PICASSO: THE BLUE AND ROSE PERIODS

SELF-PORTRAIT WITH A PALETTE, PARIS, 1906, OIL. PHILADELPHIA MUSEUM OF ART, A. E. GALLATIN COLLECTION (XVI. 28)

THE BLUE AND ROSE PERIODS

A Catalogue Raisonné of the Paintings, 1900-1906

Pierre Daix and Georges Boudaille
Catalogue compiled with the collaboration of
Joan Rosselet

New York Graphic Society Ltd. Greenwich, Connecticut

The original French edition of this book was created and
published by

EDITIONS IDES ET CALENDES, NEUCHATEL,
SWITZERLAND

Translated from the French by Phoebe Pool.
The texts of this edition were revised by Pierre Daix in 1967.
Design, André Rosselet, Auvernier.
Typography and color plates, Imprimerie Paul Attinger S.A.,
Neuchâtel.
Gravure, Imprimerie Roto Sadag S.A., Geneva.
Photolithos, Atesa, Geneva, and Courvoisier Lux,
La Chaux-de-Fonds.
Line blocks, Clichés Rapid S.A., Yverdon.
Lamination, Karl Meyer S.A., Lausanne.
Binding, Mayer et Soutter S.A., Lausanne.
Printed in Switzerland.

TABLE OF CONTENTS

El Principe, Barcelona, 1902, pen drawing.
Collection Albert Pasche, Geneva.

ACKNOWLEDGMENTS

We wish to express our deepest gratitude to all the private collectors, curators, directors and staff members of museums and art galleries who have contributed to this work through their invaluable co-operation and interest in our research. With the exception of those who wish to remain anonymous, the names of the collectors figure in the catalogue.

We are especially grateful to all those who have put at our disposal their personal archives, or who have provided indispensable information for our documentation:
Señor Juan Ainaud de Lasarte, Director general of the art museums of Barcelona.
Mr. Alfred H. Barr, Jr., New York.
Monsieur Heinz Berggruen, Paris.
Monsieur Max G. Bollag, Zurich.
Mademoiselle Suzanne Bollag, Zurich.
Monsieur Pierre Cailler, Geneva.
Monsieur François Daulte, Lausanne.
Mr. Jacques O'Hana, London.
Monsieur Maurice Jardot, Paris.
Monsieur Daniel-Henry Kahnweiler, Paris.
Madame Louise Leiris, Paris.
Monsieur Lionel Prejger, Paris.
Mr. John Rewald, New York.
Monsieur Siegfried Rosengart, Lucerne.
Mr. Germain Seligman, New York.
Mr. Justin K. Thannhauser, New York.
Monsieur Christian Zervos, Paris.

Woman with a Mirror, Paris, 1904, pen drawing. Private collection, Paris.

One institution only has refused its co-operation: the Barnes Foundation. If we have succeeded, in spite of this, in gathering the documentation necessary for the publication of the principal works by Picasso in this famous collection, we are aware that this documentation is incomplete. In addition to the paintings, the Barnes Foundation has several drawings and unpublished studies of 1904-1906, notably: five drawings of the saltimbanques period, two studies for *The Two Brothers,* two studies for *La Coiffure,* a sketch for *The Blind Man's Meal,* a gouache on paper from the Blue Period: *Crouching Woman* (about 60 × 40 cm.), and a gouache on cardboard of 1905: *Acrobat* (60 × 30 cm.). As we were unable to obtain photographs, it is unfortunately impossible to include these last documents in our catalogue.

PREFACE

Why this catalogue of Picasso's paintings from 1900–1906?

Picasso, more than any other painter of his time, has been magnificently served by the intelligence and talent of his contemporaries: Apollinaire, Reverdy, Raynal, Eluard, Kahnweiler and Sabartés, and by the devotion and ability of the specialists dedicated to his work such as Christian Zervos, Alfred H. Barr, Jr. and Bernhard Geiser. But this very abundance itself creates the need for a synthesis. Besides this, the majority of our predecessors worked when Picasso was more a subject of controversy than of study, when the years with which we are concerned were not yet open to scientific investigation, the documents were mainly out of reach, and much of the evidence of Picasso's contemporaries was considered too recent to occupy the attention of research students.

Today all institutions of art are concerned with the sources of the twentieth century. It is a subject of interest not only to the museums which classify and catalogue the works of this period, reinstating artists who have been forgotten, but also to the collectors who, with the dealers, contribute in a similar way by exhibiting their works of art and by allowing their reproduction. The importance of this phenomenon is so great one might say that within the last ten years it has completely modified both our knowledge and our views about the birth of modern art.

Picasso, from the very nature of his personality and role, has benefited more than anyone else from these investigations. The exhibitions of his early works, the stir which they cause, the pace in their circulation on account of their ever-increasing commercial value, have developed correspondingly. Not only has this excitement multiplied the collation and comparison, the general knowledge of the œuvre, and made it possible to see a great number of works which had been more or less inaccessible up to the present time, but even more it has been accompanied by remarkable progress in the analysis and description of the works.

The conventions of an œuvre catalogue enable one to draw up a balance of all the gains which we have just mentioned. At the same time it provides the means of giving prominence to the facts on a historical basis and of establishing a really scientific study.

We were also guided by our own experience of research into Picasso's work. We have been able to assess from practice the difficulties and contradictions arising from the progress in the history of the beginning of the century. The new documents which we have discovered permitted us to believe that a methodical work of research would be fruitful. The results at which we have arrived convince us that our attempt will at least be useful in showing to what extent the field of research remains to be explored, and doubtless in stimulating works which will correct us and add precision to our discoveries.

Finally, and not least important, our catalogue is the first book to show in chronological order the evolution of the works painted by Picasso in these early years when one can follow his development, his rise from an extraordinary precociousness to mastery, and finally to the break from which Cubism will emerge.

Until recently the public—and the artist himself—have been unable to study more than fragmentary sequences in the film of this creative life. This book offers the paintings in color, many of which were previously unpublished, and an illustrated catalogue which we hope is as complete and chronologically precise as possible. In this way we combine with an instrument for study a vision of the work's reality which only an œuvre catalogue can furnish.

It is also a tendency born of the progress of the history of art in our time to give precedence to the work in the biography of an artist, to what is produced rather than to the man who is dedicated to it and lives only for and by it. In any case Picasso would have forced us to adopt this attitude. But here we have been able to pursue this course without diversions, allowing the logic of the book's conception itself to guide us.

In the course of writing this book we have benefited first from the kind information and encouragement provided by Picasso and from the collaboration of Jacqueline Picasso, whose competence and efficiency are only equalled by her graciousness. Daniel-Henry Kahnweiler, Louise Leiris and Maurice Jardot have given us valuable and indispensable help. But we should like here to pay a particular tribute to Christian Zervos, whose supreme role in contributing to the knowledge of Picasso we have been able to appreciate in detail while compiling this work. The catalogue of the artist's work to which Christian Zervos has devoted himself for thirty-five years not only remains the basic book, but still forms the guide and master plan of research, a fact which, if one recalls the state of criticism on the painter at the beginning of the thirties, represents a fine example of scholarship and discrimination.

With the permission and encouragement of Christian Zervos himself, we have used and benefited from his nomenclature and his archives.

In view of the fact that when the first records of Picasso's work were made, real precision did not seem necessary either to collectors, museums, or dealers, we have undertaken the task of making this inventory from the very beginning. We have applied to all the owners, dealers and museums to obtain accurate measurements, detailed information for purposes of identification, and recent photographs.

Among the corrections which we have made in the chronology of Picasso's work, certain of them lead to the substantial revision of accepted ideas. The fact that the exhibition at the Galeries Serrurier, Boulevard Haussmann, took place in 1905 and not in 1904, as many biographers have declared, leads to the correction in the dating of several works. Even more important are the deductions which must be drawn from the fact, previously established by Barr, that Picasso's stay in the Catalan village of Gosol took place in the summer of 1906 and not in 1905. This is relevant to the whole genesis of Cubism.

We have been careful to state nothing which we cannot prove; hence the importance of the documents reproduced in the appendix, and particularly the prefaces to the catalogues of the first exhibitions at the galleries of Berthe Weill and Vollard, as well as the articles which appeared in the literary reviews of the time.

An important part of the sources of this book came from the conversations which the authors, and particularly Pierre Daix, have had with Picasso. The reader might well, then, be surprised by the relative importance played by hypothesis for the dates and places where the works were produced. There are two reasons for this. The first is that Picasso, whose memory for everything concerning his work is phenomenal, has never troubled in the least to make mental notes of dates and material circumstances. He did not date his works systematically until the Cubist period—perhaps from regret at not having done so before. The second is that at the distance of sixty years we raise problems which had not then the same meaning and importance. Picasso has always refused to be what he calls his own *connoisseur*. He loves finding again his early works, some of which he hasn't seen since their execution. It frequently happens that this brings back to him memories attached to them. But his turn of mind leads him very quickly to revert to his more recent concerns, in order not to be distracted from the work to be carried out by work already done.

Picasso has shown all possible attention, kindness and patience for this book. But let us repeat, his main preoccupation is to paint, and in no respect to turn away from the canvases which fill his studios at Mougins to unearth facts buried beneath sixty-five years of unwearied activity. Besides, Picasso detests anything vague or imprecise, and would rather say nothing at all than give an approximate or polite answer that has no meaning.

P. D. and G. B.

Each chronological section of the catalogue of paintings is followed by a selection of drawings. It being impossible to add, within the frame of this work, a complete catalogue of drawings, we reproduce only those which are of particular interest, either because they are unpublished (or not previously catalogued by Zervos), or because they constitute significant stages in Picasso's work.

The Catalogue of Paintings (1900–1906) which we give here, on the other hand, is the most complete published to date. The contribution of numerous unpublished works and the chronological arrangement of more than 750 illustrations[1] in the form of a catalogue raisonné make this a record without precedent.

We have only catalogued those works whose authenticity we could assert, leaving out, on the advice of the artist himself, a number of works, some of which have been published by our predecessors.

[1] Of which 230 are not reproduced in Volumes I and VI of Zervos.

PORTRAIT OF GUSTAVE COQUIOT, PARIS, 1901, OIL. EMIL G. BÜHRLE FOUNDATION, ZURICH (VI. 16).

Bon
Pinto

I. THE FORMATIVE YEARS IN BARCELONA, 1896–1900

1. *Pablo Ruiz Picasso, afterwards Picasso*

Until the spring of 1901 Picasso signed his works Pablo Ruiz Picasso or P.R. Picasso. Apparently it is only in the course of his visit to Madrid that pictures appear signed merely with his mother's name, Picasso, a name as rare in Spain as Ruiz, his father's name, is common. It is difficult for a foreigner to understand exactly the emotional nuances implied in such a choice, which the Spanish custom of uniting the father's and mother's name makes not only possible but usual and often necessary. It is also worth noticing that this decision coincides with others equally important to the artist: his departure for the second stay in Paris, and a new style of painting which witnesses to the assertion of the independence and individuality of a young man who will not be twenty until 25th October, 1901.

Alejandro Cirici-Pellicer has made a study of these years under the title of *Picasso before Picasso,* which doubtless puts too much emphasis on the change which the facts, as we see them, make more difficult to perceive. But this formula conceals the other danger of making us forget that from now onwards we can only approach the painter's youth in the light of the many decades of creative life and experiences which separate us from it. We cannot take as a working hypothesis the fact that the young man who signed himself Pablo Ruiz Picasso was only a virgin talent little by little fashioned by encounters and influences, to whom originality would come one fine day as a result of external forces; still less can we suppose him to have had from the first all the creative virtues which more than seventy years of activity and reflections devoted only to his art have enabled us to perceive. Whether or not we want to, we see Pablo Ruiz in the light of Picasso because he has become and *is* Picasso.

Fundamentally these difficulties do no more than express,

in the particular field of the years of apprenticeship and developing personality, the general dificulty in approaching the history of the painter Picasso. From the fact that he embodies, in the unprecedented effervescence of modern creativity, the very type of the revolutionary artist, not only the understanding but the simple knowledge of his work have suffered important alterations in time, and lead to distortions as well as pure and simple mistakes and falsifications.

Eighteen years had to pass before *Les Demoiselles d'Avignon* was revealed to the public[1], thirty before it was exhibited. And the works which followed the break of 1906 have often prevented people seeing anything in the previous works that was not classical. These chronological muddles, the mistakes in "reading" the pictures, have led to isolating Picasso from his contemporary setting and to treating him as if he lived upon another planet. These excesses have led to the opposite tendency to find for him, at all costs, models and predecessors, patrons and master minds.

These preconceptions are never more tiresome than in this period when Picasso searches for and finds himself, passing through the sequence of experiences which make up precisely the subject of this book. We find ourselves encountering a young man whose skill and precocity are both stupefying. We have no genuine way of penetrating into the depth of his thought, his hopes and desires at this time, no way of putting ourselves into his skin and seeing the world with his eyes except by way of his work. On the other hand we can try to disclose at what world and what art the painter as a child and young man was looking, as

---

[1] In *La Revue Surréaliste,* No. 4, July 15, 1925. The first reproduction was in *Architectural Record,* May, 1910, with an article by Gelette Burgess on "The Wild Men of Paris".

we bring together the ideas and books which were important for him and chronicle the friendships which he formed, in short, review the circumstances attending his development. The expression "the child painter" does not jar any more than the phrase "the child musician" as applied to Mozart. Picasso's precocity is only equalled by that of a Rimbaud, for it involves both a precocity of creation where decision is aided by a prodigious facility of execution, and a critical precocity in which the judgment of himself and others seems to be based on an unequalled memory and intelligence.

2. *The Turmoil of 1898*

The era is already distant, but not distant enough to have become really part of history. If in France the idea of the *Belle Epoque* tends to simplify problems in a tiresome way, in Spain the situation is little better. For reasons connected mainly with recent history, the study of the great intellectual events of this period, the literary movement of the *Generation of '98* and Catalan modernism, has not found much favor beyond the Pyrenees.

There is a blank between Goya and Galdos. The concept of a Spain as an empty territory on the cultural map throughout the course of the nineteenth century is scarcely exaggerated—a Spain set apart. This is as true of romanticism as it is of 1848. But as we look back from the distance of over half a century to the defeat of Spain by the United States in 1898, which confirmed the decay of state and government, we discover the deep and very rich forces of the new intellectual generation. To estimate the extent of the shock one must look back to the concept of the Empire of Charles V, that Empire on which the sun never set. The defeat of 1898 marks the loss of the few colonies of importance which Spain still possessed—Cuba, Puerto Rico, the Philippines. To be no longer anything of importance overseas was, for reflective Spaniards, something quite different from a wound to pride. It was a mighty turmoil causing a general overhaul of accepted ideas and a many-sided intellectual and political revival. In literature Galdos—born in the same year as Verlaine—is followed by Unamuno, the same age as Romain Rolland, and by men ten years junior: Machado, Baroja, Azorin, Valle-Inclan, who claim to be the generation of the year of disaster, the

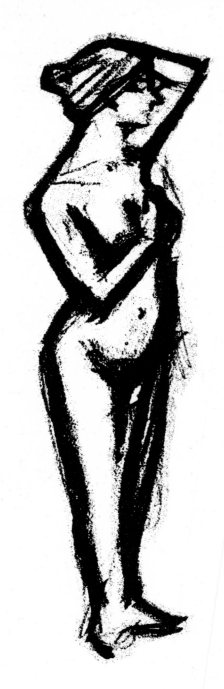

Nude, 1898-1899, Conté crayon.

Generation of '98, which breaks with the old lethargic Spain.

Picasso was nearly seventeen years old at the time of the defeat[1]. We have the evidence of Gertrude Stein as to the importance which he attached to the lessons of the Spanish-American war. And when he founded a review in Madrid, in the spring of 1901 with Francisco de Asis Soler, there

[1] He was in Horta de Ebro with his friend Pallarés when the Treaty of Paris, which put an end to Spanish rule in Cuba, was signed, August 13, 1898 (Josep Palau i Fabre, *Picasso en Cataluña*).

14

appeared quite naturally at the top of the table of contents the names of Unamuno and Pío Baroja. One must not underestimate the effect of the shock of 1898 on Picasso. However, if that landmark is useful to us in order to correct the over-simple idea of a Spain where nothing happened, it is necessary to remember that the city in which Picasso passed the decisive years of his intellectual formation was not Madrid, but Barcelona. But Picasso was not always content with Barcelona. After his first journey to Paris in the year of the Universal Exhibition and his return to Malaga, he settled in Madrid in February, 1901. But this visit did not last more than three months, and even if he scarcely stopped in Barcelona before departing again for Paris, it is in Barcelona that he lived after the important visit of 1901. Moreover, *Arte Joven,* Picasso's short-lived review in Madrid, was a review which united the Madrid writers of '98 with the Catalan "modernists".

3. *Decadence, Art Nouveau and modern art*

If the Catalan renaissance at the end of the nineteenth century was nourished and ennobled by the new developments in Madrid, it had its own foundations, and in 1898 its own assured existence. Witness, to begin with, the real literary revival of the Catalan language among writers such as Santiago Rusiñol and Joan Maragall, who in Sabartés' phrase made it "crack like a flag". Witness, too, a lively and powerful intellectual movement which participated in the development, general at that time in western Europe, which we call the style of the *fin de siècle* or of 1900, but which was also called Art Nouveau, *Jugendstil, Sezession,* according to whether one was in France, Belgium, England, Munich or Vienna. And Catalonia did not only follow, but contributed. As Norway at the other end of this small intellectual Europe brought the force of Edvard Munch to the new art, Barcelona gave it the luxuriance of Gaudi. Here certainly was a case of new art. It is mere abusive simplification and ignorance, too long the fashion in France, to reduce what occurred then only to the writhing plant forms, to Hector Guimard's entries to the Métro, to Gallé's vases and Lalique's jewels.

Since the need has been felt to understand the "sources of the twentieth century" we have grasped the fact that this first art to claim the title of *modern* was not so uncon-nected as it might seem with the birth of what today constitutes for us modern painting, modern sculpture, modern architecture, in short, modern art.

To be made aware of this it would be enough to reread, as Roger H. Guerrand[1] has done, the essay published in Germany in 1893 by Dr. Max Nordau, *Entartung,* which anticipates Hitler's campaign against the *Entartete Kunst,* degenerate art. Nordau was a disciple of the Italian criminologist Lombroso. His book was highly successful; it was translated into French in 1894 under the title of *Dégénérescence* and then into English as *Degeneration.* Charcot once said, "Neurotics seek each other's company." Nordau without hesitation compares groups of intellectuals with bands of unbalanced criminals who must be subjugated by the secular arm. "The mystics and above all egoists and filthy pseudo-realists are enemies of society of the worst kind. The latter has the strict duty of defending itself against them." Naturalists, Pre-Raphaelites, Symbolists: Ibsen, Nietzsche, Ruskin, Tolstoi, Wagner, Wilde, Zola— none of them found grace in the eyes of Nordau. "The strange style of certain painters, impressionists, pointillists or mosaic-makers, timid or dazzling, raging colorists, dyers in pale or rough colors," he wrote, "will become immediately understandable if we bear in mind the research made by Charcot's school on the visual troubles of degenerates and hysterics."

One cannot fail to be struck on discovering accusations in this book which will all be leveled at a later time against the Cubists, the Surrealists, the abstract painters, and in general against the experiments of the avant-garde. Henceforth in the eyes of the orthodox the only art worthy of the name is that which respects and ennobles traditional appearances and forms, and follows the canons of beauty. All art which questions these standards or denies them— either by exposing what society hides (naturalism) or by experimenting with new idioms in order to reach a deeper reality (impressionism, symbolism), not only turns its back on progress but can only be the sign of decadence in comparison with the history of ancient art, and more generally with Greco-Roman civilization.

What has confused everything for later generations is the fact that like the romantics, the realists and the impres-

[1] Roger H. Guerrand, *L'Art Nouveau en Europe* with a preface by Aragon, published by Plon, Paris 1965.

sionists, the "decadents" have taken the contemptuous name leveled against them and adopted it openly. But whereas the romantics were romantic, Courbet a realist, and the Impressionists impressionists indeed, the decadents themselves were the enemies of the only decadence they knew, that of bourgeois society. The same thing happened to these "decadents" as happened to the French existentialists of 1945: fashion seized on what they were not and made out of this a reality which was a caricature.

"In the literary world," wrote Sabartés of Barcelona at the turn of the century, "the center of attention is the idiocy called 'decadent poetry'. Fashionable young ladies adopt languishing gestures. Pallor is in fashion. Art Nouveau imposes corkscrew decorations made fashionable by the posters and illustrations of the Czech painter Alphonse-Marie Mucha, for all this comes to us from Paris. Santiago Rusiñol with his publications *El Pati Blau* and *Els Jardins abandonats* follows the fashion and increases the damage to public taste. Some write poems dealing with fairies and lakes... Others draw. In the drawings and illustrated books the decorations are irises or other hallmarks of this style. The poets have to be shaggy-haired or nothing, and the painters wear their jackets buttoned up to the neck in spite of the climate."

This explains the caricatured portrait in the Barcelona Museum, *Sabartés as a Decadent Poet* (see Catalogue 1. 6) which is evidence of the state of mind of the two friends. But it would be rash to conclude from this that Picasso turned away from Art Nouveau. From 1898 when he drew a menu card for *Els Quatre Gats* he practised with perfect ease and naturalness the simplification of outlines and the play of curves of this style like the lash of a whip. And this style, as Jean Cassou[1] and Aragon[2] have rightly shown, belongs not only to decorative art, but to art itself, to Munch, to Gauguin, to Lautrec and Seurat.

Precisely those which seem modern to us now among works in this style are those which had the greatest circulation at the time; Sabartés rightly emphasizes the role of posters and illustrations. It was their circulation which really popularized Art Nouveau, introduced it into the streets and to the young and sent it across frontiers. Picasso more than anyone perceived its influence.

[1] Jean Cassou, *Les Sources du XXᵉ Siècle*.
[2] Aragon, preface to *L'Art Nouveau en Europe* by Roger H. Guerrand.

4. *Art Nouveau, Techniques and Science*

The progress in photography on one hand and in the optical science of colors on the other, coincided at the beginning of the last third of the nineteenth century with the discovery of Japanese prints and the new needs of the press and advertising in the field of illustration. It would take too long—and be irrelevant to our subject—to describe the influence of photography on the experiments of painters, but from Delacroix to Degas one can see how photography, by allowing painters to compare their vision with the colorless two-dimensional reproduction of the real, prepares the visual understanding of the use of flat colors in Japanese prints. One of the results of this was the *cloisonnisme* of Emile Bernard and the group of Pont-Aven which led to Gauguin. But without doubt the growing fashion for lithography was linked in some way to this process.

One finds, besides, that the use of flat tints is encouraged for another technical reason; photography in halftones does not yet exist—it is not until 1903 that the use of ruled halftone screens becomes common, and in Paris *Le Matin* publishes as a special event the first photograph made by this process. Illustrations not needing halftones thus benefited from the massive circulation by printing at the very time when the eye was accustomed to their simplification. The path of lithography from Degas to Lautrec, passing by way of Maurice Denis, Vuillard and Bonnard, includes a considerable amount of experiments in abstraction, deformation and ellipse which advertising often extends to the street poster. Similarly Aubrey Beardsley is about to transform English posters and illustrations, in his case starting from another experience of flat tints, the silhouettes of the eighteenth century.

These demands of the printing press have another result: the present function of the news photograph was at that time assigned to drawings which could be engraved. Steinlen's draughtmanship was formed in this school.

These relationships between art and technology have become so familiar to us that we are in danger of neglecting the real revolution which they produced in the concept of art. Certainly in 1885 *Le Figaro* wrote: "There is more skill in a poster than in many of these sensational pictures." And if Picasso at the age of seventeen designs a menu, Lautrec with his menu for the Société des Indépendants had set an example, the same Lautrec who draws an advertisement for a serial story in *Le Matin* or for *l'Entôleuse, chanson vécue*. The painter's feeling for technique is traditional. Delacroix grinds his own colors, and Degas, when he develops a passion for photography or the technique of engraving is not lowering himself any more than is Lautrec with his lithography. But from a conventional viewpoint these are noble techniques, like printing. On the other hand, the new techniques as seen by the gentlemen of the Institute have all the coarseness of the common people. Now it is precisely these techniques which invade the towns and countryside.

Intoxication with iron is the mark of the century, with its infinite tentacles of rails and also with the giant tower of M. Eiffel. There is an invasion of industry into the countryside much more serious than the factories in the suburbs which can always be avoided. The novelty of iron in architecture is everywhere and extends even to the design of locomotives and steamers, and this is in keeping with scientific progress and the modernity of the period. But painting also is affected. This "different" kind of painting creates a scandal when Claude Monet, for instance, portrays the Saint-Lazare station with its architecture of stone and glass and the engines, and when Pissarro paints the coal barges, smoke and fog of the industrial port of Rouen. This kind of painting not only harmonizes with the period by choosing contemporary subjects, but is in accordance with the changing nature of the period itself.

Impressionism is not only a new way of reaching the truth of reality, it is a reversal both of technique and of the painter's view of the world and his role. In fact it is a revolution as important as the replacement stage by stage of manuscript illumination by classical perspective. But whereas on the threshold of the Renaissance this revolution in the painter's way of seeing appeared as a philosophical revolution, a new expression of the relationship between man and the cosmos which concealed its directly optical and geometrical origin, the popularization of Chevreul's theory of colors became the crude, one might even say chemical, justification of the new painting. The painters of the Renaissance started from the conviction that perspective was a part of nature and thus allowed them a more faithful representation of appearances than the previous methods had permitted. The Impressionists, however, depended on physical laws which allowed them to attain a realism of color and light at the price of an open break with appearances. Chevreul's theory, as is well known, divides colors into two groups: the primaries which are red, yellow and blue, the secondary colors which are orange (red and yellow), green (yellow and blue) and violet (red and blue). This theory carried further shows that a primary color juxtaposed to the secondary color composed of the other two primaries heightens it; thus blue heightens orange, red, green, etc. These colors are called the complementaries of the secondary colors. But another result is that two complementary colors neutralize each other when mixed in equal quantities.

Doubtless painters had known this dialectic of colors by instinct for a long time, but it is one thing to experience a sensation contradicted by common sense and quite another to learn by scientific progress that you are right and the appearances wrong. Add to this the justification given by photography allowing painters to abandon the conception of light illuminating all people and things in the same way, and also the lesson of Delacroix showing that color can produce the effect of movement if one makes it do the work of drawing, plus the complementary dictum of Ingres that there is no right or wrong way of drawing, and we have assembled the fundamental ideas for the liberation of painting which the Impressionist revolution brought into play.

Picasso was born after this revolution and its gains seemed natural to him. The abbreviations and abstractions in the lithographs and posters, the graphic compositions employing the most unusual effects of perspective in order to provoke surprise, the end of the separation between major and minor arts, all this he could take for granted.

It is not difficult for us, who know what was to follow in Picasso's work, to discern in these ideas the beginning of the process which will lead to the relief constructions and the collages of Cubism. In more than one respect modern art is Art Nouveau restored to health. The continuity is obvious in the sculpture and ceramics of Picasso, who continues in a masterful way to dignify the non-noble arts with his ceramic tiles and the *Head of a Bull* (1943) made from the handlebar and saddle of a bicycle. Picasso has seized on what was the new art at the time of his apprenticeship, has realized its innermost meaning and has destroyed the compromise which it represents between art and work by identifying art no longer with the ornamental and decorative but with the *work* of the painter, sculptor or ceramist, and at the same time making beauty not a super-added quality but the *result* of the effort to seize and express the world.

5. *Catalan Modernism*

Phoebe Pool, following Alejandro Cirici-Pellicer, has applied herself to studying in more detail the atmosphere of the artistic discussions in the Barcelona circles known to the young Picasso. One must admit that an essential thing is missing. In what way were these discussions carried on? And we have little more than a catalogue of names. But such as it is, it gives us some valuable clues, particularly on the importance of the German and Northern influences.

IN FRONT OF THE CHURCH, SPAIN, 1901, OIL. EMIL G. BÜHRLE FOUNDATION, ZURICH. UNPUBLISHED IN COLOR (V. 49).

We have the testimony of Picasso himself who wrote in November 1897, when he was just sixteen, to his friend Bas, "If I had a son who wanted to be a painter, I wouldn't let him remain in Spain for a moment, and don't imagine that I would send him to Paris (where I should be very glad to be myself) but to Munik *(sic)*... That's a city where they study painting seriously without worrying about fashions like pointillism and so on." Rusiñol describes *Els Quatre Gats* which was the usual haunt of young Picasso as "a Gothic tavern for those in love with the North." For Catalan intellectuals at that time Germany meant Schopenhauer, Nietzsche and Wagner. Joan Maragall, whose poetry we know Picasso appreciated, was one of the principal leaders in introducing Nietzsche's ideas to Spain, also the works of Goethe and Novalis, which he translated. Although it would be naïve to identify what we know of the young Picasso's ideas with those of Nietzsche, and although the statement on this subject made by Leo Stein in 1905 is no more than an anecdote, it is easy to imagine how Nietzsche's denunciations of bourgeois Philistinism would have been received by the young Catalan intellectuals. The North also meant Maeterlinck and Ibsen, who were then the leaders of the new drama, and also Verhaeren, who was frequently translated.

What is striking in the choice made by the Catalan modernists from among the new developments in philosophy and literature is the honor given to anything tending to support Catalan national claims, which, as A. Cirici-Pellicer appropriately reminds us, had their first electoral triumph in 1901. But in a more general way this flow of ideas led to the affirmation of the self. Joan Oliva Bridgman, in a poem which Picasso illustrated for *Joventut*, August 16, 1900, proclaims:

Ser o no ser amics! la gran questió és aquesta;

Ser o no ser del tot: mostrem-nos francament.

To be or not to be friends, that is the great question;

To be or not to be at all: we must look at it openly.

One cannot infer from the fact that Picasso read this poem that he adopted its ideas, but these ideas correspond with the thought of Maragall and with the opinion of Verhaeren, who points out that "the poets of today look for their individual style in themselves, forging for themselves an order of their own and submitting to nothing except the personal rules arising from their own way of thinking and feeling."

El Clam de las Verges, Barcelona, 1900, charcoal. Illustration for a poem by Joan Oliva Bridgman, reproduced in Joventut, *July 19, 1900.*

Picasso's drawing, like another of the same time and for the same review which illustrates another poem of the same Joan Oliva Bridgman: *El Clam de las Verges* (The cry of the Virgins who want to be free and to enjoy the delights of love), is above all symbolic in character. Unlike other charcoal drawings of the same period, one might say that Picasso has weakened the liveliness of his line and the sharpness of his observation in the interests of a certain blurring which was perhaps demanded by the poet. It would seem useless to try to extract influences from minor works made to supply the needs of illustration. One might see here a wish to recall the Pre-Raphaelites, since Picasso's friend Junyent said that "Turner, Rossetti, Holman Hunt and Millais have attained the highest summits ever reached by painters." Phoebe Pool, on the other hand, compares *The Cry of the Virgins* with Edvard Munch, who illustrated similar proclamations of sexual freedom. None of this is convincing. A third drawing (see Catalogue 1. 25) which appeared on September 6, 1900 in *Cataluña Artistica, La Boja* (The Mad Woman) is quite another matter. It is the title of a story by Suriñach Senties in which the heroine has first lost her husband in tragic circumstances, then her house which the local lord destroyed in order to build himself a castle; now it is the title of a drawing whose violence remains in the memory. This time one really does think of Edvard Munch—no one work in particular, but of his way of creating an expression of anguish, torment, heartbreak which later shows up as a characteristic of German Expressionism. It is enough to compare *The Mad Woman* with such paintings as *The Cry* or *The Vampire* to see that if Picasso were inspired by Munch, who lived in Paris at this time and whose works were frequently reproduced, he has grasped his meaning, undergone the shock of impact and not simply copied some trick such as making a face emerge from a dark background.

Each problem that we meet admits different solutions which are not necessarily in contradiction. The Expressionism of Munch and Ensor was as much in the air as Art Nouveau. Is it simply coincidence or influence? This brings us back to the question of whether the intellectual climate of Barcelona was favorable to the blossoming of a genius or whether we only ask this question because of the existence itself of Picasso. We must be satisfied with a multiplicity of answers. It is not in this case the effect of optics, illusion, imagination or ignorance on the part of the observer. This multiplicity is part of the phenomenon which is being studied. When Delacroix learns to understand Turner, Constable or simply Bonington, it is possible to define his encounters—some in Paris, some in London during Delacroix's visit in 1826. But in Picasso's time, precisely because we have without any doubt reached the modern period, this has become impossible. Doubtless nothing can replace direct knowledge, above all for a painter, and when Picasso in Paris sees Van Goghs at Vollard's or Daumiers in the big retrospective exhibition at the Palais des Beaux-Arts in 1901, his paintings immediately show signs of it. But Picasso could have seen the woodcuts of Munch or of Käthe Kollwitz, the engravings of Beardsley, the drawings of Steinlen or of Carrière, the lithographs of Lautrec no matter where they were reproduced. And here the question of when or where Picasso came across them is pointless.

Picasso is not a modern painter born in an age which was not modern, but the modern painter of a period which precisely was becoming modern, and he knows it. We shall see besides that with Picasso one must never argue in terms of influence, since he never leaves anything in the state in which he finds it. Looking for likenesses when one is dealing with a man whose capacity for recording and visual memory is truly stupefying, often leads one to neglect the real problems. When Picasso borrows it is to experiment and to go further. In this too he is the child of the new age. When painters Millet and Théodore Rousseau, and especially Manet, Degas, Monet, Mary Cassatt, Van Gogh, Gauguin, Lautrec and Seurat, set about collecting Japanese prints, a different relationship was established between them and this earlier and non-Western art. They were not dealing with a model of beauty like the antique, but with a model of ways of seeing, a model which was not to be copied in the academic sense since it translated a distant reality, but a model which must be understood and transformed. Picasso as a Spaniard had already met a similar problem with Goya, who often departed from the illusionist tradition of the Renaissance, and with El Greco, whom the modernists of Barcelona rediscovered. It was perhaps even the case with Turner, in whose defense Ruskin had written his *Modern Painters,* and it was certainly so with Edvard Munch.

"I am going to make a drawing for you to take to *Barcelona Comica.* We'll see whether they'll buy it. It must be modernist for a paper like that. Neither Nonell, that young mystic, nor Pichet nor anybody else has reached the extravagance I attain in this drawing." This quotation is taken from the letter to his friend Bas (Madrid, November 3, 1897).

It must not be forgotten that Picasso was then just sixteen, and that everything inclines one to think that at eighteen, when we find him in Barcelona again, he had no less independence of mind and confidence in his powers.

6. *The Beginnings of the œuvre*

It is not the least of the paradoxes in Picasso's life that we are now better informed about his first childhood paintings than about the more conscious products of his originality. The only landmark is in 1898, his convalescence at Horta de Ebro with Manuel Pallarés after the scarlet fever which put an end to his first stay in Madrid. But it is an uncertain landmark. Nevertheless it seems that there has been a tendency to predate a fair number of Picasso's works by placing them in 1898, a year in which, if one adds together the period of his illness and the months passed in the mountains, Picasso did not spend much time in Barcelona.[1] One example among several others of this predating is the portrait in charcoal and turpentine wash of Manuel Pallarés against a background of factories with smoke going up obliquely into the sky (1. 7); Zervos dates it 1898, whereas it falls quite naturally into the series of portraits which were made in Barcelona between the middle of 1899 and 1900.

A series of colored drawings in watercolor or turpentine wash, traditionally dated 1898, seems to us Picasso's first advance into originality. We refer to *Redemption* (The End of the Road) Thannhauser Foundation, Guggenheim Museum (see Catalogue 1. 2); to *The Mother and Little Boy* (z. 1. 12), which develops two of the figures in *Redemption,* and to *Old Man and Young Girl* (z. 1. 378). The first has a definite symbolic meaning: a row of carriages and another row of old people, women and children, trudging painfully, come together at the end of a road where death awaits them. What is striking is the rapid way of suggesting form and making silhouettes while eliminating all detail. Phoebe Pool compares this drawing with one by Nonell, showing a long line of peasants, but this elliptical method is to some extent merely the result of the technique of charcoal drawing, and one can find similarities in Steinlen. More interesting is the idea suggested by the drawing of *The Mother and Little Boy,* which is closely related to *Redemption* since the same group appears, shown front view this time against a background of mountains reminiscent of Horta de Ebro. The elongation of the forms is characteristic. One thinks of El Greco here and again with still more justification in *The Old Man and Young Girl.*

[1] Our statement concerning the predating of the works of this period has since been confirmed by Josep Palau i Fabre's accurate history of Picasso's early years, in *Picasso en Cataluña.*

As Cirici-Pellicer says: "There is no doubt that Picasso found El Greco a very strong moral support." This does not mean that there is nothing gothic in the drawings just discussed, but it is only later, towards 1902, that one begins to find traces of borrowings from mediaeval sculpture, often romanesque, in Picasso's painting. El Greco was a nearer, more direct example. Besides, he was studied and admired in the intellectual circles of Barcelona. Santiago Rusiñol had bought two paintings by El Greco in 1894, although this was in Paris. Miguel Utrillo contributed a great deal towards making the Master of Toledo known, even before the publication of his monograph on the artist in 1906. Utrillo, the adoptive father of Maurice Utrillo since 1891, was an editor of the review *Pèl y Ploma (Brush and Pen),* and he was responsible for the first article of

Self-Portrait, Barcelona, 1899, charcoal. Private collection, New York.

BOOTH AT THE FAIR, PARIS, 1900-1901, OIL.   COLLECTION FRITZ ANDREAE, SEN., COLOGNE.   UNPUBLISHED IN COLOR   (V. 63).

importance on Picasso published in Spain,[1] on the pastels exhibited in the Sala Parés. As Barr observed, Miguel Utrillo was also a connoisseur of Catalan mediaeval art, and he influenced Picasso simultaneously in the two directions.

These experiments of Picasso are limited to a few works, but the important thing is that they did take place. It was scarcely conceivable that a boy of seventeen should keep to one sharply defined direction. Nevertheless this first experiment in deformation and simplification throws a new light on those which follow, and particularly on the second period of El Greco's influence in 1906, in the Gosol compositions with peasants, flowers and oxen. Picasso's progress is consistently marked by these sorties for reconnaissance which seem to be halted as soon as they are begun, but the artist takes them up again, often years later, strengthened by all he has learned and created in the meantime. And from the *Peasants* of Gosol to the *Demoiselles d'Avignon,* as Barr has well observed, is not a long way from the artistic point of view.

The series of portraits made in Barcelona after the return from Horta de Ebro is abundant; it extends from the spring of 1899 to the first months of 1900. Raynal has described them admirably: "His prodigious satirical instinct, which is not akin to caricature, leads him to make portraits with harsh, contrasted thrusts of the plastic medium, painted in violent strokes, crudely outlined and drawn with a mastery surprising in a young man. It is not so much skill as vigor, brutality, a certain haughty bitterness which is not without grandeur. One can already see in the young artist a constant dissatisfaction and a ceaseless torment, and above all that revolutionary instinct which is common to the greatest sons of Spain."[2]

Everything suggests that this activity is linked with the work of Ramón Casas, the most celebrated painter in the *Quatre Gats* group. He was the artistic director of *Pèl y Ploma,* at this time a weekly paper, but its first monthly number in 1901 was to contain the account of Picasso's exhibition at the Sala Parés. Casas became the editor of *Forma* in 1902. His part in the research on El Greco and Catalan romanesque art was as important as that of Utrillo,

although less direct. Besides, Casas knew Paris well. He knew both Steinlen and Lautrec. Like them he did drawings for newspapers. Picasso made portraits because they were of his friends. They are works which bear the signs of a long contact with the models. Doubtless there was a kind of competition within the group. Why should Picasso not think of being published in *Pèl y Ploma?* In fact, this occurred first in *Joventut,* and with illustrations which were commissioned.

But here again once an influence has been observed, it must not be overemphasized. It is enough to compare the portrait of Picasso by Casas,[3] published in *Pèl y Ploma* in 1901, with those by Picasso to be struck by the difference. Picasso penetrates to the essentials. He accepts the pose, but uses it to probe beyond anything which the model could conceivably have offered him. Casas' portraits are no more than likenesses; he seems insipid, almost studious in his facility. With Picasso the placement of the drawing on the page seems so natural that it is only after a time that one detects the oddities. For example, he always cuts the legs at the knees or above, but the subject comes to life, even springs to life, every time. Casas is skillful; with Picasso everything is intensified.

When one surveys this gallery of friends one feels that he can see how our painter of eighteen has taken stock of them. He has drawn from them everything he could.

In 1900, the year of the Universal Exhibition, many of the *Quatre Gats* painters were in Paris; Isidro Nonell, Joaquin Sunyer, Ricardo Canals, not to mention the sculptor Manolo. This means many conversations about Paris, many overtures from Paris. But Picasso needed to go further and to discover new horizons. The fidgets which possessed him in the autumn of 1900 were in fact to last eight months and to lead him from Barcelona to Paris, then from Paris to Malaga, from Malaga to Madrid, from Madrid to Barcelona and again from Barcelona to Paris. It was more than an apprentice's journey, it was a search for himself.

When Picasso settled again for a time in Paris, his painting had completely changed.

---

[1] Cf. Appendix, p. 333. An anonymous article on Picasso was published in *La Vanguardia,* February 3, 1900, on his first exhibition (in the *Quatre Gats*).

[2] Special number of the review *Le Point,* Souillac (Lot), October, 1952.

[3] Reproduced in Appendix, page 337.

II.   THE FIRST TWO JOURNEYS TO PARIS, 1900–1901

1. *Going to the Source*

There were three who undertook the adventure of Paris at the same time. Three friends, three painters: Picasso, Pallarés and Casegemas. Pallarés was Picasso's oldest Catalan friend, his comrade ever since his convalescence at Horta de Ebro after scarlet fever in 1898. Casagemas had been his companion through thick and thin. He now had only three and a half months to live, for he was to commit suicide in Paris on February 17, 1901, over an unhappy love affair. Pallarés, a few years older than Picasso, would be with him at Horta de Ebro again in 1908, at the dawn of Cubism. In 1960 he was still in Picasso's circle, photographed by Duncan at the artist's villa in Cannes, *La Californie.*

Who would have attached any importance to the arrival of these very young men? It was the time, as Fagus wrote shortly thereafter, of *L'Invasion espagnole,* the invasion of Paris by Spanish painters. But who took notice of Rimbaud when he too came to Paris thirty years earlier? Rimbaud came for poetry, Picasso for painting, simply that.

When we try to distinguish what comes from Barcelona and what comes from Paris in the work of the autumn of 1900 the most striking thing on reflection is that nothing in the sketches or in the finished paintings shows that there was a Universal Exhibition in Paris from May to November. The Exhibition completely transformed the fine western districts of Paris, the Concorde, the Champs-Elysées and the approach to the Invalides. It left us the Pont Alexandre III, the Grand-Palais and the Petit-Palais, but Picasso had certainly not come to Paris to inspect these showpieces. There were however also two painting retrospectives, a centennial and a decennial. Thanks to Roger Marx, and much to the horror of Monsieur Gérome of the Institut, both exhibitions included the Impressionists. There were even three Cézannes to be seen at the centennial exhibition. This had a Spanish section; No. 79 was called *The Last Moments*[1] and it was the work of somebody called Pablo Ruiz Picasso.

Of Paris, only Montmartre and the *fortifs,* the poor quarters of the outlying boulevards, meant anything to Picasso. The misery of the town and its night life. Lautrec and Steinlen above all dealt with the same themes. Does this prove that Picasso copied them? Or does it mean only that he was interested in the same things as his older contemporaries? Or did Picasso see only the Paris of those artists who endowed the new century with a new vision? In any case it was the darkness of a city which was already called *The City of Light,* ever since the appearance of the *fairy electricity* at the preceding Universal Exhibition in 1889. It was a different city from the Paris which the official painters or the Impressionists cared to see, the former through blindness, the latter by choice. Nor was it the Paris of Seurat, of Signac or the Nabis. But what Picasso found he had already seen and remembered from Barcelona. This accords with what we know or guess of his modernism, of his *Nietzscheism,* of his rebellion.

It was also a way of following in the steps of his predecessors in the narrowest sense, the painters of the Spanish colony, and particularly Nonell whose studio in Montmartre he took over. Nonell exhibited in Paris with the *Peintres Impressionistes et Symbolistes* in 1897, then at Le Barc de Bouteville's and finally at Vollard's in 1899.[2] These exhibitions were reviewed in *La Revue Blanche* by Félicien

[1] Perhaps the painting *Science and Charity* which had already gained prizes at Madrid and Malaga; or perhaps another painting depicting a young priest praying by the bedside of a dying woman, which was hung in the *Quatre Gats* exhibition in February, 1900. Picasso no longer knows exactly.
[2] Joan Merli, page 36.

Fagus which shows that he was already interested in modern Spanish painting and that his article on Picasso's exhibition at Vollard's in 1901 was part of a more general preoccupation. Fagus was struck by "the Spanish types, beggars and sorceresses, repatriated soldiers (from Cuba) who are eaten up by fever and consumption, dazed women praying... everything which could make the abasement of a noble people unbearable, a people who had been brutalized and dulled by poverty, slavish ignorance and bigotry. Scenes and people like these recall, without flinching, the gloomy news items of Goya, as does their technique."[1]

Nonell must be included with Steinlen and Lautrec when one attempts to find out what interested and influenced Picasso at this period of his life. But when their influence is pointed out in the usual way, it is above all the difference between Picasso and those painters who had not seen the blackness of Paris which is remarked on. The fact is that Picasso appears as a "committed" painter (if this anachronism is permitted) when he is compared with everyone of importance in painting at the time and even with the younger painters, Matisse, Marquet and Bonnard, for example. The parallel with Nonell and Steinlen is in the manner of approaching life rather than in that of painting it. With Lautrec, the ties are profound and complex, but of a different kind, as we shall see.

But Picasso did not decide to go to Paris merely to find Nonell again. He went to see the new painting, to study on the spot the Impressionists and the Pointillists, of whom he spoke so badly in 1897 in his letter to Bas that he must have known their work already. Picasso undoubtedly did everything he could to familiarize himself with what was being painted and there was certainly no lack of occasions in that autumn of 1900, not only in the retrospectives of the Exhibition but also at the dealers. At Vollard's there was an exhibition of Cézanne and there were also Van Goghs, Gauguins and the Nabis. Berthe Weill no doubt already had Matisses and Marquets. Picasso's curiosity was indefatigable; the certainty of his glance, his flair and his visual memory were unbeatable.

The most remarkable thing is that Picasso was going to take his time to digest and integrate what he had learned. This perhaps was one of the reasons for his return to Spain at Christmas. In fact the influence of what was stirring in

painting in Paris is not noticeable in his work until about six months later, not before April or May, 1901, in Barcelona. It was only then that the divisionist method, for example, came to maturity, at the same time as the heightening of color. It was as if Picasso had assimilated all the most advanced experiments and then created all at once the Fauvism *avant la lettre,* whose exuberance struck his contemporaries at the Vollard exhibition. But it will make itself known in another conception of the role of painting, one which dealt equally with bohemian and decadent subjects, and with the luxuries and pleasures of the *belle époque.*

The relationship between Picasso and the outside world seems to have been established from this period. It is a direct, sincere, natural relationship. Picasso the painter expresses what influences and conditions his existence. In Barcelona he painted arenas because he had been going to bullfights since childhood. In Paris he went to horse races, just as he went to the cafés, to the Moulin-Rouge and to the Moulin de la Galette. He needed this nocturnal life and so it must become part of his painting. We can be sure that he never went out looking for a scene to paint. First it must have impregnated him; it must have become so familiar that it became part of him. It is probable that *Street Scene* (11. 11) shows one of his familiar routes from the rue Gabrielle.

This sort of reaction and also, no doubt, the unfamiliar sadness of the Parisian autumn accounts for the rather low production of the first stay and, inversely, for the extraordinary richness of the second. He had certainly prepared himself for the second trip, knowing already what awaited him, and having in a way forged the instrument that was necessary to capture what he wanted to paint of Paris. Not that this first stay caught him entirely unawares, for Picasso had not arrived from the depths of the provinces.

In his adolescent drawings it is noticeable that he never worries about finish except for the Ecole des Beaux-Arts. His drawings from the model of 1897, like his painting *Science and Charity,* are conscientious exercises. They are very well done but Picasso is not in them, except when he shows his father as a doctor. He knew, one might say from birth, that his integrity as a painter lay in what he saw and understood of reality, and not in anecdote or in rules of presentation. The contradiction that was Courbet's stumbling block was alien to him. Courbet wrote, with

[1] *La Revue Blanche,* December 15, 1900.

The Artist's Father, 1898, Conté crayon.

L'Après-Dîner à Ornans in mind: "An artificial color, whose real nature escapes us, cannot be painted." But Jean Cassou recalled that when Courbet was painting a pile of faggots which was too far away for him to identify precisely, he simply noted down its optical appearance with a few patches of color. He left it to a friend to go to the spot to identify the object which was represented, but not described, in this way. As Pierre Francastel said, "Courbet's vision was more modern than his theory."

For the young Picasso, on the other hand, immediate legibility was secondary; and it was contrary to art and building on a lie to add details which were not meaningful in the vision of reality but important only for legibility.

The paintings of his youth which Picasso keeps in his villa, *La Californie,* those reproduced for the first time by David Douglas Duncan, are perfectly explicit in this respect. When the fourteen year old boy needed to use the resources of the academy in order to pass an examination he knew how to use them all: the *Old Couple* in the Provincial Museum of Malaga or the *Portrait of a Man* done at La Corogne, both of which date from 1895, are remarkable demonstrations of this.

But in the same year, 1895, Picasso painted for himself at home a *Flight into Egypt* (Duncan, p. 41) in which everything is invention. The truly oriental appearance of the house astonished Duncan, who for a long time was a reporter in the Middle East. The originality is also notable in the dates hanging on the palm tree, which Duncan interprets as an image of the Holy Spirit, in the glow of the sky and in the depiction of the Holy Family. Their forms are barely distinguished from the dark brown of the earth by a light which falls on Joseph's tender glance and the Child's face. Nothing is painted which is not necessary; the dates are there "because they really had to eat something!" as Picasso exclaimed to Duncan some sixty-five years afterwards. But the faces are scarcely indicated and the silhouettes still less. It is as if already, at the age of fourteen, Picasso had eliminated everything from his painting that was not indispensable for the plastic vision he wanted to produce, instinctively joining the truth of art to the truth of content in his painting.

The year of *Science and Charity* also saw the production of a small portrait of his father (Duncan, p. 47), full-length, a silhouette which seems to be against a background of sea and night. There is only a portion of the face between the hair and the collar of the vast overcoat; all the rest is abstract in the real meaning of the term. And yet anyone who is familiar with the more highly-developed portraits of his father (for example, the watercolor of 1895 reproduced by Penrose or the drawing reproduced here) will find in this featureless image not only his father's likeness but also his stance, his state of mind and his profound melancholy at this time.

The painting with which we commence this catalogue (I. 1.) is also a night piece. This scene in the *Barrio Chino,* the prostitutes' quarter in Barcelona, is at the same time a work of extreme brutality and of great sobriety. Nothing is shown and yet everything is said. Four gas lamps piercing the darkness, the silhouettes of drinkers and prostitutes—that is enough. But it is not the audacity of the subject that limits the painter. He paints all that a passer-by would have seen, nothing more. He shows only what is necessary to construct the rest mentally. Once more Picasso shows that he has total confidence in his vision, that he understands it and that he bases his painting on it alone—not on the reality outside him, not on details of local color, not on what he could not see, what he would have had to reconstruct or add. He is not a theoretical painter. He paints the essential, only what is necessary. He asks of the spectator the same labor that reality itself would have exacted from him.

Streetwalker (I. 1) is not a small painting and it foreshadows *Le Moulin de la Galette* (II. 10), painted about a year later. This time it is the Montmartre night; not a night scene of sailors' dives and gaslight, but a night with modern lights, electricity. Of course Lautrec had been here before. But while *Streetwalker,* very appropriately named, reveals Picasso's spontaneous taste for subjects that in Paris would have seemed the province of Lautrec, it also shows that what Picasso borrowed from Lautrec was above all the certainty that painting could concern itself with such scenes, that it could say everything. In fact there is no real pictorial borrowing from Lautrec here or anywhere else. And before the Blue Period Picasso hardly ever utilized the flat, pale colors of his predecessor, or Lautrec's taste for the arabesque in composition. *The Café-Theater del Paralelo* (I. 8) is further evidence, as it goes just as far as *Streetwalker* in its elisions. It seizes the movement of the dancers on the stage and the postures of the spectators in a few touches of color, the impasto and ruggedness of the paint

indicating at the same time the forms, relief, gestures, depth.

The methodical way in which this nineteen year old boy experimented with the possibilities or more exactly, the specific qualities of different media, is symptomatic. Henceforth Picasso is a pragmatic painter. His charcoal drawings play upon the relationship between the line and the grain of the paper, as do his drawings in colored crayon. He utilized the irridescence of pastel with the virtuosity of Degas and, as soon as he mastered this, blended the pastels with oils or turpentine wash. When he used oils he respected the nature of his material, retaining in the brushstroke the imprint of the gesture which applied it.

This does not mean that Picasso had already found his way but only that he was precociously posing for himself many problems at the same time. In fact paintings in a classical technique do exist. The *Portrait of Lola* (I. 17) or *The Encounter* (I. 20) remind us that Picasso was at the age of hesitations. However it is more important to discern the significant stages in his development, rather than to interpret works whose chronological sequence is unknown in military terms of advances and retreats. Picasso was groping in a world that was also groping. We see that now with the clear perception of those who know that Cézanne and Van Gogh were right. But we must forget this when dealing with a boy who certainly had not seen paintings by Cézanne or Van Gogh before his first stay in Paris and probably not even works by Manet or Degas.

Perhaps the most moving aspect of these youthful experiments is the evidence they give that the fundamental problems of Impressionism were not just the concern of a limited group but were the real problems of a whole epoch. The taste for non-classical *mises-en-page,* for example, came spontaneously to Picasso. Studying the *Café-Theater del Paralelo* (I. 8), *The Divan* (I. 10) or the *Woman with a Shawl* (I. 19) one can see how he gave long reflection to this problem. The framing of the *Moulin de la Galette* is the result; it cuts diagonally two-thirds of the woman in the left foreground and diverts the couple on the extreme right from the spectacle. Should one see here only reactions to or imitations of Degas and his new concept of pictorial space? It would be foolhardy to assert this, first because there is no reason to believe that Picasso had already seen the works which could have led him in this direction (*The Woman with a Vase, A Ballet seen from a Box, Le Café-Concert des Ambassadeurs* or the various *Tubs* of 1886), but above

LE MOULIN DE LA GALETTE, PARIS, 1900, OIL. THE SOLOMON R. GUGGENHEIM MUSEUM, NEW YORK, JUSTIN K. THANNHAUSER FOUNDATION (II. 10).

all because it was literally only after Cubism that we understood to what degree Degas had broken with classical perspective. It is exactly the same in the case of Lautrec. Pierre Francastel, who has contributed more than anybody to understanding the importance of the new pictorial space created by the Impressionists, notes for example that "Degas' *Woman with a Vase* is the most typical example of a whole series of disarticulations of Alberti's cube which are nevertheless based on the conservation of the cube. It is more a question of irregularities of *mise-en-page* than of a rupture. It does not go beyond an academic exercise." To imagine that painters felt the necessity of breaking away from classical perspective when they clearly did not believe it to be possible only amounts to reversing the problem.

The important thing here is not the compromise but the novelty. The novelty lies in the fact that the painter—Degas, Lautrec, Gauguin[1], Picasso or Bonnard—abandons both the *mise-en-scène* of his subject and its corollary, the reproduction of this *mise-en-scène* for a well-placed spectator. The space of the painting is no longer the same as the space of those who are looking at it. It is possible that the cutting of people or objects by the *mise-en-page* resulted from the naturalist concern to reproduce the accidents of real appearances, and that for the young Picasso these bold framing devices brought the added satisfaction of clashing with the dictates of the *Ecole*. But this is secondary to the result of these experiments: painters learned that classical perspective was neither indispensable nor a natural law. And as a side effect they learned intuitively what science was then saying in its own language, namely that homogeneous three-dimensional space is a convenient abstraction and a special case.

Street Scene (II.11) does not pose any particular problems in its concept of space, showing simply Picasso's interest in the plunging views over the city from the Hill of Montmartre. But the series of *Lovers* (II.12, 13, 14) shows characteristically how Picasso, from the beginning of his stay in Paris, was no longer satisfied with traditional solutions implying homogeneous space whose depth is given by triangulation towards the vanishing point.

In the two open-air scenes, *Lovers in the Street* (II.12) and

Idyll on the Outer Boulevards (II.13), the couple is in both cases disproportionate to the landscape, which is itself treated in normal perspective. As a result this background emphasizes even more the disproportion of the couple. This disproportion is internal this time and of an expressionist nature[2]. It is as if the space of the couple were separate from the urban space, which is not shown merely to give breadth, like the *veduta* of the quattrocento, but to serve at the same time both the meaning of the theme—the embrace in public—and its plastic significance.

The interior version of the *Embrace,* in the Pushkin Museum (II.14), the most famous of the series, is also the one in which the distortions are most striking because this time the contrast is between two nontraditional spaces. The couple has perhaps even more breadth, especially the man, who now completely envelops the woman he embraces. The sloping attic allows an unusual framing which plays upon the classical illusion of depth. The result is that the effort of interpretation demanded of the spectator is a double one, and this too underlines the meaning: the meeting of this proletarian couple, the physical urge which throws them towards each other, the enormous bed in the very small room.

This series is of interest for the understanding it gives of Picasso's creative process. It seems likely that it is based on the sight of lovers embracing in public, an unusual one for a Spaniard just arrived in Paris, and that he treated it first as one way of taking possession of Paris by capturing both the formal and social content of the subject with the maximum of decision and clarity. The preparatory drawing (page 118) is notable for the deliberate nature of its abstractions, its elisions. The pastel version (II.12) is neither more clumsy nor less finished than the Barcelona portraits, but Picasso was no longer interested in the same things. He was no longer concerned with recording the folds of clothing or the details of faces. He sought the gesture, and in the same way that Degas treated *In the Loge,* an exactly contemporary work, it was enough for Picasso to indicate the red patch of the lips, the black mark of the eye and the shape of the coiffure for the woman to be there; there was no longer any need to distinguish the man's profile: just the shadows

[1] Gauguin's contract with Vollard dates from March, 1900. Picasso could have seen at Vollard's, Rue Lafitte, canvases from Pont-Aven, interesting for their *mise-en-page*.

[2] Cf. Jean Adhémar, who has noted this characteristic of Lautrec in his catalogue of the lithographs: "He is above all an Expressionist, one of the very first French Expressionists, after Daumier."

HARLOT WITH HAND ON HER SHOULDER, PARIS, 1901, OIL. PICASSO MUSEUM, BARCELONA (V. 11).

beneath the arch of the eyebrows and jaw and everything is said, everything is implied by its absence.

Picasso had undoubtedly seen how Lautrec handled the professional kiss of *Reine de Joie* and, in certain respects, his *Lovers in the Street* are pastel versions of the lithographs of his older contemporary. In *The Embrace,* the flat patch of the skirt, the movement of the woman's arms and the elisions in the sleeves of the man's blue shirt show similarly the transposition into oils of the simplifications of lithography. Lautrec in some way had a direct effect on Picasso's vision and plastic ideas, but not in details or through his picturesque subject matter. What is significant is that the lithographs and posters—more accessible certainly, but also more modern—first influenced Picasso. However he transformed, transcribed and experimented with his sources as a scientist would proceed from an experiment carried out by a colleague.

These paintings define the questions that Picasso was already asking himself about the meaning, the content of his work as a painter, questions about composition, the objectivity of the work of art. They also demonstrate a way of working which would become characteristic, the exploration of problems through a series of paintings on the same theme. They are not simply variations dictated by external circumstances, as in the case of Monet, nor are they even repeated struggles with the world and nature, as in the case of Cézanne's *Card Players* or the *Mont Sainte-Victoire* series, but rather they represent a reasoned, deliberate exploration of ways of realizing the creative idea that the painter carried within himself.

Picasso at the age of twenty had no intention either of sacrificing the expression of his feelings or of sacrificing plastic coherence to the requirements of the composition. If that led to a deformation of appearances, so be it! *The Embrace* proclaims this with so much force that it is surprising not to find it remarked upon by the commentators of the period.

It is true that Picasso's paintings in 1900 did not correspond to any of the current concepts, either on the art of the time or on the progress of the painter. The idea of *The Embrace* had also occurred to Munch, who produced a series of woodcuts between 1897 and 1902 in which the entwined lovers gradually dissolve into one another, but the preliminary drawings for *The Embrace* show that the pictorial development was Picasso's own. And one must

Young Woman, Paris, July 1901, colored crayons.

remember that this first series of *Lovers* in 1900 is the prelude not only to *The Embrace* of 1903 and to *La Vie*, but equally to everything in the work to come in which "deformation" resulted from respect for the essential nature of the object painted.

Le Moulin de la Galette (II. 10) and *Le Cancan* (II. 16) strike us first by their subjects, and these are works, especially *Le Cancan*, which most clearly recall the anecdotal content of Lautrec; but in fact they are part of an inventory of Paris by night which leads to *The Shirt Fronts, The Conversation* (II. 17 and 18), and to *The Blue Dancer* (II. 23). In these Picasso continued to experiment with the solutions which he found in Lautrec's posters and lithographs, and the solutions here may have been developed from *La Goulue at the Moulin Rouge* or the *May Milton* poster which Picasso represented on the wall of his Boulevard de Clichy studio in his painting *The Blue Room*. But his personal contribution is all the more striking.

Now that he had settled in Montmartre it was normal that Picasso should go to the places which his elders had just made fashionable. His temperament led him to measure himself against new and difficult visual realities like the shows illuminated by electric light, then in its infancy. Lautrec's *Dance at the Moulin Rouge* of 1890 may be painting's first attempt to master this new light, and the electric light bulbs are perhaps the clearest point of comparison with Picasso's painting. Jean Adhémar[1] recalls the remark of Lucien Muhlfeld who said apropos of Lautrec's *Moulin Rouge*, that there the electric light bulbs diffused "a dazzling, false day, dull whites and brutal shadows, an artificial light like the theater." In *La Goulue Entering the Moulin Rouge between Two Women, At the Moulin Rouge* and *Loïe Fuller at the Folies-Bergère*, which date from 1892–1893, Lautrec struggled with Muhlfeld's "dazzling, false day", the bluish, greenish reflections of this cold light, the patches of light breaking the rule of uniform distribution.

Picasso himself painted the night, pierced now by electricity, as in Barcelona he had painted it pierced by gaslight. But the subject is not the same for the two painters. Lautrec paints La Goulue, Valentin le Désossé, the Moulin Rouge, while Picasso represents an anonymous dance which he had seen one night in Montmartre and which turned out to be *Le Moulin de la Galette*. Lautrec painted his world with complicity, amusement and sympathy; Picasso painted the spectacle which he seized through its very novelty. The women's lipstick, the feathers in their hats, the flesh of their faces, everything which catches the artificial light, and nothing more, set against the black background of the men's suits and the patches of shadow—this treatment created a type of painting never seen before. With amazing audacity Picasso chose to distinguish only what his own vision distinguished, and yet everything is there—the brightness of the electricty, the winter costumes, the mixture of fashionable people slumming and the girls. The result is not at all like a Lautrec but it is clear that Lautrec has passed this way. Lautrec but not Renoir.

As in the case of the Impressionists and Van Gogh, Lautrec's influence on the twenty-year-old Picasso as we understand it did not operate definitively nor all at once. On the contrary, he displayed extreme care in dealing with the fundamental questions of his art, never ceasing to explore all the possibilities, all the consequences of his experiments; his prudence in this respect was in contrast to his remarkable rapidity in execution. He has never hesitated to measure himself against the painters who were important to him, but always after a long, very intimate acquaintance. The impatience and ardor of his twenty years cannot be dealt with in terms of years but in months; nevertheless, haste is one thing that can never be seen in Picasso.

2. *The Return to Spain*

We are no better informed about Picasso's return to Spain than we are about his departure for Paris. Was it because of lack of money,[2] fatigue, the need to digest what he had learned? At the end of three months Picasso left for Malaga in the company of Casagemas who shortly thereafter committed suicide on his return to Paris. Picasso was in Madrid in January; he intended to settle there and founded a review, *Arte Joven*, but he stayed briefly, probably just long enough to see the first number come out, March 31, 1901. He made a quick trip to Barcelona, but as his painting

---

[1] *Lithographies de Toulouse-Lautrec*, page x.

[2] It seems unlikely because the dealer Pedro Mañach paid him a monthly salary... (see Sabartés, *Picasso, Portraits et Souvenirs*). But when we were speaking about this period Picasso remarked that the train journey from Paris to Barcelona was then comparatively much more expensive than today; 150 francs, he said.

reveals he had already decided to return to Paris, where he arrived in May at the latest.

If we examine the surviving works, we form the impression that Picasso had left Paris without any desire to return. What we know of the work done in Malaga shows no trace of the three months in Paris. Were it not for the dates, these drawings could be associated with those done in the summer of 1900 in Barcelona. And yet they are distinguished by a certain hardness, a sort of bitterness, or perhaps anger, which continued to characterize the works done in Madrid. It is not simply the restricting influence of the return to his native country. Picasso makes us feel that he was returning to the attack as if nothing had happened in Paris, as if he had painted neither *Le Moulin de la Galette* nor the series of *Lovers*.

On the whole, however, his vision appears more satirical. The relatively large number of drawings for *Arte Joven* are often in a grating style and the important paintings also show the same state of mind. The model for the *Woman with a Plumed Hat* (III. 4) is treated with a cruel objectivity which foreshadows the portraits of courtesans of the summer of 1901 in Paris. The large canvas, *Woman in Blue* (III. 5) has something about it perhaps even more brutal and animal, a quality which will be found again in the heroines of the pastels. Should this be seen as a misogyny resulting from the circumstances of Casagemas' suicide or as a more general bitterness? In any case, it is an attitude without complacency or illusions, not only towards his female models but towards life as well. We know from Sabartés that Picasso suffered from the cold that winter and that he had barely enough to live on.

The long, decisive brush marks of the *Woman with a Plumed Hat* or the *Woman in Blue* are almost a translation into oil of the pastel strokes in works like the *Woman in Green* (III. 7), the *Lady in Blue* (III. 12) or the *Seated Woman* (III. 8). But just as at the end of the preceding period at Barcelona we found complex pastels combined with turpentine or even oil, so the Madrid period includes *Woman with a Dog* (III. 9) and *The Spanish Woman* (III. 11), oils that in reproduction have often been confused with pastels. They have an additional interest in that they offer, treating similar subjects, what are probably the first attempts to introduce the distinct brush marks, divided and highly colored, which were to characterize the paintings at the Vollard exhibition.

Paris could only have reinforced Picasso's liking for high color, already seen in complex pastels like *Entrance to the Bullring* (II. 8) or *The Gipsy Girl* (II. 9), executed in Barcelona. What was born under the Spanish sun was soon enriched by a wider knowledge of painting, by the experiments of the Impressionists, by acquaintance with the work of Van Gogh and, as we saw, by the exploration of electrically-illuminated nights, in the wake of Toulouse-Lautrec. It is difficult to decide if what was hatching under Picasso's brushes is Impressionism fertilized by the sun of Barcelona and by the lessons of Seurat and Van Gogh or if it was already something quite different, a sort of pre-Fauvism. In the long run, its name is not important. Picasso's originality in this field is undeniable. It helps one to understand the meaning of the subsequent encounters with Braque and Derain, when they abandoned Fauvism.

We are now approaching an important and unjustly neglected moment in the painter's formation. This neglect is perhaps due to the first accounts of this period. They were written at a time when most of the works in question had become inaccessible and could only be known through black and white reproductions, and their polemic purpose has probably falsified the facts of the problem in a lasting way. These accounts are all the more important in that they come from two of Picasso's earliest supporters, two art

Reclining Nude, Barcelona, 1902, pencil drawing.

AT THE RACES, PARIS, 1901, OIL. PRIVATE COLLECTION, FRANCE. UNPUBLISHED IN COLOR (V. 31).

critics: Gustave Coquiot, who was the organizer of his first exhibition in Paris, and Maurice Raynal. "The coloristic problems then posed in Paris," Raynal wrote in 1952 for the special issue of *Le Point,* "worried Picasso immediately, but not for long. In his humanity he considered the brilliant void of Impressionist recipes or naturalist notations rather stupefying." In Maurice Raynal too we find the expressions "the coloristic kitchen of divisionism", or "mining in exhausted veins", phrases which have been repeated often, as well as the more inclusive judgment that these "refined and highly colored notations in Picasso's work represent in the end a sacrifice to fashion".

Raynal's judgment will be more easily assessed if it is noted that in his first important study of Picasso (that of 1921 published by Delphin Verlag, Munich, on which the Crès edition of 1922 is based), he does not reproduce or comment on any of the important paintings of the Vollard exhibition, and he also commits certain chronological errors (since repeated by numerous biographers) relating to the emergence of the blue paintings. The first painting he lists is *Mother and Child* (IX. 7) which he dates 1901, whereas it was done in 1903. After *Mother and Child by a Fountain* (VI. 9), correctly dated 1901, come two works also of 1901, the *Portrait of Sabartés* (VI. 19), which he dates 1902, and *The Fugitives* (VI. 1), which he dates 1903 like *The Soler Family.* In fact it is not until 1906 that one finds a series of correct datings and then it is Raynal who is right and not Zervos; but these paintings date from the time when Raynal was very closely linked with Picasso. However, to be fair to Raynal let us not forget that in 1940 Jean Cassou himself was misled by the resemblance between the *Bullfight* in the Niarchos collection (IV. 6) and *The Wounded Horse* of 1923, displacing the earlier painting by twenty-one years, although he reproduced it in color.

As for Gustave Coquiot, he sums up the period just discussed in the following way: "Arriving in Paris very young, Picasso entered upon his Steinlen period. He painted the street, gardens, houses, the boys and the women of the town. He painted them very quickly, up to as many as ten paintings per day. Soon there were so many that his first exhibition was organized, at Vollard's in June, 1901... He was getting tired of this plagiarism; and from Steinlen he went on to Lautrec..."[1] There is the source of the labels "Steinlen period" and "Lautrec period".

Today we have a better knowledge of the paintings, and it becomes possible to consider the evolution of Picasso's work in 1901, and the numerical and aesthetic importance of the paintings which show his research into color. This knowledge allows only one part of Raynal's judgment to stand: the implication that these experiments did not last very long. They continued for three or four months at most, from May to September. As for the rest of his statement, it is that of a partisan, both the idea of a "sacrifice to fashion" and of "the already exhausted veins".

When we examine closely a major painting like the *Bullfight* in the Niarchos collection (IV. 6) it is evident that the use of pure, high color has nothing to do with divisionism or with anything done before, but it does make it possible for Picasso to deal in oils with a reality of major importance to him, the contrast of light and shade in the arena and the internal movement of this contrast. The other *Bullfight* (IV. 5) which shows almost the whole of the arena, remains impressionist in its use of blue for the shadows, but their opposition to the violent red of the *barrera* in the sun and the brilliance of the red patches of the women's costumes are signs of different preoccupations.

Let us return to the painting in the Niarchos collection which is much more positive. Here, Picasso is concerned only with the small portion of the arena almost entirely in the shade, the zone of sunlight being in the upper right background. The vivid blues which represent the crowd or the bodies of the horses arbitrarily go beyond the reproduction of sense impressions in order to express the violence of the scene. It is as if the deformation of the *Lovers* series was followed by this dazzling dissonance of color, this pursuit of paroxysm with the aid of touches of pure color, in broad areas or broken. The clash of the reds of the capes and the costumes with the red of the *barrera* explores a combination of colors which generate new constructions. The composition in oblique areas stems from the body of a disembowelled horse directly in the foreground, a motif which reappears in 1923, and then in the *Guernica* period.

If this painting is compared with the most highly finished of the complex pastels from the autumn of 1900 representing the same subject (especially II. 5 and II. 6) one can judge how much Picasso has gained in liberty and in power of plastic

[1] Gustave Coquiot, *Cubistes, Futuristes, Passéistes,* published by Ollendorf, Paris, 1914.

BULLFIGHT, BARCELONA, 1901, OIL. COLLECTION STAVROS S. NIARCHOS, ST. MORITZ (IV. 6).

Torero, Barcelona, 1900, India ink.

expression. These *Bullfights* mark Picasso's new mastery in the face of the stimulation of actuality; they demonstrate an ability to reconstruct freely from reality which was to come to fruition half a century later in the paintings done in Cannes or in Mougins. What was to become the essence of Fauvism, "the use of color which has been experienced *(la couleur vécue)*", as Jean Cassou said, is already here in germ. There is no question of establishing a factitious precedence for Picasso, as the names of Delacroix, Gauguin and Van Gogh can also be cited, but simply of underlining the originality and the sincerity of Picasso's experiment in this last spring before his twentieth birthday.

Another painting which is as clearly Spanish as the *Bullfights,* and doubtless from Barcelona, is *The Dwarf Dancer* (IV. 2). It also confirms the nature of Picasso's investi-

gations. Once again it is a subject of the night world, typically Spanish in the flower in the hair and even in the exotic kind of ugliness. It is a reply to Velasquez's dwarf in *Las Meninas,* according to Phoebe Pool, or more probably a souvenir of Goya, but that question is secondary. Just as Picasso experimented with his new manner in bullfight subjects in order to express them with more inner truth, so it is with the dwarf. It is not the sight of the deformity he presents but the way she bears our examination of this deformity without compliance in her glance, as she is spotlighted like a Degas dancer or Lautrec's Jane Avril. The contrasts and dissonances of color are produced against a background of brilliant patches of arbitrary colors. But the colorist's virtuosity is no more gratuitous here than it is in the bullfights. This attempt to represent the transformations of artificial light through color corresponds to the study of the oppositions in the natural play of shadow and light in the bullfights.

This can be seen in a closely related painting, whose subject could equally well be from Barcelona or Paris, *Harlot with Hand on her Shoulder* (V. 11) which was most probably the painting titled *The Morphine Addict* in the Vollard exhibition. If the apparent subject is reminiscent of Lautrec, it is enough to compare this painting with its predecessors to see that Picasso is pursuing a project which is his very own. The same chords of vermilion express different things, the painted lips, the hat, the dress, as well as the rouged cheeks and the multicolored background; the same contrasts with blues represent the hair, the shadow, the hand and the circles under the eyes. In the same way as in *The Dwarf Dancer* he brings us face to face with an extraordinary person, to submit us to her glance and oblige us to go beyond the anecdotal in order to judge both her and her interrogation of us. None of this comes out of imitation or fashion. Its source is in the paintings done in 1900 in Paris but the role of color has changed.

Each time in his life that Picasso undertakes an experiment in form, he verifies it through persons and things that are familiar to him, in order to express what means most to him. There is no doubt that such paintings were influenced by Lautrec and Van Gogh, by the Manet of *The Bar at the Folies-Bergère* and the Seurat of *The Grande Jatte,* but what Picasso seeks in these sources, and shows to us is his alone. *The Dwarf Dancer* or the *Harlot* could be characters from the Blue Period. Then the monochrome will carry the same

PORTRAIT OF PEDRO MAÑACH, PARIS, 1901, OIL. THE NATIONAL GALLERY OF ART, WASHINGTON, D.C., CHESTER DALE COLLECTION (V. 4).

message that the heightening of color and the use of broken brushwork already conveys here. But to master this monochrome Picasso must learn by himself the formal values resulting from encounters of pure colors.

This experiment was very brief. Even if the whole of the Barcelona phase was devoted to it—that is, the month of April—it can scarcely have been continued in Paris for more than a few months, until August. But we have about sixty works, many of them of great importance, and they alone constitute a true period, as rich as it is varied. It would be very wrong to neglect it or to mix it with the Blue Period, under the pretext that Picasso merely flashed through it with the speed of a meteor, sometimes painting two or three canvases a day, piling up pastels and watercolors with the prodigious vitality of his twenty years.

3. *The Vollard Exhibition*

The dates and the subjects of the paintings just discussed, Picasso's habit of subordinating his life to his painting, this new style and this new vision, probably played their part in his decision to leave Spain at the end of such a short stay. Other factors confirm this hypothesis. If Mañach was still giving Picasso a monthly income of 150 francs he expected some pictures in return, so it is extremely improbable that Picasso returned to Paris empty-handed. In any case, it is difficult to imagine how he could have left Barcelona even at the end of April—which seems to be the latest possible date—without some preliminary studies. Equally it is hard

to see how he could have invented his new style, how he could have painted the sixty paintings of the exhibition or how Mañach could have negotiated the exhibition with Coquiot and Vollard, all for June 24, if much had not already been done in Spain.

Moreover, the exhibition itself makes the point very clearly. There are easily a dozen titles which refer to Spanish subjects. Of course Vollard, Coquiot or Mañach emphasized the Spanish note for commercial reasons and because of the presence of Francisco de Iturrino.[1] But even allowing for this, everything compels us to give much more importance to the stay in Barcelona, between Madrid and the return to Paris, than is normally given in Picasso's *œuvre*. In fact, besides the bullfight paintings, *In Front of the Church* (v. 49) and *Spanish Dancer* (IV. 3) must also be assigned to this period, as well as the paintings listed in the Vollard exhibition catalogue under the titles *Montjuich, Spanish Village, Don Tancredo,* and *Toledo* (these we have not been able to identify). There are also two female heads: v. 57, traditionally ascribed to the Spanish period, and v. 58 which is very much of the same type. The flower paintings could have been done in Spain or Paris. One can be sure that Picasso was already carrying some of his new works in the folder seen under his right arm in the drawing in which he represented himself arriving in Paris in the company of Jaume Andreu Bonsons.[2]

But he knew that this style could only be developed in Paris. We shall never know, since Picasso no longer remembers the details, if these canvases were executed and finished in Barcelona or if they were taken up again in Paris, for the facts are more complex than they are normally considered to be. Raynal's idea that Picasso sacrificed himself to fashion is too opposed to everything we know of the painter's character to be retained, but it is nonetheless true that the experiments with heightened color, and the use to that end of divided brushwork—in brief the state of mind that we can call pre-Fauvism—were discernible at the same moment in certain painters of the new generation. And they were not the least important of this generation—first, Marquet and Matisse, who we see, from 1898 onwards, heading towards that next stage after Impressionism in

[1] Iturrino, the Basque painter who exhibited at the same time as Picasso at Vollard's, was born in Bilbao in 1864 and died in Switzerland June 20, 1924.
[2] Reproduced: D. IV. 12.

AT THE CAFÉ DE LA ROTONDE, PARIS, 1901, OIL. COLLECTION MR. AND MRS. DAVID LLOYD KREEGER, WASHINGTON, D.C. (V. 45).

which the painting is given an almost Cézannesque structure based on that strength of color revealed by Seurat's divisionism. This direction is especially clear in their experiment of painting two nudes at the same time and from the same angle.[1]

We have no way of telling if Picasso knew of these researches. But it is certain that he was aiming at almost the same thing: a rapid painting in which color constructs the picture, in which it ceases to be a fugitive effect of light as it was with the Impressionists, and becomes the major reality, the language and means of expression. All this is very close to what Bonnard was trying to do at the same time, and even if the relationship which Pierre de Champris[2]

suggests between Bonnard's painting *The Races* and Picasso's *Longchamp* is not entirely convincing, the resemblances are many and striking. Once again this does not mean that Picasso knew Bonnard's work, but the convergence is all the more interesting for that. If Picasso did not go so far as the chromatic exaggerations which constitute Fauvism, he displayed towards immediate sensorial analysis exactly the same sort of liberty as Bonnard. And in fact, if the manifesto-paintings of the Vollard exhibition are compared with contemporary works of Matisse and Marquet, one is

[1] Cf. the exhibition: *Le Fauvisme français et les débuts de l'expressionisme allemand,* Musée National d'Art Moderne, Paris, 1965.
[2] *Ombre et soleil,* Nos. 254 and 255.

astonished both by their close relationship and by the tranquillity with which Picasso followed his own course, bending the data of nature to what he had to say, and then expressing it above all by the power of color.

If Picasso's future had been that of Matisse, these paintings would unquestionably be seen as the announcement of Fauvism. It is absurd to neglect them because of the subsequent monochrome of the more well-known Blue Period, or because of the absence of color in Cubism, for if they are reintegrated in Picasso's development, their premature Fauvism explains perfectly how Picasso has always maintained this intimacy with the energy of color which illuminated his palette in the spring of 1901. The blue, pink or red monochrome is the sign of somebody who knows, as Jean Cassou wrote of the Fauves, that "every liberty is permitted towards painting as towards reality, as towards the relationship between painting and reality which sclerotic codes claimed to have established forever." To say everything with blues, pinks or ochres, or not to use any color at all, could only be the act of a colorist. It is enough to recall Braque's cry of joy. Braque, the former Fauve, said during the period of colorless Cubism: "We succeeded in clearly disassociating color from form, and in seeing its independence with regard to form, for that was the important thing. Color acts simultaneously with form but has nothing to do with it."

Although we have not been able to study the original versions of a regrettably large number of paintings, especially many belonging to the earliest collectors and not easily accessible, we have enough data to identify the body of works shown at Vollard's. Along with the paintings already discussed, the *Vase of Flowers* in the Tate Gallery (v. 22), and the one in the Phoenix Museum (v. 28), *Woman with Blue Stockings* (v. 62), *Young Girl with a Red Flower* (v. 60), *Old Woman* (Woman with Jewels) (iv. 4), the two *Female Heads* (v. 57, v. 58), *Woman at the Theater* (v. 71), *The Fourteenth of July* (v. 70), *The Café de la Rotonde* (v. 45) and *French Cancan* (v. 55) seem to be particularly representative of this pre-Fauvism which Fagus noted when he wrote: "Like all pure painters, Picasso adores color for itself." The *Little Girl with a Hat* (v. 69), the *Blue Roofs* (v. 21), the *Reclining Nude* (v. 52) show the whole range of Picasso's experiments.

But as always with Picasso this exploration of color has some relationship to the content. One tends to fail to observe the color experiment in a painting such as the *Woman with Blue Stockings* (v. 62) because of the entirely expressionist cruelty of this portrait of an old prostitute. Elsewhere, as in the astonishing series on the races at Auteuil and Longchamp, the spectator is first struck by the virtuosity of the scene; in *Little Girls Dancing* (v. 15) he is overwhelmed by the frantic movement. And if we look at these paintings in context, as part of his total production in the spring of 1901, we are astounded by the number of problems he posed at the same time. In *Longchamp* (v. 34) the finesse of the details, worthy of a miniature, is combined with a play of colors that shows the same boldness as in the preceding interpretations of arenas. As Raynal correctly observed, Picasso may be inspired by reality but he recomposes with great freedom, the freedom of color. Those paintings in which the racecourse scene is seen in detail show on the other hand one of the contradictions in this exploration of color. In these, notably in *At the Races* (v. 31), Picasso felt bound to reintroduce contours to characterize the faces. This also occurs in a painting technically very close to *At the Races, The Diners* (v. 66). Here the connection between the whites of the tablecloth, the dress, the skin, the cuff and the shirt front reminds us very appropriately that white is always an inseparable part of Picasso's experiments with color. In fact, he only indicates contours where a break in the color justifies it, the red of the lips, for example, while he treats the man's shirt front and cuff as one patch of pure white. Thus the unrealistic interpretation of colors and their free confrontation are accompanied by the opposite principle, that is to say by fidelity to the immediate sense impression.

Little Girls Dancing (v. 15) extends the subtle relationships that are seen in *Longchamp*. Blue on green, green on white, a multicolored white streaked with the blue and green of a belt, three light chestnut patches of hair, all against a background in which blue and green are mixed, softened, broken with white or ochre. We can understand Fagus' enthusiasm in the face of this precision of observation but still more striking certainly is the insolence of this man in love with color, on which he relies to express rhythm, movement, forms, and the deformations resulting from the movement. Everything is audacity in this painting; the *mise-en-page* which cuts off the feet of the girl to the left and accentuates her flying movement, the creation of space exclusively by colored rhythms, the representation of gestures as a function of plastic movement. This conflicts with all

WOMAN WITH A JEWELED COLLAR, PARIS, 1901, OIL.
COLLECTION AYALA AND SAM ZACKS, TORONTO (V. 48).

COURTESAN WITH A JEWELED COLLAR, PARIS, 1901, OIL.
LOS ANGELES COUNTY MUSEUM OF ART,
MR. AND MRS. GEORGE GARD DE SYLVA COLLECTION (VI. 17).

academic ideas of resemblance and even with immediate legibility, but in compensation there is an accuracy in the wild movement of the girls which one could believe inspired by the invention of the cinema.

French Cancan (v. 55) displays a similar freedom, and a similar originality, too, in comparison with the pastel of the same subject from the first stay in Paris (II. 16). This vivid, demonic, supple style seems to have been perfectly adapted to his new capturing of Paris which occurred when the cherries were beginning to flower: the Paris of the Boulevard de Clichy, the *bateaux-mouches,* the Moulin-Rouge, the squares and gardens full of children playing. This style con-

tinued after the Vollard exhibition in the *Portrait of Gustave Coquiot* (v. 64) in the Musée National d'Art Moderne, and in *The Fourteenth of July* (v. 70) in the Thannhauser Foundation, Guggenheim Museum.

The Café de la Rotonde (v. 45), the bistro almost directly beneath Picasso's studio, where Casagemas committed suicide, is perhaps the painting which best sums up the audacities of the whole period. Here the *mise-en-page* goes so far as to decapitate the waiter. The colored architecture creates by itself a complete space, as if seating us at the table with the young women. It can be seen how Picasso goes beyond Impressionism to compose a new plastic world through the liberty given to color, similar to that of the Fauves or of Bonnard.

Contrary to the opinion frequently repeated in spite of Zervos' accurate account, Picasso was successful at the time of the Vollard exhibition. The catalogue mentions fifteen works sold before the exhibition and Picasso himself has confirmed that this was true. Success seems to have gone to those paintings which were most Impressionist in appearance but doubtless also to those which show as little sentimentality as Lautrec. The most brutal were not bought right away. *Nude with Cats* (v. 16) must have stayed at Vollard's until Paul Guillaume acquired it. Like the *Woman with Blue Stockings* this painting shows the way in which Picasso challenged the academic theme of the female nude, approaching it with a brutality which had scarcely been known since the end of the Middle Ages. Lautrec showed sympathy for the women in the brothels, a sympathy which was not characteristic of this young man who coldly stripped them, just as he scrutinized the manoeuvres of women intriguing at the races or dining with some old man, just as he painted professional courtesans in all their brazenness.

Jean Sutherland Boggs remarked that Picasso painted his first nudes in Paris, the traditional Spanish prudery having prevented him from dealing with the subject until then. But one should not conclude from this that the cruelty Picasso showed in his portraits of prostitutes had anything to do with Spanish austerity. In the first place the accounts of Picasso's frequent visits to the places where his models were found are precise and numerous. Then, his work itself shows that this was not always his attitude to women. The *Reclining Nude* (v. 52) shows a tenderness and sensuality which are also found in such a drawing as *The Snob and the Naked Woman* (z. 1. 143), done on the back of one of the commercial cards used by Junyer's father in Barcelona, and which were also present in the paintings of the *Lovers* series. Picasso was precocious in his lack of illusions—about Paris, about the fashionable world as well as about the brothels. His painting, which is never unfaithful to his feelings, states this forthrightly. He treats the elegant women at Auteuil or Longchamp as he does the men of the *cuadrilla* in the arena, searching for their truth. Too bad if it is not beautiful. Too bad if the prostitute's body has been hard used. It is not really that Picasso decides for us; rather he presents us with the means of judging. It

is an instantaneous art like that of the camera which seizes on the wing the posture, the gesture and the glance which tell all.

Perhaps we should look in this direction for the reasons behind the change in style after the Vollard exhibition. In fact, comparing three paintings—*The Woman in a Plumed Hat* (III. 4), painted in Madrid and showing the beginning of the evolution towards broken brushwork, the *Woman with a Jeweled Collar* (v. 48), and the *Courtesan* (VI. 17) a later painting dealing with the same subject—it can be seen that the freedom with respect to the model has become increasingly more pronounced. The Madrid painting still seems to be determined by the girl's position, like a snapshot except for the movement of the long, vigorous brush marks which embrace the form in a sort of blue-green monochrome, curiously anticipating the Blue Period proper by a good six months. The *Woman with a Jeweled Collar* is harder. There is no doubt that the model has changed. She has the greedy, insensitive, bestial mask of the *Nude with Cats* (v. 16). But above all the painter has stepped away. He has diverted her gaze from us, fastened on the curves of the hat and has sketched the rhythm of the body. Finally, with the *Courtesan,* the transformation is complete. Everything contributes to the expression of the subject: the hat itself is a symbol of conquest, the line of the ringlets on the forehead, the plunge of the decolletage with the movement of the arms cut short by the edge of the canvas. The expressionist deformation of *The Lovers* is here fertilized both by the experiment with strong color and by the return to line, a line which shows an awareness of the arabesques of Art Nouveau and the whiplash line of Lautrec.

Already in the Madrid painting Picasso had emphasized the effect of the many-stranded jeweled necklace which raises the head and evokes the predatory female aspect of the character at the same time as it provides a play of light drawn from the real object. In the second painting the necklace has as it were subsided into the decolletage, while the third on the contrary accentuates the giraffe neck and derives its strength and its poise from this distortion. Basically it is as if, in Madrid, Picasso had still been searching for his plastic language and was still dominated by his experiments; in Paris, in June, he was guided by them, docile to their suggestions; while in the autumn he treated them on equal terms, making use of them for what he had to express, using the reality of what was to be said to give free rein to color, arabesque and the rhythms resulting from their combinations.

Picasso's creative ferment should not be reduced to this linear scheme. The painting most like the *Woman in the Plumed Hat* is *The Absinthe Drinker* (v. 12) which is generally agreed to have been painted in Paris because of the glass of absinthe. This was almost certainly the *Absinthe* of the Vollard exhibition which was not sold at the exhibition and stayed at Vollard's until purchased, by Paul Guillaume once again. The color and the divided brushwork already show themselves but whereas the Madrid painting is in a general blue-green tonality, here Picasso contrasts pure colors. In view of its general character and its naturalism, should this painting be included in the Madrid period? Or was Picasso stimulated by a particular Parisian scene to take up again a technique tried and abandoned in Madrid? Even at this tender age Picasso was the experimentalist we know today. Nothing prevents him from painting several canvases simultaneously in different modes. We never have more than the dates of completion or publication, a fact we should always bear in mind. This does not contradict another fact, namely that the moment Picasso ceases to find any interest in a particular line of research, he abandons it once and for all. He often uses the same theme again as a basis for new experiments but without ever adopting the easy way out of relying on a formula that has already been verified.

4. *The Stained Glass Period*

This expression, used to describe works like the *Courtesan with a Jeweled Collar* (VI. 17), was coined by Félicien Fagus, Picasso's first critic. His notice of Picasso's exhibition at Vollard's, published in *La Revue Blanche* of July, 1901, is extremely important and he wrote a second article in September, 1902, devoted to the April exhibition at Berthe Weill's. Fagus was aware of Picasso's novelty and force. He was then a twenty-eight year old anarchist and poet, but later changed his ideas sufficiently to become a royalist and he disappeared from Picasso's horizon almost immediately. But the testimony he left us on the painter is of capital importance. (Cf. Documents, appendix.)

At least three paintings of the summer of 1901 bear witness to the persistence of Picasso's chromatic experiments: the *Portrait of Gustave Coquiot* (v. 64) in the Musée

National d'Art Moderne, *The Flower Seller* (v. 65) which could be taken for a Bonnard, and *The Fourteenth of July* (v. 70), which was to be seen again at the Berthe Weill exhibition in April, 1902, with a certain number of paintings in the new style that concerns us now. *The Fourteenth of July* is probably one of the earliest examples of the pre-Fauvism which was already seen in the Barcelona pictures. *Little Girl with a Hat* (v. 69) and *Bibi la Purée* (v. 74) are less clearly datable, but are among the most characteristic examples of Picasso's divisionist experiments. The *Still Life (La Desserte)* (v. 72)—most probably identifiable with the *Still Life,* the only one from this period, at the Berthe Weill exhibition—was foreshadowed to some extent in *The Diners. Le Gourmand* (v. 53), traditionally identified with the *White Child* of the Vollard exhibition, is hardly distinguishable in technique from the *Child Holding a Dove* (VI. 14). The contours in the former are more emphatic, but the long, melting touches and the harmonies of greens, blues and whites are much closer to *Little Girls Dancing* than to the flat areas of the Stained Glass Period proper. The fact that the tonality of the *White Child* is predominantly blue simply confirms the danger of attempting to classify everything too neatly.

The admirable *Woman at the Theater* (v. 71) in the Charles Im Obersteg collection is one of the most characteristic canvases in the style of the Vollard exhibition. We do not know if it was shown there, and in any case it was not sold as it was in Picasso's possession again in the autumn when he painted *Girl with Folded Arms* (VI. 25) on the back of the canvas. Exactly the same thing happened to *Little Girl with a Hat* (v. 69), on the back of which is *Woman with a Chignon* (VI. 23). These canvases painted on both sides point to Picasso's material difficulties at the beginning of the autumn and probably to the fact that Vollard must have found himself saturated with the young artist's overabundant production. Picasso not only painted the versos of his pictures but practiced an even greater economy by barely covering the canvas in contrast to the thick paint used in the preceding summer.

Examining this transitional period more closely, we are struck by the existence of a group of works which show that the passage from the Vollard exhibition style to the stained glass style could not have happened as simply as the series of courtesans' heads might lead one to think. In this group of paintings the emphasis is placed on the composition, on the rhythm of the contours. Unfortunately they are often very little known, especially *Children in the Luxembourg Gardens* (VI. 3) and *The Fugitives* (VI. 1), which reminds us that at that very moment there was a great Daumier exhibition at the Ecole des Beaux-Arts. On the other hand, the four paintings on the death of Casagemas are particularly significant for the change in the painter's state of mind (VI. 2, 4, 5 and 6). They are grouped here for the first time thanks to Picasso who has revealed the two unpublished works that remained in his collection.

Picasso turned abruptly away from the spectacle of the outside world to explore his inmost feelings. We have already encountered Casagemas, Picasso's companion in the adventures of Barcelona and of the first journey to Paris. He killed himself on February 17, 1901, as established by the police report, which we were able to locate through Picasso's reminiscences and publish here for the first time[1]. The report confirms the reasons for the suicide which were already known, but it also informs us that Casagemas and Pallarés, that is to say both of Picasso's close friends that autumn, and Manuel Hugué (Manolo), lived at 130 *ter* Boulevard de Clichy, perhaps in Mañach's apartment. In any case, when Picasso settled there during his second stay in Paris, the café in which his friend killed himself was literally beaneath his eyes, four houses away at no. 128.[2] As we have seen, he preserved the appearance of the café in the painting traditionally called *Café de la Rotonde* (V. 45), almost certainly exhibited at Vollard's. It is possible that this was the name of the café then, although today it is called *Palace-Clichy*.

Picasso was badly stricken by this event which happened in his absence. The first work (VI. 5) directly related to this death must date from the summer of 1901. It is in bright colors with thick impasto and is fairly close to the Vollard style. The second (VI. 6) is larger and less naturalistic, already foreshadowing *Evocation (The Burial of Casagemas)* (VI. 4), as much by the blue monochrome as the kind of idealization it breathes.

The Mourners (VI. 2) marks a new stage, an increased remoteness, as if Picasso had started from a close-up, then retreated to take in more and more of the field with each stage. Here the details are eliminated; only the contours of the faces remain and the group of mourners is reduced to a general silhouette. As in *The Fugitives,* Picasso proceeds by elisions, in the manner of Cézanne with his series of *Bathers*. *Evocation* treats the same scene from an even greater distance, from so far that the distances of memory are also abolished and the group in mourning around Casagemas' deathbed is placed beneath figures of naked girls in the sky, and still higher there is a scene of romantic parting between a horseman and a nude woman who embraces him. The dominant blue is very marked here too, in spite of the red and green patches of the girls' stockings.

The surviving studies for *Evocation* show that Picasso hesitated between an idea for an entombment, rather in the tradition of that of Christ, and a scene placing in opposition the stiff corpse of Casagemas and a naked woman floating above him in front of the group of mourners. Phoebe Pool compares this painting with Odilon Redon's *Temptation of St. Anthony* and Cézanne's *Apotheosis of Delacroix*. It is certain in any case that Picasso here gives a powerful impetus towards plastic construction, towards the dominance of the compositional rhythms and it is not out of the question, as Joan Merli believes, that he was thinking again of El Greco, *The Martyrdom of St. Maurice* in particular.

With the exception of the three *Mother and Child* paintings (V. 7, 8 and 10), which belong to the beginning of the style of the Vollard exhibition, the other *Maternities* of 1901 are difficult to classify with precision; in one case, as we shall see, Picasso's help proved invaluable. *The Mother* (V. 9) seems a link between the style of the Vollard exhibition and the experiments of the Stained Glass Period. It has the emphatic, thick brushwork and the brilliant chromatism of the former style, the interest in landscape, here with its summer light, its background of fields waiting to be harvested and a village with slate and tile roofs. But the simplifications within the powerfully stressed contours and the solid construction belong to the Stained Glass Period. The characteristics of the style of the Vollard exhibition are seen again in the *Mother and Child* (X. 9) in the Niarchos collection. This is the painting, traditionally dated 1903–1904, which Picasso told us was done in 1901. Here the curvilinear construction is accompanied by the rigid mannerist elongations of the arms, and especially of the hands. This style marks the very beginning of the Blue Period in

---

[1] Reproduced in appendix: Documents, page 338.

[2] In fact there is a 128 *bis,* a 128 *ter,* a 130 and a 130 *bis.* The quarter has been considerably changed since 1901 by the construction of a big cinema and a lycée, but the group of buildings in question has not been touched. (Cf. *Boulevard de Clichy,* v. 30.)

WOMAN WITH A CAP, PARIS, 1901, OIL.
COLLECTION OF THE ARTIST. UNPUBLISHED IN COLOR (VI. 12).

WOMAN IN A BATHROBE, PARIS, 1901, OIL.
COLLECTION OF THE ARTIST. UNPUBLISHED IN COLOR (VI. 13).

the winter of 1901 and it is particularly evident in *Woman with a Cigarette* (VI. 26). In our opinion, these *Mother and Child* paintings are works that were either begun in the summer and finished later, or they formed part of Picasso's first experiments with the emphasizing of formal compositional rhythms. The style of *The Mother* (V. 9) and *Mother and Child* (X. 9), as well as the landscapes seen in them, indicate that they were painted in the summer of 1901.

The other *Maternities* of this transitional period seem later than these two works, especially VI. 11 and *Mother and Child by a Fountain* (VI. 9), in which can be seen indications of the painting in the Goetz collection (VI. 29). But *Child Holding*

a Dove (VI. 14) and *Woman with a Cap* (VI. 12) belong apparently to the same series of experiments, and *The Blue Room* (VI. 15) and its related study, *Woman in a Bathrobe* (VI. 13), can also be associated with it. We should not be misled by the general bluish tonality. It was already encountered in *The Woman in a Plumed Hat* which dates from the Madrid period, then in *Le Gourmand* and also in *The Blue Roofs;* in fact it is only a dominant color, quite different from the monochrome which characterizes the Blue Period itself.

The rhythm of the composition in some of these paintings is clearly taken from Degas, but the study of the light on the naked body of the woman in *The Blue Room,* the interruptions in the color introduced by the reds of the carpet, the flowers on the table, the back of the divan beneath the window are not so far from the colored patches of *Longchamp.* The unreality of the blue monochrome, which is beginning to show, offers us a variation in blue of Lautrec's *May Milton* poster which graced the studio-living quarters in the Boulevard de Clichy represented in *The Blue Room.* Basically we are closer to the pre-Fauve concerns already discussed than to a style in which pre-eminence is given to contours.

The *Courtesan with a Jeweled Collar* (VI. 17) already mentioned clearly belongs to the stained glass style. Blue is also dominant, but this is because of the flat background and the large, deep-blue plume in the hat. Distinct brush strokes give way here to fusion, to flat areas of color, representing the flesh, for example. This technique will be found again in this brief period which is rich in masterpieces: *The Two Saltimbanques* (VI. 20), *Harlequin* (VI. 22), *Portrait of Sabartés* (VI. 19), *Mother and Child* (VI. 28).

At this point the technique of the Lautrec lithographs reappeared, after a very different course from that which led Picasso to *The Embrace.* In the Lautrec lithographs the quality of the skin was rendered by almost colorless flat tints which were given life by the decisiveness of the contours. Picasso's intention was not the same. The inspiration from within, the intimate exploration we saw in *Evocation,* predominates now. This first plunge into the world of the circus in *The Two Saltimbanques* and *Harlequin* already shows everything Picasso would endow it with in 1905—solitude, vagrancy and exile. The *Portrait of Sabartés,* done shortly after the arrival of Picasso's friend in Paris and in the confusion of transplantation, expresses the same thoughts in an unforgettable way. *La Gommeuse* (VI. 18), on one hand, and *Mother and Child* (VI. 28) on the other, represent the extreme limits of this line of research. *La Gommeuse* is the most pitiless of those paintings stripping prostitutes, the application of the new style to brutal naturalism. The *Mother and Child* in the Goetz collection is all sweetness and tenderness, a bending of forms and draperies, a style already glimpsed in the series of *Lovers,* and taken up again in *The Fugitives* (VI. 1) and also in *Mother and Child* (X. 9). The novelty, apart from the blue tonality, is in the importance now given to drapery. *Woman with a White Mantilla* (XV. 42) which, according to Picasso, is contemporary with the *Mother and*

Child series of 1901 (VI. 28, 29, 30, 31), marks a significant stage in Picasso's work: it anticipates the experiments he carried out in 1906, in Gosol, in which the mantilla or kerchief is used to emphasize the mask-like treatment of the face. The elaboration of the contour is developed beyond that of the most characteristic works of the Stained Glass Period—for example, *Harlequin* (VI. 22)—and this development tends towards an increased austerity, towards less concern with the representation of reality, towards what might be termed a form of abstraction.

It is remarkable that, at this time, Picasso made personal use of the arabesque of Art Nouveau, linking it to the real art of the Middle Ages, to the Romanesque constructions which he could have seen in Catalonia, and not to the fake Gothic inherited from the Romantics which inspired so many of his contemporaries. The Blue Period systematically developed these curved, arch-like constructions.

Here we must note Picasso's continual experimentation throughout his different manners. At one moment we saw him verifying the potentialities of different media. Then in the course of the year following his first Parisian works, he passed from the formal expressionism of the *Lovers* to the heightening of color by divided brushwork to give constructive strength; and then he came back to contour, helped not only by his own experiments but by what they taught him about cloisonnism, the art of Degas, Lautrec's line and Cézanne's composition. In each case the experimentation was always towards the same end, the truth of painting; to adapt painting to what was to be said, to make it equal to this requirement. In reality it seems as if Picasso were making a systematic inventory of everything his seniors had left him.[1]

---

[1] This return to the contour, to a stained glass character, evokes the *cloisonnisme* of Emile Bernard and Gauguin. There are many proofs of the importance Picasso attached to Gauguin's painting and to his experience. In 1903 he covered a copy of *Noa-Noa* with drawings. But it is worth remarking that in 1901 none of his contemporaries were aware of the relationship to Gauguin in the paintings just discussed. In any case, as with Lautrec, it is not the resemblances of detail that matter. There is a quite striking parallel between the way in which Picasso charged his contours with a spiritual content and the way in which Gauguin transformed Emile Bernard's *cloisonnisme* into a means of expressing his personal symbolism. But Picasso seems to have been more responsive to Lautrec's technique. It must not be forgotten that for a boy of his generation the use of flat colors and the importance given to contour belonged to contemporary life, to Art Nouveau. And what was original for Picasso was what was done with this technique, what Lautrec and Gauguin had done with it.

HARLEQUIN, PARIS, 1901, OIL. THE METROPOLITAN MUSEUM OF ART, NEW YORK, GIFT OF MR. AND MRS. JOHN L. LOEB, 1960 (VI. 22).

In the same way that the style of the Vollard exhibition was born in Spain, the blue monochrome was born in Paris. We have already noticed the invasion of blue in *Evocation* and in *The Blue Room*. But the *Portrait of Sabartés* (VI. 19) already shows something quite different. Picasso here returned to that way of creating space by juxtaposing two almost identical colors which was already encountered in the *Bullfight* in the Niarchos collection. From now on however the setting is simplified as much as possible. One broad, deep-blue flat area, almost totally uniform, and a white plane standing for the table, that is all. There is no trace of the anecdotal. The unorthodox deformation is as evident as it is in the *Lovers,* not only in the disproportion of the hands and of the tankard, which gives the impression of relief, but also in the way the blue plane of the background and Sabartés' body are cut off by the edge of the table; this suggests depth and denies it at the same time, as if Sabartés had no thickness. And it is precisely the indications of the relief of his figure, the shadows on his jacket and the contour line which create Sabartés' volume, and at the same time construct in our minds the void around him, a void which becomes all the more immense and desert-like, the mark of solitude itself.

The series of women in a café: *Woman with a Chignon* (VI. 23), *The Apéritif* (VI. 24), *The Girl with Folded Arms* (VI. 25), *The Woman with a Cigarette* (VI. 26) served as experiments in his new style on a subject that he had been dealing with for a long time, as was always his practice. After *The Harlot with Hand on her Shoulder* (V. 11) and *The Absinthe Drinker* (V. 12), *The Woman Seated on a Café Terrace* (V. 14) provides us with the intermediate point of reference for the period of the Vollard exhibition. She is the most clearly implanted in the exterior world; the environment is presented through color alone in *The Harlot* and just suggested in *The Absinthe Drinker*. Now in the later paintings in the stained glass style, only the bare minimum remains: a bench, a table, a glass with a siphon or a carafe. Each of these women is alone, alone in a public place. Who or what she is waiting for we do not know, or perhaps, like *The Girl with Folded Arms,* she is no longer waiting for anything, lost, drunk from absinthe. Now nothing distracts from them, their faces, their gestures. The hands and the fingers of the woman in *The Apéritif* seem endlessly drawn out in the strange fold of her arms. It is a whole new language that Picasso is working out here, one in which the absence of details gives maximum impact to everything that is noted, even to the mannerisms.[1]

The contrasts of the stained glass style lead on to a paler painting, with very slight impasto, which blue monochrome soon lights up with a new force.

[1] The exacerbation of form has already been linked with the exacerbation of color at the time of the manifestations of Tuscan Mannerism at the beginning of the sixteenth century. We note this in order to emphasize the dialectical relationship between Picasso's successive investigations in 1901. Cf. Rodolfo Palluchini in René Huyghe, *L'Art et l'Homme,* III, p. 17: "Form and space, color and light are also problems discussed and resolved in an original way: a freer fantasy of rhythms developed in opposition to the concept of harmony characteristic of the Renaissance: an exasperated search for form to be put at the service of a very intense spiritual anxiety; reality was transformed to the point of deformation." It should not be forgotten, moreover, that Picasso looked at El Greco a great deal.

Other beggars are worn out by life. They seem amazed to have reached the goal, which has remained blue, but is no longer the horizon.

Picasso lived this painting of tears, blue as the humid depths of the abyss, and full of pity.

Guillaume Apollinaire

III.   BLUE AS A MEANS OF EXPRESSION

1. *The Blue Style*

The testimony of Sabartés is extremely important in studying the development of the Blue Period. First of all, he lived with Picasso in Paris at the beginning of this phase—the two portraits of him (VI. 19 and 34) serve as landmarks in its evolution. He rejoined Picasso in Barcelona in the spring of 1902, the few months' separation giving him a certain perspective. Above all he understood his friend and shared his ideas completely. According to Sabartés, *The Glass of Beer* (VI. 19) belongs to the actual *formation* of the Blue Period. This corresponds with our idea of the sequence of pictures in this period as we have just re-established it.

"From the threshold of the studio (in the Boulevard de Clichy)," wrote Sabartés,[1] "one saw immediately the large painting, *The Burial of Casagemas,* supported from behind by heaven knows what, jutting out a little from the wall like a screen... The palette was on the floor: a thick mound of white in the middle formed the base of a kind of cement made up mainly of blue. The other colors circled the edges. I cannot recall ever having seen Picasso with the palette in his hand. He assures me that he has often held it in the usual way. It is possible, but I always saw him mixing his colors leaning on a table or a chair or sitting on the ground. When he made the second oil portrait of me, he was standing up, with the palette on a chair... He is not bothered by discomfort and seems to look for it, as if he took pleasure in this kind of mortification, keeping his wits alert by a hair shirt of difficulties. He would put the canvas in the lowest notch of the easel, which obliged him to paint bent almost in two."

The second *Portrait of Sabartés,* the *Portrait of Mateu F. de Soto* and the *Self-Portrait* (VI. 34, 33 and 35) are extremely close to one another. In comparison with the portraits made in the autumn, one is struck not merely by the fact that the sitters have let their hair grow long and the extent to which they are marked by the winter and presumably by cold and hunger, but also by the way in which the paintings are at the same time interiorized and simplified. We find ourselves admitted to a confidential conversation, plunged into an empty world where everything is blue except the reddish beards of Picasso and Mateu F. de Soto, which are painted in the minutely detailed style of a primitive. The painter has retained no accidental or external fact.

The *Child Seated in a Chair,* also known as *The Blue Baby* (VI. 32) belongs to the same series. It is a solid picture, remarkable for the intense blue, a royal blue, of the child's dress.

Picasso chose to paint misfortune. Sabartés rightly speaks of "beggars, sick people, the crippled, the hungry and prostitutes painted in the same style. The work of the Blue Period is made up of all these," he says. His testimony leads one to think that the origins of this style were more Parisian than is generally conceded, though admittedly Sabartés has a tendency to consider as blue the pictures belonging to the Stained Glass Period. However he states categorically that the *Seated Woman with a Fichu* (VII. 6), traditionally dated as from Barcelona, was in fact painted before Picasso left Paris, since Sabartés described it in the article which he says he read to Picasso in the Boulevard de Clichy. "I alluded to the bluish-white of a moonbeam coming through the window in this picture which shows a woman seated in a prison cell; the pale moon coming to caress her, finds her huddled up and makes her bent shoulders shiver still more with cold."[2]

It is possible that Sabartés' memory is at fault. It seems

[1] *Picasso, Portraits et Souvenirs,* p. 79 and p. 88.
[2] *Op. Cit.,* page 75.

difficult, for example, to date *Roofs of Barcelona* (IX. 2), as he does, in the period when Picasso's atelier was in the Calle Conde del Asalto, that is, January-October 1902. The gray in the blue of this picture certainly seems to date from 1903, a dating which also corresponds with the fact that the studio Picasso occupied then, the one in the Calle Riera de Sant Joan, was on the top floor; the one in the Calle Conde del Asalto, on the other hand, was on the first, without a view of the roofs. But in general the evidence of Sabartés about these first blue pictures is borne out by our impression of the sequence of works from that time onwards; we seem to be dealing with an uninterrupted series, consistent except for the fact that Picasso is growing less and less interested in portraits, and at the same time his drawing is becoming softer, as in the *Dozing Absinthe Drinker* (VII. 3) and the *Crouching Woman* (VII. 5). It can be taken for granted that these last two pictures are from Barcelona in 1902. But we are still uncertain about the *Woman with Folded Arms* (VII. 7) which, moreover, Barr dates Paris, 1901, about the second *Crouching Woman* (VII. 4) and about the *Woman with a Hood* (VII. 2) born of the same inspiration as the *Seated Woman with a Fichu.*

We lack the data provided by exhibitions. When Picasso left Paris for Barcelona in January, 1902, he left Mañach at the same time; the latter kept some of his work which he showed at Berthe Weill's gallery at the beginning of April, 1902, but no pictures properly called blue were included. Picasso had surely taken any in this style with him to Barcelona, as he did the second portrait of Sabartés. It should be noted that the signatures of the pictures painted in Barcelona are underlined with a curved stroke, but pictures painted in Paris could have been signed later in Barcelona, and moreover Picasso may have continued for a time in Barcelona the straight underlined signature of Paris. In fact the *Woman with Folded Arms* still has a signature with the straight underlining, but the *Seated Woman with a Fichu* has not.

More important for following Picasso's artistic development is the fact that, in this series of pictures, he evidently is attempting to give the effect of despair by using drapery and poses in a way that requires the renunciation of precise drawing, an impression confirmed by the expressionless faces with closed eyes or elusive gaze. The testimony of Sabartés about Picasso's state of mind during the Blue Period applies particularly to these pictures and to the

Old Woman, Barcelona, 1901-1902, charcoal. Collection O'Hana, London.

CROUCHING WOMAN, BARCELONA, 1902, OIL. THE ART GALLERY OF TORONTO (VII. 5).

mother-and-child series which heralded them. "At this time we eagerly upheld the idea, which came from Picasso, that the true artist should know nothing; that knowledge hampered him, prevented his seeing and constrained the expression by lack of spontaneity... We called pure the direct expression of the artist, but not the expression which grew out of a style misdirected by the artist's inability to do more than pass on his knowledge without adding anything of his own. The works of the Primitives in the Museums showed us the value of our doctrine; they were evidence of an innocence uncontaminated by artifice. We demanded sincerity from the artist and would not acknowledge that it could be found apart from sorrow."[1]

Sabartés adds: "We divined this in Picasso's painting of 1901." His statement would be made more exact by excluding the pictures of the Vollard exhibition, limiting it to the works produced since the *Death of Casagemas* series, that is to say, to the works of the second half of 1901.

The evidence of Sabartés also throws light on Picasso's development in 1902. He records a letter to Max Jacob which should no doubt be dated in the summer of 1902, which contains a very revealing remark: "I show what I'm doing to my friends, the local *artists,* but they think it has too much soul and no form." Picasso at once took issue with this verdict: "It's funny. You can talk with people like that, but they write worthless books and paint idiotic pictures. That's life." The "no form", which in the original is written *pas forme* (Picasso's knowledge of French was still slight), expresses the "artists'" reaction to that softness of draperies which seems to be derived from Carrière. It also presumably expresses a lack of understanding of what, for convenience, we call Mannerism, which is really expressive distortion similar to that in the series of *Lovers* of 1900.

If the *Odalisque* of Ingres has three vertebrae too many, according to Kératry, how many has the mother in the *Mother and Child* (VI. 30) of 1901? The "no form" here is possibly a kind of parallel to Ingres, who had similarly been accused of having "neither bones, nor blood, nor life, nor relief, in short nothing which makes for imitation." When Picasso painted his *Nude from the Back* (VII. 17) in 1902 it seems likely that he had in mind one of Ingres' bathers seen from the back, either the one of *Valpinçon,* the one in the *Harem* or in the *Turkish Bath,* all three on exhibition in the Louvre that year. And some fifteen years later, what Picasso found of interest in Ingres was precisely his mannerism

and his forms, which were expressive rather than imitative.

However that may be, Picasso reacted to the accusation, "no form". There is a series of pictures never brought together before this catalogue which show this reaction very clearly. First, the *Woman with a Shawl (Portrait of Germaine Pichot)* (VII. 8) and the *Mother and Child in Profile* (VII. 20); these lead to two well-known pictures, *The Two Sisters* (VII. 22) and *La Soupe* (VII. 11). *Germaine Pichot* is portrayed bursting with youth, her resolute face framed by the strong oval of a scarf, anticipating the heads of Fernande wearing a kerchief at Gosol in 1906. This earlier *Woman with a Shawl* is shown beside an arcade, a new motif no doubt influenced by the arches in the old quarters of Barcelona, shown in *The Blue House* (VII. 1); it would be too soon to speak of the influence of Romanesque art.

The *Mother and Child in Profile* (VII. 20) is very close to *Mother and Child* (VI. 30) of 1901, but distinguished from it by an intense and warmer blue, and by the burst of red in the flower which breaks the monochrome. It marks the appearance of a much firmer drawing in the draperies. In the play of curves, which soon take on an almost geometrical stiffness in *The Two Sisters,* the influence of Gothic sculpture—not Romanesque—is obvious. The opposition between the movement of the cape and the line of the legs imprisoned in the long dress of the mother is clearly indicated in the studies for *The Two Sisters*[2] and it also dominates the movements of the man in *The Offering* (D. VII. 1). Sir Anthony Blunt rightly draws attention to *The Visitation* at Chartres in this connection, but Picasso could have seen other examples of Gothic stylization and geometrical forms in the sculptures of Notre Dame in Paris or in Barcelona. This development illustrates the way Picasso in his experimentation oscillated between spontaneous lyrical outbursts on the one hand and austere compositions in the mathematical tradition on the other. It also enables us to understand, to some extent, what prepared Picasso to confront the preoccupations of Cézanne and then to create Cubism.

The Two Sisters, also called *The Meeting* (VII. 22) is the key picture in this development, and not only because of its large size: 152×100 cm.

Picasso wrote to Max Jacob: "I want to make a picture from this drawing I'm sending you *(The Two Sisters).* I

[1] *Op. Cit.,* page 74.
[2] Especially the one in the artist's collection. See Addenda No. A. 14.

Self-Portrait, 1903, pen drawing.

drew it from a prostitute at Saint-Lazare and a Sister (of Mercy)."

In one of the studies for this picture (D. VII. 4) the forms of the two women follow the curve of the Romanesque vault above them. The other study (D. VII. 6) carries this construction further in its simplification and geometrical opposition of the draperies. Picasso eventually abandoned this simplified treatment, although he did retain and accentuate the hieratic stiffness of the Sister, while the prostitute remains in the bowed position of the preceding studies.

This new geometrical severity gives *La Soupe* (VII. 11) its grandeur. Again the woman's back is curved like a Romanesque vault, and the draperies are rigorously constructed. This picture is presumably later than *The Two Sisters*; *The Offering* (D. VII. 1) which is a study for *La Soupe*, includes a bearded man who appears in the works done in the autumn of 1902 from Paris, and a variation on the theme (Z. VI. 409) is dated December 1902.

Sir Anthony Blunt has compared the profile of the Sister in *The Two Sisters* with that of the effigy of Queen Ensea in the monastery of Pedralbes near Barcelona. Whatever his inspiration, Picasso has sought a modern transcription of motifs taken from both Romanesque arches and Gothic stylizations. He has renewed contact with sources of the past, adopting their majesty of form but secularizing them, applying them to human subjects and even, in *The Two Sisters*, confronting religion with a fall from grace. This is not a contradiction of what Sabartés calls "the direct expression of the artist," since there is a break with traditional connotations, and it is a sincere expression into which the artist is compelled to put all of himself and all of his resources.

Thus, *The Two Sisters* sums up and surpasses all the subjects of crouching women, huddled, withdrawn into themselves by drink, hunger, cold and poverty, and also the studies of anonymity, women seen from the back, *Two Women at a Bar* (VII. 13) and *Mother and Child* (VII. 18). It is certainly the painting which marks the turning point of this new stay in Barcelona. It can almost certainly be dated in the summer of 1902 in view of his reference to it in the letter to Max Jacob, "It's a long time since I've written to you..." which is made more definite by the sketch on one page of the letter, where he shows himself in front of the Plaza de Toros in Barcelona, a sketch which has the atmosphere of summer.

Picasso has now finished with drapery and headdresses. A hood reappears only in a realistic picture like *Celestina* of 1903. When he painted the *Woman Ironing* (XI. 6) in 1904 he replaced the arbitrary vaulting of the woman's back in his 1901–1902 picture (VI. 27) by the angular movement which was observed and re-created from experience. To some extent the year 1902 represents the imaginary and intellectual side of the Blue Period; it is a time when Picasso paints more from his conceptions than from reality and projects his ideas onto reality.

This development must be kept in mind if one wishes to understand the role of the dominating blue color. In the Paris phase it is almost equivalent to the blue of photographic proofs, a way, in keeping with the disillusion of his twenty years, to embody his expressionist conception through monochrome. It is the blue of Lautrec's nights by gaslight and electricity. It is also, no doubt, a pursuit of the impressionist experiment with blues to indicate shadow. And perhaps also it is related to the blues of Cézanne, unrealistic, but very forceful in indicating relief and plastic construction. Everything justified Picasso's return to this color, and his lasting taste for it is well-known. Moreover, it was characteristic of him to push this experiment as far as it would go, right to the renunciation of color. It is the opposite of the sparkling play of colors of the Vollard exhibition period, but it involved an equally arbitrary attitude towards color. The poverty of Picasso, who had sold nothing since the autumn of 1901, no doubt impelled him to put as little paint as possible on his canvas and perhaps, as tradition has it, to use laundering blue in his paintings on paper, but this poverty was not so much the cause of the Blue Period, as is often said, as the result of it. We must not forget that Picasso knew very well what was pleasing in his earlier work, and if he turned his back on it so obstinately it was because, for him, art does not exist on the level of its success nor on material circumstances, but is the very meaning of life. The blue was a conception of painting.

He may have found that the coldness of blue suited the cold of a winter without fires, the cold of poverty and hunger, but it did not exclude the pleasure of color. There are paintings which show that the return to Barcelona produced a warming of his palette with yellows, greens and bright light. This is particularly the case with *The Blue House* (VII. 1) (called *House in Barcelona* at the Berthe Weill exhibition in November 1902); it is a comparatively gay and brightly-colored picture, dominated more by green than blue and with broad expanses of yellow. Where blue is still the dominant color, it is more intense than the somber blue of Paris, as Sabartés has rightly noticed. It is also a blue which calls up other colors and is warmed and heightened by them. The *Portrait of Corina Pere Romeu* (VII. 15) is no longer even "blue". The blue, laid on very lightly, is used as background and for the outline and shadow on the white of the shawl. The *Crouching Nude with Green Stocking* (VII. 16) and the drawings of *Nude Woman* and *The Toilette*[1] belonging to the artist, bear witness that with the return to Barcelona youth took the upper hand again. If Picasso returned to the study of misfortune he did it deliberately and not as a simple reflection of his own despondency.

When Picasso left for Paris in the company of Sebastián Junyer in the autumn of 1902, he had finished with the phase which began with the blue paintings of *Mother and Child* and ended with *The Two Sisters*. He did not abandon blue, but in the future it was to be used more realistically, and in painting equally charged with meaning but dominated by observation rather than by imagination.

2. *Paris and Friendship with Max Jacob*

Commenting on *Man in Blue* (VIII. 1), which he has kept himself, Picasso told us that it was the portrait of a character who was slightly mad, a man well-known in Barcelona and often seen in the cafés. We did not know exactly where to place this picture, which looked different from those of 1902, so we asked him, "Then you painted it at Barcelona?" He shrugged his shoulders. "Models stay in one place, but artists travel."

The same problem is presented by the pastel, *Woman and Child on the Shore* (VII. 21). There too the theme comes from Barcelona, but it is almost certainly the work which Picasso sold in Paris to pay for his journey back to Barcelona in 1903. Did he bring it to Paris, or paint it in Paris? The insistent stare of the woman, the more realistic look of the shawl and the child's worn clothes bear signs of the development which was to mark the work of 1903.

The failure of Picasso's third journey to Paris, the poverty he shared with Max Jacob and his participation in a group

[1] Reproduced in the Addenda No. A. 12 and A. 13.

MOTHER AND CHILD IN PROFILE, BARCELONA, 1902, OIL. PRIVATE COLLECTION, U.S.A. (VII. 20).

exhibition at Berthe Weill's, November 15 – December 15, 1902, is well known. He can scarcely have sold much there, since everything indicates that by the end of the year he was in desperate straits. He had probably read the article Charles Morice wrote about him in the *Mercure de France* of December, but in view of the mixture of old and recent works in the exhibition, this report can scarcely have given him anything new to think about, apart from compliments.

The best surviving evidence of Picasso's activities during this visit is still unpublished—his marginal drawings on a copy of Gauguin's *Noa-Noa* which had been given him by Charles Morice and is still in the artist's possession. Picasso told us that these drawings were almost the only ones saved from the fire when he burned his drawings to keep warm, before going back to Barcelona in January.

All that remains from this stay in Paris is the pastel *Intimacy* (VIII. 3), where Picasso was trying to please; the watercolor of the *Poet Cornuty* (VIII. 2) which heralds the greater realism of the bistro scenes to come; and the *Mistletoe Seller* (VIII. 4), in which there suddenly appears for the first time the figure of the famished old man with a beard, accompanied by a child, which was to haunt Picasso on his return to Barcelona.

Scarcely twenty-five paintings are catalogued for the whole of 1902. Doubtless it is possible that some pictures may reappear, but they could not appreciably change this number, which is amazing compared with some one hundred pictures for 1901. Picasso must have painted much less because of his poverty and lack of materials, but also because he went through a kind of crisis. Here the testimony of Sabartés is significant: "What Picasso wants is to work. And to work every day. If he does not work it is because he lacks inspiration and the elements necessary; and if he is not in the mood to work, he does not enjoy anything else. Luckily this does not happen every day."

3. *The Great Pictures of the Blue Period*

On his return to Barcelona, Picasso again joined his friend Angel F. de Soto in the studio in the Calle Riera de Sant Joan which he had occupied in 1900. This is the great period of his painting in Barcelona and the most fruitful of the periods he spent there. From January 1903 to April 1904, there are some fifty works, many of them very important, and it was a great year for portraits. Picasso is no longer interested in abstract, anonymous human types as he was at the beginning of 1902; now he questions his subjects searchingly and allows their glances to seize the onlooker. The style of 1902 continues, but it is enriched, as Zervos perceived, by a new study of El Greco, reflected both in the figures and the distortions. If Mannerism returned it was charged with a new expressive content; the masterpiece of this style is *The Old Guitarist* (IX. 34).

The chronological data are provided mainly by dated drawings. The drawing dated January 1903 (z. VI. 599) confirms that the *Mother and Child (The Sick Child)* (IX. 7) and *Ménage de Pauvres* (IX. 9) are from the beginning of the year (IX. 9 is dated April 1903). One of the studies for *La Vie* (D. IX. 5) is dated May 2. The sketchbook of drawings from October 1903 is evidence that Picasso was working on *The Blind Man* (IX. 31) at that time, but the earlier drawing (D. IX. 6) of *The Blind Woman,* dated May 23, shows that he had this theme in mind for some months. The drawing of the *Nude Woman in Profile* (z. VI. 564), an imitation of Gauguin signed Paul Picasso, is dated December.

It is possible then to reconstruct roughly a journey beginning with *Poverty* and *Figures by the Sea* (IX. 4, 5) which descend directly from the blue pictures of 1902, passing by way of *The Sick Child,* which is sepia-colored on a blue background, to the nudes in *The Embrace* (IX. 11, 12) and *La Vie.* The summer is richest in portraits, with the *Head of a Woman* (IX. 17), *The Painter Sebastián Junyer* (IX. 21) and the pictures of the Soler family. The end of the year was probably devoted to the themes of *The Blind Man* and of the old men inspired by El Greco, leading to *The Beggar's Meal* and *The Madman* of 1904.

The two views of Barcelona seen from the studio in the Calle Riera de Sant Joan show an astonishing mastery in plastic construction and handling of colors within the dominant blue. *Barcelona at Night* (IX. 3) is reddened by fires lighted for warmth in the half-light of dawn. Doubtless these pictures are from the winter when Picasso was again in the studio he had in 1900, for he liked to take possession of each of his homes by seizing its image.

The variants on the theme of *Les Misérables* are significant. The large oil, *The Tragedy* (IX. 6), develops the idea of *Woman and Child on the Shore* (VII. 21) but with harder drawing and deeper color; the wash drawing *Poverty* (IX. 4), anticipates the stiffness and simplicity of *The Blind Man*

THE TRAGEDY, BARCELONA, 1903, OIL. THE NATIONAL GALLERY OF ART, WASHINGTON, D.C.,
CHESTER DALE COLLECTION (IX. 6).

(IX. 31). The *Ménage de Pauvres* (IX. 9) is the last of the inquiries into the solitude of couples in cafés which had begun with *The Two Saltimbanques* (VI. 20) of autumn 1901. Similarly *The Sick Child* is the final picture in the mournful series of mothers. Here the visage and the insistent gaze, calling the spectator to account, convey the meaning that formerly would have been expressed by the curve of the body.

La Vie (IX. 13) of May 1903, goes beyond earlier paintings not only in its prominent and considered symbolism but also in its complex internal oppositions, contrasting nude figures with clothed, and reality with the painted image. Picasso would play with such oppositions in a number of different ways in his later work, from *La Toilette,* painted at Gosol, to the innumerable paintings of studio interiors, pictures of the painter and his model, and the *Meninas.*

In its final state, *La Vie* is a confrontation of a young couple, standing, nude (the man is given the head of Casagemas), with a mother whose gaze is frozen by unhappiness. The canvas in the background shows a nude couple crushed by grief, with the insistent gaze seen in works from the beginning of the year. The canvas in front of it represents a solitary nude even more overcome with misery. It is interesting that the standing man with the face of Casagemas originally (in the studies) had the features of Picasso himself.[1] The final portrait of Casagemas is executed with extraordinary mastery. Since the portraits made at the end of 1901 Picasso's art had matured.

This second evocation of Casagemas evolving at the very time of Gauguin's death—May 8, 1903—is evidence of the new area of Picasso's reflections. The master of Tahiti had posed a similar question in his painting, *"Where do we come from, what are we, where are we going?"* Picasso had meditated on *Noa-Noa* during the past winter, and in the light of it he returned to the question which had haunted him since his break with the painting of the Vollard exhibition, the question of the meaning painting should convey. He had first raised the problem, we must remember, when painting the death of Casagemas. *La Vie* is openly a philosophical inquiry, but Picasso answers the complaint of the "artists" of Barcelona, "too much soul and no form", by a composition constructed with masterly firmness. It even has a touch of bravura and of the "Salon machine", as Barr says.

The Embrace (IX. 12), which was probably painted at the same time, shows that Picasso was now trying to stay close to reality to express what he had to say. It is probably the first nude study of a pregnant woman in western painting since the Middle Ages. In the *Embrace* (II. 14) of 1900 Picasso had conveyed his meaning by expressionist deformation, but now he did so by recording his observations—the frail arm of the woman on the powerful arm of the man, her head buried on his shoulder, her swollen stomach. The precision of gesture and anatomical representation are remarkable. Picasso does not seek reality, nor limit himself to copying it. But he bases what he has to say about anguish and anxiety on his knowledge of the physical world.

The attraction towards reality is evident in the gallery of women's portraits produced in the summer. Here Picasso shows a new curiosity in the movement of locks of hair and the structure of the face. This taste for likeness also dominates the portraits of his friends of the café, *Angel Fernández de Soto* and *Sebastián Junyer* (IX. 20, 21), and those of the Soler family (IX. 22, 23, 24). The respect for observed detail in *The Soler Family (The Picnic on the Grass)* (IX. 23) gives the picture a naïve aspect which explains Picasso's later interest in the Douanier Rousseau. Admittedly Picasso did not finish this large picture himself and left to Sebastián Junyer the task of painting a glade in the background, doubtless because Picasso had already put into it all that he cared about. But it would be wrong to attribute insincerity to this painting commissioned by his tailor. Rather, it shows that Picasso was beginning to tire of blue monochrome and to take pleasure in the incitements and colors of summer.

Before the break with the dominant blue, which does not occur until 1904, clearly after the return to Paris,[2] Picasso was first to pass through a new phase of violent simplification and expressionism. One may assume, however, that all the watercolors on themes taken from the Catalan countryside (D. IX. 13–21) also date from the summer of *The Soler Family.* When questioned by Josep Palau i Fabre, Picasso replied that they were evocations of his stay at Horta de Ebro, without explaining whether he was speaking about the visit of 1898 or a new excursion.

Celestina (IX. 26) seems to be one of the crucial works of the summer of 1903. The charcoal study (IX. 25) derives from the caricature sketches of Junyer produced at the same

---

[1] Cf. D. IX. 4 and 5.

[2] It still dominates *The Woman in a Chemise* (XII. 5).

CROUCHING WOMAN, BARCELONA, 1903, GOUACHE. COLLECTION MAX G. BOLLAG, ZURICH.
UNPUBLISHED IN COLOR (IX. 10).

time as the portrait, in June. The old one-eyed procuress has the solidity of Fernando de Rojas' heroine.

Soon reality again served as a springboard for Picasso. This time the catalyst was not Romanesque art but the mysticism of El Greco. *The Ascetic* (IX. 33), *The Old Jew* (IX. 30), *The Blind Man* (IX. 31), *The Old Guitarist* (IX. 34) and *The Blind Man's Meal* (IX. 32) are the five great pictures which result from this secular translation of the dramatic and religious tensions of El Greco into poverty and unhappiness. This new expressionist phase—the most blue— marks the twenty-two year old painter's attainment of maturity. No more mannerisms, properly speaking. The rigorous drawing expresses only the essentials. The simple hieratic composition and the strict palette of intense blues combine to attain unforgettable force. It is the silence of suffering humanity, the world's movement arrested at the moment of gravest misfortune.

This tension slackens a little with the blue *Madman* (X. 5, 6) which follow at the beginning of 1904. The last two portraits painted in Barcelona, those of Sabartés (X. 11) and Vilaro (X. 12) show signs of new interests. Sabartés has described this relaxation better than anyone else: "The blue of this last portrait is very intense... Until now there were no metallic highlights such as the one at the edge of my tie-pin... This detail and the pleasant red color of the lips herald the approach of a new manner. Before, in Paris, Picasso would not have noted the shining gold of the pin, even if the sun had caught it. The still livelier tone of my lips would not have mattered to him; then he needed simplification and violence. Little by little all that now passes; because his experiments had taught him the possibilities of blue, he wanted to see to what extent he could do without it."[1]

4. *The Blue Pictures of Montmartre*

For the first time we are well informed about one of Picasso's departures for Paris because he had been prepared and reflected on this trip. In March Picasso sent packing cases containing his work to his new address, 13 Rue Ravignan, where he would install himself on the top floor of the strange building which Max Jacob called the *Bateau-Lavoir,* the Floating Laundry, on the side of the Butte de

The Blind Beggar, Barcelona, 1903, 15 × 10 cm. Pen drawing on a postcard sent by Picasso from Barcelona to a friend in Paris, November 30, 1903. Unpublished. Collection M. Knoedler & Co., Paris.

[1] *Picasso, Portraits et Souvenirs,* page 109.

THE OLD GUITARIST, BARCELONA, 1903, OIL. THE ART INSTITUTE OF CHICAGO,
HELEN BIRCH BARTLETT MEMORIAL COLLECTION (IX. 34).

Montmartre. Picasso also described his journey with Junyer in a series of cheerful sketches called *Alleluias* in the manner of traditional Spanish engravings which show human existence as a valley of tears. But these *Alleluias* end with the meeting between Junyer, a picture under his arm, and Durand-Ruel, the most important picture dealer of the time, who is offering him a sack full of gold.

At the beginning of his twenty-third year, Picasso knew that he had done with what is now called his Blue Period. As Sabartés says, he needed "to breathe another air, speak another language, have a change of conversation, compare himself with others, change the faces round him and the manner of his life." It was this which he demanded from Paris.

Picasso prowled through Montmartre; he discovered new subjects and new models there. He drew couples taking their apéritifs and amused himself by recording the fashion of the moment and the plumes adorning the hats of the elegant ladies. He gave the same attention to the working-class couples sitting at table and above all to the begging, staring street urchins (XI. 2, 3). Rarely has he been so close to life in all its aspects. With rare good fortune everything found a place in his work. He was always alert for incidents which could inspire him and give still more meaning to his line, which grew increasingly vigorous and incisive. It was a suicide by hanging which inspired the *Christ of Montmartre* (D. XI. 9).

Margot, the daughter of Frédé, owner of the Lapin Agile which Picasso had frequented on his previous visits, became the strange *Woman with a Crow* (XI. 10 and Addenda No. A. 7). She is seen in the light of the candles which illuminated the cabaret like a picture by Georges de La Tour. With Margot, Picasso began a series of portraits glorifying a new type of woman, a woman with a fine, sharp, severe profile, a somber, direct gaze and well-shaped eyes. The delicacy of the features and the intensity of the gaze are emphasized by the mass of hair piled up in the shape of a casque in the *Woman with a Helmet of Hair* (XI. 7). Here she has the provocative boldness of a "Marianne" but the same woman seems to be sinking under the burden of life and inhuman toil when she leans on the iron with all her weight in *Woman Ironing* (XI. 6). Within a short period Picasso painted these contrasting images, the dignity of woman opposed to the slavery to which circumstances have reduced her.

The Two Friends, Paris, 1904, pen drawing. Collection Berggruen, Paris.

The importance of these works, after sixty years, depends upon their combination of beauty and humanity. *Woman with a Crow* and *Woman with a Helmet of Hair* are masterpieces of the Blue Period, and together with *The Old Jew, The Old Guitarist* and *Celestina,* they mark its highest point. The *Woman Ironing,* a very colorless picture, marks a turning point; here, as in *The Couple* (XI. 5), the expressive deformation is accompanied by a new simplification, a greater degree of abstraction in the unimportant details. Picasso strips from the faces and the clothing everything not essential to his purpose. The monochrome color is carried to the maximum point of austerity.

Picasso's drawing can be supple or stiff, truthfully incisive or free and improvised, but it is always faithful to the conception of the painting. From this period with symbolical, philosophical and humanitarian themes, Picasso is a modern painter, perhaps partly because of these themes or perhaps despite them. His modernity does not depend upon his subjects, even if he sometimes gives them a touch of contemporary reality, nor upon the deliberate boldness of his draughtmanship, which always aims to invest the subject with the maximum expressive intensity rather than to assert itself. Nothing is further from Picasso than art for art's sake. Drawing is a medium with its own rules, an instrument capable of capturing and expressing the external world. This world is a new and modern world and must find expression in an appropriate style, in harmony with the men of this time.

Picasso has understood not only the lessons of Gauguin, Cézanne and Van Gogh, but he has also reflected on the example of the Primitives. He has not ignored the pronouncements of Maurice Denis on "the flat surface covered with forms and colors brought together in a certain order," but he no longer makes concessions to this kind of modernism. He will not sacrifice to it either the likeness of the drawing or its expressive value. Picasso, who knows everything, feels everything, sees everything, even before he rationalizes his discoveries, knows how to play with color, line and contour in such a way as to avoid the effects of relief which might break the picture plane. He can be sculptural in a strictly two-dimensional picture. In this too, from 1904 onwards, he is a twentieth century painter.

The chronology of the works produced in the first months of the 1904 period in Paris is particularly difficult to determine because there are no outstanding landmarks. The portraits, and even the projects for theater posters, bear no marks of a development which we can check.

Each time Picasso becomes interested in portraits, his style becomes less aggressive, less wilfully original, as in the portraits of *Gaby* (XI. 17), the future wife of the actor Harry Baur, and the singer *Suzanne Bloch* (XI. 18). It becomes supple and poetic in the watercolor of the latter (XI. 16), and more incisive when he is portraying his friend *Manolo* (D. XI. 10).

The new face of the sharp-featured woman becomes more and more graceful, marked by youth and tenderness. The watercolor *Mother and Child* (XI. 21) and the preparatory drawing (D. XI. 26) for the gouache *Mother and Child* (XII. 4) show these pleasing qualities in the drawing style. The latter is dated 1905 but this is not necessarily the date when it was finished, but more probably the date when it was signed. Furthermore, it seems highly probable that the first Harlequins shown at the Galeries Serrurier in February 1905, and also *The Actor* (XII. 1), should be dated in the last months of 1904.

You cannot confuse these saltimbanques with actors. The spectator must be pious for they are celebrating silent rites with a difficult agility. It is this that distinguishes this painter from the Greek vase painters although his drawing sometimes approaches theirs.

Guillaume Apollinaire *(La Plume,* May 15, 1905)

IV. THE NOSTALGIA OF THE ETERNAL WANDERERS

1. *The Atmosphere of Paris*

Chronologically we are entering the unknown. The vagueness is not the fault of Picasso's memory even if he has often confused 1905 and 1906. Rather, we are discussing a type of painting in which time is abolished and hardly anything tells us the order in which the work was done. This is the situation for the two years between Picasso's settling in the Bateau-Lavoir, in April 1904, and his departure for Gosol. Even then the problem is not solved, for there is almost an overabundance of works apparently painted at Gosol. Picasso was capable of painting and drawing this much in a few weeks but it is difficult to see how he could have carried all these works to and from this remote place. But let us not anticipate.

Something has changed in Picasso's painting which goes beyond the transformation of his palette and the break with the blue monochrome. What is it exactly? The themes? The color? These are not basic matters for Picasso. Rather the change lies in something that controls simultaneously his choice of themes and the composition of his palette.

The essential characteristics remain the same. Mannerism, for example, is quite as evident in *The Actor* (XII. 1) as in the maternities of 1901. The denial of strong color continues and does not reappear until the period of *Les Demoiselles d'Avignon.* The new element is described by Apollinaire better than anyone else: it is the relaxation, the *détente,* of the drawing. There is a new preference for a purified line, limpid and warm, close to that of the Greek potters, as Apollinaire said. This reference is not a poetic fantasy, but the opinion of someone who may have gone to the Louvre with Picasso to look at the Greek *lekythoi* or who heard him talk about them.

The preference for classical draughtsmanship—the great word finally appears. Let us return to Apollinaire, the only eyewitness of interest to us. Writing of the February 1905 exhibition at the Galeries Serrurier in the May issue of *La Plume,* Apollinaire referred to "Picasso's taste for a line which eludes, changes and penetrates, and produces almost unique examples of linear drypoints in which the general appearance of the world is not altered by the light which modifies forms as it changes colors." (Extract from the article reproduced p. 335.)

Besides the fact that this text proves that the drypoints—not only the *Head of a Woman in Profile* (Geiser 7b), but also the harlequins of *The Bath* (G. 14b), the *Toilette de la mère* (G. 15a), etc.—date from the very beginning of the year, it gives as well extremely important information about Picasso's ideas. It is almost certain that the technical precision came not from Apollinaire but Picasso. Apollinaire's great merit was to know how to listen to Picasso. The ideas expressed in that passage announce Cubism, though only in Picasso's head, of course. One sees the historical perspective immediately when one compares the lines quoted with Picasso's words, "Only line drawing escapes imitation. Yes, line drawing has its own light, created, not imitated." Compare also Braque's statement, written, like Picasso's, after Cubism: "Color acts simultaneously with form but has nothing to do with it."

A new feeling for drawing. A freer sensuality in the line which gradually called forth a growing warmth in the color. Even if blue was more cause than consequence of the artist's poverty, it is not paradoxical to state that rose was the cause and not the consequence of the improvement in his material situation; however, this only became really sound in the last months of 1905 when the Rose Period was nearly at an end.

Nor is it possible to identify this change entirely with the appearance of Fernande Olivier in Picasso's life. This transformation certainly played its part but we shall never know exactly when it took place. It was certainly before the trip to Holland, however; that is, before the summer of 1905.

In 1933 Fernande wrote a little book, sometimes bitter, *Picasso et ses amis*. It is really done from memory, with the imprecision that this implies, but there is no doubt that she sought authenticity.

There is no reason to disbelieve her description of their meeting: "Living in the same house (the Bateau-Lavoir) I came across him often. He seemed at that time to spend his whole life on the little Montmartre square and I said to myself, 'Whenever does he work?' I learned afterwards that he preferred to paint at night undisturbed, for throughout the day there was a continual stream of Spaniards through his room. I met Picasso as I was coming home one stormy night. He was holding a very young cat which he offered to me, laughing, stopping me from getting by. I laughed too. He had me visit his studio (p. 25).

"There was nothing very attractive about him when you didn't know him; yet his strange appearance compelled attention. It was hardly possible to place him socially but one felt his radiation, his interior fire, which gave off a sort of magnetism which I didn't resist. And when he wanted to know me, that was what I wanted too."

We can read Picasso's feelings for Fernande in his paintings. He painted her portrait over and over. Her first appearance is perhaps in the marginal sketches in *Study for the Actor* (XII. 2). At first these portraits were only intended for Fernande herself, but then she began to invade his painting, not just because she was always available to model and without a fee, but because Picasso liked her roundness and grace and she embodied a delight in life. This transformation took place slowly and Fernande, who met Picasso at the end of 1904 and was living in his studio by the end of 1905, did not play an important role in his painting until the ochre nudes of 1906.

Once more, the evolution in Picasso's style was determined only by interior needs and psychological factors. The revolutions which were going to convulse the art of the time did not unsettle him. He was familiar with the chromatic explosion of the Fauves but did not deviate from his line; he had already considered the effects of the riot of color four years before.

The Equilibrist, Paris, 1904-1905, pen drawing. Collection Berggruen, Paris.

No doubt the failure of his exhibition at Berthe Weill's gallery, October 24–November 20, 1904, did not surprise him. He had exhibited mostly old paintings except for a few particularly aggressive, large watercolor drawings such as *The Madman* (x. 6). Picasso sought something else from now on; he showed neither impatience nor haste, as if he knew exactly where he was going and how much time he needed.

Let us look back and imagine the artistic situation in 1905. Never was the division between progressives and conservatives so complete and for more than ten years it was to be an absolute division. The conservative side was represented by the Salon, whose image Grün fixed for posterity in the painting commissioned by the State in 1911: a worldly gathering amusing itself at the Grand Palais. Among the green plants slender, sentimental nudes seem to take flight with a clumsy movement which makes the whiteness of their overpolished marble gleam. Members of the Institut pay court to one another; fashionable ladies in big hats surround themselves with young beaux who talk of art in the language of the preceding century. The painters of the moment are Albert and Jean-Paul Laurens, Bonnat, Rochegrosse, Béraud, Gervex, Boldini, Caro-Delvaille, Alfred Stevens and many others now forgotten; today their lack of substance permits only ridicule. The favorite themes are portraits of fashionable ladies and descriptions of elegant social gatherings, men in evening dress grouped around buffets, the singer leaning on the piano. Everything contributes to the creation of a single type of painting, the portrait of a society which secludes itself and looks inwards, perhaps to escape anguish and the vision of a world undergoing complete transformation. These precious interiors are self-portraits of complacency too. They sometimes include children and always include overdressed figures in elaborate, rustling dishabilles.

But since the creation of the Salon d'Automne in 1903 by Desvallières, Rouault, Matisse, Marquet and Bonnard, a reaction had set in. The earlier reaction of the Salon des Indépendants went back to 1884 and already in the eyes of young painters Signac and his friends must have figured as ancestors.

The aims of the Salon Committees are evident from the retrospectives they organized and the artists they invited to exhibit. In 1902 Toulouse-Lautrec was the special guest of the Indépendants; in 1903 Gauguin was honored at the

Studies for **The Jester** *(detail), Paris, 1905, pen drawing. Collection Lionel Prejger, Paris* (D. XII. 26).

Salon d'Automne; in 1904 (the first Salon Picasso could have seen) it was the turn of Cézanne and Odilon Redon, while Kandinsky could be seen in a small room. In 1905 Seurat and van Gogh had a room each at the Indépendants. That year the first group of Fauves exhibited at the Salon d'Automne, and they were to find themselves together again at the Indépendants in 1906.

Picasso already knew the French poets but he did not begin to meet the most dynamic French artists of his generation until the end of 1905. He had not yet emerged from his circle of Spanish painters; among them, Iturrino, Pichot and Canals were exhibiting at the Salon d'Automne. However he was not unaware of the investigations of the progressive painters, who were still essentially landscape artists. Landscape authorizes every kind of transformation, every liberty, and does not require the artist to aim for the seemingly immutable harmony, nobility and dignity of the human figure. Thus it was the favored terrain for all those artists who wanted to strike out for a new art, men like Derain, Vlaminck, Dufy, Matisse and Marquet, many of whom came from the atelier of Gustave Moreau at the Ecole des Beaux-Arts.

As for Picasso, the years 1902–1904 saw the production of very few landscapes; they are souvenirs rather than studies, and even fragmentary, because almost all are views from his studio. On the other hand there are hundreds of figure studies and these were his constant preoccupation.

2. Picasso's Commedia dell'arte

The new type of sharp, slender woman who appeared shortly after the return to Paris is soon joined by a corresponding character who had already held Picasso's attention during the summer of 1901—Harlequin.

At first Picasso seems to have thought of him as a sort of representation of himself. The period of the return to Paris is particularly rich in self-portraits: Picasso painted himself looking at a sleeping woman in *Meditation* (XI. 12); in D. XI. 28 and 29 he was amused to show himself smoking a pipe and wearing a driver's cap; finally he clearly gave his features to the Harlequin in *At the Lapin Agile* (XII. 23). This last representation certainly does not mean that the increasingly numerous harlequins were so many self-projections, but such personal motives in the elaboration of the

character should not be altogether disregarded. Picasso returned to Harlequin in the new classicism after 1914 and did not abandon him until the middle of the twenties. Then he would appeal directly to the image of the painter, the sculptor or to that other complex figure, the minotaur, to express his feelings.

It is difficult to interpret *Pierrette's Wedding* (XI. 22) from the black and white photographs which may be all that remains of it. It seems, as Phoebe Pool has noted, that Pierrette-Colombine is going to marry a rich old man and that Harlequin is giving her a farewell kiss. It is enough to describe the apparent subject to show how far we are already from the intimate expressions of misery in the Blue Period.

It should be noted that Cézanne's *Mardi Gras* (now in the Pushkin Museum), in which a bluish-white Pierrot follows Harlequin in his blue and red checkered costume, was hung as number 19 in the Cézanne room at the Salon d'Automne of 1904. *Pierrette's Wedding* surely belongs to the end of 1904, and this coincidence in the dates is too significant to be fortuitous. While there is no direct pictorial borrowing from Cézanne, Picasso may have found there a kind of authorization to paint this character, or at least the suggestion that there was something to be extracted from it for the new painting.

The Actor (XII. 1), tall, skinny and awkward, is a focusing of the characterization. Dusky-pink, sky-blue, red—there is no trace of the blue world even if the hands of both the prompter and the actor have the customary mannerist elongation. This theater caught in the emptiness of a rehearsal is a real world. Harlequin too was to evolve in a real world; in his company we find ourselves behind scenes at the circus or at the Lapin Agile. And we realize immediately that the important thing is not the costume which makes the character actor, harlequin, juggler or acrobat, and which really exists only to please the painter's eye; the important thing is that by means of this character which is at once individual and general, concrete and abstract, Picasso was able to resolve the contradiction he faced throughout the Blue Period. The dilemma was that in seeking the symbol he risked abstracting too much from reality, or on the other hand, in soaking himself in the real he was in danger of limiting himself to the anecdotal. With Harlequin there was no longer any need for deformations, simplifications and the rejection of color. The precision of the drawing and the joy in the color are one with the content.

THE ORGAN-GRINDER, PARIS, 1905, GOUACHE. KUNSTHAUS, ZURICH (XII. 22).

The catalogue of the exhibition at the Galeries Serrurier, February 25–March 6, 1905, shows that Picasso threw himself feverishly into his new investigations. There were eight paintings of saltimbanques; among them, as we know from Apollinaire's article in *La Plume,* May 15, 1905, were *Seated Harlequin with Red Background* (XII. 10), *Acrobat and Young Harlequin* (XII. 9), *Two Acrobats with a Dog* (XII. 17), and *The Harlequin's Family* (XII. 6). The "adolescent sisters balancing on the balls of the saltimbanques," which Apollinaire described, refers to *Circus Family* (XII. 18) and to *Young Acrobat on a Ball* (XII. 19). In three or four months, let us say from November 1904 to February 1905 if our hypothesis as to the liberating role of Cézanne is correct, Picasso created his new world: mothers (primiparas, as Apollinaire said perceptively), the svelte harlequin ("beardless manhood... transfigured by paternity"), the serious youth, older than his years, sometimes accompanied by a gaunt and shivering acrobat, brother of the blue blind man, sometimes by a little boy even more mature than himself.

Although the background landscapes already announce the desert-like setting of the *Family of Saltimbanques* (XII. 35), the dominant characteristic here is the radiation of human warmth, the group, the circus community; as Apollinaire marvellously expressed it, "a domestic hearth warms the gypsy caravan." The intimate warmth of the family makes the atmosphere of the Blue Period appear in contrast as one of cold and solitude in public places.

Perhaps it is one of the characteristics of Picasso's genius to be able to discover what is most profound in man, what all men have in common beneath the uniforms of their professions, whether that of clown or toreador. This desire or need is felt still more in the few studies which survive from this period. In the line, in the light touch of color there is tenderness without sentimentality.

Picasso's position takes on its full value when it is compared with that of his immediate predecessors. At the end of the nineteenth century the circus became a classic theme for painters. Seurat painted *Le Cirque.* He loved the circus as a repertory of forms, for its colors and lights. He disembodied it to subject it to the frame of his pointillist and divisionist aesthetic, as rigid as the bed of Procrustes. Toulouse-Lautrec painted *The Clowness* and the *Stage of the Music Hall.* He too loved the light and color of the show, but what fascinated him was the element of caricature, of exaggeration in the types, who become something other

than what they are and achieve a tragic inhumanity. Picasso's attitude is different still. He goes behind the scenes to show us what lies there and the moment when these marionettes become human again; his attitude is modern and at the same time original for the period.

Picasso's genius lies in his subtle legerdemain with technique. Some of his most beautiful and moving works are the watercolors; they are made of nothing, of an almost imperceptible film of color just sufficient to give presence and relief to the figures. Their postures are barely indicated by the line, precisely controlled even in the deformations, suggesting the modeling without breaking the surface of the canvas or paper. Highlights of India ink suffice to note the stresses where they are needed. Even today we are astonished by such virtuosity.

Mother and Child, Paris, 1905, pen drawing and wash. Baltimore Museum of Art, The Cone Collection.

THE ACROBAT'S FAMILY WITH A MONKEY, PARIS, 1905, GOUACHE, WATERCOLOR AND PASTEL. GÖTEBORGS KONSTMUSEUM (XII. 7).

The rose which has given its name to this period is never a dominant color as was the blue. It appears as a dusky rose tone over a gray ground, usually blue-gray, almost metallic, remarkably luminous. It is used for the blouse of the *Woman with a Crow* (XI. 10 and Addenda No. A. 7), the lozenges of harlequin's tights, the costume of *The Actor*. But *Woman in a Chemise* (XII. 5) is still part of the blue world which at its most intense forms the cobalt background of the *Woman with a Crow*. Red, warm as circus bunting, bursts out in the right hand corner of the stage in *The Actor* (XII. 1); it provides the general tonality of *Seated Harlequin* (XII. 10), then of *The Athlete* (XII. 20). It lights *At the Lapin Agile* (XII. 23), bathing Harlequin and his companion in a friendly atmosphere although they are both in their own dream worlds.

The name "Rose Period", in spite of its imprecision and the fact that it covers very different preoccupations, as we shall see, does have real meaning, especially in opposition to the Blue Period. Its significance lies in Picasso's choice of colors, which is not dictated by imitation of appearances or by the more subtle illusionism of the Impressionists. Color has its own meaning. It is a language inside the language of painting. It has its own laws. "If you set down a black," said Picasso, "the spectator thinks 'That turns,' and in fact you can only represent depth in this way. While if you paint a sculpture rose, it will be rose."

The changes in Picasso's painting after the Galeries Serrurier exhibition seem to be linked with the friendship and companionship of Apollinaire. Picasso liked Apollinaire's article in *La Plume* very much. When we recently showed him the photostat he read the first lines aloud with an emotion to which he does not yield easily. It seems that Picasso was also deeply impressed by Apollinaire's size and corpulence and the feeling of strength which emanated from him. The only significant difference between the caricature of Apollinaire (D. XII. 24) and a study of *Giants* (D. XII. 23), is more precise indication of the features in the portrait. And, in their turn, these giants are closely related to the athletes and fairground strongmen who were to take their place in the *Saltimbanques* series.

Nothing is ever unimportant in Picasso's life; facts, apparently without meaning, often have repercussions in his work and find their place there one day when they have been forgotten. This is the case with the displays of muscular strength, that tranquil virile power which makes the little dancers fly at the end of the athletes' arms with even more grace than on the broad backs of circus horses. As always Picasso exaggerates the disparity between the figures. These athletes represent the same glorification of masculine power as the Kings, and it is interesting that when Picasso designed an ex-libris for Apollinaire, it was on the theme of a drinking king (D. XII. 9).

An analogous character emerged: the gross jester, inspired by a real actor, *El Tio Pepe Don José* (XII. 30). The jester is always dressed in red. In the admirable watercolor in the Cone Collection (XII. 29), a little boy, frail and pink, leans casually against him, wearing bright blue tights of the same color as the cube on which the jester is sitting and also as his own hair, because Picasso needed a touch of blue in this spot.

We have arrived at the period of the *Family of Saltimbanques* (XII. 35).

3. *The Saltimbanques*

This is the largest composition yet undertaken by Picasso. He has since shown that there is no fixed scale or limit to the dimensions of his work, and that he could paint enormous surfaces. But these later works all have a precise architectural destination, responding to the imperious requirements of the artist's inspiration: *Guernica* for the Spanish Pavilion at the Paris International Exhibition of 1937, and the post-war paintings, *War* and *Peace* in a chapel at Vallauris and *The Fall of Icarus* for the UNESCO headquarters in Paris.

Family of Saltimbanques (XII. 35) was not commissioned. Picasso undertook this enormous painting for his own pleasure, a very costly one so far as canvas, stretcher and paints were concerned: it is about 2.12 by 2.30 meters. This gives some indication of the importance it had for him.

Several preliminary studies leading up to the final painting are known. In fact, most of the earlier works of 1905 can also be considered as studies, as all the characters he painted from the beginning of the year can be found in *Family of Saltimbanques*.

We are in the presence of six people. In the middle is the *Buffoon* (cf. XII. 28, 29, 30). He appears to be the leader not only from his central position but from the authority which can be read in his face and which emanates from every part of his bulky person. On the left is *Harlequin* in his multi-

The Equestrienne, Paris, 1905, pen drawing. Baltimore Museum of Art, The Cone Collection.

colored checkered tights. He is the first of the acrobats to have appeared, at the end of 1904. By now his angular body and his mannered gestures have been replaced by a more strongly modeled body which suggests a certain virile maturity. The Harlequin is holding a dancer by the hand, the little girl with a basket of flowers, represented with a dog in the preliminary study (XII. 31) and in the compositional study (XII. 33), these being her only appearances in Picasso's work. To the right of the Buffoon is the *Boy with a Barrel* (XII. 32), one of those adolescents Picasso used as a model until very late in the year.

The sixth figure, the *Woman of Majorca* (XII. 34), is a Spanish provincial type; she is sitting beside a pitcher of a kind found in Catalonia which Picasso painted during the summer of 1906 at Gosol. Her presence seems indispensable to the equilibrium of the composition, which could not have been conceived without a figure in this position. And yet she is missing from the compositional study (XII. 33). Was she added later in place of another figure now disappeared? That is not likely. It is more probable that Picasso, who had never before stayed so long in Paris, was feeling nostalgic for Spain and that he found a way to express his longing here. Thus he was anticipating in a way the journey he was going to make the following year. The landscape itself has a rugged, arid quality that recalls Southern Spain.

The most important study for the *Family of Saltimbanques* is that from the Tschukin collection in the Pushkin Museum, Moscow (XII. 33). It differs in many details from the final version. The Harlequin on the left is wearing a top hat and a cloak over his checkered tights and carries a valise. These details connect him with one of the figures in *Pierrette's Wedding* (XI. 22).

The little girl does not yet have her basket of flowers but the dog is present, as in the study, *Little Girl with a Dog* (XII. 31), although it is somewhat further away. The other figures are similar to those in the final painting, except of course the *Woman of Majorca* is absent.

A landscape scene is the background for this study: one can see houses, a crowd, and a horse race. Thus Picasso had originally conceived an even more complex work, a synthesis of multiple themes. He gave up this idea, painting a landscape as neutral as possible to give full value to the great figures.

There is a watercolor which can be associated with the *Family of Saltimbanques,* in the Cone Collection, Baltimore

75

(XII. 18). It is a work of great beauty, consisting of several groups of figures, two maternal groups, a harlequin and the *Young Acrobat on a Ball* (cf. XII. 19). It is a very different conception which Picasso did not develop in oil and as it dates from the beginning of 1905, it is probably the first idea for the *Family of Saltimbanques*.

It is possible that Picasso, in painting this halt of a wandering circus, had in mind Manet's *Old Musician,* as he has always found Manet particularly stimulating (see the series of *Déjeuners sur l'herbe,* 1959–1961). The *Old Musician* was at the Salon d'Automne of 1905, but for this exhibition of the Manet to have influenced Picasso would require much too late a date for the *Family of Saltimbanques.* Everything else indicates that it was painted before the trip to Holland.

As is often the case with Picasso, it seems that this great painting which sums up months of work, is the end of something, as if he were assembling all the characters of his rose world to take leave of them. Time is stopped, a stillness which caused Rilke to speak of a *tapis perdu dans l'univers.* The same question is asked as in the great blue paintings, above all in *La Vie:* where are we going? The rose world is still a painting of ideas, like the blue series, but the content that was abstracted in 1902, sustained by reality in 1903 and even more in 1904 (let us say at the time of the *Woman Ironing),* is here supported by a new kind of abstraction. It is based on a kind of dislocation, on the transplantation of a particular reality, that of the circus, into an empty, naked world, an uninhabited desert in which we too are plunged by the will of the painter.

The *Woman Ironing* (XI. 6) of 1904, was close to the lesson of *Celestina* (IX. 26). Picasso began with what cannot be imagined, what only the reality of life can give—here the gesture breaking on the iron, there the one-eyed glance. But as Pierre de Champris[1] has shown very clearly: "It is enough to compare the brutally naturalistic *Women Ironing* by Degas with that of Picasso. How incomparably superior Picasso is! Degas pursues rudimentary images, situating the model in her familiar setting, concerned with the professional gesture which he stresses with a line as base as her conversation. Picasso raises the level of the debate. Out of the vulgar accessories, a bowl, an iron, he makes the instruments of tragedy, expressed in a few essential lines and colors: the blue speaks of mental apathy, of the absence of physical life."

[1] *Picasso, Ombre et Soleil,* Gallimard, Paris, 1960, page 17.

Picasso

Circus Horse Kneeling, Paris, 1905, pen drawing. Baltimore Museum of Art, The Cone Collection.

MOTHER AND CHILD (SALTIMBANQUES), PARIS, 1905, GOUACHE. STAATSGALERIE, STUTTGART (XII. 8).

Between *Woman Ironing* and the *Family of Saltimbanques,* the nature of the reference to reality has not changed but in *The Saltimbanques* Picasso has chosen models he can dispose exactly as he wishes to, to whom he can give the expression he has decided on, as if he were both author and director of the play and they were actors. Thus he has extraordinary liberty. The colossal size of Tio Pepe, the powerful, stocky body of his friend Apollinaire were no more than incitements, pretexts for something else (including Herod, in the drypoint, *Salomé*).

"But who are they, tell me, these wanderers,

These men a little more fleeting even than we ourselves..." asked Rilke, after having lived with the picture for many months at Hertha von König's in 1916.[1] The poet captured Picasso's state of mind at a moment when he, too, was planning to leave home (for Holland), when he was engaged in a painting of escape, perhaps experimenting with opium, as Fernande Olivier relates, and about to astound us with great classical nudes, the triumph of rose. Then at Gosol, he transformed rose into ochre and shattered harmony against an elementary, fundamental reality.

4. *The Trip to Holland*

However little we know about Picasso's trip to Holland in the summer of 1905, its importance cannot be minimized. Picasso did not paint a great deal during the few weeks of his journey but the paintings he brought back were surprising in more than one sense. They were like nothing he had painted before and thus had the direct consequence of bringing about distinct changes in his work.

A young writer and lover of painting, Tom Schilperoort, had invited Picasso to stay with him in June at Schoorl, near Alkmaar. Fernande Olivier tells the story that Picasso, fearing her jealousy when he unpacked the paintings of nudes that he brought back from his journey, made jokes about the women of the Low Countries with their "military" proportions.

When we see these nudes we can understand why Picasso anticipated Fernande's jealousy. The *Dutch Girl* (XIII. 1) breathes a powerful sensuality. Fair, pearly, abundant flesh spreads out across the whole surface. The young Spaniard,

with his dark hair and skin, discovered in Nordic women an exotic quality comparable to that which Scandinavians find in Mediterranean women.

The group, *Three Dutch Girls* (XIII. 2), from the Lefèvre collection, now in the Musée National d'Art Moderne, Paris, has perhaps an element of humor. It is this first contact with a national group that disconcerts the painter. But the nude studies show clearly what fascination those large, strong, fair women had for Picasso. In front of these women he did not think, he no longer tried to compose works full of meaning, of symbolism or of mystery. His eye was captivated, and that was enough for his hand to follow and for his brush to obey, fixing these models on the canvas definitively.

It is as if Picasso was anticipating the presence of Fernande in his painting, in the works done in 1906 at Gosol. In any case, the Dutch adventure ended the reign of the thin, delicate female model who flourished in the time of the harlequins. The enigmatic *Woman with a Fan* (XIII. 14), frozen in a hieratic position, and the portrait of the beautiful, sculptural *Madame Canals* (XIII. 9) were perhaps affected by the stay in Holland although nothing justifies a definite statement unless it is their break with a type of woman still found in the *Woman of Majorca* (XII. 34).

The Death of Harlequin (XII. 27) is probably another transitional work, linking Harlequin with the two young boys who were to dominate the paintings at the end of the year. It seemed then as if Picasso were interested only in adolescents and in fact he did not abandon them until he went to Gosol, after the period of the big, rose nudes. What attracted him to them was their capacity for dreaming. The *Boy with a Pipe* (XIII. 13), *Boy with a Frilled Collar* (XIII. 19), *Juggler with a Still Life* (XIII. 20), and *Blue Boy* (XIII. 21) are among the successes of a pleasing, clearly constructed painting, filled with the magic of expectation.

The *Girl with a Basket of Flowers* (XIII. 8) is perhaps the most characteristic painting of this series, although it represents a single nude figure, a young girl just at the end of adolescence. She has an awkward, unformed body, and her face is already no longer that of a child, with a large painted mouth and a heavy glance, lacking in innocence.

Picasso enjoyed the ambiguous eroticism of this body; he made the warm black of the hair, the fiery red of the flowers sing. Gertrude Stein, whose brother Leo bought the painting from the dealer Clovis Sagot, was repelled by

[1] Rainer Maria Rilke, *Duino Elegies.*

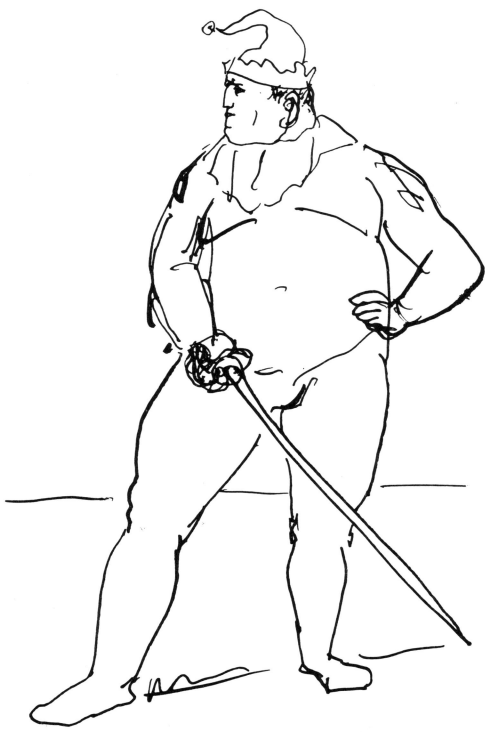

El tio Pepe Don José
¿ 40 años

El Tio Pepe Don José, Paris, 1905, pen drawing. Collection Mr. and Mrs. Lee A. Ault, New York (XII. 30).

the ugly legs, the overlarge feet. With great simplicity Clovis Sagot suggested cutting off the bottom of the canvas, "guillotining" it.

The blue world was one of exhaustion, of consumption, of total solitude. The harlequins opened the door to freedom. But other worlds were still to come.

5. *The Return of Success*

At this stage in Picasso's life one must ask how he supported himself in Paris. Even supposing that the Galeries Serrurier exhibition had resulted in several sales, the money earned could not have lasted forever. Like everybody else Picasso had to pay the rent of his studio in the Bateau-Lavoir and eat every day.

The memoirs of Fernande Olivier give an idea of how young artists lived then. It was a bohemian life which has changed little; its permanent secret is well-known—credit. There was a bistro near the Boulevard de Clichy[1] where the artists from the Bateau-Lavoir, along with the poets Apollinaire, Max Jacob, and André Salmon, used to celebrate from time to time. The extravagant customers of one day, they lived on credit the rest of the time. It was the same with the baker, the butcher and the other tradesmen. They would have goods sent home while they were out, or would not reply when the goods were delivered—nothing to pay for the time being. Fernande once stayed in bed for two months because she had no shoes, but whatever the stratagems invented to economize money was still needed.

The year 1905 was a period of intense activity for Picasso. Not only was he painting a great deal, but he was also making sculptures[2] and executing a series of sixteen etchings and drypoints in which the principal themes of his painting recur.

Picasso had several sources of income at this time. First, he knew two people, since become legendary, who were prepared to buy his pictures, Père Soulier and Clovis Sagot. The first remained a secondhand dealer, happy to share the adventures of those who passed through his shop; the second was an art dealer and his descendants today are specialists in prints. In 1905 Picasso received an average of one hundred gold francs for each painting sold at Clovis Sagot's. In emergencies Père Soulier would give him forty or fifty francs for a packet of drawings.

Then in addition, before the end of 1905, several collectors began to make direct purchases. The first was Leo Stein, who bought *Girl with a Basket of Flowers* from Clovis Sagot and then went to the studio to make the painter's acquaintance. He took along his sister Gertrude, and a long friendship was born. It was profitable for both sides, and was not merely due to the Steins' purchases. The German writer, Wilhelm Uhde, also made direct purchases, and later the Russian collector, Tschukin. At last, before the end of the year, the dealer who had exhibited Picasso a few years earlier, Ambroise Vollard, came to the studio. For the lump sum of 2000 francs he became the owner of a considerable part of the work of the Rose Period. From this time Picasso was the center of a wide circle, as he has never ceased to be since. His friends were not only artists like himself who lived from day to day but also poets and writers who often had a second profession, among them Apollinaire, Salmon, Max Jacob.

6. *A Year of Transition*

Kahnweiler notes rather dryly that the sculptures of 1905 reveal in Picasso "a state of mind which was satisfied with the means of the period, whose efficacy he did not feel obliged to contest as they were adequate to his ends." However, we must state that although the simultaneous recourse to sculpture and graphics[3] shows an increasing technical assurance, it nevertheless betrays a certain anxiety with regard to painting. We have been following Picasso long enough through 1905 to know that he had begun to fear too much facility.

The supple, fluid line of the drawing, the rapid grace of the watercolors and gouaches, could not fail to make Picasso dissatisfied with a charm too easily achieved, even if the final works were the result of very hard work. The hundreds of sketches, studies, and instantaneous notations recorded in volume VI of Zervos give eloquent, although still incomplete, witness to his labor. Success in his eyes is a danger

---

[1] Vernin, rue Cavallotti.

[2] This was his first important series of sculptures; in Barcelona, in 1903, he had made a seated woman, a head of a blind man, and a head of a picador with a broken nose.

[3] Picasso studied the technique with Ricardo Canals in Paris in 1904.

HARLEQUIN ON HORSEBACK, PARIS, 1905, OIL. COLLECTION MR. AND MRS. PAUL MELLON, U.S.A. (XII. 24).

sign, as we have already seen after the Vollard exhibition, when he was twenty.

His painting very quickly showed signs that Picasso was setting new problems for himself. The *Woman with a Fan* (XIII. 14), and the *Boy with a Frilled Collar* (XIII. 19), together with a certain number of studies and related drawings, mark a renewed interest in Egyptian bas-reliefs and a preoccupation with expressing volumes on a flat surface. The role of color seems to have changed a great deal since the return from Holland; most of the young people in the paintings from the end of the year are blue figures against a rose background.

This is most striking in the *Boy with a Pipe* (XIII. 13), who is relieved against a flowery background, and the *Boy with a Bouquet* (XII. 12), who also stands out against a contrasting background. Picasso never tired of playing with oppositions of color and sometimes simply amused himself in this way.

These new paintings must not be judged in the same way as one "felt" their predecessors. In the previous year, color gave its psychological and emotive nuance to each picture. Now it is no longer charged with meaning; it has become an accessory again. Picasso no longer painted pictures to express misery, hunger and cold, nor to celebrate the nostalgia of those eternal wanderers, the saltimbanques and the circus people. Since he became aware of the presence of the human body—of its beauty—he aimed only to make us see and even experience that beauty.

The boys in blue first came from the circus, but are soon no longer harlequins. They are now only elegant adolescents, rich in their dreamy poetry and in the seductiveness of their age. Dealers and critics have given them whimsical names. Their ages vary; some are still children; in others the first signs of manhood can be seen. All of them have a characteristic disdainful or disillusioned pout; they gaze far into the distance. Their state of mind, this psychological emanation, is a legacy from the Blue and Rose Periods. They are still romantics. Soon they will become mere anatomies, animals with unfocused gaze, their eyes drowned in shadow like those of primitive statues. One more step in the direction of emphasizing volume and Cubism would be on the verge of birth. The blue jacket was no longer a uniform nor a working garment; it was still however something more than a blue area heightening the pinks of the background; it was intended to be neutral in order to

Study for Young Acrobat on a Ball, *Paris, 1905, pen drawing.*

YOUNG ACROBAT ON A BALL, PARIS, 1905, OIL. THE PUSHKIN MUSEUM, MOSCOW (XII. 19).

give full importance to the face and intensity to the glance. Logically the jacket should disappear and in fact it does. Picasso was to devote his whole talent as a painter to the nude adolescents whose carnal presence is accompanied by a psychological vacuity and emptiness of gaze.

By the end of 1905 Picasso's years of formation and investigation were over. His painting would never again look as it did from 1900 to 1905. 1906 was to be a crucial year, decisive from all points of view.

The apparent content of the painting and whatever literary association there might have been were to disappear once and for all. Picasso could say the same things through his work but he would say them in another way, no longer formulating them through characterizations in a pictorial form, however perfect. Henceforth he would express what he had to say through painting itself, by giving up all anecdotal associations to let line and color stand on their own, that is to say, by establishing the primacy of the visual detached from all literary references.

This new attitude gave rise to his need to consult archaic or archaicizing forms.

PORTRAIT OF MADAME CANALS, PARIS, 1905, OIL. PICASSO MUSEUM, BARCELONA (XIII. 9).

The man who invents a pattern of imitation is a man of genius.

Diderot

V.   1906, THE YEAR OF THE GREAT TURNING POINT

1. Return to Mediterranean Sources

If one takes Picasso's creative activity during the year 1906 as a whole, it seems paradoxically one long plunge into the art of the Mediterranean past. Picasso began by a return to the classical Greek tradition, then went further back to sculpture of the archaic period and finally he broke with the lineage of western art by studying the arts of different cultures, arts which have another approach towards perceptible reality. One would be tempted to call these arts barbaric, because the Greeks did, if this word had not acquired a pejorative sense; in this case they are the arts which belong to the oldest Western Mediterranean legacy accessible to us—Carthaginian and Iberian art.

We know that the end of the exploration is *Les Demoiselles d'Avignon,* and therefore this search takes on a different significance from that suggested by a simple account. It is not flight, or submission to tradition, but rather a revaluation. When Picasso studied Greek art it was to cleanse himself of the art surrounding him, which was already outmoded, already in a sense the art of the nineteenth century. It is important to point out that this quest involved a search for equilibrium, harmony and perfection, but Picasso never yielded to the temptation to prettify, to produce a beauty which conformed to the recognized canons. On the contrary this classical phase is above all lively, natural and well-observed, and it is this which gives it force and grandeur. It also allows Picasso to eliminate from his painting every element of charm, everything which would please, in order to paint the essence of people and things, their substance, their description in volumes purged of every detail, every sign particularizing the model.

It was as if Picasso took up the lesson of the Greeks in opposition to everything which had been painted since the Renaissance, examining the act of creation from above and from afar in order to find a true and solid point of departure and also to discover more general laws. The experiments of Cézanne as much as those of Gauguin pointed the way. When we write "took up the lesson of the Greeks", we mean Picasso took up the conventions of Greek classical art as if they were new conventions, as modern as Cézanne's perspective, for example.

We are not concerned here with establishing a critical study from external evidence, of trying to place Picasso's pictures in relation, for instance, to historical events such as the impact of the Russian revolution of 1905. We are simply working within the framework of Picasso's progress, trying to suggest the correct chronological sequences. The dates have only this relative value. As the pictures were not produced in public, references and means of verifying their order are missing, and Picasso has involuntarily made confusion worse. The complexity of Picasso's work justifies this attempt to isolate its various stages.

The confusion is made greater by the fact that in his painting Picasso anticipated his journey in 1906 to Gosol, in Spain. He painted his longing for Spain well before his return, to be exact in 1905. *The Woman of Majorca* (XII. 34) bears witness to this, and even stronger testimony is given by the barren landscapes that can be seen from the beginning of the Circus Period, and which dominate the *The Watering Place* series of the winter 1905–1906. But this is not a turning point in Picasso's art. In dealing with 1900–1901, we tried to base the dating of pictures as painted in Paris or Barcelona on differences of subject, but for that period there was justification in the painting Picasso was then producing, impressionist in nature and often anecdotal. However, even in dating that group we took more account of the saturation of the atmosphere and the quality of the

87

light than of what is properly speaking the subject matter.

At the point we have now reached, the adult Picasso deliberately projects his inner world into his painting. As always, reality is for him the basis of creation, but it is only the working material, the matter, not the inspiration. The picture goes beyond, made up of desire, dreams, recollections, memory and the work of the memory. It is extremely important to insist upon this in order to understand the deep mechanism of the re-evaluation which Picasso is undertaking. He has put enough distance between himself and crude reality to grant himself freedom of interpretation and reconstruction.

As a landmark for Picasso's "classical Greek" period one can take the moment when the figures are represented nude. Assuming a proportionate rate for Picasso's production during the winter of 1905–1906, the pictures with nudes should be placed right at the beginning of 1906, and doubtless they go on into the spring, but not too long, for Picasso left then for Gosol.

The problem of the Gosol paintings is purely one of chronology. It is known which pictures derive from Gosol with its landscape of bare reddish-brown earth, and the rose-red monochrome of 1906 is evidence born of this saturation. The quantity of work done there (even admitting that under the most favorable conditions he may have produced more than one picture a day, as in 1901) leads us to assume a stay of at least three months; and as Picasso left Gosol before mid-August, he must have left Paris in May. Fernande Olivier speaks of a stay in Gosol of several months, which justifies the hypothesis of a departure in April. But the altitude of Gosol is fairly high (more than 4,500 feet), so the weather conditions are hardly favorable there as early as April. This brings us to the beginning of May, which seems the earliest moment for settling there under satisfactory conditions.

The financial possibility of the visit to Gosol was provided by a large sale of the paintings of 1905 to Vollard, a sale which must be placed at the end of that year in the absence of more exact details. Page 28 in the *Carnet Catalan* mentions two exhibitions in Paris: "Chez Bing, 10 rue St. Georges, from the 25th to 29th of April," and "Durand-Ruel, from the 3rd to 5th of May. Open to the public Durand-Ruel May 6th from 2 to 6." This does not indicate that Picasso was present at these exhibitions, but only that he owned the notebook and was probably still in Paris when these exhibi-

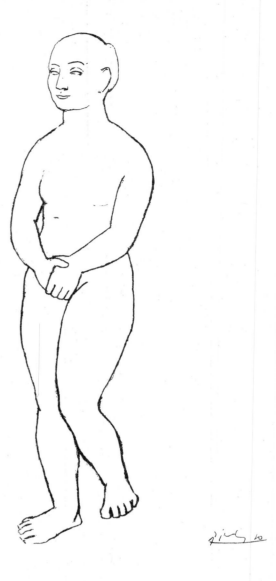

Study for Standing Female Nude (XV. 27), *Gosol, 1906, charcoal. Private collection, Paris.*

tions were announced. Nevertheless it gives more weight to the hypothesis of a departure in the middle of May, and we shall hold that opinion until more ample information is available. Douglas Cooper tends to restrict the stay at Gosol to the summer proper, but his "a few weeks" are in contradiction with the "few months" of Fernande Olivier's recollections. In addition Picasso is categorical on the point that *all the notes contained in the carnet* (except naturally the two on the Paris exhibitions) *were made or drawn during the stay at Gosol.*

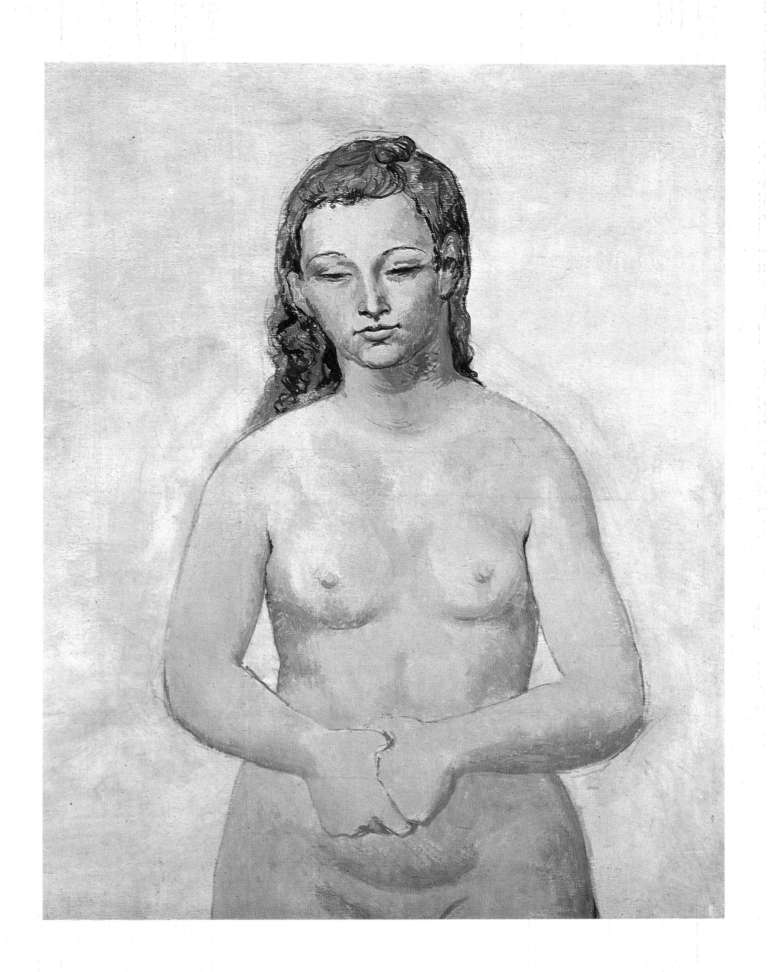

NUDE WITH HANDS CLASPED, GOSOL, 1906, GOUACHE. COLLECTION AYALA AND SAM ZACKS, TORONTO (XV. 28).

Picasso's renewed interest in the nude goes back to 1905 and took place in two ways, on the one hand through the female nudes made on the journey to Holland, and on the other through engravings: *Salomé* (Geiser 17b), *The Dance* (Geiser 18b), *At the Circus* (Geiser 11b), *The Watering Place* (Geiser 10b). No doubt engraving helped Picasso to make his line rounder, to free himself from the harsh angles of the Blue Period and to take pleasure in plastic harmony. But the experience of Holland brought him new ideas of equilibrium. He brought back images of solid strength, of well-built, somewhat heavy Dutch women, images which increased the attraction he felt towards sculpture. Fernande and the sensual attraction he felt for her was a catalyst in this. In the end he attained that "unpretentious and natural nobility of compositional order and gesture" of which Barr speaks, and which he says "makes the official guardians of the Greek tradition, such as Ingres and Puvis de Chavannes, appear insipid or vulgar."

2. *The Search for Objectivity*

The *Carnet Catalan* affords proof that *The Two Brothers* (xv. 9) and the *Young Girl with a Goat* (xv. 35) date from the visit to Gosol, which leads to linking them with the *Two Youths* (xv. 10), and also with *The Adolescents* (xv. 11), both paintings traditionally dated from the Gosol period. In the same way it is now proved that the execution of the big composition called *The Peasants* (xv. 62) in the Barnes Foundation dates not from 1905 but from the end of the summer of 1906, after the Gosol visit. The *Still Life with a Portrait* (xv. 14), dated Paris 1905 by Zervos, contains a preliminary drawing of *The Two Brothers* and thus becomes contemporary with the *Still Life with Vases* (xv. 13) from Gosol. All this falls into place without any difficulty and brings to light connections and lasting preoccupations which the traditional splitting up of these works prevented one from grasping. Only one difficulty remains—the date of that major work, *La Coiffure* (xiv. 20), in The Metropolitan Museum of Art, New York. From the evidence, as Barr observes, it is contemporary in its present state with the portrait of *Gertrude Stein* and the *Self-Portrait* of autumn 1906. But the studies known enable us to envisage the possibility of an earlier state which perhaps was abandoned by Picasso at the time of his departure for Gosol and taken

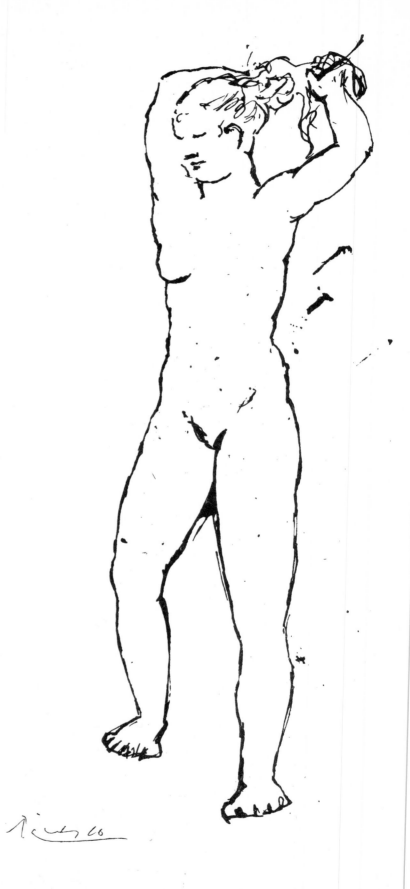

Nude Combing her Hair, Gosol, 1906, pen drawing.
Collection Gustav Zumsteg, Zurich.

90

LA TOILETTE, GOSOL, 1906, OIL. ALBRIGHT-KNOX ART GALLERY, BUFFALO, N.Y. (XV. 34).

up afterwards, as he did with the portrait of *Gertrude Stein*. In any case, Picasso's testimony confirming the date as 1905 must be considered with caution.[1] In fact Picasso has constantly muddled up 1905 and 1906, as one can see from the date which he wrote, after the event, on the *Woman with Loaves* (xv. 46). Unquestionably *La Coiffure* in its final state is later than *La Toilette*; it bears the imprint of the investigations made at the end of the stay at Gosol and traces of corrections, particularly visible in the treatment of the faces.

From the evidence of the paintings themselves, four periods of work can be distinguished in 1906, preceding the transition to *Les Demoiselles d'Avignon*. First there is a change in Paris before the departure for Gosol. The boy leading the horse sheds his clothes. This is the time when Picasso is planning *The Watering Place*, and the art of the *Saltimbanques* period is stripped of references to the circus to give place to a natural world where men are nude with their horses in an uninhabited desert. Then this classicism broadens; it is the beginning of the visit to Gosol, the time of the large rose-ochre nudes. The third period, the Gosol period proper, encroaches on the preceding one. Picasso took possession of the village, the countryside, the people; he returned to nature and to the concrete fact. Finally, strengthened by his double experiment, the search for the classical ideal and then for reality in its harshness and roughness, Picasso undertook an absolutely new quest. He freed himself from immediate impressions and remade them, either utilizing El Greco's distortions, or seeking to express volume and three-dimensional form above all. In this he anticipated once more his imitation and assimilation of the art of Iberian sculpture, although these sculptures were not at Gosol but in the Louvre. One feels that through the inspiration of the austere forms of upper Catalonia, Picasso has literally re-created these sculptures before seeing them—or seeing them again—after his return to Paris. This fourth period includes the end of his stay at Gosol and the return to Paris.

Picasso knew, up to a point, what awaited him at Gosol, having already lived in the Catalan mountains at Horta de Ebro during his convalescence from scarlet fever in 1898; and he had kept a happy memory of this rough and peaceful life. But although the stay at Gosol marks the break with classical idealization in favor of the primitive and sculptural roughness of an objective art, one cannot conclude that

Picasso went to Gosol with this end in view. In fact at the beginning of this visit, Picasso at first developed the classicism of *The Watering Place,* seeing only the Gosol which suited his purpose, the vases and pottery. It was *at* Gosol that the transformation took place.

Let us return to the winter of 1905, to the nude figures in the studies which lead towards the three compositional projects for *The Watering Place* (xiv. 14, 15 and 16). In both *Girl on Horseback and Boy* (xiv. 3) and *Boy with a Horse* (xiv. 4) the boy is still clothed and very like the *Blue Boy* (xiii. 21). The sheet of studies (D. xiii. 12) which shows this young man along with caricatures of Apollinaire is interesting by reason of its date: "Paris December 24, 1905, midnight." From this one can deduce, as we have done already simply on the basis of the logical unfolding of Picasso's work, that the period of *The Watering Place* must begin at that time, even if the drypoint of the same title is slightly earlier.

The watercolor, *Boy with a Horse,* is still somewhat stiff and very close in style to *Girl on Horseback and Boy;* then suddenly in the studies (xiv. 5 and 6) the body of the boy becomes freer and more supple, and attains already the sovereign ease of the masterpiece *Boy Leading a Horse* (xiv. 7). Picasso has given himself up to the pleasure of the natural plastic rhythms arising from the body's movement, in its balance, harmony and beauty. Jean Sutherland Boggs very rightly reminds us in this context[2] that as a student Picasso worked on casts from the Parthenon frieze. But this is especially significant for the draughtsmanship, which one can follow from the studies to the painting, and which has the same flexibility and decisiveness as the line of Picasso's engravings. The greatness of the painting depends on other elements, in which Picasso has profited as much from his experiments in blue monochrome as from his investigations in the Rose Period. In fact the large canvas of the *Boy Leading a Horse* has only two colors: the boy's body is the rose color of the earth, while the gray of the horse is lightly reddened, and the gray of the sky touched with blue. The modeling is scarcely indicated—the way in which the black contour line is applied is enough.

The classicism of Picasso is pictorially the fruit both of his own research, and of the modern experiments which

---

[1] Alfred H. Barr, Jr., *Picasso, Fifty Years of his Art,* page 43.
[2] *Picasso and Man,* page 45.

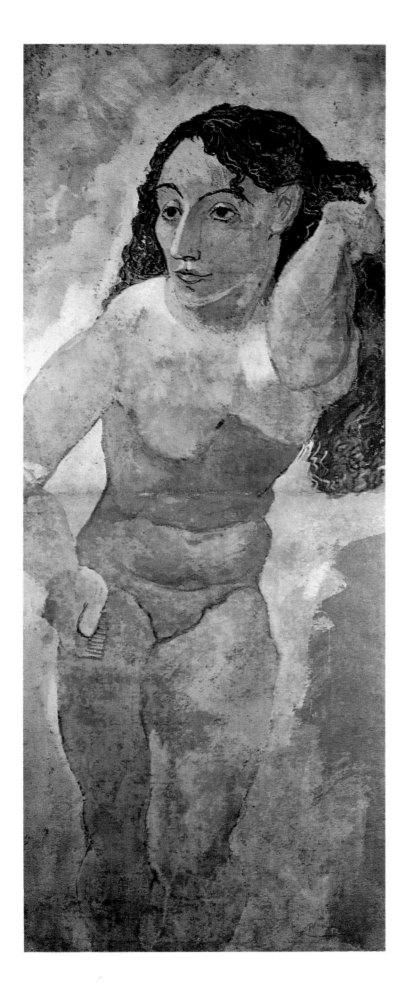

seem to him the most conclusive. The comparisons suggested by Phoebe Pool with Gauguin and Cézanne are convincing. Similarly, from the time of the *Young Acrobat on a Ball,* it is clear that this world, empty to the horizon, is akin to that of Puvis de Chavannes. The change is not in the technique but in what is being said. There is no longer any outside element between the painted setting and the spectator, no circus or figures in the background. It is a desert of light and beauty. The two gouache studies for *The Watering Place* have this absolute simplicity (XIV. 15, 16).

The final painting was never carried out. Perhaps Picasso thought that he could not go any further without copying himself, without repeating the *Boy Leading a Horse,* and to some extent the *Family of Saltimbanques.* Perhaps at this stage of his work he simply felt the need to steep himself again in the sources of his art and therefore he put off the execution of the great picture he dreamed of until his stay in Catalonia. Zervos rightly emphasizes the fact that "an undertaking carried through, or simply sketched out, is exhausted in Picasso's eyes. For Picasso, as for Goya, of whom I cannot help thinking when writing about Picasso, once a problem is solved there arises from it an unbelievable number of others which are not." But the research into classicism, strictly speaking, the research into the Greek, began precisely with *The Watering Place.*

As we shall see this classical research fills all the first part of the stay in Gosol—and it is here that chronological corrections take on their full value. The abandonment of *The Watering Place* is only the abandonment of a given subject, of something which derived from the circus. Picasso is about to return to the study of the nude bodies of young boys and young women, deliberately, in their own right, for their harmony and beauty. At the same time as *The Watering Place* he abandoned the *Portrait of Gertrude Stein,* but he returned to the portrait when he left Gosol and finished it in his new style, a procedure which was obviously impossible with *The Watering Place.*

The *Portrait of Gertrude Stein* shows signs of other interests related to those revealed in Picasso's sculpture, particularly the *Head of Fernande* (z. 1. 323) and *La Coiffure* (z. 1. 329). The traditional date is 1905, although some of the sculptures

WOMAN WITH A COMB, PARIS, 1906, GOUACHE.
COLLECTION JEAN WALTER—PAUL GUILLAUME, PARIS (XVI. 5).

seem considerably later than Gosol. However, the exact dates or chronological sequence are not so important as the evidence of Picasso's interest in sculpture.

The *Head of Fernande* has the distant majesty of the *Dutch Girl*. No doubt Picasso was more and more obsessed with a new way of representing volume, and his interest in engraving confirms this as strongly as do the sculptures, yet he was still seeking something else. In the strict sense of the word it was objectivity. "A term in modern philosophy," Littré wrote, "the quality of what is objective; the existence of objects outside ourselves." It was as if sculpture cut the umbilical cord between the painter and his picture.

Now at last we can understand better the difference between the series of *The Watering Place* and that of the *Saltimbanques*. Sentimentality has disappeared. Making the bodies nude not only corresponds with freer plastic qualities, it also eliminates from our assessment any reaction founded on nonaesthetic criteria.

This does not mean that Picasso's taste for sculpture owes nothing to the sculptural qualities of Fernande's body. Quite the reverse. It would be absurd to assert that Picasso's investigations do not originate in the plastic suggestions offered by reality. It would also be totally incompatible with his way of living a painter's life, because he is first and foremost a painter. In Fernande we can see the first of Picasso's great dialogues with his models, his women-models. Again and again Picasso's art is fertilized by his love for the model. It is not only a dialogue between himself and his model or between himself and his painting, it is also a dialogue between himself and what he is learning.

This did not escape Fernande, who observes in her book that at Gosol Picasso's painting became the painting of an adult man. We must not forget that in fact Picasso was not twenty-five until October 25, 1906.

In the *Portrait of Gertrude Stein* Picasso also began from the accidental facts provided by reality. "Seduced by the physical appearance of the woman," Fernande says. Here one might say Picasso is even anticipating the women he would paint on his return to Paris after the stay in Gosol. There was nothing graceful about Gertrude Stein. She was solid and masculine; her attractions were intellectual. All the evidence confirms that the conception of the portrait belongs to the autumn of 1905, that is, it coincides with the transition from the *Family of Saltimbanques* to *The Watering Place*. Of course this does not mean that the final state we

know was already conceived of in the first project. Picasso did not have Gertrude Stein pose for more than a hundred sittings without learning anything, but one might think that the original idea of the picture already contained his desire for objectivity reflected in the female nudes painted at the moment when Picasso gave final definition to the portrait.

3. *External Sources of Inspiration*

It is intellectually satisfying to connect Picasso's taste for subjects related to classical Greece with the fact that he used to go with Apollinaire to listen to Jean Moréas at the Closerie des Lilas. The revival of interest in Mediterranean antiquity appeared to some extent everywhere in French literature at this period, in Maurras and Barrès, and also in Suarès and Gide. Thus it was a phenomenon sufficiently widespread to stimulate Picasso, although this literature must often have seemed to him very academic. But it is likely that something of it, even if distorted, would have reached him from the discussions of his poet friends, especially Apollinaire and Max Jacob. However, we must not forget that Nietzsche was at the source of the revival, and that Picasso had no need of a mediator to look at the Greek statues in the Louvre in the light of *The Birth of Tragedy*.

There is no reason to disassociate Picasso from literature and poetry, but on the other hand one must not assign too much importance to the role of literature in his development. The great event for him at the end of this year 1905 was obviously one in the realm of painting, the scandal of the *Cage of Wild Beasts* (the *Fauves*) at the Salon d'Automne. Of course for him the event was not a scandal, nor was it an obvious source of one. He had surely seen works by Matisse and Marquet before, and doubtless Derain, Vlaminck and Van Dongen too. The event was the great break made by painters of his generation with Impressionism and its followers. Once again painting was on the move. Picasso was too conscious of his own development and his own modernity to be shaken by it, but one can be sure that he looked at and studied, judged and gauged the pictures exhibited.

We have seen how he exalted the role of color at the time of the Vollard exhibition in 1901, but he did this to give full expression to what he was trying to convey; to satisfy and

PORTRAIT OF GERTRUDE STEIN, PARIS, 1906, OIL. THE METROPOLITAN MUSEUM OF ART, NEW YORK, BEQUEST OF GERTRUDE STEIN, 1946 (XVI. 10).

give free play to his passion for expression. Zervos has noted well his differences and divergences from the Fauves. "Picasso took good care not to fall in with the eccentricities of Vlaminck, who used vermilions and cobalts in order to set fire to the Ecole des Beaux-Arts. Picasso used pure colors only to satisfy his natural inclination to go every time as far as his nervous tension would allow, although it cost him a swift reaction from his exaltation. He had no need, as Derain had, to make color into a cartridge of dynamite destined only to burst into light in a frantic apotheosis."[1]

Yet Picasso could not have been insensible to this affair and the scandal arising from it. Despite his indifference to the Fauve position one cannot infer that he learned nothing from it. The revolution in brilliance of 1905 came at a time when Picasso was making his way towards a new use of monochrome, towards almost colorless pictures, and he continued in this direction with his usual independence. Color did not return until eighteen months later in the extraordinarily luminous gouaches of the spring of 1907, the spring of *Les Demoiselles d' Avignon*. But the architecture of his pictures was then radically new.

It was on this level that Picasso received the impact of Fauvism. He had no need to be taught the expressive power of color or the possibilities it offered of liberating pictorial construction from immediate sensory data. But he found in Fauvism the justification for pushing his own daring to even greater lengths.

If one compares the *Cage of Wild Beasts* with Picasso's "classical Greek" period one does not understand this. One might even deduce that Picasso was turning his back on his own times and escaping into the past, or at the very least was making his own Marquesas Islands out of the age of Pericles. But looking at Matisse's *Luxe, Calme et Volupté*[2] and considering what Picasso was painting in the spring of 1906, one finds that he may have found support in Fauvism for his experiments towards objectivity in painting the nude.

Since Douglas Cooper's publication of the *Carnet Catalan,* it would certainly seem that all the "Greek" works must be placed at Gosol. In fact they have a profound unity and reveal in Picasso a sensual peace which seems clearly the result of the return to Spain, of the Catalan mountains and the presence of Fernande. But Gosol is also the land of red-ochre earth, the effect of that extraordinary light of the Spanish sun on soil the color of terracotta. One does not go to Gosol by accident[3], because one thinks it pretty at the turn of a road, for the very good reason that even in 1966 there is still no road leading there, only some twenty kilometers of beaten path. The natives can cover it in their little cars but strangers brave it only in jeeps. Picasso was looking for the harshness of the Catalan mountains; he found there the color of baked earth. The result was that extraordinary experience of ochre monochrome, bathed, flooded and permeated with a light which is always warm, the color of flesh and fire.

Picasso was already preoccupied with luminosity when he started to work on *The Watering Place,* but when we compare the studies for it or the *Boy Leading a Horse* with the works done at Gosol, the former give the impression of having been seen in a Dutch light. Picasso had wanted this test of strength with the light, and he won it in a masterly way. He had already attempted it at the time he was painting the circus world; *The Athlete* tosses his little partner about against a brick red background.

The Two Brothers (xv. 9) seems to have initiated the new period. The childish slenderness of the figures relates them to the rose world of 1905 (the *Head of a Young Man* (xv. 7) which heralds them is dated 1905), as does the sort of tenderness or compassion shown by Picasso. But the novelty of the painting lies in the use of the new monochrome.

In the course of the previous two years Picasso had experimented enough with rose to have mastered its properties, its translucence, its quality of leaving objects unchanged, of opposing the effects of chiaroscuro. Rose does not shape in the round; by instinct we read it as relief.

But Picasso's experiment was just as much an experiment in psychology. The blue monochrome had been the blue of cold, hunger, misery, and solitude. Even if Jungian psychoanalysis has caricatured its implications, Picasso himself learned its qualities of expression. And it was precisely this knowledge which would serve him henceforth in a totally different adventure, an adventure into the warmth

---

[1] Zervos II, page 1.

[2] Shown at the Salon des Indépendants in 1905. *La Joie de Vivre* was shown at the Salon des Indépendants of 1906. That year the Salon was held from April 20th to 30th, that is to say, Picasso could have visited it before going to Gosol.

[3] Picasso's friends in Barcelona knew Gosol well; Casanovas, the sculptor, often stayed there, and Doctor Cinto Reventos chose Gosol as a health resort for some of his patients.

Little Girl Playing Ball, 1906, pen drawing.
Baltimore Museum of Art, The Cone Collection.

of physical understanding, into the fullness of life, into material security and also, we may say, the confirmation of success.

It is now possible to assess the importance of the revised chronology of the ochre or rose monochrome pictures of Gosol. Hitherto, association of the two large canvases, *Two Youths* and *The Adolescents* (XV. 10 and 11), and the *Young Girl with a Goat* (XV. 35), with the pictures belonging to the *Saltimbanques* sequence could only lead to attributing to Picasso a changeability and indecision quite alien to him; he certainly allows himself every kind of change, and above all any kind of break, but never vacillation of that kind. Antonina Vallentin, who followed the old chronology, nevertheless characterized perfectly the differences between the two periods. "The bodies... become thick-set with shorter, square heads and sightless eyes full of brown shadows; the features are drawn with a brown brush... the bodies seem to be torn out of an almost monochrome background by a brown contour line." But above all they are glowing and serene. Picasso has stopped the world. It is the moment of which Faust dreamed, "Stay then awhile, you are so beautiful." In the earlier paintings Picasso also fixed the moment, though in a different way. The *Seated Harlequin with Red Background* (XII. 10), seated before a background as stridently red as a theater curtain, is immobile, but fixed in his own being, like the *Blue Boy* (XIII. 21) of a few months later. Now in the works of Gosol, we have all the force of candid photography applied by the painter to a privileged moment, to the beloved gesture of the woman doing her hair. This gesture more than any other produces the effect of surprise, and *The Harem* (XV. 40), better than any other picture, gives the impression of intruding and of time suspended. *The Harem* sums up precisely a whole phase of research as the *Family of Saltimbanques* or *The Watering Place* did earlier.

This intimacy is seized in stealth as if by a housebreaker, without disturbing these young girls and women, peaceful and confident in their nudity. It dominates the paintings of nudes from *The Young Girl with a Goat* to the large *Standing Female Nude* (XV. 27), one of the works with the boldest use of monochrome. The intimacy flowers into grace and delicacy in the gouache, *Nude with Hands Clasped* (XV. 28), which has the almond eyes of Fernande, and which is treated with tenderness and limpid sensuality in an incomparably natural way.

97

The chronological regrouping also brings to light other relationships, not only between *Two Youths* (xv. 10) and *The Adolescents* (xv. 11), but also, for example, between these two large pictures and the *Standing Female Nude* (xv. 27), which have traditionally been considered separately. These works have in common their size and their color, which varies from red ochre to ochre and to rose (flesh-color as André Level says), applied in a very light, fluid way on the canvas, with the contours marked by an extremely fine brush stroke, browner in tone. They are alike, too, in their almost total lack of modeling except by subtle intensification and lightening of color, and in the hieratic, serene posture reminiscent as much of archaic Greek Kouroi as of Gauguin or the *Large Bather* of Cézanne. Here time has stopped completely. We plunge into a bright, bare eternity. In the *Two Youths* the figures stand in front of marble blocks on which pots are placed, but in *The Adolescents* only the jar the young girl carries gives any particularity to the scene. The boy is as much out of the world as *Standing Female Nude* (xv. 27). He stands with his arms crossed above his head in a pose which Picasso noted in the *Carnet Catalan* for *The Two Brothers* as well (cf. xv. 1–4).

Picasso's ease in these great pictures seems to derive from spontaneous mastery, but contrary to what one might expect, the studies which have been preserved suggest very careful placing and deep reflection. The final balance is the fruit of long struggles with the dazzling successes of improvisation.

This paganism, this pride in the body, this Grecian balance of nudity, all take their power and novelty from what the work of refining them reveals of their intimate source in the painter himself. There is nothing less academic. This classicism which adorns itself effortlessly with all the ancient researches and gives them a new meaning is by no means a corset or restraint. It seems to be produced or catalyzed by the sumptuous body, the elusive gaze, the peaceful smile and the flowering of Fernande.

La Toilette (xv. 34), the only work of this period which breaks with the ochre monochrome, is a masterpiece which brings together abruptly the new achievements with the investigations which had been begun in Paris. The young woman doing her hair and the servant opposite her belong to two worlds, to two styles of painting, to two different kinds of space. The studies show that Picasso only arrived at the opposition which gives this picture its power when

he gave the nude young girl a heightened, upward movement in contrast to the servant (cf. xv. 29–34). The young girl is seized on the wing, in the rapid gesture with which she draws back her hair; the servant, in profile, holds her mirror with the statuesque immobility of the *Standing Female Nude*. Her blue garments hang rigidly, like the garments of Gertrude Stein or of the girls in *La Coiffure*. In her hieratic stillness she anticipates the nudes from the end of the stay at Gosol.

This kind of contrast goes back, as we have seen, to the pictures of 1900 in Paris in the series of *Lovers*. The *Family of Saltimbanques,* in which the figure of the *Woman of Majorca* is set flat in the foreground, shows a revival of it. *Les Demoiselles d'Avignon* makes a well-known use of it. But what is noteworthy is the fact that Picasso always used this kind of stereoscopic effect as a test in crucial periods. The

Self-Portrait in Profile, Paris, 1906, pen drawing.
Private collection, Santa Barbara.

pictures of the *Painter and his Model* in 1963 and 1964 have to some extent made a system out of such contrasts. Moreover *La Toilette* also shows that Picasso maintained a continued interest in the paintings he had left behind in Paris.

Picasso was soaked in the colors of Gosol, but up to this time he had done no more than develop the preoccupations which he had brought with him. Besides the light of Gosol he had borrowed little except the earthenware, the vases which appear in nearly all the major pictures as a distinctive mark of this period. They will lead Picasso back to still life, a genre which he had only practiced once before, in *La Desserte* (v. 72) of 1901. The *Still Life with a Portrait* (xv. 14) is really a view of the studio with an unknown framed picture on the wall and beside it a pen and ink study for *The Two Brothers* (see xv. 6). But now the *Still Life with Vases* (xv. 13) is only concerned with the pots and the *porrón* painted for their substance, their volume and their appearance as objects, anticipating the clearly Cézanne-like still lifes of the winter 1907–1908. The *Still Life: Flowers in a Vase* (xv. 16) combines the bowl and the chocolate pot of the *Still Life with a Portrait* with mountain flowers, a much more usual subject for Picasso.

It was not until later that the village itself, its landscape and its inhabitants, forced themselves upon Picasso. But instead of submitting himself to them and simply receiving them passively, Picasso used them as a springboard for a new experiment, ending the classical period with its themes brought from Paris with a brutal rupture, a plunge into the harsh and crude reality of the high Catalan mountains.

4. *The Materials of Gosol*

This is the decisive moment. Up to now Picasso had allowed himself innumerable audacities, but always respected as essential the law which unites antique sculpture to the easel picture composed in depth according to normal geometrical perspective. He had carried almost to the limit his liberties with proportions, framing, the visual reconstruction of elisions, the rejection of chiaroscuro, division of brush stroke, the use of monochrome and expressionist distortion of line. Since he was twenty he had constantly appealed to the spectator's power of interpreting what was left unsaid, in such a way as to deny traditional illusionism.

To put it crudely, Picasso mocked at illusionism, but nevertheless he respected the rules of the game, which the impetuous flow of his natural impulses, the ebb of concentration and critical wariness, regulated successively. Now in 1906, at twenty-five, he possessed a body of work already worthy of setting him among the great. He had arrived at a mastery in which likeness, harmony and beauty seemed to burst at will from his brush.

But signs of disquiet and dissatisfaction have already been encountered even within the expansiveness of his creative impulses. He abandoned *The Watering Place* just when he seemed to be reaching his goal. According to Gertrude Stein her *Portrait* originated from a sketch of startling likeness, but instead of being satisfied, Picasso worked at it so long and so hard that he finally rapped out at his model, "I don't see you any longer when I look at you." And he abandoned the portrait.

The great turning point in Picasso's painting comes at the moment we now have reached. It alone did not determine all that was to follow, but it was the first uncoupling of the link, the rupture. The re-established chronology gives a coherent view of it.

The portraits of Fernande reflect the change. The one listed as xv. 41 is very near to the face of the *Standing Female Nude* (xv. 27) or to the attitude of the *Nude with Hands Clasped* (xv. 28). The impression of distance derives perhaps from the sketchy treatment of the blouse in contrast to the searching representation of the face, where the modeling is strongly expressed by hatchings. But here we are again back to earth, in everyday life. A feature of everyday life which could be only accidental among the classical nudes appears in other portraits of Fernande, where she is shown wearing a mantilla (xv. 43 and 44). (Later, on her first journey to Spain, Olga was also painted in the traditional mantilla, and doubtless when in his own country with the woman he loves, Picasso feels the need to see her dressed in this way.) But this accidental feature which links Fernande with *Madame Canals* (xiii. 9) was to be continued: the *Carnet Catalan* reveals Picasso's interest in the faces of women framed by the Catalan headdress; the face is reduced to its oval.

Picasso is aware of the resulting austerity and also of the expressive power of the mask. This type of headdress really reveals the mask, the unvarying nature of the face which changes of hair style disturb. The mask is not a likeness and it does not correspond with the mental construction we make from the play of features, which is the sentimental image of the model. But has not the mask a truer reality, a deeper authenticity? Does it not show the very nature of the woman without the affectations of fashion? In this way it expresses these natural women, linked to nature as the peasant women of Gosol are.

The *Woman with Loaves* (xv. 46) is a remarkable example of the way in which Picasso seizes what the reality of Gosol provides. What interests him is the dignity of carriage, which he notes with the same vigor in his drawing, *Woman Returning from Market* (D. xv. 34), taking from life what he has already tried to express in nudes like *Torso of a Young Girl* (xv. 24) or *Nude with a Pitcher* (xv. 23). Perhaps it is the austere landscape, the roughness of the people which influence him. One gets the impression that there is a reaction against the harmony and joy of the classical nudes. Emerging from a period of idealization Picasso seems to feel the need to get back to earth and to confront the challenges of everyday life.

But the spirit of his search is no longer the same. The period of classical nudes seems to have released him from a certain reserve towards heightened plasticity. With the Fauves, such a liberation results in becoming drunk with color, but with Picasso it allows him to obey the divergencies, the "distortions", suggested by experiment. The *Woman with Loaves* shows Picasso's response to the monastic appearance of her garments, to her natural balance under the weight of the round loaves, to the way in which her headdress emphasizes the face. The two gouaches, *Fernande with Kerchief* (xv. 45) and the *Reclining Nude* (xv. 47), show still greater signs of freedom. Here Picasso records from life, instantaneously, the different responses Fernande's unusual appearance elicits from him. In *Reclining Nude* he unexpectedly adds this kerchief-framed head to the sketch of a naked body, but without harmonizing them, as if to accentuate still more the mask-like appearance, the rupture and isolation produced in this way by the face. *Reclining Nude* is perhaps the first work which breaks so deliberately with normal and especially with unified proportions. Picasso is here consciously making a mistake or being clumsy, if this gouache is judged by ordinary standards, but he is also experimenting with the license which he will use to finish the *Portrait of Gertrude Stein* after the researches which fill the last part of the stay at Gosol.

During the period of the nudes Picasso was working towards the establishment and refinement of rhythms, towards the search for the harmony and equilibrium of the body to obtain an ideal unity. Now he was concerned with extracting from the innovations of reality the fundamental and essential secrets which they concealed and revealed. The way in which Picasso treated the face in the *Head of a Man* is in this respect instructive. The two versions (xv. 52 and 53) no doubt lead to the sculpture *Man's Head* (z. 1. 380), but we believe it would be a mistake to explain Picasso's interest in the old man's mask (treated as such in the drawing xv. 54) entirely as a project for this sculpture.

The look of painted sculpture, acquired more and more clearly by Picasso's painting during this period, did not spring from the concerns of a sculptor. Plainly it was the reverse. When Picasso executed the sculptures, *Man's Head* and *La Coiffure* (z. 1. 329) in the autumn (doubtless on the return to Paris considering their weight and bulk), he was transposing his experiences as a painter. The face of the *Head of a Man* does not need the contrivance of a kerchief to make it look like a mask; old age, the stretched, dry skin on the cheek-bones are enough. And Picasso will not rest before he has picked out from it the distinctive marks and basic forms.

During the outburst of experiments that appeared midway in the stay at Gosol, and before developing consistently the reduction of the human body to its essential elements, Picasso became involved in another experiment closely united with the two previous ones, but one which already anticipated the freedom of reconstruction which flowered at the time of *Les Demoiselles d'Avignon*. This search led to the large-scale *Composition: The Peasants* (xv. 62), a painting of cardinal interest for understanding the birth of Cubism.

Here also, at the beginning, are scenes which seem to be noted down from life: *Boy with Cattle* (xv. 56) and *Study for The Peasants* (xv. 57). Then Picasso devoted himself to disengaging the mask of the man (xv. 60) and at the same time to giving the composition its movement and rhythm by reducing the figure of the young girl in front of the legs of her companion and making her lean in the same way (xv. 61).

It is now certain that because of its very large size the final composition in oil was only painted on the return to Paris, on the basis of elements brought back from Gosol.

This was Barr's hypothesis[1] and it is now confirmed by Picasso's letter.[2] A drawing (xv. 57) which is added for the first time to the other studies, attests that the source of the picture was something living and actually seen. It does not negate Picasso's statement that he had not seen a blind flower seller guided by a little girl, for clearly it was the man's mask-like look which made Barr think he was blind; in fact, the man was simply a peasant with a basket on his back, bringing back wild flowers from the mountains.

On the other hand Barr is very convincing when he compares the free reconstruction of the figures with the distortions of El Greco, particularly with *Saint Joseph and the Child Jesus,* which was reproduced not only in Miguel Utrillo's monograph published in Barcelona in 1906, but also in *Les Arts* of October 1906 and the *Gazette des Beaux-Arts* of November, both published in Paris. The influence of El Greco has already been emphasized by the man who bought this picture from Vollard in 1913, Dr. Albert C. Barnes, who added in a letter of December 1944, to Barr: "The dominant impression in this picture is of El Greco, but when I talk to students about it, I put it beside a number of works by Cézanne, and this shows that Picasso's use of color in the form of distinct planes is as predominant and as clearly visible as the distortions imitated from El Greco..." It is very remarkable that ten years later, when Picasso was beginning a new classical phase while simultaneously continuing his cubist experiments, he was to make use of Mannerism or rather of mannerisms, as a means of translating his cubist liberties into the language of traditional drawing. The elongations, the thickenings, in short the distortion was to be the equivalent of the perspective separation of the cubist planes. In *The Peasants* on the other hand the distortions will lead to Cubism. But in fact we construe the distortions from our experience of Picasso; we already interpret this painting as if it had been done in 1920. To say this is to recognize the strength of the new principles with which Picasso was experimenting, and to realize, too, the significance which the archaic visual languages had for him. These principles were the road to a true expression of reality, not so much because they preceded or were more objective than the classical methods, but rather because they called them into question, almost in the way that a

kerchief on the head makes one question the ordinary life-like expression of the face.

If it were only the support of El Greco and the wealth of experience of the preceding years which now gave Picasso authority for much greater liberties than the expressionist liberties of the *Lovers* series, one might say that it was all part of the same advance. And probably we are now dealing with one of the constants of Picasso's nature, one which we believe determines his character and the continuity of his art. One must carry one's experiments right to the end, that is his rule. Push distortion right to the limit, where it will multiply the meanings through surprise; push elision and abstraction to the final point where the spectator's vision will be most enriched by the essential images. Go to the lengths of paroxysm. With *The Peasants* Picasso accomplished his break with the aesthetic of verisimilitude or likeness, whichever one calls it. He mobilized the forces of the plastic "composition" (the name given to *The Peasants,* and remarkably well-chosen by Picasso, which with *Guernica* and *Massacre in Korea,* is one of the four or five titles which he has chosen himself) to evoke peasants carrying flowers, a pagan image *par excellence,* a song of nature. It is as if he restored El Greco to health, without his religion and mysticism, to bestow on man the discoveries of his painting. The conception of painting which Picasso was in the course of forming included the fact that for him painting was not only the complete expression of appearances, but also of the sense of life and of the world. The Fauve-like dazzle of the discoveries of spring, 1901, in Paris, the cruelty of the stained glass pictures, the hunger and misery of the blue pictures, the pagan song of the ochre nudes, everything must be interpreted in this light. The change which had just taken place in Picasso's painting through contact with the rough realities of the high Catalan mountain was not only aesthetic but philosophical in the widest sense. Painting is also a way of understanding. It reaches out not only to appearances, but to the physical truth of the world.

5. The Birth of Cubism

For the moment one can set aside the experiment of *Composition: The Peasants,* which directly anticipated the period of *Les Demoiselles d'Avignon.* On his return from Gosol Picasso worked in four directions. He took up the theme

---

[1] *Fifty Years,* page 256.
[2] Cf. Appendix, Picasso's letter to Leo Stein dated August 17, 1906, and also the study (xv. 59).

of the nude woman doing her hair in a more abstract way, developing the method of the mask and applying it to the treatment of the body. In the same spirit he devoted himself to the problems of representing two full-length figures, the theme of two nude women standing, in some cases with their arms round each other. He continued his researches into the expression of volumes on his own face and body shown half-length, and at the same time on the female body treated in spheres and cylinders. Finally from there he went on to indicate modeling by hatchings, emphasizing the meeting of planes, the angles, and preparing the way for constructions which were really Cubist.

The revised chronology allows us to put the question of the influence of Iberian sculpture on Picasso in a different way. Picasso's statement to Zervos that *Les Demoiselles d'Avignon* had been conceived before he knew negro sculpture and that he had drawn his inspiration from Iberian sculpture in the Louvre, dates from 1939. This gave rise to James Johnson Sweeney's study of Picasso and Iberian Art published in 1941[1], which remained the source of all the comparisons attempted since. But Sweeney in this article placed works like the *Woman with a Comb* (XVI. 5) in 1905 and this led him to state, "Picasso's visit to Spain in the summer of 1906 was apparently not the original stimulus for his interest in Iberian sculpture." This thesis was taken up in 1956 by John Golding[2], who rightly observed that there is no Iberian sculpture at Gosol. But we have seen the real inspiration which, on the contrary, did derive from the stay at Gosol; it seems as if there Picasso had verified the profound reality of the so-called clumsiness and naïveté[3] of Iberian sculpture. And on his return to Paris he seemed determined to enlarge the scope of his experiments.

There is no reason to doubt the statement of Gertrude Stein that Picasso gave the final expression to the face in her portrait on the very day of his return from Gosol. This mask does in fact resemble Iberian votive bronzes, but this means only that the work done at Gosol, whether deriving from Fernande and the women with kerchiefs or from the *Head of a Man,* was a return to these archaic conventions. It seems very likely that Picasso finished *La Coiffure* at the same time. His two self-portraits, *Self-Portrait with a Palette* (XVI. 28) and *Bust of a Man* (XVI. 26), have the same mask-like treatment of the face, but they belong to quite another style of painting, one which is extremely colorless, with the shadows for modeling reduced to a few significant marks.

All the experiments of this autumn seem to have some reference to both the investigations at Gosol and to Iberian sculpture. The empty eyes and closed eyes are already to be found in the studies which derive from the face of Fernande (*Standing Female Nude, Head of a Woman,* XV. 27 and 22). Only the enlarged and stylized eyes in the series of *Two Nudes* (XVI. 15–19) obviously come from the votive bronzes of Osuna and Cerro de los Santos. But the series of *Two Nudes* with their arms round each other (XVI. 11, 12, 13) derives directly from the *Peasants of Andorra,* as the preparatory drawing reproduced by Zervos (z. VI. 875) bears witness (See also p. 292).

It is extremely important to grasp and understand this double movement. Cubism did not parachute into Picasso's painting through the discovery of primitive Iberian sculpture. Picasso rediscovered through his own experience of reality the point of view which had impressed him in primitive art. Thus, having understood the reasons for their creation, he went to the sculptures themselves for lessons.

The *Two Nudes* (XVI. 15), now in the Museum of Modern Art, New York, gives the fullest expression of these lessons. Picasso is not so much concerned with grasping the hieratic power of the mask, with which he was now familiar, as with appropriating the sculptural weight, the massive force which emanates from the small Iberian ex voto statues. The *Two Nudes* do not owe their solidity and the impression of calm majesty which they give the spectator to any traditional attractions. Rather, they draw us into their own space, their own world, which the perspective effect places above us. This is the same way Cézanne leads us to see his *Three Bathers* of 1879, in the Musee d'Art Moderne de la Ville de Paris; and suddenly we understand another source of Picasso's reflections at this turning point in his painting. Just as the woman at left in the *Two Nudes* clearly heralds the girl at extreme left holding the curtain in *Les Demoiselles d'Avignon,* we see now that the crouching bather at the extreme right of Cézanne's picture has bequeathed her body and her quartered posture to the crouching girl at the far right of the Picasso.[4]

[1] *Art Bulletin,* September 1941, pages 191–198.

[2] *Cubism,* page 43 and note.

[3] Expressions used by Pierre Paris, published in 1906.

[4] From this time numerous elements which were to find a place in *Les Demoiselles d'Avignon* occur in Picasso's painting (See Catalogue XVI).

Seated Nude, Paris, 1906, pencil drawing.

The *Two Nudes* has always been placed at the end of 1906. It is possible that it was painted after the Salon d'Automne of 1906, in which there were ten works by Cézanne. The *Three Bathers* had been exhibited in the second Salon d'Automne, that of 1904, the first which Picasso had been able to see.

These are the elements of reflection which sum up our study of this period. Picasso had arrived at what we should call today a point of no return. Certainly we say this without risk, because we know the sequel, but the significant thing is that the experiments which followed after Picasso had unclothed his boy leading a horse, led him to prove that classical conventions do not exist in nature or reality. This is true not only of perspective, but also of the traditional representation of the human face and the modeling of the body. Picasso had just discovered that this representation can be obtained by other methods and other symbols, choosing other guiding marks than those by means of which beauty and likeness had traditionally been achieved. Picasso's boldness and revolutionary determination are in no way diminished, but rather they are oriented if we recall here some lines from Elie Faure's preface for the third Salon d'Automne, that of 1905: "To put ourselves in contact with the young generations of artists, we must be free to hear and we must wish to understand an absolutely new language. Let us hear them, these primitives..."

This was written with reference, among other things, to "Gauguin's sensuality, to the austerity of Cézanne." This was the autumn of Cézanne's death, 1906. Picasso had just learned the lesson of the older painter's *Bathers* and knew that the majority of Cézanne's pictures were more than a quarter of a century old. He must have said to himself that it was time, high time, to go forward. It is there that we shall leave him in this book. He was just twenty-five. Behind him was a body of work which would have crushed anyone else. But in front of him, in the direction which he was taking, there was nobody.

Can we draw up a balance sheet of our investigation? In re-evaluating Picasso's art during this formative period, our book does not destroy the traditional conception of the Blue and the Rose Period, but it includes them within the framework of two other periods at least equally important: the pre-Fauvism of the painter's twentieth year, that we have called the style of the Vollard exhibition, and the pre-Cubism which corresponds with the period at Gosol. In reality these two re-evaluations complete each other. Cubism would seem a capricious adventure, and Picasso's development illogical and incomprehensible, if we deny the experiments with color in 1901 to integrate them by force with the period of blue monochrome, or extend the Rose Period unduly into the reaction by which Picasso broke with likeness and classical beauty. We have applied the opposite method strictly, starting from the idea that it was possible to establish a series of artistic developments which were chronologically coherent, and through this to clarify most of the mysteries and to disclose Picasso's fundamental continuity with regard to reality and the means of mastering it in his art.

Through the paintings themselves, we have revealed the profound unity of the artist, the continuity of his themes, his curiosity, his emotions and general attitude towards life, all of which restores to his work a more human dimension, whose true quality is sometimes hidden by anecdotes too widely current.

At the end of this re-assessment, it seems to us that this quality is the never-failing interest which Picasso takes in whatever mankind and the reality of the world provide for him. From this he draws the challenges and inspirations for painting. He imitates and contradicts, loves and rejects, records and transfigures. To him everything is his subject, his material, his tool, his means of expression. He nourishes himself upon all the experience accumulated since men first painted or made sculpture, upon the plastic suggestions provided by natural forms or by objects called utilitarian. Life is a whole. Painting is a whole. At the time we leave him, Picasso is on the verge of producing a radically new kind of painting in order to express what he sees and knows. If Cubism has profoundly transformed our way of seeing, such as the shapes which men give objects and the buildings they create, it is because Cubism had its roots in the reality of our time.

This book, with the chronology unfolded by the illustrations, is a description of the stages in this evolution.

Malaga, 1885 : Picasso, four years old.

Picasso, seven years old, with his sister, Lola.

Barcelona, 1896 : Picasso, fifteen years old.

Picasso in 1904. Photograph taken in Paris by Ricardo Canals.
Inscribed and signed, top right : To my dear friends, Suzanne and Henri (Bloch), Picasso, 1904.

Photographs from the archives of Pierre Cailler, Geneva.

Picasso in Barcelona, 1898-1900

The year 1900 brought Picasso his first real studio, on Calle Riera de San Juan, but the turn of the century is not reflected in his work. He returned from Horta de Ebro in April 1899, according to Sabartés, and worked in the quarters of the brother of the sculptor Cardona at No. 1 Calle de Escudillers Blancs. "The other part of the apartment," wrote Sabartés, "housed the workshop of a corset-maker. Sometimes, in spare moments, Picasso took pleasure in operating the machine for punching eyelets in the corsets... while observing the activities of the workmen and the functioning of the machines. Then he would go to his room to draw and paint, paint and draw incessantly. I can see him now, buried beneath a stack of drawings..."

Outstanding during this period is the large number of portraits, generally in charcoal on paper, sometimes finished with pastel, watercolor or turpentine wash. Sabartés relates how Picasso's friends prodded him to compete with Ramón Casas (1866-1932), who at the time was a portrait painter of some repute in Barcelona working in the Parisian manner, and who played a part in bringing Lautrec and Steinlen to the attention of Picasso. A sort of exhibition resulted, at the beginning of 1900, at the *Quatre Gats*, with the drawings pinned up on the walls.

We have included only four examples of this type of work: the portraits of Cardona, Pallarés and Sabartés, because of their biographical relevance to Picasso, and the portrait of Vidal y Ventosa, which Zervos did not catalogue. For the others we refer to Vol. VI of the Zervos Catalogue. They teem with the sense of life that so struck Sabartés. Although they constitute a fine illustration of Picasso's early mastery of technique and his psychological acumen even in adolescence, they are nevertheless outside our inquiry. They belong to his juvenile work in its last phase.

In these eighteen months in which we lack enough information to construct a certain chronology and there is little variation in signatures, we have sought above all for works which are characteristic of this formative period. We list, for example, the majority of the oils known to us and a series of portraits of Picasso's sister, Lola. We continue our custom of including previously uncatalogued works, whatever their importance [1].

At the start of 1900, Picasso moved to the Calle Riera de San Juan. He had a studio "on the top floor of an old house on the heights of the old city, the sort of place designed for industrial use, an *obrador*, without furnishings but with large windows." [2] Picasso lived there with his friend Carlos Casagemas, a young painter in whose company he spent the whole of 1900.

[1] This catalogue covers the years 1900 to 1906. We have catalogued, for the sake of documentation, a part of the works from 1898-1899.

[2] Sabartés, *Picasso, Portraits et Souvenirs*, pp. 40-41.

A Chronology of Picasso's Early Years

1881 *October 25*
Birth at Malaga, at 11:15 p.m., according to the baptismal record, of Pablo, Diego, José, Francisco de Paula, Juan Nepomuceno, Maria de los Remedios, Cipriano de la Santisima Trinidad, legitimate son of Don José Ruiz Blasco, teacher at the School of Arts and Crafts of San Telmo in Malaga, and Doña Maria Picasso y Lopez, of this city.

1884 *December 25*
Birth of Lola, younger sister of Pablo Picasso.

1891 Removal of the whole family to Corunna in Galicia where Don José was a drawing master at the Instituto da Guarda.

1894 José Ruiz hands his brushes and paints over to his son Pablo and decides to renounce painting.

1895 *September 25*
After vacation in Malaga, Don José took his family to Barcelona where he had an appointment as instructor at the provincial School of Fine Arts. Pablo followed his father's wish that he study an art curriculum. He took the entrance examination. Sabartés wrote, "Only the mature risked this test, and only after having taken all the classes and having steadily won prizes." Pablo passed the exam.

1897 *June 8*
The jury at the National Exhibition of Fine Arts in Madrid awarded honorable mention to Pablo Ruiz Picasso for his picture *Science and Charity*, which subsequently won a gold medal in Malaga.

1897 *October*
Passed the entrance examination for the Academy San Fernando in Madrid. Stayed in Madrid.

1898 *Spring*
Pablo came down with scarlet fever, left Madrid for Barcelona and then convalesced at Horta de Ebro at the home of his friend Pallarés.

1899 *Spring*
Returned to Barcelona. He worked in the lodgings of the brother of the sculptor Cardona, and participated in the group that met at the café *Els Quatre Gats*, which he frequented even before leaving for Madrid.

1900 *Beginning of the year*
Picasso moved into a studio on the Calle Riera de San Juan with Carlos Casagemas, a painter slightly older than himself, who had literary aspirations and was, according to Sabartés, quite well off. The drawing (cf. D.I.7) which shows the two friends bundled up in coats and walking side by side was done after the return from Horta de Ebro.

1900 *February*
Picasso's first exhibition, at the café *Els Quatre Gats*, contained portraits of his friends, in charcoal finished with pastel and watercolor. There was only one painting; it depicted a young priest standing by the bedside of a dying woman. An admonishing commentary on this exhibition was printed in *La Vanguardia*, February 3, 1900. According to Josep Palau i Fabre (*Picasso en Cataluña*, pp. 62-70), this unsigned article was written by Rodríguez Codolá, art teacher at *La Lonja*.

1900 *July 19*
Picasso's first published drawing, in the magazine *Joventut*.

1900 *October*
Departure for Paris with Casagemas and Pallarés. Picasso was nineteen.

I. 1
STREETWALKER
Barcelona, 1898–1899.
Oil on canvas.
Size : 46 x 55 cm.
Signed bottom right : P. Ruiz Picasso.

Exh. Never exhibited.

Bibl. Not in Z. Duncan, *Picasso's Picassos,* p. 49, repr. in color (dated 1899 by Duncan).

Owned by the artist.

This work remained in the artist's possession, never exhibited or reproduced until David Douglas Duncan included it in *Picasso's Picassos,* a work done at the villa La Californie in Cannes, 1960. From this point on Picasso did not follow academic dictates about a finished appearance. He renders the figures with a few strokes of color in a bold style reminiscent of Daumier's oils.

I. 2
END OF THE ROAD (Redemption)
Barcelona, 1898–1899.
Watercolor and conté crayon on paper.
Size : 45.5 x 29.8 cm.
Signed bottom right : P. Ruiz Picasso.

Exh. Museum of Modern Art, New York, 1957 : *Picasso, 75th Anniversary Exhibition,* repr. in cat. p. 14. Philadelphia Museum of Art, 1958 : *Picasso,* No. 1, repr. in cat. Museum of Modern Art, New York, 1960 : *Art Nouveau, Art and Design at the Turn of the Century,* No. 222, repr. in cat. p. 65. The Solomon R. Guggenheim Museum, New York, April–

September 1965 : *First Showing of Masterpieces of Modern Art from the Thannhauser Foundation,* No. 27, repr. in color in cat. p. 36.

Bibl. Not in Z. Blunt and Pool, No. 64. John Richardson, 1964, No. 1 (repr. in color).

Coll. Private collection, Barcelona ; Justin K. Thannhauser, New York ;

The Solomon R. Guggenheim Museum, New York, Justin K. Thannhauser Foundation.

I. 3
PORTRAIT OF JUAN VIDAL Y VENTOSA
Barcelona, 1899–1900.
Watercolor and charcoal on paper.
Size : 52.5 x 34.5 cm.
Signed bottom right : P. Ruiz Picasso.

Exh. Musée de Lyon, June 1953, No. 1. Musée des Arts Décoratifs, Paris, 1955, No. 1 (entitled *Portrait d'un écrivain*), repr. in cat.

Bibl. Not in Z. (Zervos reproduces as No. VI. 252 another portrait of Juan Vidal y Ventosa, against a plain background and less elaborate. Zervos dates it 1899, which makes it earlier than this one, done —according to the sitter—in 1900). John Richardson : *Picasso, aquarelles et gouaches,* Basel, 1964, No. 2 (repr. in color).

Coll. Juan Vidal y Ventosa, Barcelona.

Collection Maître Maurice Rheims, Paris.

Juan Vidal y Ventosa, a year older than Picasso, intended to be a sculptor but became a photographer and worked for museums in Barcelona. His studio was the gathering place of a group nicknamed "El Guayaba." It was similar to the one which met at *Els Quatre Gats,* but it was more sensitive to trends from England than Germany. (See photograph in the Appendix.) Picasso visited Vidal y Ventosa and his friends often and continued to keep in touch with him.

I. 4
PORTRAIT OF RENART
Barcelona, 1899.
Oil on canvas.
Size : 44.5 x 36.8 cm.
Signed top left : P. Ruiz P.

Bibl. Not in Z. Penrose, *Portrait of Picasso.*

Coll. Cardona, Barcelona ;

Collection O'Hana Gallery, London.

This portrait is thought to have been painted in the studio of the sculptor Cardona.

I. 5
PORTRAIT OF SABARTÉS SEATED
Barcelona, 1899–1900.
Charcoal and watercolor on paper.
Size : 48.4 x 32.5 cm.
Signed bottom left : P. Ruiz Picasso.
Exh. Musée Réattu, Arles, July 6–September 2, 1957 : *Picasso, Dessins, gouaches, aquarelles 1898–1957,* No. 4. Sala Gaspar, Barcelona, 1961 : *Picasso, Dibujos - Gouaches - Acuarelas,* No. 2.
Bibl. Z. VI. 247. Sabartés, *Picasso, Portraits et souvenirs,* 1946, No. 1.

Sabartés, *Picasso, Retratos y Recuerdos,* Madrid, 1953, p. 80. Palau i Fabre, No. 26 (repr. in color).

Coll. Jaime Sabartés, Paris ;

Picasso Museum, Barcelona.

Sabartés hesitates to date this portrait in the period when Picasso was working at Cardona's ; he seems inclined to place it at the beginning of Picasso's residence in the Calle Riera de San Juan. Technically this portrait is very close to the one of Vidal (I. 3).

I. 6
SABARTÉS AS A DECADENT POET
Barcelona, 1900.
Charcoal and color wash on paper.
Size : 48 x 32 cm.
Signed bottom left : Picasso, with the inscription : "Recuerdo para J. Sabartés de antes de siglo de su amigo Picasso, hoy 31 de octubre de 1950."
Inscribed top right : *Poeta Decadente.*

Exh. Musée Réattu, Arles, July 6–September 2, 1957 : *Picasso, Dessins, gouaches, aquarelles, 1898–1957,* No. 3, repr. in cat. pl. 2. Sala Gaspar,

Barcelona, 1961 : *Picasso, Dibujos - Gouaches - Acuarelas,* No. 1, repr.

Bibl. Not in Z. Sabartés, *Picasso, Retratos y Recuerdos,* Madrid, 1953, p. 65. Blunt and Pool, No. 47. Sabartés, *Picasso, Les bleus de Barcelone,* Paris, 1963, pl. 10 (repr. in color). Palau i Fabre, No. 25 (repr. in color).

Coll. Jaime Sabartés, Paris ;

Picasso Museum, Barcelona.

Sabartés dates this portrait in the summer of 1900.

I. 7
PORTRAIT OF MANUEL PALLARÉS
Barcelona, 1899.
Charcoal and color wash.
Dimensions not known.
Signed bottom left : P. Ruiz Picasso.

Bibl. Z. I. 13.

Present location unknown.

This sketch of Picasso's oldest Catalan

friend is dated 1898 by Zervos. But it seems to have been done after Picasso's return from the village of Pallarés, Horta de Ebro, where he convalesced after an attack of scarlet fever—that is, in the spring of 1899. This date is supported both by similarity of handling in the other portraits of this period and by the landscape of Barcelona factories in the background.

I. 8
THE CAFÉ-THEATER DEL PARALELO
Barcelona, 1899–1900.
Oil on panel.
Size : 36 x 48 cm.
Signed top right : P. Ruiz Picasso.

Bibl. Z.I. 11. C.-P. No. 11.

Collection J. Barbey, Barcelona.

I. 9
INTERIOR OF THE QUATRE GATS
Barcelona, 1899–1900.
Oil.
Size : 41 x 28 cm.
Signed bottom right : Picasso.
(The signature was added later. It is very close to those of the return to Barcelona at the beginning of 1902.)

Exh. Museum of Fine Arts, Boston, 1957 : *European Masters of our Time,* No. 112, repr. in cat. pl. 7 (entitled *Night Café*).

Bibl. Z.I.21. C.-P. No. 14. Palau i Fabre, No. 23 (repr. in color).

Coll. Madame Helena Rubinstein (Princess Gourielli), New York ; Parke-Bernet, New York, April 20, 1966 : Sale of the *Helena Rubinstein Collection of Modern Paintings and Sculpture* (First Part), No. 27, repr. in color in cat. p. 45, sold for $40.000 ;

Private collection, U.S.A.

The man with the pipe is the poet Rafael Nogueras Oller. His companion's red skirt stands out vividly against the dark background of this oil of 1899.

I. 10
THE DIVAN
Barcelona, 1899–1900.
Drawing with watercolor on paper.
Size : 25 x 29 cm.
Signed bottom right : P. Ruiz Picasso.

Exh. III Bienal Hispanoamericana de Arte, Barcelona, 1955 : *Precursores y maestros del arte Español contemporáneo,* No. 33. Tokyo, 1964 : *Picasso,* No. 1, repr. in color in cat. pl. 1.

Bibl. Z.I.23. C.-P. No. 26. Sabartés and Boeck, p. 358. Sabartés, *Picasso les bleus de Barcelone,* Paris, 1963, pl. 4 (repr. in color). Palau i Fabre, No. 67 (repr. in color).

Coll. L. Plandiura, Barcelona ; Museo de Arte Moderno, Barcelona ;

Picasso Museum, Barcelona.

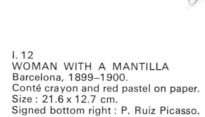

I. 11
THE POOR VIOLINIST
Barcelona, 1899–1900.
Pastel and chalk.
Size : 25 x 23 cm.
Unsigned.
Inscribed top left : Dispens.

Bibl. Z. VI. 285 (dated 1899). C.-P.
No. 87 (dated 1901). W.C.A. XII.
No. 156.

Coll. Junyer Vidal, Barcelona; Galerie
Charpentier, Paris, Sale, June 17, 1960
(entitled *Interior Scene*), sold for
63,000 fr.

Private collection, U.S.A.

I. 12
WOMAN WITH A MANTILLA
Barcelona, 1899–1900.
Conté crayon and red pastel on paper.
Size : 21.6 x 12.7 cm.
Signed bottom right : P. Ruiz Picasso.

Exh. Sidney Janis Gallery, New York,
April 25–May 21, 1960; O'Hana
Gallery, London, June 23–July 28,
1960; Stoneleigh Abbey, Warwick-
shire, July 30–August 14, 1960;
Galerie Motte, Geneva and Paris,
August 23–September 10, 1960 : *Pi-
casso, his Blue Period,* No. 17, repr.

in cat. Galerie Katia Granoff, Paris,
April 29–June 8, 1963 : *Collection
d'un amateur,* No. 57, repr. in color in
cat. (entitled *Spanish Woman*).

Bibl. Not in Z.

Coll. Private collection, Barcelona;
O'Hana Gallery, London;

Private collection, Paris.

Authenticated by the artist.

I. 13
PORTRAIT OF LOLA,
THE ARTIST'S SISTER
Barcelona, 1899–1900.
Pastel.
Size : 44.5 x 30.5 cm.
Signed top left : P. Ruiz Picasso.

Exh. Sidney Janis Gallery, New York,
April 25–May 21, 1960; O'Hana
Gallery, London, June 23–July 28,
1960; Stoneleigh Abbey, Warwick-
shire, July 30–August 14, 1960;
Galerie Motte, Geneva and Paris,

August 23–September 10, 1960 : *Picasso, his Blue Period,* No. 2, repr. in
color in cat.

Bibl. Not in Z. Jacques O'Hana,
Picasso, his Blue Period, No. 2 (repr.
in color).

Coll. Private collection, Barcelona;

Present location unknown.

Authenticated by the artist.

I. 14
LOLA, THE ARTIST'S SISTER
Barcelona, 1899–1900.
Charcoal and colored chalk with color
wash, on paper.
Size : 44 x 29 cm.
Signed top left : P. Ruiz Picasso.

Exh. III Bienal Hispanoamericana de
Arte, Barcelona, 1955; *Precursores y
maestros del arte Español contemporáneo,* No. 35. Musée d'Art et d'Histoire, Geneva, 1956 : *Sélection de la
IIIe Biennale Hispano-Américaine :*

Picasso, Nonell, Manolo, No. 18. Musée Réattu, Arles, 1957 : *Picasso, Dessins, Aquarelles, Gouaches 1898–
1957,* No. 2, repr. in cat. pl. I. Tokyo,
1964 : *Picasso.*

Bibl. Z. I. 29. C.-P. No. 16. Sabartés,
Picasso, les bleus de Barcelone, Paris,
1963, pl. 2 (repr. in color). Palau i
Fabre, No. 17 (repr. in color).

Coll. L. Plandiura, Barcelona; Museo
de Arte Moderno, Barcelona;
Picasso Museum, Barcelona.

I. 15
PORTRAIT OF LOLA
(L'ESPAGNOLE)
Barcelona, 1899–1900.
Pastel.
Size : 44.5 x 21 cm.
Signed top right : P. Ruiz Picasso.

Exh. Musée de l'Athénée, Geneva, July 16–September 29, 1960 : *De l'Impressionnisme à l'Ecole de Paris,* No. 62, repr. in cat.

Bibl. Not in Z. Palau i Fabre, No. 18 (repr. in color).

Coll. Robert Rey, Geneva ; Mr. and Mrs. Norman B. Woolworth, New York ; Knoedler & Co., New York ;

Collection Miss Barbara Thurston, New York.

Authenticated by the artist in Cannes, April 9, 1960.

I. 16
PORTRAIT OF LOLA
Barcelona, 1899–1900.
Ink and watercolor on paper.
Size : 16.5 x 11.4 cm.
Signed top left : P. Ruiz Picasso.

Bibl. Not in Z.

Coll. O'Hana Gallery, London ;

Collection Max Rayne, London.

Authenticated by the artist.

Lola Maria de los Dolores Ruiz Picasso, the artist's sister, married the doctor Don Juan Vilato Gomez of Barcelona.

I. 17
LOLA PICASSO
Barcelona, 1899–1900.
Oil on canvas.
Size : 150 x 100 cm.
Signed bottom left : P. Ruiz Picasso.

Exh. Museum of Modern Art, New York, and The Art Institute of Chicago, 1939–1940 : *Picasso, Forty Years of his Art,* No. 2, repr. in cat. The Arts Council of Great Britain, Tate Gallery, London, 1960 : *Picasso,* No. 3, repr. in cat., pl. 4c (entitled *Portrait of the Artist's Sister*).

Bibl. Z. I. 377. Barr, *Forty Years,* p. 22. Barr, *Fifty Years,* p. 15. C.-P. No. 17.

Lieberman, 1961, pl. 5. Duncan, *Picasso's Picassos,* p. 203.

Owned by the artist.

It is hard to put this series of portraits in chronological order. They must have been done between the spring of 1899 and the autumn of 1900. In any case, this large canvas seems earlier than the small oil on wood in the Mellon Collection, which we describe among the works that might have appeared in the Vollard exhibition. (Cf. V. 56.)

I. 18
LA COIFFURE
Barcelona, 1899–1900.
Pastel and watercolor.
Size : 30 x 19 cm.
Signed bottom left : P. Ruiz Picasso.

Bibl. Z. I. 28. C.-P. No. 13 *(Scène de la vie de bohème).* W.C.A. Vol. XV, 1963, No. 3789.

Coll. Señora de Aguirre, Buenos Aires ; Parke-Bernet, New York, Sale, December 11, 1963 ; sold for $18.500 ;

Private collection, U.S.A.

I. 19
WOMAN WITH A SHAWL
Barcelona, 1899–1900.
Pastel on paper.
Size : 21.4 x 25 cm.
Signed top right : P. Ruiz Picasso.

Exh. III Bienal Hispanoamericana de
Arte, Barcelona, 1955 : *Precursores y
maestros del arte Español contemporáneo,* No. 34.

Bibl. Z. I. 17. C.-P. No. 23 *(Woman
on a Sofa).* Sabartés, *Picasso, les
bleus de Barcelone,* Paris, 1963, pl. II
(repr. in color).

Coll. L. Plandiura, Barcelona ; Museo
de Arte Moderno, Barcelona ;

Picasso Museum, Barcelona.

I. 20
THE ENCOUNTER
Barcelona, 1899–1900.
Pastel on paper.
Signed bottom left : P. Ruiz Picasso.

Bibl. Z. I. 15. C.-P. No. 15.

Coll. Gifreda, Barcelona ; Junyer
Vidal, Barcelona ; O'Hana Gallery,
London ;

Private collection, Paris.

I. 21
PORTRAIT OF ANGEL FERNÁNDEZ
DE SOTO
Barcelona 1899–1900.
Oil on canvas.
Size : 62 x 50 cm.
Signed bottom left : P. Ruiz Picasso.

Bibl. Z. VI. 197. Joan Merli, *Picasso,
el artista y la obra de nuestro tiempo,*
Buenos Aires, 1942, color plate No. 11
(entitled *Head of a Man).*

Coll. Augusto Palanza, Buenos Aires ;
Sale of the Palanza collection at the

Galeria Witcomb, Buenos Aires, September 3, 1963 : sold for 4,550,000
pesos ;

*Collection Alejandro Leonescu,
Buenos Aires.*

This is the only oil we know that is
definitely connected to the series of
portraits of Picasso's friends ; usually
the medium is charcoal or chalk with
watercolor or color wash.

I. 22
PORTRAIT OF ANGEL FERNÁNDEZ
DE SOTO
Barcelona, 1900.
Blue and white chalk and Conté
crayon, on beige paper.
Size : 30.5 x 22.9 cm.
Signed bottom right : P.R.P.
Inscribed bottom right, above the
signature : "A la mi Amigo Fernández."

Exh. National College of Art, Dublin,
1944 : *Exhibition of Modern Continental Paintings.*

Bibl. Not in Z. Blunt and Pool, No. 143.

Coll. Madame Zack, Paris ;

*Collection Roberts Richmond Figgis,
Ballybrack, Ireland.*

In comparison to I. 21, this new
portrait is much more decisive, related
by mastery of expressive detail to the
self-portraits of the spring of 1901.

I. 23
ROOFS OF BARCELONA
Barcelona, 1899–1900.
Pastel.
Size : 37.8 x 50.9 cm.
Unsigned.

Bibl. Z. VI. 250.

Present location unknown.

Known to us only through Zervos. Instead of pastel, it might be charcoal or colored chalk finished with watercolor or color wash, which were more usual for Picasso in 1899, the date proposed by Zervos.

I. 24
HOUSES IN BARCELONA
Barcelona, 1900.
Oil on canvas.
Size : 48.1 x 48.3 cm.
Signed bottom left : P. Ruiz Picasso.

Exh. Never exhibited.

Bibl. Unpublished.

Owned by the artist.

These two landscapes, I. 23 and 24, are views from Picasso's studios in Barcelona.

I. 25
LA BOJA (THE MADWOMAN)
Barcelona, 1900.
Ink, watercolor, and gouache on paper.
Size : 13.5 x 9.5 cm.
Signed bottom left : P. Ruiz Picasso.

Exh. Musée des Beaux-Arts, Paris, 1900 : *L'Aquarelle française.* Frankfurt and Hamburg, summer, 1965 : *Picasso, 150 Handzeichnungen aus sieben Jahrzehnten,* No. 6, repr. in cat. Galerie Knoedler, Paris, November–December 1966 : *Picasso, Dessins et Aquarelles 1899–1965,* No. 4, repr. in cat.

Bibl. This is the original of the reproduction published in *Cataluña Artistica,* Barcelona, September 6, 1900. Z. VI. 271 (charcoal, according to Zervos). C.-P., documents (charcoal, according to C.-P.). Blunt and Pool, No. 41.

Collection Maître Maurice Rheims, Paris.

An illustration published in *Cataluña Artistica,* September 6, 1900, for a short story by Suriñach Senties entitled *La Boja* (*Madwoman* in Catalan. *Boja* in Spanish also means absinthe).

I. 26
THE OLD BEGGAR
Barcelona, 1900.
Ink, gouache and watercolor on paper.
Size : 15.9 x 10.8 cm.
Signed bottom right : P. Ruiz Picasso.

Bibl. Not in Z.

Coll. O'Hana Gallery, London ;

Collection Max Rayne, London.

Authenticated by the artist.

I. 27
PORTRAIT OF THE TAILOR SOLER
Barcelona, 1900.
Gouache, ink and watercolor on paper.
Size : 22.2 x 10.8 cm.
Signed bottom left : P. Ruiz Picasso.

Bibl. Not in Z.

Coll. O'Hana Gallery, London ;

Collection Max Rayne, London.

Authenticated by the artist.

I. 28
BULLFIGHT
Barcelona, 1900.
Watercolor.
Size : 26 x 21 cm.
Signed bottom right : P. Ruiz Picasso.

Bibl. Z. I. 383. W.C.A. Vol. XV, 1963,
No. 3767.

Coll. Barbara Church ; Sotheby & Co.,
London, Sale, April 24, 1963 ; sold for
£3,800.

Present location unknown.

If one eliminates The Picador, which
dates from Picasso's youth (Z. VI. 3),
this watercolor may well be the earliest
of Picasso's existing bullfight scenes.
The picador in the foreground on the
right is similar to El Zurdo (The Left-
Handed Man, Geiser 1), the first
etching made by Picasso, in 1899.

I. 29
MATADORS
Barcelona, 1900.
Conté crayon and gouache on paper.
Size : 23.1 x 21.2 cm.
Unsigned.

Bibl. Z. VI. 280.

Present location unknown.

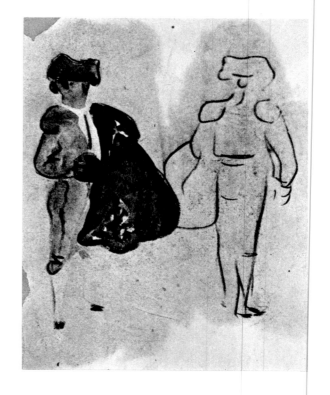

D. I. 1
LA CHATA
Barcelona, 1899.
Watercolor on paper.
Size : 31.6 x 7.6 cm.
Signed top left : P.R.P.
Dated bottom left : Año de 1899.
Inscribed top left : La Chata.

Coll. L. Garriga Roig, Paris ;

Picasso Museum, Barcelona.

D. I. 2
ELS QUATRE GATS
Barcelona, 1899–1900.
Pastel on paper.
Size : 30 x 28 cm.
Signed bottom right : P. Ruiz Picasso.

Exh. Stoliar, Galerie des Etats-Unis, Cannes.

Bibl. Not in Z. Tomás Caballé y Clos, *Los viejos cafés de Barcelona* (frontispiece). Palau i Fabre, No. 22.

Coll. Soleboils ; Palais Galliera, Paris, Sale, June 17, 1965, No. 21, repr. pl. II, sold for 23,000 fr. ;

Collection Serge Stoliar, Cannes.

D. I. 3
THE LETTER
Barcelona, 1899.
Watercolor and charcoal on paper.
Size : 26.5 x 7.5 cm.
Signed bottom right : P.R.P.
Signed on the back : Picasso.

Exh. Frankfurt and Hamburg, 1965, No. 2, repr. in cat. Galerie Knoedler, Paris, November–December 1966 : *Picasso, Dessins et Aquarelles 1899–1965,* No. 2, repr. in cat.

Bibl. Not in Z.

Collection Maître Maurice Rheims, Paris.

D. I. 4
PORTRAIT OF TORENT
Barcelona, 1899.
Charcoal on paper.
Size : 48.8 x 32.3 cm.
Signed and dedicated, bottom left : A mi amigo E. Torent—P. Ruiz Picasso.

Exh. Toronto and Montreal, 1964 : *Picasso and Man,* No. 3, repr. in cat. p. 24.

Bibl. Not in Z.

Coll. Mrs. Cornelius J. Sullivan ; Acquired in 1938 by

The Detroit Institute of Arts.

This drawing was unpublished until the Toronto exhibition. It is a portrait of Evilio Torent Marsans (1875–1945), a Spanish painter and friend of Picasso.

D. I. 5
PORTRAIT OF JOSEF CARDONA
Barcelona, 1899.
Conté crayon on paper.
Size : 38 x 30.4 cm.
Signed and dedicated, center left :
Al volgut amich Cardona—P. Ruiz Picasso.

Exh. UCLA, Los Angeles, 1961 : *Bonne Fête M. Picasso,* No. 48. Toronto and Montreal, 1964 : *Picasso and Man,* No. 2, repr. in cat. p. 23.

Bibl. Not in Z.

Collection Miss Barbara Mallory, Santa Barbara.

Dated 1898 (Toronto catalogue), this portrait should be dated instead in the spring of 1899, after Picasso's return from Horta de Ebro, when he moved into Cardona's studio in the Calle de Escudillers Blancs.

D. I. 6
EL MAESTRO ENRIQUE MORERA
Barcelona, 1899–1900.
Conté crayon on paper.
Size : 18 x 13 cm.
Signed (in ink) left : P. Ruiz Picasso.

Exh. Sala Gaspar, Barcelona, 1954 : *Els Quatre Gats et son époque,* repr. in cat. No. 112.

Bibl. Not in Z. Palau i Fabre, No. 42.

Coll. Enrique Morera and his heirs ; Alberto Puig, Palau (1953) ; Sala Gaspar, Barcelona (1958) ;

Private collection, Barcelona.

Authenticated by the artist, August 20, 1960.

D. I. 7
PICASSO AND CASAGEMAS
Barcelona, 1899–1900.
Ink and watercolor on paper.
Dimensions not known.
Unsigned.

Bibl. Z. VI. 219. C.-P. No. 10. Sabartés, *Picasso, documents iconographiques*, No. 56.

Present location unknown.

According to Sabartés, this drawing, showing the two friends walking side by side, should be dated at the period following Picasso's return from Horta de Ebro.

D. I. 8
THE ARTIST CARLOS CASAGEMAS
Barcelona, 1900.
Ink and watercolor on paper. Size : 18.5 x 14.5 cm.
Unsigned.

Bibl. Z. VI. 240.

Formerly collection Jacques Seligmann, New York.

Casagemas was perhaps Picasso's closest friend at this time. Later he would accompany Picasso to Paris on his first trip in the autumn of 1900, return with Picasso to Malaga, and eventually return to Paris to commit suicide over a love affair, February 17, 1901. His death is responsible for the series of canvases done in the summer of 1901 (see VI. 5 and VI. 6), which culminates in *The Mourners* in the Edward G. Robinson Collection (VI. 2) and in *Evocation* (or *The Burial of Casagemas*, VI. 4). See also Addenda, A. 6 and A. 8.

D. I. 9
ANGEL F. DE SOTO
Barcelona, 1900.
Ink and watercolor on paper.
Size : 19 x 14.5 cm.
Signed top left : Picasso.

Bibl. Z. VI. 278.

Collection Marshall Field.

Angel Fernández de Soto, like his brother Mateo, belonged to the group of Catalan intellectuals who gathered at the *Quatre Gats*. Picasso remembers him as his most loyal and considerate friend. According to the questionnaire done for Barr by Carlos Junyer (*Fifty Years*, p. 252), at the time of these portraits Angel F. de Soto helped Picasso financially by paying a large part of his rent.

D. I. 10
THE DANCER
Barcelona, 1900.
Conté crayon on paper.
Size : 17.8 x 12 cm.
Signed bottom right : P.R.P.

Bibl. Not in Z.

Coll. Junyer Vidal, Barcelona ; O'Hana Gallery, London ;

Collection Max Hermanos, New York.

D. I. 11
TWO WOMEN WALKING ON A WINDY DAY
Barcelona, 1900.
Charcoal and colored chalk on paper.
Size : 13.4 x 20.3 cm.
Signed bottom left : Pablo Ruiz Picasso.

Bibl. Not in Z. Catalogue, paintings and drawings, "Cau Ferrat" (Rusiñol Foundation), Sitges, 1942, p. 27.

Coll. Ignacio Zuloaga, Barcelona ; Santiago Rusiñol, Barcelona ;

Museo del "Cau Ferrat," Sitges.

D. I. 12
THE DANCER
Barcelona, 1900.
Conté crayon on paper.
Size : 17.8 x 12 cm.
Signed top right : P.R.P.

Bibl. Not in Z.

Coll. Junyer Vidal, Barcelona ; O'Hana Gallery, London ;

Collection Max Hermanos, New York.

THE BLUE DANCER (PIERROT AND DANCER), PARIS, 1900, OIL. PRIVATE COLLECTION, FRANCE. UNPUBLISHED (II.23).

Charcoal sketch for The Embrace (II.14), *Paris, 1900.*

The First Trip to Paris, September-December 1900

Again we rely on the account of Sabartés to portray the fascination Paris held for the intellectuals in Barcelona— they thought they had to go there to be able to speak from the source—and to give details of Picasso's departure. "It was an enterprise we could not explain. He just gave up his studio, parted with his family and said goodbye to us all. . ."

"Where was the money for it ?" Sabartés asked.

"The three of us were to pay for ourselves, Casagemas, Pallarés and I. My father paid the travel cost. He went with me to the station, along with my mother. They went home with nothing but small change. They had to skimp for the rest of the month. My mother told me long afterward."

The departure was discussed many times with his reluctant father. After all, Picasso was not yet nineteen. Still, he would be in the company of two close friends. Pallarés was his first Catalan friend and had acquainted him with the wild interior of Catalonia and his own village, Horta de Ebro, when Picasso was recuperating there from an attack of scarlet fever at the end of 1898. And Casagemas was his companion of the Calle Riera de San Juan. Nevertheless, it was a bold venture. The first idea was to settle on the Rue Campagne-Première in the artists' quarter of Montparnasse. But he met Nonell who was about to leave again for Barcelona and was in a position to offer Picasso his own studio in Montmartre at 49 Rue Gabrielle.

Isidro Nonell was almost ten years older than Picasso; he died at 38 in 1911. Nonell is the painter who brought brutal subjects, real life scenes, into the idealizing atmosphere of Catalan painting typical of that period, putting an end to Pre-Raphaelite and Art Nouveau mannerisms, and the insipid echoes of Impressionism. Far more than Ramón Casas and Santiago Rusiñol, who never escaped from a certain provincialism, Nonell was the one painter in the circle Picasso knew who was a real link with what was happening in Paris. After Picasso's second trip to Paris in 1902, when both painters were back in Barcelona, there was a time when the two were following a common course. But Nonell was not an influence at the time of the first trip. Remember that Picasso said it was not until he got to Paris that he knew how great a painter Lautrec was. He had to experience the works themselves and the environment that inspired them. But Nonell in some respects prepared him.

At the end of the summer of 1900, Picasso shows a remarkable stylistic development. He suddenly seemed confident of himself, ambitious to tackle high themes, and impatient of the lessons imposed on him. The series of pastels of the bullring shows this advance. We know from Berthe Weill's memoirs that Picasso had brought with him to Paris, in October 1900, scenes of the bullfights. She purchased three of them for 100 francs and sold them to Adolphe Brisson, the editor of *Annales*, forthwith, at a profit of 50 francs. We know of the existence of nine pastels clearly in the style of the summer of 1900. It is almost certain, in view of Picasso's work habits, that these pastels were done in Barcelona, and may have been intended for sale in Paris. They portray the commonplace subjects of Spain, in full sunlight and Mediterranean air. Picasso is always deeply sensitive to the atmosphere in which he lives, and his work reflects this.

In Paris, the signature "P. R. Picasso" takes the place of "P. Ruiz Picasso."

II. 1
THE PICADOR
Barcelona, 1900.
Pastel.
Dimensions not known.
Signed bottom left : P. Ruiz Picasso.

Bibl. Z. VI. 379. C.-P. No. 78. (Both date it 1901, a date that seems a little too late.)

Present location unknown.

II. 2
OUTSIDE THE ARENA
Barcelona, 1900.
Pastel on cardboard.
Size : 28 x 28 cm.
Signed bottom left : P. Ruiz Picasso.

Bibl. Z. VI. 382. C.-P. No. 79. Elgar and Maillard, p. 5 (entitled *L'entrée aux arènes*, repr. in color). Dated 1901 by Z., C.-P., and Elgar and Maillard.

Coll. Riera, Barcelona ;

Private collection, Paris.

II. 3
BULLFIGHTERS
Barcelona, 1900.
Pastel.
Dimensions (square) unknown (Cf. note).
Signed bottom left : P. Ruiz Picasso.

Bibl. Z. VI. 380. C.-P. No. 80 (dated 1901).

Formerly Riera Collection, Barcelona.

In many ways this seems to be the companion piece to the preceding work, No. II. 2. In that case the dimensions would be : 28 x 28 cm.

II. 4
THE BULLRING
Barcelona, 1900.
Pastel and gouache on paper.
Size : 19 x 25 cm.
Signed bottom right : P. Ruiz Picasso.

Bibl. Z. VI. 299. C.-P. No. 81. (Dated 1900, Barcelona, by Z. ; 1901 by C.-P.)

Coll. Barbey, Barcelona ;

Collection Mr. and Mrs. Leigh B. Block, Chicago.

In commenting on this work Picasso pointed his finger at the empty seats in the arena and said : "It was really like that. In those days there weren't many spectators. It wasn't at all like today."

II. 5
IN THE BULLRING
Barcelona, 1900.
Pastel and oil on canvas.
Size : 23 x 32 cm.
Signed bottom right : P. Ruiz Picasso.

Exh. Frankfurt and Hamburg, summer, 1965 : *Picasso, 150 Handzeichnungen aus sieben Jahrzehnten,* No. 3, repr. in cat.

Bibl. Not in Z.

Coll. Enrique Morera, Barcelona ;

Collection Wilhelm Reinold, Hamburg.

Inscribed on the back : Ce tableau est fait par moi Picasso, Cannes 24-9-58.

II. 6
BULLFIGHT
Barcelona, 1900.
Pastel and gouache on canvas.
Size : 45.8 x 68.6 cm.
Signed bottom left : P. Ruiz Picasso.

Exh. Yale University Art Gallery, New Haven, 1960 : *Alumni Collection.* Knoedler, New York, 1962 : *Picasso, An American Tribute,* No. 6, repr. in cat. The Art Gallery of Toronto and The Montreal Museum of Fine Arts, 1964 : *Picasso and Man,* No. 5, repr. in cat. p. 26. Fort Worth Art Center Museum, 1967 : *Picasso,* No. 142.

Bibl. Not in Z. Dated 1900, Barcelona, by John Richardson *(An American Tribute)* and by Jean Sutherland Boggs *(Picasso and Man).*

Coll. Acquired in March, 1959, by the present owners :

Collection Mr. and Mrs. Henry John Heinz II, Pittsburgh.

The simultaneous use of pastel and oil or gouache, and the choice of canvas for the support, really make these works the "paintings" that Picasso himself calls them. Presumably they belong to the same series as the three Picasso sold to Berthe Weill in 1900. Perhaps this one, which does not seem to come from a Barcelona collection, is one of those three. All this supports the idea that this group of pastels was done in Barcelona during the summer of 1900.

II. 7
BULLFIGHT
Barcelona, 1900.
Pastel and gouache on paper.
Size : 16.2 x 30.3 cm.
Signed bottom right : P. Ruiz Picasso.

Bibl. Not in Z. Catalogue of paintings and drawings in the "Cau Ferrat" (Rusiñol Foundation), Sitges, 1942, p. 27. Palau i Fabre, No. 63 (repr. in color).

Coll. Ignacio Zuloaga, Barcelona ; Santiago Rusiñol, Barcelona ;

Museo del "Cau Ferrat," Sitges.

This beautiful bullfight scene has never been out of Spain. Except for the catalogue of the Rusiñol Foundation, it was not reproduced until 1966.

II. 8
ENTRANCE TO THE BULLRING
Barcelona, 1900.
Pastel on cardboard.
Size : 51 x 69 cm.
Signed bottom left : P. R. Picasso.

Exh. Galerie Charpentier, Paris, 1944 : *Paris.*

Bibl. Unpublished.

Coll. Emmanuel Virenque, who bought it directly from the artist, around 1900 ;

Private collection, France.

This "pure" pastel—very vivid, highly colored—was probably bought by Emmanuel Virenque as early as the autumn of 1900. In fact, Virenque was one of Picasso's first purchasers and owned a painting done by Picasso at the time of his first stay in Paris.

Color plate, page 17.

II. 9
GYPSY GIRL
Barcelona, 1900.
Pastel and oil.
Size : 44.5 x 59.7 cm.
Signed bottom right : P. Ruiz Picasso.

Exh. Museum of Modern Art, New York and The Art Institute of Chicago, 1957 : *Picasso, 75th Anniversary Exhibition,* repr. in cat. p. 14.

Bibl. Not in Z. Raynal, Geneva, 1959, p. 19 (repr. in color).

Private collection, Paris.

Raynal's comment is apt : "The intensity of color gives this work a play of pure, bright tones that seems Fauve." This description also fits the preceding pastels (II. 5, 6, 7 and especially 8), but Raynal dates this work 1898. This scene in front of the sea was certainly not painted either in Madrid or at Horta de Ebro. It does not relate to anything we know of Picasso's short stay in Barcelona after his attack of scarlet fever. Barr also dates it 1898, followed by a question mark. In our opinion this painting dates at least from the summer of 1900, in Barcelona, just before the journey to Paris. The handling of the face, with no attention to details, and the grasping of the general rhythm—in short, the overall manner—foreshadows the series of pastels of women done after the first trip to Paris. It might be related to the stay in Malaga, especially because of the smoking chimney and the bundled-up gypsy girl, possible indications of a sunny winter day.

II.10
LE MOULIN DE LA GALETTE
Paris, 1900.
Oil on canvas.
Size: 90.2 x 117 cm.
Signed bottom right: P. R. Picasso.

Exh. New York and Chicago, 1939–1940: *Picasso, Forty Years of his Art,* No. 5, repr. in cat. p. 24. Museum of Modern Art, New York, 1946: *Picasso, Fifty Years of his Art,* repr. in cat. p. 18. Museum of Modern Art and The Art Institute of Chicago, 1957: *Picasso, 75th Anniversary Exhibition,* repr. in cat. p. 15. Philadelphia Museum of Art, 1958: *Picasso,* No. 4. The Arts Council of Great Britain, Tate Gallery, London, 1960: *Picasso,* No. 4, repr. in cat. pl. 1 b. The Solomon R. Guggenheim Museum, New York, April–September 1965: *First Showing of Masterpieces of Modern Art from the Thannhauser Foundation,* No. 30, repr. in color in cat. p. 39. Grand Palais, Paris, November 1966–February 1967: *Hommage à Pablo Picasso,* No. 3, repr. in cat.

Bibl. Z. I. 41. Barr, *Forty Years,* p. 24. Barr, *Fifty Years,* p. 18. C.-P. No. 18.

Penrose, 1958, pl. I, No. 8. Lieberman, 1961, pl. 12 (repr. in color). Daulte in *Connaissance des Arts,* May, 1966, p. 68 (in color).

Coll. According to Berthe Weill, sold by her in 1900 to M. Huc for 250 fr.; Galerie Thannhauser, Berlin;

The Solomon R. Guggenheim Museum, New York, Justin K. Thannhauser Foundation.

Picasso remembers this as his first painting done in Paris. Pierre de Champris emphasizes the similarity with Lautrec's *Bal du Moulin-Rouge.* In any case it is a kind of personal assimilation of the night life of Montmartre and at the same time a tribute to Lautrec. Note also the change in the signature: P. Ruiz becomes P. R., which may be explained by a desire to simplify his name for French use.

Color plate, page 29.

II. 11
STREET SCENE
Paris, 1900.
(Also titled: *Paris Street* and *Old Man, Woman and Child in the Street.*)
Oil on canvas.
Size: 44.5 x 62.3 cm.
Signed bottom left: P. R. Picasso.

Exh. Galerie Berthe Weill, Paris, October 24–November 20, 1904, No. 33 (?). Museum of Modern Art, New York, 1939, and The Art Institute of Chicago, 1940: *Picasso, Forty Years of his Art,* No. 7. California Palace of the Legion of Honor. Santa Barbara Museum of Art, 1960. The Art Gallery of Toronto and The Montreal Museum of Fine Arts, 1964: *Picasso and Man,* No. 6, repr. in cat. Dallas Museum

of Fine Arts, February 8–March 26, 1967: *Picasso,* No. 3.

Bibl. Z. VI. 302. Barr, *Forty Years,* p. 25. Lieberman, 1961, pl. 6.

Coll. Harriet Lane Levy, San Francisco;

San Francisco Museum of Art, Harriet Lane Levy Bequest.

Jean Sutherland Boggs emphasizes here the influence of Steinlen and also of Isidro Nonell. The latter's work is especially apparent in this cheerless, miserable winter landscape, which offers a sad daytime Montmartre in contrast to the gay Montmartre by night shown in *Le Moulin de la Galette* (II.10).

II. 12
LOVERS IN THE STREET
Paris, 1900.
Pastel on paper.
Size: 60 x 36 cm.
Signed bottom left: P. Ruiz Picasso.
Inscribed, under the signature: A el amigo Bilaro.

Exh. III Bienal Hispanoamericana de Arte, Barcelona, 1955: *Precursores y maestros del arte Español contemporáneo,* No. 10. Musée d'Art et d'Histoire, Geneva, 1956: *Sélection de la IIIe Biennale Hispano-Américaine: Picasso, Nonell, Manolo,* No. 22.

Bibl. Z. I. 24. C.-P. No. 84 (dated 1901). Blunt and Pool, No. 85. Sabartés, *Picasso, les bleus de Barcelone,* Paris, 1963, pl. 9 (repr. in color).

Coll. L. Plandiura, Barcelona; Museo de Arte Moderno, Barcelona;

Picasso Museum, Barcelona.

II. 13
LOVERS IN THE STREET
(Idyll on the Outer Boulevards)
Paris, 1900.
Oil.
Size : 65 x 50 cm.
Signed bottom left : P. R. Picasso.

Exh. Galerie Berthe Weill, Paris, October 24–November 20, 1904, No. 32.

Bibl. Z. I. 25. Catalogue of the Berthe Weill Exhibition, 1904, preface by Maurice Le Sieutre ("... on the ramparts are vulgar couples ..."). C.-P. No. 83 (dated 1901).

Coll. G. Swarzenski, Boston ;

Private collection, U.S.A.

Picasso told us that the landscape behind the couple is a street on a slope of the hill of Montmartre.

II. 14
THE EMBRACE
Paris, 1900.
Oil on cardboard.
Size : 53 x 56 cm.
Signed bottom left : P. R. Picasso.
Verso : an oil sketch showing a seated woman with a book ; the top of the head is cut off. Also a red sofa against a brown background.

Exh. Maison de la Pensée française, Paris, 1954, No. 2. Pushkin Museum, Moscow, 1955 and The Hermitage Museum, Leningrad, 1956 : *Art français du XVᵉ au XXᵉ siècle,* repr. in cat. Arts Council of Great Britain, Tate Gallery, London, 1960, No. 271. Tokyo, 1964, No. 2.

Bibl. Z. I. 26. Catalogue of paintings in the Tschukin Collection, Moscow, 1913, No. 182, p. 40. Touguenhold : *Le premier musée de la peinture moderne occidentale, l'ancienne collection Chtchoukine,* Mos-cow-Petrograd, 1923, p. 112. Réau, *L'Art français dans les musées russes,* 1929, No. 1006. Javorskaïa, *Pablo Picasso,* Moscow, 1933, p. 14. Kahnweiler and Parmelin, *Picasso,* 1955. Elgar and Maillard, 1955 (catalogue). Sutton, 1955, pl. II (repr. in color). Diehl, 1960, p. 14 (repr. in color). Blunt and Pool, No. 87. Daix, 1964, p. 26 (repr. in color).

Coll. S. I. Tschukin (until 1918) ; Museum of Modern Western Art, Moscow (1918–1948) ;

Pushkin Museum, Moscow.

The theme of *The Embrace,* treated here directly and boldly, reoccurs often in future work (cf. in 1903, IX.11 and 12). See also a hitherto unknown version of this oil, reproduced in the Addenda, No. A. 3.

II. 15
WOMAN BEFORE A MIRROR
(The Dressing-Room)
Paris, 1900.
Pastel on paper.
Size : 50 x 55 cm.
Signed and dated, bottom right : P. Ruiz Picasso, Paris 1900.

Exh. III Bienal Hispanoamericana de Arte, Barcelona, 1955 : *Precursores y maestros del arte Español contemporáneo,* No. 7.

Bibl. Z. I. 38. C.-P. No. 22 *(Dans la loge).* Sabartés, *Picasso, les bleus de Barcelone,* Paris, 1963, pl. 6 (repr. in color).

Coll. L. Plandiura, Barcelona ; Museo de Arte Moderno, Barcelona ;

Picasso Museum, Barcelona.

II. 16
LE CANCAN
Paris, 1900.
Pastel.
Size : 41 x 55 cm.
Signed bottom right : P. R. Picasso.

Bibl. Z. I. 40. Cassou, 1940, No. 36.
C.-P. No. 19. Blunt and Pool, No. 32.

Coll. Hess, Berlin ;

Collection Paul Pétridès, Paris.

Phoebe Pool relates this pastel to Lautrec's poster for the *Troupe of Mlle Eglantine.* Granted the influence, what is significant is that again Picasso proceeds from his own way of seeing to master the lesson of an older artist.

II. 17
THE SHIRT FRONTS
Paris, 1900.
Oil.
Size : 17 x 26 cm.
Signed top left : P. R. Picasso.

Bibl. Z. I. 35. C.-P. No. 53 (dated 1901).

Formerly collection Josef Stransky, New York.

II. 18
THE CONVERSATION
Paris, 1900.
Oil.
Size : 17 x 26 cm.
Signed top right : P. Ruiz Picasso.

Bibl. Z. I. 34. C.-P. No. 51 (dated 1901). Blunt and Pool, No. 36.

Formerly collection Josef Stransky, New York.

These two small canvases continue Picasso's conquest of Parisian night life. They anticipate the larger oils painted at the time of the Vollard exhibition in 1901, such as *The Diners* (V. 66) or *Au Moulin Rouge* (V. 13).

II. 19
WOMAN WITH A VEIL
Paris, 1900.
Oil on canvas.
Size : 66 x 51 cm.
Signed top left : P. R. Picasso.

Exh. Boyer Galleries, Philadelphia, 1936 : *19th and 20th Century French Paintings,* No. 7, repr. in cat. Jacques Seligmann & Co., New York, 1936 : *Picasso, Blue and Rose Periods,* No.10, repr. in cat. Florida Gulf Coast Center, 1958 : *The Collection of Mrs. C. Shillard Smith.*

Bibl. Z. VI. 383. W. Aubrey Cartwright, *A Guide to Art Museums in the United States (East Coast),* 1958, p. 180.

Coll. Dikran Kelekian ; J. B. Neumann; Sale of the Neumann collection, 1936, No. 60 ; Mrs. C. Shillard Smith, Florida (1936–1955) ;

Collection Mr. and Mrs. James Howley, New York.

Because of the signature, we hesitate between Picasso's stay in Paris and Malaga. Zervos dates it 1901. Feminine fashion more than anything inclines us toward Picasso's stay in Paris in 1900.

II. 20
CAFÉ SCENE
Paris, 1900.
Oil on canvas.
Size : 25.5 x 33.7 cm.
Signed bottom right : P. R. Picasso.

Bibl. Z. I. 33. Gertrude Stein, *Picasso,* Paris 1938, pl. 6.

Coll. Gertrude Stein, Paris ;

Yale University Library, Gertrude Stein Collection.

Zervos dates this work 1900, from the Barcelona period. Since it shows nothing typically Spanish and nothing guarantees the signature "P. R. Picasso" before the Paris paintings, we put it here in the absence of other documentation.

II. 21
MAN IN A CLOAK
Paris, 1900.
Oil on canvas.
Size : 80.5 x 50 cm.
Signed bottom left : P. R. Picasso.

Exh. Munich, Cologne and Hamburg, 1955–1956 : *Picasso 1900–1955,* No. 1. Wolfsburg, 1961: *Französische Malerei von Delacroix bis Picasso,* No. 240.

Bibl. Z. I. 16. Catalogue of the Sale of la Peau de l'Ours, Paris, March 2, 1914, No. 65 *(L'Homme à la Houppelande : Debout, coiffé d'un feutre noir, la pipe à la bouche ; autour du cou un foulard violet).* Carl Georg Heise, *Die Sammlung des Freiherrn August von der Heydt,* Elberfeld, 1918, No. 211. Catalogue, von der Heydt-Museum der Stadt Wuppertal, 1964, p. 30, repr. p. 87.

Coll. La Peau de l'Ours, Paris ; Sold, March 2, 1914, to Thannhauser for 1,350 fr. ; Baron August von der Heydt, Elberfeld ; Baron Eduard von der Heydt, who gave it to the museum:

Von der Heydt-Museum der Stadt Wuppertal.

II. 22
YOUNG WOMAN WITH A HAT
Paris, 1900.
Pastel on cardboard.
Size : 36 x 26 cm.
Unsigned.

Bibl. Not in Z. The Art Institute of Chicago, *Catalogue of Paintings,* 1961, p. 355 (not reproduced), inv. No. 54.319.

Coll. Joseph Winterbotham, Chicago ;

The Art Institute of Chicago, Gift of Joseph Winterbotham.

Picasso stated that this work was done in Paris in 1900. He told us, "Mañach sent me his friends so I could draw their portraits. This is one of them."

II. 23
THE BLUE DANCER
(Pierrot and Dancer)
Paris, 1900. .
Oil on canvas.
Size : 38 x 46 cm.
Signed bottom left : P. R. Picasso.

Exh. Galerie Charpentier, Paris, 1944 :
Paris.

Bibl. Unpublished.

Coll. Bought directly from the artist by
M. Emmanuel Virenque ;

Private collection, France.

Color plate, page 117.

II. 24
HEAD OF A WOMAN
Paris, 1900.
Oil on canvas.
Size : 35.5 x 33 cm.
Signed left : P. Ruiz Picasso.

Exh. The Arts Council of Great Britain,
Tate Gallery, London, 1960 : *Picasso,*
No. 5, repr. in cat. pl. 4 e (lent by the
Hon. Michael Astor).

Bibl. Z. I. 27.

Coll. The Hon. Michael Astor, London ;

Private collection, London.

II. 25
CANCAN DANCER
Paris, 1900.
Brush drawing on sprayed ground,
on white Ingres paper.
Size : 47 x 31.3 cm.
Signed bottom left : Ruiz.
Later signature, above Ruiz : Picasso.
On the back : Two Women with a Cat
(see D. II. 2).

Exh. Frankfurt and Hamburg, 1965 :
*Picasso, 150 Handzeichnungen aus
sieben Jahrzehnten,* No. 4, repr. in cat.

Bibl. Not in Z.

Sale : Kornfeld & Klipstein, Bern,
May 1963, Sale No. 110, catalogue
No. 893, repr. pl. 24. Estimate (recto
and verso) : 40,000 Swiss fr.

Collection Madame Lilo Behr, Stuttgart.

D. II. 1
TWO WOMEN
Paris, 1900.
Colored crayons on white paper.
Size : 20.5 x 27 cm.
Signed top left : Picasso.

Bibl. Not in Z. Jaffé, *Picasso,* Abrams,
New York.

*The Abrams Family Collection, New
York.*

Although the signature does not
match others of this period, we put
this drawing here because of the
obvious relationship of subject and
handling to D. II. 2 and D. II. 3.

D. II. 2
TWO WOMEN WITH A CAT
Paris, 1900.
Charcoal on white Ingres paper.
Size : 47 x 31.3 cm.
Unsigned. Signed on the back.
Recto : Cancan Dancer (II. 25).

Exh. Frankfurt and Hamburg, 1965,
No. 4, repr. in cat. (recto and verso).

Bibl. Not in Z.

Sale : Kornfeld & Klipstein, Bern, May
1963, Sale No. 110, cat. No. 893,
repr. pl. 25, estimated price (recto and
verso) : 40,000 Swiss fr.

*Collection Madame Lilo Behr, Stutt-
gart.*

D. II. 3
WOMAN WITH A CAT
Paris, 1900.
Pastel on cardboard.
Size : 45 x 51 cm.
Signed bottom left : P. Ruiz Picasso.

Exh. Musée de Lyon, June 1953 :
Picasso, No. 9 (entitled *Femme
étendue*).

Bibl. Unpublished.

Coll. Léon Bloch, Paris ;

Private collection, Paris.

D. II. 4
THREE CANCAN DANCERS
Paris, 1900.
Colored chalks on paper.
Size : 13.3 x 19.5 cm.
Signed bottom left : P. Ruiz Picasso.

Bibl. Not in Z. MUSEION, Office International des
Musées, supplément mensuel, April 1940, pp. 1–2 :
*Disparition des dessins de Picasso au Musée du
Cau Ferrat.*

Coll. Ignacio Zuloaga, Barcelona ; Santiago Rusiñol,
Barcelona ;

Museo del "Cau Ferrat," Sitges.

Stolen in 1940 with other Picasso drawings from the
"Cau Ferrat" Museum at Sitges, near Barcelona.
It has never been found.

D. II. 5
THE DANCER SADA YACCO
Paris, 1900.
Pastel.
Size : 35.5 x 24.5 cm.

Bibl. Z. I. 44 (dated by Z. Paris, 1900).

Coll. Galerie Percier, Paris ;

Present location unknown.

D. II. 6
LITTLE GIRL SEEN FROM THE BACK
Paris, 1900.
Watercolor drawing.
Size : 16.6 x 9 cm.
Signed top left : P.R.P.
Later signature, beneath the initials : Picasso.

Bibl. Not in Z. Helen Kay, 1965, p. 19.

Collection Dr. and Mrs. Andrew Linz, New York.

D. II. 7
STANDING WOMAN WITH A BLUE HAT
Paris, 1900.
Ink and colored pencils.
Size : 15.3 x 5.5 cm.
Signed bottom : P. Ruiz Picasso.

Exh. Kunsthaus, Zurich, 1932 : *Picasso,* No. 253
(for sale).

Bibl. Z. I. 43 (dated Paris, 1900. Medium, according
to Z. : watercolor).

Present location unknown.

D. II. 8
PICASSO, CASAGEMAS AND ROSITA
Paris, 1900.
India ink and watercolor.
Size : 14 x 10 cm.
Signed bottom center : Picasso.

Exh. Los Angeles Municipal Art Gallery, 1959.

Bibl. Elgar and Maillard, p. 10. W.C.A. XII, No. 4167.

Coll. John Rewald, New York ; Sotheby & Co.,
London, Sale, July 7, 1960, No. 83 ;

Present location unknown.

Until now this work was known as *Picasso, Casagemas, and his Concierge.* Picasso's comment :
"She was never a *concierge.* She was a friend
called Rosita."

WOMAN WITH A PLUMED HAT, MADRID, 1901, OIL. THE MARION KOOGLER MCNAY ART INSTITUTE, SAN ANTONIO, TEXAS (III. 4).

Picasso in Malaga and in Madrid, January-February 1901

Picasso returned to Spain with Casagemas and spent New Year's Day, 1901, in Malaga.

"For almost two weeks he dallied between café and brothel. In short time, he regretted this dissipation. Leaving Malaga, he gave the impression of wanting to get free of himself. He badly needed a different atmosphere, in order to take stock before considering new moves. When he got to Madrid, he thought he would stay there forever—a year anyway. He moved into a boardinghouse on the Calle Caballera de Gracia.

marble-top table. The exact date is February 4. A room on the top floor of the building at Number 28, belonging to the widow Doña Concepcion Gomez, leased for one year."

Since Sabartés is the only reliable source of information for this whole period, his version here of the facts must stand by itself. Our chronology is determined by the signatures. "P. R. Picasso" now is more often just "Picasso," though pastels and drawings are still signed "P. Ruiz Picasso." The reproductions in *Arte Joven* also provide some dates, although Picasso sometimes included drawings done in Paris; this is

Advertisement for the review Madrid, *published in* Arte Joven, *Madrid, June 1901. Picasso and Francisco de A. Soler were to be the directors of* Madrid, *a review which, finally, was never published.*

He described it as "nothing but fried eggs." Already by the first of February, he was living in a garret on the Calle Zurbano.

"It's a lovely street," I said to him. "A very elegant district."

"Oh yes, but I live in an attic. With no heat or light. I was never so cold."

"In the diningroom of the apartment on Rue La Boétie (in Paris), just by chance I found the lease that was signed in Madrid in February 1901, lying in a pile of old papers on a

certainly the case with *Lovers in the Street* (z. VI. 396) and *The Parisienne* (D. III. 10).

Our predecessors, especially Zervos, had every reason to think that the originals of these drawings were lost. Now that *La Boja* has come to light and *Woman with a Large Hat* has been identified, we see that this fear is not in all cases justified. (Cf. I. 25 and III. 6).

III. 1
AT THE THEATER
Malaga or Madrid, 1901.
Black chalk with white wash on paper.
Size : 20.7 x 35.7 cm.
Unsigned. Signed on the back.
Recto : Dancer, III. 2.

Bibl. Not in Z.

Coll. Bought in 1915 in Germany ;

Rijksmuseum Kröller-Müller, Otterlo.

The woman in the foreground resembles
The Courtesan (see III. 3).

III. 2
DANCER
Malaga, 1901.
Pastel and charcoal on paper mounted on
cardboard.
Size : 35.7 x 20.7 cm.
Signed bottom left : Malaga, P. R. Picasso.
Verso : At the Theater, III. 1.

Bibl. Not in Z.

Coll. Bought in 1915 in Germany ;

Rijksmuseum Kröller-Müller, Otterlo.

If this pastel foretells the Madrid series, in
a way it recaptures the theme of Goya's
Marquésa de Solana. Like all the works
exactly dated from this period, this one is
an extremely valuable reference.

III. 3
AT THE THEATER
(The Courtesan)
Madrid, 1901.
Oil on wood panel.
Size : 14 x 20 cm.
Signed bottom right : P. R. Picasso.

Bibl. Z. I. 32 (*La Courtisane,* wrongly dated
Madrid, 1900). Barnes Foundation,
Inventory No. 177 *(The Courtesan).*

Barnes Foundation, Merion, Pa.

Listed in the Kahnweiler archives as *La
Loge* and dated Madrid, spring, 1901.

III. 4
WOMAN WITH A PLUMED HAT
Madrid, 1901.
Oil on canvas.
Size : 46.5 x 38.5 cm.
Signed bottom right : P. R. Picasso,
Madrid.

Exh. San Antonio 1954, No. 3. Milwaukee Art Institute, 1957 : *Inaugural Exhibition,* No. 95. University of California, Berkeley, 1960 : *From Ingres to Pollock,* cat. pp. 39–40. Knoedler, New York, 1962 : *Picasso, an American Tribute,* No. 4, repr. in cat. The Art Gallery of Toronto and The Montreal Museum of Fine Arts, 1964 : *Picasso and Man,* No. 9, repr. in cat. Dallas Museum of Fine Arts, February 8–March 26, 1967 : *Picasso,* No. 2 (dated 1900 by error).

Bibl. Z. I. 39 (dated by Z. 1900, which should be corrected to 1901 as showh by the inscription "Madrid" benenat the signature). C.-P. No. 64.

Coll. Reinhard Galleries, New York ; Dalzell Hatfield, Los Angeles ;

The Marion Koogler McNay Art Institute, San Antonio, Texas.

Except for postcards recently issued, this work has never before been reproduced in color.

Color plate, page 129.

III. 5
WOMAN IN BLUE
Madrid, 1901.
Oil on canvas.
Size : 133.5 x 101 cm.
Signed top right : P. Ruiz Picasso.

Exh. Madrid, 1901 : *Exposicion de Bellas Artes.* Museum of Modern Art, New York and The Art Institute of Chicago, 1957 : *Picasso, 75th Anniversary Exhibition,* repr. in cat. p. 16. Philadelphia Museum of Art, 1958, No. 8, repr. in cat. Musée Cantini, Marseilles, 1959 : *Picasso,* No. 1, repr. in cat. Musée National d'Art Moderne, Paris, 1960 : *Les sources du XXe siècle,* No. 548. Grand Palais, Paris, November 1966–February 1967 : *Hommage à Pablo Picasso,* No. 5, repr. in cat.

Bibl. Not in Z. Raymond Cogniat, *Picasso, Figures,* Lausanne, 1959, p. 7 (repr. in color). Daix, Paris, 1964, p. 29 (repr. in color).

Museo Nacional de Arte Moderno, Madrid.

According to Douglas Cooper, author of the catalogue for the Marseilles exhibition, this painting, intended for an exhibition in Madrid, was abandoned by the artist at the time of his departure for Barcelona in March 1901. According to Barr (catalogue of the New York exhibition in 1957), this painting was shown in Madrid in 1901 but then remained completely unknown for almost fifty years.

III. 6
WOMAN WITH A LARGE HAT
Madrid, 1901.
Crayon and white chalk on paper.
Size : 21.8 x 13.9 cm.
Signed bottom right : P. R. Picasso.

Exh. Musée de l'Orangerie, Paris,
April-May 1941 : *Donation Paul Jamot.*

Bibl. The first page of *Arte Joven,* No. 1,
Madrid, March 31, 1901. Z. VI. 393
(reproduction of the whole page of
Arte Joven). C.-P. No. 28 (idem).

Sabartés, *Picasso, documents iconographiques,* No. 57 (idem).

Coll. Paul Jamot, Paris ;

Musée des Beaux-Arts, Reims.

This is the original drawing, which as
far as we know is unpublished. The
reproductions published by Zervos,
Cirici-Pellicier, and Sabartés were
made from the cover of *Arte Joven.*

III. 7
WOMAN IN GREEN
Madrid, 1901.
Pastel on paper.
Size : 50.8 x 34.3 cm.
Signed top left : P. Ruiz Picasso.

Exh. Sala Parés, Barcelona, 1901.

Bibl. Not in Z.

Coll. Delmiro de Caralt, Barcelona
(1901–1960) ;   M. Knoedler & Co.,
New York ;

*The Metropolitan Museum of Art,
New York, Gift of Mr. and Mrs. John
L. Loeb, 1961.*

III. 8
SEATED WOMAN
Madrid, 1901.
Pastel on paper.
Size : 52 x 36 cm.
Signed top left : P. Ruiz Picasso.

Bibl. Not in Z. Sabartés and Boeck,
p. 481, No. 246.

Collection Madame Pagésy, Paris.

III. 9
WOMAN WITH A DOG
Madrid, 1901.
Oil on cardboard mounted on canvas.
Size : 37.5 x 42 cm.
Signed bottom left : P. R. Picasso.

Exh. Musée des Arts Décoratifs, Paris, June–October 1955 : *Picasso, peintures 1900–1955,* No. 2, repr. in cat. Grand Palais, Paris, November 1966–February 1967 : *Hommage à Pablo Picasso,* No. 4, repr. in cat.

Bibl. Not in Z. Raymond Escholier, *La Peinture française, XXᵉ siècle,* 1937, p. 73. Elgar and Maillard, 1955, p. 16 (repr. in color).

Private collection, Paris.

Authenticated by Picasso for the authors (September 3, 1965) with the attestation : "Painted in Madrid."

III. 10
THE BOUDOIR
Madrid, 1901.
Pastel.
Size : 32 x 40 cm.
Signed top left : P. Ruiz Picasso.

Bibl. Z. VI. 386. C.-P. p. 64 (repr. in color).

Collection Masoliver, Barcelona.

III. 11
THE SPANISH WOMAN
Madrid, 1901.
Oil on wood.
Size : 51 x 64 cm.
Signed top left : Picasso.

Bibl. Not in Z. André Level, *Picasso,* 1928, pl. 3. Cassou, *Picasso,* 1959, p. 9.

Coll. Julius Stern, Berlin ; Sale of the Stern collection, Berlin, May 22, 1916, No. 74 ;

Ny Carlsberg Glyptotek, Copenhagen.

The Spanish Woman is a kind of transposition into oil of the style of the pastels. Thus it offers a new source for the impressionistic use of color which appears full-blown in the paintings for the Vollard exhibition.

III. 12
LADY IN BLUE
Madrid, 1901.
Pastel on cardboard.
Size : 50 x 35 cm.
Signed top left : Picasso.

Exh. Galerie Charpentier, Paris 1960 : *Cent tableaux de collections privées,* No. 85 (entitled *Madame X*). Alex Maguy, Galerie de l'Elysée, Paris, November 19–December 25, 1966 : *Hommage à Picasso,* repr. in color on catalogue cover.

Bibl. Not in Z. Cirici-Pellicer, *Picasso antes de Picasso,* Barcelona, 1946, No. 126 (withdrawn from the French edition).

Coll. Alberto Puig, Barcelona;

Collection Alex Maguy, Paris.

Authenticated by Picasso in Cannes, February 3, 1959.

In spite of the variation in signature, all these works (III. 4 to III. 12), whether pastel or oil, have an obvious resemblance which relates them to this period. For nine works we now have four indisputable references to Madrid. In addition a fifth one was exhibited at the Sala Parés, Barcelona—that is, before Picasso's departure for Paris.

III. 13
THE RED SKIRT
Madrid, 1901.
Pastel on cardboard.
Size : 55 x 47 cm.
Signed top left : Picasso.

Exh. Kunstnernes Hus, Oslo, October–November 1956 : *Picasso,* No. 2.

Bibl. Not in Z.

Coll. Jens Thüs, Oslo ;   Sale of the Jens Thüs collection, Oslo, December 1942, sold for 15,000 N. Kr. ;

Private collection, Oslo.

III. 14
SELF-PORTRAIT
Madrid, 1901.
Conté crayon.
Size : 34.3 x 15.3 cm.
Signed bottom left : Picasso.

Exh. Kunsthaus, Zurich, 1932, No. 251. Museum of Modern Art, New York, 1939, and The Art Institute of Chicago, 1940 : *Picasso, Forty Years of his Art,* No. 3, repr. in cat.

Bibl. Z. I. 49. Barr. *Forty Years,* p. 23. Cassou, 1940, p. 8.

Collection Justin K. Thannhauser, New York.

This is the original drawing, printed in *Arte Joven,* Madrid, 1901. There is an almost identical version which is in fact a copy of the authentic drawing catalogued here. It is charcoal with watercolor, size : 46 x 31 cm., with an unauthentic signature bottom right. It is this copy which was catalogued by C.-P. (No. 25), Bouret (p. 17), and Sabartés (*Picasso, Documents iconographiques,* No. 60). It is now in a private collection in Paris.

D. III. 1
TWO HEADS OF WOMAN AND A STANDING
WOMAN
Malaga, 1901.
Conté crayon and colored crayons.
Size : 14.5 x 22,5 cm.
Signed top right : Picasso.

Bibl. Z. VI. 325.

Present location unknown.

The woman's head in the center of this sketch
sheet is related to the one in *At the Theater* (III. 1)
and in *At the Theater (The Courtesan)* (III. 3).

D. III. 2
STUDIES OF HEADS
(Man with a Cigar and Two Women)
Malaga, January 9, 1901.
Chalk drawing on paper.
Size : 15.3 x 23.4 cm.
Signed bottom left : Picasso.
Dated top left : Malaga—9 enero—1901.

Exh. Kunsthaus, Zurich, 1932, No. 254.

Bibl. Unpublished.

Coll. G. and L. Bollag, Zurich ; Acquired in December
1919 by Mme Hahnloser, Winterthur ;

Formerly collection Hahnloser, Winterthur.

D. III. 3
THE SPANISH WOMAN
Malaga or Madrid, 1901.
Charcoal, colored crayons and wash on paper
mounted on cardboard.
Size : 28 x 20,5 cm.
Signed bottom left : P. Ruiz Picasso.

Exh. Galerie Charpentier, Paris, 1960 : *Cent tableaux
de collections privées,* No. 86.

Bibl. Not in Z.

Coll. Maître M. Blum, Paris ; Raphael Gérard,
Paris ; A. C., Paris ;

Private collection, Paris.

A continous line in sepia wash frames this colored
drawing. In the photograph reproduced here, this
line is only visible at the left.

D. III. 4
CAFÉ-CONCERT IN MALAGA
Malaga, 1901.
Conté crayon.
Dimensions not known.

Bibl. Not in Z.

Present location unknown.

Reproduced in *Pèl y Ploma,* No. 77, Barcelona,
June 1901, p. 15, at the head of an article by Miguel
Utrillo (signed "Pincell").

D. III. 5
PICASSO IN MADRID
Madrid, 1901.
Charcoal.   Size : 23.5 x 30.5 cm.
Signed bottom right : P. Ruiz Picasso.

Exh. Galerie Knoedler Paris, November–December
1966 : *Picasso, Dessins et Aquarelles 1899–1965,*
No. 11, repr.

Bibl. Z. I. 36.   C.-P. No. 34.   Sabartés, *Picasso,
documents iconographiques,* No. 67.   Blunt and
Pool, No. 53.

Coll. Louis Goldschmit ;   Christie's, London, Sale,
May 20, 1960, No. 77 ;   M. Knoedler & Co., New
York ;

Collection Mr. and Mrs. Walter Bick, Canada.

This is the original of the drawing printed in *Arte
Joven,* Madrid 1901.   Shown in this group from left
to right are an unidentified figure, the poet Cornuty,
Francisco de Asis Soler, Picasso, and Alberto
Lozano.

D. III. 6
THE POET ALBERTO LOZANO
Madrid, 1901.
Pastel.
Size : 21 x 12.7 cm.
Signed top right : P. Ruiz Picasso.

Exh. Sidney Janis Gallery, New York ; O'Hana
Gallery, London ; Stoneleigh Abbey, Warwickshire ;
Galerie Motte, Geneva, 1960 : *Picasso, his Blue
Period,* No. 18.

Bibl. Not in Z.   Jacques O'Hana, No. 18 (wrongly
dated 1900).   Blunt and Pool, No. 54.

Coll. Private collection, Barcelona ;

Private collection, London.

D. III. 7
IN THE CAFÉ
Madrid, 1901.
Pastel.
Size : 30 x 42 cm.
Signed bottom left : P. Ruiz Picasso.

Bibl. Reproduced in *Arte Joven,* Madrid, 1901.
Z. VI. 373.   C.-P. No. 39.

Collection Masoliver, Barcelona.

D. III. 8
WOMAN WITH FLOWERS IN HER HAIR
Madrid, 1901.
Pastel.
Dimensions not known.
Signed bottom left : P. Ruiz Picasso.

Bibl. Published in *Arte Joven,* Madrid, 1901.
Z. VI. 398.   C.-P. No. 36.   Blunt and Pool, No. 18.

Present location unknown.

D. III. 9
THE AMATEUR
Madrid, 1901.
Charcoal drawing.
Size : 21.5 x 16 cm.
Signed bottom right : P. Ruiz P.

Exh. Musée de l'Athénée, Geneva, July 11–September 21, 1963 : *Picasso,* No. 5 (dated 1902).

Bibl. Not in Z.

Private collection, Switzerland.

D. III. 10
THE PARISIENNE
Pastel. Dimensions not known.
Signed bottom right : P. Ruiz Picasso, Paris.

Bibl. Published in *Arte Joven,* Madrid, 1901.
Z. VI. 394. C.-P. No. 29.

Present location unknown.

This drawing, reproduced in *Arte Joven* in Madrid, 1901, might have been done earlier in Paris.

D. III. 11
YOUNG WOMAN WITH A HAT
Madrid, 1901.
Pastel.
Dimensions not known.
Signed bottom left : P. Ruiz Picasso.

Bibl. Published in *Arte Joven,* Madrid, 1901.
Z. VI. 371. C.-P. No. 31.

Present location unknown.

D. III. 12
TWO WOMEN SEATED
Madrid, 1901.
Left : pen drawing with touches of color.
Right : colored crayons.
Size : 13.4 x 20.3 cm.
Signed bottom left : P. R. Picasso.

Bibl. Not in Z. Catalogue of paintings and drawings of the "Cau Ferrat" (Rusiñol Foundation), Sitges, 1942, p. 27.

Coll. Ignacio Zuloaga, Barcelona ; Santiago Rusiñol, Barcelona ;

Museo del "Cau Ferrat," Sitges.

D. III. 13
YOUNG WOMAN WITH A HAT
Madrid, 1901.
Pastel on paper. Size : 21.5 x 12.6 cm.
Signed bottom right : P. Ruiz Picasso.

Exh. Sidney Janis Gallery, New York ; O'Hana Gallery, London ; Stoneleigh Abbey, Warwickshire ; Galerie Motte, Geneva, 1960 : *Picasso, his Blue Period,* No. 19, repr. in cat.

Bibl. Not in Z. Jacques O'Hana, No. 19. Blunt and Pool, No. 35.

Coll. Private collection, Barcelona ;

Present location unknown.

Authenticated by the artist.

OLD WOMAN (WOMAN WITH JEWELS), BARCELONA, 1901, OIL. THE PHILADELPHIA MUSEUM OF ART, LOUISE AND WALTER ARENSBERG COLLECTION (IV. 4).

Barcelona, Spring 1901, and the Return to Paris

Picasso is reluctant to speak about this phase of his career. It could be because his decision to leave Spain for Paris, for the second time, was the only thing that mattered. We do not know if he left Madrid already determined to go to Paris, or if he decided all this in Barcelona.

A month is unaccounted for between the first issue of *Arte Joven*, dated March 31, and the probable date of his arrival in

middle position, weighted in favor of emphasizing the stay in Barcelona.

If one follows Sabartés in dating the poster for *Els Quatre Gats* (reproduced below) as 1902, which is logical, there is no justification for dating from the return to Spain, in 1902, all the drawings on the backs of the Junyer commercial cards, or the *Parody of Manet's Olympia* (D. IV. 7). In fact, on the evidence of the last self-portrait of 1901, Picasso was wearing a beard when he went back to Barcelona in 1902. The *Parody* shows him with only a mustache, and so do the two first self-portraits

Poster design for Els Quatre Gats, *Barcelona, 1902, India ink (31 × 34 cm.).*
In the foreground : Picasso ; from left to right : Pere Romeu, Rocarol, Fontbona,
Angel F. de Soto, Sabartés.
Collection Mr. and Mrs. Walter Bick, Canada.

Paris with Jaume Andreu Bonsons (not with Casagemas, who had committed suicide in February). If we judge the place itself—Paris or Barcelona—to have been irrelevant to the extraordinary speed of execution of the canvases in the "Vollard style," then we may conclude that some of the Spanish canvases must have been painted in Barcelona during what Sabartés considers a "stopping-off place." Zervos, like Sabartés, would attribute to Paris nearly everything exhibited at Vollard's. On the other hand Picasso had to justify the monthly stipend Mañach was sending. Barr (*Fifty Years*, p. 19) thinks that the Exhibition was made up of work "mostly done in Spain." We take a

of 1901 that we place in Paris during the spring. In the drawing in which he appears with Jaume Andreu Bonsons, the lower part of his face is hidden, but the poster for *Els Quatre Gats* shows him quite bearded. Further evidence is given by the photograph taken by Torrés Fuster in 1901 in the studio on the Boulevard de Clichy, which must have been made between the two trips to Barcelona and in the summer, judging by the clothes. This shows Picasso with a mustache and strikingly like the first self-portraits in oil. One last point is that this photograph is autographed with the same signature as the canvases in the Vollard Exhibition (cf. Appendix, p. 340).

IV. 1
SEATED WOMAN
Barcelona or Paris, 1901.
Pastel and oil on canvas (Cf. note).
Size : 40.6 x 52 cm.
Signed bottom left : Picasso.

Exh. Toronto and Montreal, 1964 : *Picasso and Man,*
No. 7, repr. in cat.

Bibl. Z. VI. 335. Diehl, 1960, p. 6 (entitled *L'Attente*).

Coll. Robert Lebel, Paris ; Bought in January 1957
by the present owner :

Collection Mrs. John A. MacAulay, Winnipeg.

Dated 1900 by Zervos. Jean Sutherland Boggs
suggested a later date—Madrid, 1901. Given the
signature and the nature of the work, it seems fair
to suggest a date still later. We might even be
tempted, because of the hair style and the pose, to
imagine a Parisian model. Zervos and the Toronto
catalogue call the medium conté crayon and pastel.
The present owner states that it is pastel and oil on
canvas.

IV. 2
THE DWARF DANCER (La Nana)
Barcelona, 1901.
Oil on cardboard.
Size : 104.5 x 61 cm.
Signed bottom left : Picasso.

Exh. III Bienal Hispanoamericana de Arte, Barcelona,
1955 : *Precursores y maestros del arte Español
contemporáneo,* No. 20. Musée d'Art et d'Histoire,
Geneva, 1956 : *Sélection de la IIIe Biennale Hispano-
Américaine : Picasso, Nonell, Manolo,* No. 3.
Museum of Modern Art, New York, and The Art
Institute of Chicago, 1957 : *Picasso, 75th Anniversary
Exhibition,* repr. in cat. p. 17. Arts Council of Great
Britain, Tate Gallery, London, 1960 : *Picasso,* No. 9,
repr. in cat. pl. 2 b. Grand Palais, Paris, No-
vember 1966—February 1967 : *Hommage à Pablo
Picasso,* No. 6, repr. in cat.

Bibl. Z. I. 66. C.-P. p. 33 and cover (repr. in color).
Blunt and Pool, No. 48.

Coll. L. Plandiura, Barcelona ; Museo de Arte
Moderno, Barcelona ;

Picasso Museum, Barcelona.

Everything supports the theory that this work with a
typically Spanish theme was done before Picasso
left Spain. Even if Picasso works from memory,
there are not many precedents in his work of
characteristic local themes which he transplanted
elsewhere. There is an agreement between what he
paints and the atmosphere, the light, and the sur-
roundings. With *Old Woman* (IV. 4) and *Bullfight*
(IV. 5), this is really Picasso's first example of a style
which uses divisionist brushwork and pure color.

IV. 3
THE SPANISH DANCER
Barcelona, 1901.
Oil on cardboard.
Size : 49.5 x 34 cm.
Signed bottom right : Picasso.

Exh. Wadsworth Atheneum, Hartford, Connecticut, July 9–August 9, 1959 : *Music Makers.* Knoedler & Co., New York, April 25–May 12, 1962 : *Picasso, an American Tribute,* No. 7, repr. in cat.

Bibl. Not in Z.

Coll. Joseph Gottschalk, Munich ; Bought for $25.000 by the present owners :

Collection Mr. and Mrs. Richard Rodgers, New York.

This work is similar in every way to the preceding one. It is interesting that Picasso tries out his new style on theater subjects, as he had during the previous winter in Paris, combining it with the unusual placement of forms that suggests the influence of Degas.

IV. 4
OLD WOMAN
(Woman with Gloves, Woman with Jewels)
Barcelona, 1901.
Oil on cardboard.
Size : 67.4 x 52 cm.
Signed bottom left : Picasso.

Philadelphia Museum of Art, The Louise and Walter Arensberg Collection.

Exh. The California Palace of the Legion of Honor, San Francisco, 1934 : *French Painting,* No. 217, repr. in cat. The Art Institute of Chicago, 1949 : *The Arensberg Collection,* No. 163, repr. in cat. p. 92. The Solomon R. Guggenheim Museum, New York, 1961: *The Arensberg and Gallatin Collections.*

Bibl. Z. VI. 389. A. J. Eddy, *Cubism and Post-Impressionism,* Chicago, 1914, p. 140. Lieberman, New York, 1954, pl. 11 (repr. in color). John Canaday, *Mainstreams of Modern Art,* New York, 1959, p. 451, fig. 551. Blunt and Pool, No. 59.

Coll. Jerome Eddy, New York ; Walter Arensberg, Hollywood ;

The pointillist technique, the vividness and brilliance of color, relate this beautiful oil to the *Dwarf Dancer* (IV. 2) and suggest that it was painted in Spain, although the subject itself neither confirms nor denies a setting. Phoebe Pool dates this painting from Picasso's stay in Madrid, a proposal not compatible with what we know of other works from that time. In fact, the pointillist technique is still barely developed in the *Woman with a Plumed Hat* (III. 4), and the freedom of color in particular is unlike this. Note also that the signature at least is indisputably from the Barcelona period.

Color plate, page 139.

IV. 5
BULLFIGHT
Barcelona, 1901.
Oil on canvas.
Size : 47 x 56 cm.
Signed bottom left : Picasso.

Exh. Galerie Georges Petit, Paris, summer, 1932 : *Picasso,* No. 2. Kunsthaus, Zurich, autumn, 1932 : *Picasso,* No. 3 (lent by Ambroise Vollard). Grand Palais, Paris, November 1966–February 1967 : *Hommage à Pablo Picasso,* No. 7, repr. in cat.

Bibl. Z. I. 88. Sabartés, *Picasso,* 1946, pl. 1 (repr. in color). Sabartés and Boeck, p. 115 (repr. in color). Cassou, 1959, p. 11 (repr. in color). Diehl, 1960, p. 10 (repr. in color).

Coll. Ambroise Vollard, Paris ; Mrs. Chester Beatty, London ; Max Pellequer, Paris ;

Private collection, Paris.

It is likely that this bullfight scene, so characteristic of Picasso's change in style before the Vollard exhibition, was done in Barcelona and brought by Picasso to Paris. See Introduction to Catalogue V, Nos. 33, 34, and 35 of the catalogue of the Vollard exhibition.

IV. 6
BULLFIGHT
Barcelona, 1901.
Oil on cardboard mounted on panel.
Size : 49.5 x 64.7 cm.
Signed bottom right : Picasso.

Exh. Arts Council of Great Britain, Tate Gallery, London, 1960 : *Picasso,* No. 6, repr. in cat. pl. 4 d.

Bibl. Z. VI. 378. Cassou, 1940, p. 123 (wrongly dated 1923). Palau i Fabre, No. 64 (repr. in color).

Coll. Albert Henraux, Paris ; Knoedler & Co., New York, 1958 ;

Collection Stavros S. Niarchos, Saint-Moritz.

Zervos justifiably dates this painting Barcelona, 1901. It is a development from the preceding work and the most remarkable example of the brilliant pre-Fauvism which appears at the end of Picasso's stay in Spain. This work is far less known than the preceding one, even though it is clearly freer and more elaborate.

Color plate, page 37.

IV. 7
PORTRAIT OF JULIO GONZALEZ
Barcelona, 1901.
Watercolor and ink on paper.
Size : 29 x 24 cm.
Signed and inscribed, bottom left :
Recuerdo para Julio Gonzalez de su amigo Picasso.

Exh. Musée Réattu, Arles, July 6—September 2, 1957, No. 7, repr. in cat., pl. 4.

Bibl. Not in Z. Catalogue of the Julio Gonzalez retrospective, Museum of Modern Art, New York, 1956.

Coll. Given by the artist to Julio Gonzalez ;

Collection Madame Roberta Gonzalez, Arcueil.

As Picasso remembers it, this watercolor shows Gonzalez seated on the hillside of the Tibidabo in Barcelona. Julio Gonzalez was in Paris the summer of 1901. In style,

this work is either 1901 or 1902. Doubtless it was done at the time of a meeting in Barcelona which we cannot date more precisely. Julio Gonzalez, born in Barcelona in 1876, died in Arcueil (Seine) in 1942. A sculptor in iron, he played a large part in the artistic life of Picasso, who relied many times on his experiments and technique. The *Still Life with a Bull's Skull,* one of the most tragic works of the Occupation, was painted by Picasso April 5, 1942, in the week following the death of Julio Gonzalez. In 1935 Gonzalez wrote in *Cahiers d'Art* : "I have known Picasso more than thirty years. And every time I have seen and talked to him —which is often—we spoke about Catalan people. I have heard his nostalgic words about Barcelona and Perpignan. He conjured up the holidays, the fairs, the public displays and events of all kinds. And he did it with vigorous details. Everything over there interests him. He is one of us."

IV. 8
CHILD WITH A DOLL
Barcelona, 1900—1901.
Oil on wood.
Size : 23 x 31 cm.
Signed top left : Picasso.

Exh. Kunsthaus, Zurich, 1948 : *Musée et bibliothèque de Grenoble,* No. 185.

Bibl. Not in Z. Helen Kay, *Picasso's World of Children,* New York, 1965, p. 40.

Coll. Acquired in 1935 by the

Musée des Beaux-Arts, Grenoble.

According to Gabrielle Kueny, Curator of the Museum of Grenoble, this work was done in Spain before Picasso's arrival in Paris.

IV. 9
THE COMEDIENNE
Paris, 1901.
Pastel.
Dimensions not known.
Signed top right : Picasso.

Bibl. Z. VI. 277. C.-P. No. 24. (Both Zervos and Cirici-Pellicer date this pastel 1900, which does not correspond with the signature or with the treatment of forms.)

Present location unknown.

IV. 10
THE COMEDIENNE
Paris, 1901.
Pastel on paper.   Size : 49 x 31 cm.
Signed bottom left : Picasso.

Exh. III Bienal Hispanoamericana de Arte, Barcelona, 1955 : *Precursores y maestros del arte Español contemporáneo,* No. 18.

Bibl. Z. I. 31. C.-P. No. 55. Sabartés, *Picasso, les bleus de Barcelone,* Paris 1963, pl. 8 (repr. in color).

Coll. L. Plandiura, Barcelona ; Museo de Arte Moderno, Barcelona ;

Picasso Museum, Barcelona.

V. 11
THE END OF THE NUMBER
Paris, 1901.
Pastel on canvas.
Size : 74 x 48 cm.
Signed bottom right : Picasso.

Exh. Probably : Galerie Berthe Weill, Paris, October 24–November 20, 1904, No. 35 : *Romancière of the Music Hall.* (See, in the Introduction to Catalogue XI, the description given it by Maurice Le Sieutre : "... a woman dressed in pastel yellow, ... bony, over-taxing her consumptive form.") III Bienal Hispano-americana de Arte, Barcelona, 1955 : *Precursores y maestros del arte Español contemporáneo,* No. 13.

Bibl. Z. I. 30. C.-P., frontispiece in color. Florent Fels, *L'Art vivant, de 1900 à nos jours,* Geneva, 1950, p. 233 (repr. in color).

Coll. L. Plandiura, Barcelona ; Museo de Arte Moderno, Barcelona ;

Picasso Museum, Barcelona.

The bright yellow dress of this *"romancière"* of the music hall, her pallor, and her gautness fit so perfectly the pastel described by Maurice Le Sieutre (cf. *Exh.* above), that its presence at the Berthe Weill exhibition three years later seems beyond question. It cannot be mistaken for *The Comedienne,* above (IV. 10), where the dress is blue.

IV. 12
THE DANCER
Paris, 1901.   Pastel.   Size : 47 x 31 cm.
Signed bottom left : Picasso.

Bibl. Z. VI. 368.   C.-P. No. 54 (entitled *Cancan*).

Collection Masoliver, Barcelona.

IV. 13
BALLERINA
Paris, 1901.   Pastel.   Size : 38 x 31 cm.
Signed bottom right : Picasso.

Bibl. Not in Z.   Sabartés and Boeck, p. 458, No. 9
(wrongly dated 1900).

Private collection.

IV. 14
CANCAN DANCER
Paris, 1901.
India ink and watercolor on paper.
Size : 17.5 x 11.5 cm.
Signed bottom right : Picasso.

Exh. Musée d'Art et d'Histoire, Geneva, 1956 : *Sélection
de la IIIe Biennale Hispano-Américaine : Picasso,
Nonell, Manolo,* No. 36.

Bibl. Z. VI. 369.   C.-P. No. 90.

Coll. L. Plandiura, Barcelona ;   Museo de Arte Moderno,
Barcelona ;

Picasso Museum, Barcelona

IV. 15
JARDIN DE PARIS (Poster design)
Paris, 1901.   Watercolor.   Size : 63.5 x 48.3 cm.
Signed bottom right : Picasso.

Exh. Perls Galleries, New York, 1937 : *Picasso.*   The
Art Institute of Chicago, March 23–May 14, 1939 :
International Watercolor Exhibition, No. 135.   Museum
of Modern Art, New York, 1939, The Art Institute of
Chicago, and The Museum of Fine Arts, Boston, 1940 :
Picasso, Forty Years of his Art, No. 14.   The Virginia
Museum of Fine Arts, The Philadelphia Museum of Art,
1941 : *The Collection of Walter P. Chrysler, Jr.,* No. 194.

Bibl. Z. VI. 367.   Barr, *Forty Years,* p. 28.   Barr, *Fifty
Years,* p. 20.

Coll. Bellier, Paris ;   Sale of the Bellier collection,
Hôtel Drouot, Paris ;   Georges Lévy, Paris ;   Perls
Galleries, New York ;   Walter P. Chrysler, Jr., New York ;
Ira Hotchkiss, New York ;   Parke-Bernet, New York,
Sale, June 28, 1961, sold for $18.500 ;

Private collection (Mr. C.M.P.), New York.

IV. 16
NUDE DRESSING HER HAIR
Paris, 1901.
Pastel.
Dimensions not known.
Signed bottom left : P. R. Picasso.

Bibl. Z. VI. 377 (dated Paris 1901).

Present location unknown.

From the signature, this pastel seems earlier than Paris, 1901, but we relate it to the following pastel (IV. 17) because of the way in which the woman's body is drawn.

IV. 17
LA TOILETTE
Paris, 1901.
Pastel on cardboard.
Size : 26 x 28 cm.
Signed middle left : Picasso.
Verso : Sketch of a Head of a Woman
(IV. 18).

Bibl. Z. VI. 397.

Coll. Mr. and Mrs. Herbert L. Matthews, New York (1937–1964) ; Sotheby & Co., London, Sale, April 29, 1964, No. 43 (recto and verso) ;

Collection Mr. and Mrs. John A. Beck, Houston.

Herbert L. Matthews bought this pastel in 1937 when he was in Spain as a war correspondent. It is a work still very close to the pastels of 1900.

IV. 18
SKETCH OF A HEAD OF A WOMAN
Paris, 1901.
Charcoal drawing on cardboard.
Size : 26 x 28 cm.
Unsigned. (Signed on the front.)
Recto : La Toilette (IV. 17).

Bibl. Unpublished.

Coll. Mr. and Mrs. Herbert L. Matthews, New York (1937–1964) ; Sotheby & Co., London, Sale, April 29, 1964, No. 43 (recto and verso) ;

Collection Mr. and Mrs. John A. Beck, Houston.

We owe the discovery of this sketch on the back of *La Toilette* (IV. 17) to the kindness of the present owners. To our knowledge it has never been catalogued or reproduced.

D. IV. 1
AT THE CABARET
Barcelona, 1901.
Black, orange and blue crayons on paper.
Size : 12.7 x 21.5 cm.
Signed bottom right : Picasso.

Bibl. Not in Z.

The Art Institute of Chicago, The Lewis L. Coburn Memorial Collection.

D. IV. 2
THREE SKETCHES OF WOMEN
Barcelona, 1901.
Ink and colored crayons on paper.
Size : 13 x 20.5 cm.
Unsigned.

Bibl. Z. VI. 366. C.-P. No. 20. Bouret, 1950, p. 19.

Coll. L. Plandiura, Barcelona ;

Picasso Museum, Barcelona.

D. IV. 3
TWO WOMEN
Barcelona, 1901.
Watercolor and ink on paper.
Size : 13.4 x 20.3 cm.
Signed top left : P. R. Picasso.

Bibl. Not in Z. Catalogue of paintings and drawings of the "Cau Ferrat" (Rusiñol Foundation), Sitges, 1942, p. 27. Palau i Fabre, No. 65 (repr. in color).

Coll. Ignacio Zuloaga, Barcelona ; Santiago Rusiñol Barcelona ;

Museo del "Cau Ferrat," Sitges.

D. IV. 4
THE D. PACO FAMILY AT HOME
Barcelona, 1901.
Pen with touches of watercolor on paper.
Size : 13.4 x 20 cm.
Signed bottom left : P. R. Picasso.
Inscribed top right : *La familia de D. Paco en su casa.*

Bibl. Not in Z. MUSEION, Office International des Musées, April 1940, p. 1–2 : *Disparition de dessins de Picasso au musée de Cau Ferrat.*

Coll. Ignacio Zuloaga, Barcelona ; Santiago Rusiñol, Barcelona ;

Museo del "Cau Ferrat," Sitges.

Stolen in 1940 from the "Cau Ferrat" and afterwards recovered.

D. IV. 5
RECLINING NUDE, WITH PICASSO
AT HER FEET
Barcelona, 1901.
Ink and watercolor on paper.
Size : 17.6 x 23.2 cm.
Signed top left : Picasso (signature
not authentic).

Bibl. Unpublished.

Coll. L. Garriga Roig, Paris ;

Picasso Museum, Barcelona.

See Addenda No. 11.

D. IV. 6
TWO NUDES
Barcelona, 1901.
Ink and colored pencils on paper.
Size : 9 x 13.3 cm.
Unsigned.

Bibl. Unpublished.

Coll. L. Garriga Roig, Paris ;

Picasso Museum, Barcelona.

D. IV. 7
PARODY OF MANET'S OLYMPIA
Barcelona, 1901.
Pen drawing and colored crayons.
Size : 15.3 x 23 cm.
Signed top left : Picasso (later).

Exh. Sidney Janis Gallery, New York ;
O'Hana Gallery, London ; Stoneleigh
Abbey, Warwickshire ; Galerie Motte,
Geneva, 1960, No. 23, repr. in cat.
Galerie Knoedler, Paris, November–
December 1966 : *Picasso, dessins et
aquarelles 1899–1965,* No. 12, repr.
in cat.

Bibl. Z. VI. 343. C.-P. No. 100. Sabartés, *Picasso, documents iconographiques,* No. 69. (Z., C.-P. and Sabartés reproduce a retouched photograph.)

Coll. Junyer Vidal, Barcelona ;

Private collection, Paris.

At the left, behind the bed, Sebastián
Junyer Vidal ; at the right, Picasso.

148

D. IV. 8
MAN AND WOMAN IN EVENING DRESS
Barcelona, 1901.
Ink and colored pencil on back of Junyer business card.
Size : 13.5 x 9 cm.
Unauthentic signature, bottom right ; re-signed by the artist, top right : Picasso.

Exh. Frankfurt and Hamburg, 1965, No. 11 *(La Rencontre),* repr. in cat. Galerie Knoedler, Paris, November–December 1966 : *Picasso, Dessins et Aquarelles 1899–1965,* No. 10, repr. in cat.

Bibl. Z. VI. 493.

Collection Lionel Prejger, Paris.

D. IV. 9
STUDIES : HANDS AND FIGURES
Paris, 1901.
India ink.
Size : 13 x 20.2 cm.
Unsigned.
Authenticated by the artist.

Bibl. Unpublished.

Collection Galerie Berggruen, Paris.

Berggruen proposes the date 1900. The use of ink inclines us toward 1901, or even the beginning of 1902.

D. IV. 10
THE SNOBS
Barcelona, 1901.
Ink and colored pencil on back of Junyer business card.
Size : 14 x 9 cm.
Re-signed top right, over the unauthentic signature : Picasso.

Exh. Sidney Janis Gallery, New York ; O'Hana Gallery, London ; Stoneleigh Abbey, Warwickshire ; Galerie Motte, Geneva, 1960, No. 37, repr. in cat. Galerie Knoedler, Paris, November–December 1966, No. 16, repr. in cat.

Bibl. Z. I. 147.

Coll. Junyer Vidal, Barcelona ;

Collection Henri Prejger, Le Cannet.

D. IV. 11
WOMAN, DOG AND HORSE
Paris, 1901.
Charcoal and colored crayons on paper.
Size : 20 x 13 cm.
Signed bottom left : Picasso (later signature).

Exh. Galerie Knoedler, Paris, November–December 1966, No. 3, repr. in cat.

Bibl. Not in Z.

Coll. Galerie Berggruen, Paris ; M. Knoedler & Co., New York ;

Collection Mrs. Loewy, New York.

D. IV. 12
PICASSO ARRIVING IN PARIS WITH JAUME ANDREU BONSONS
Paris, 1901.
Ink and colored crayons.
Size : 31 x 37 cm.
Signed and dated bottom left : Año de 1901, Picasso.

Bibl. Z. VI. 342. C.-P. (documents). Sabartés, 1954, No. 62. Penrose, 1956, p. 70.

Coll. Junyer Vidal, Barcelona ; Galerie Berggruen, Paris ;

Collection Max Rayne, London.

D. IV. 13
SKETCHES : IN THE STREET
Paris, 1901.
Charcoal and colored crayons on paper.
Size : 20 x 13 cm.
Signed bottom right : Picasso (later signature).

Bibl. Unpublished.

Collection Galerie Berggruen, Paris.

D. IV. 14
WOMEN HOLDING THEIR SKIRTS
Paris, 1901.
Charcoal and colored crayons on paper.
Size : 12.5 x 16 cm.
Signed bottom left : Picasso (later).

Bibl. Unpublished.

Collection Galerie Berggruen, Paris.

D. IV. 15
FOUR HEADS OF WOMEN
Paris, 1901.
Charcoal and colored crayons on paper.
Size : 13 x 17.5 cm.
Signed bottom right : Picasso (later).

Exh. Frankfurt and Hamburg, 1965, No. 7, repr. in cat.

Bibl. Not in Z.

Collection Galerie Berggruen, Paris.

D. IV. 16
PAGE OF STUDIES : THREE WOMEN
Paris, 1901.
Charcoal and colored crayons on paper
Size : 13 x 18.5 cm.
Signed bottom left : Picasso (later).

Exh. Frankfurt and Hamburg, 1965, No. 8, repr. in cat.

Bibl. Not in Z.

Collection Galerie Berggruen, Paris.

D. IV. 17
DANCING COUPLES
Paris, 1901.
Colored pencils.
Size : 13.5 x 22 cm.
Signed center right : Picasso.

Bibl. Unpublished.

Collection Galerie Berggruen, Paris.

The Galerie Berggruen dates this drawing 1903, but
because of the signature and also the nature of the
theme, it seems to us that it should be dated 1901.
The simplifications of outline are close to the other
sketches reproduced above, which show Steinlen's
influence. On the other hand, these studies can be
connected to those done the preceding autumn for
The Embrace (II. 14).

D. IV. 18
HEAD OF A WOMAN IN PROFILE
Paris, 1901.
Charcoal.
Size : 13 x 12 cm.
Signed bottom right : Picasso (later signature).

Bibl. Unpublished.

Collection Galerie Berggruen, Paris.

D. IV. 19
THE ENTERTAINER
Paris, 1901.
Colored pencils.
Size : 21 x 13 cm.
Signed and dated bottom right : Picasso, Año de 1901.

Bibl. Unpublished.

Collection Galerie Berggruen, Paris.

D. IV. 20
ENTERTAINER
Paris, 1901.
Charcoal, with touches of color, on paper.
Size : 21 x 12.5 cm.
Signed bottom left : Picasso.

Exh. Musée d'Art et d'Histoire, Geneva, 1956 : *Sélection de la IIIᵉ Biennale Hispano-Américaine : Picasso, Nonell, Manolo,* No. 30.

Bibl. Z. VI. 376. C.-P. No. 42.

Coll. L. Plandiura, Barcelona ;   Museo de Arte Moderno, Barcelona ;

Picasso Museum, Barcelona.

D. IV. 21
HEAD OF BLANCHE
Paris, 1901.
Charcoal and colored crayons on paper.
Size : 20 x 12 cm.
Signed bottom left : Picasso (later signature).

Bibl. Unpublished.

Collection Galerie Berggruen, Paris.

D. IV. 22
JEANNE BLOCH AT THE FOLIES-BERGÈRE
Paris, 1901.
Ink and watercolor on paper.
Size : 15.5 x 10.5 cm.
Signed bottom left : Picasso.

Exh. Frankfurt and Hamburg, 1965, No. 5, repr. in cat.   Galerie Knoedler, Paris, November–December 1966, No. 5, repr. in cat.

Bibl. Not in Z.

Collection Lionel Prejger, Paris.

D. IV. 23
SELF-PORTRAIT
IN FRONT OF THE MOULIN-ROUGE
Paris, 1901.
Ink and colored pencil on paper.
Size : 18 x 11.5 cm.
Signed bottom right : Picasso.

Bibl. Not in Z. Penrose, 1958, pl. 1, No. 5. Lothar-Gunther Buchheim, *Picasso, eine Bildbiographie,* Munich, 1960, p. 12.

Collection Mrs. E. Heywood Lonsdale, London.

At bottom right : Jaume Andreu Bonsons (see also D. IV. 12).

LITTLE GIRLS DANCING, PARIS, 1901, OIL. PRIVATE COLLECTION, PARIS (V. 15).

The Vollard Exhibition, Paris, 1901

The Vollard Exhibition was organized by Gustave Coquiot, who at 36 already had a voluminous production as a Parisian journalist behind him. He had published books with such evocative titles as *Les Bals Publics*, 1895; *Les Café-concerts*, 1896; *Dimaï̇̇cs d'été*, 1897; and also *Les Villas de Paris*. He was a close ï̇̇end of Huysmans, Rodin, Jean Lorrain and also of the Impressionists. He loved Bonnard's work. And, doubtless, he believed he had found another "harmonist of luminous coloring" in the work of Picasso at the time. His interest could only decline rapidly when Picasso changed his style during the summer. In fact, in 1914, Coquiot wrote: "Besides, Picasso is artful... His clowns, his harlequins of that period seem to be borrowed at times from other painters. These figures are more colorful than deeply significant."

In Coquiot's book, *Cubistes, Futuristes, Passéistes*, which contains a slightly modified version of his preface to the Vollard Exhibition, he expresses another opinion: "Bookmakers willingly give Picasso four to one odds, Matisse even odds, and Derain is favored. Let me repeat that in my opinion Picasso will be the first to drop out of the running..."

We should remember that it was from Coquiot that such expressions as "Steinlen period," and "Lautrec period" came, and have been used constantly ever since without any clear meaning, which is not surprising if you consider that for our critic the "Steinlen period" covered the Vollard Exhibition! We owe to Coquiot also this other kind appraisal: "Picasso is ignorant of everything, absorbs everything, but retains nothing." This makes clearer the later relations between the critic and the painter, then nineteen and a half. In reality, Coquiot is the one chiefly responsible for the misunderstanding which still persists about this major formative period of Picasso.

The exhibition was made up of 65 numbers, but actually consisted of more works, since number 65 designated the group of drawings. The catalogue gives only titles, without dimensions, a customary practice then, and it does not specify the medium. Inasmuch as an exhibition of Picasso's pastels was held at the Sala Parés in Barcelona at the same time as the Vollard Exhibition, we presume that the works shown in Paris were oils. But despite its vagueness, this catalogue is fundamental to the classification of Picasso's work in 1901. The Vollard catalogue, plus Sabartés' account and the catalogue of the Berthe Weill Exhibition of April 1902, with information about the last works painted in 1901, allow us to follow rather closely Picasso's stylistic evolution.

According to Sabartés, he rejoined Picasso in Paris "at the end of autumn." Actually, when we read his memoirs, we realize that he spent a good deal of time with Picasso in Paris. As Picasso left for Spain again in January 1902, it is more logical to date Sabartés' appearance at the end of October or the beginning of November rather than in December. This would also agree with the "dense fog" which prevented Sabartés from seeing Paris on his arrival. And his first reaction at Picasso's studio was: "The pictures Picasso showed me had violent tonalities and the colors at first sight reminded me of the shades of playing cards. This series of works was done in four or five months."

"Here I was, suddenly, my mind far away, unprepared to withstand this unexpected feeling, in the face of a new aspect of Picasso's work. His latest works were too alien for me to understand them: there had been too long a gap in my usual close attention to his development. What he had done in Madrid and Barcelona, before he returned here, was so different from what I had before me!... There was more difference between the paintings brought from Madrid to Barcelona a few months before and those of Paris on my arrival than between the work of Madrid and that shown at Barcelona."

This narrative by Sabartés, in spite of appearances, does not prove that he thought he was seeing only work done in Paris. He referred to the work exhibited in Barcelona—that is, the pastels of the Sala Parés—as close to the Madrid work we have analyzed, for the excellent reason that a number of these pastels must have come from Madrid.

The precision of the date remains. Four or five months of work—if we adopt a date in May for Picasso's arrival in Paris, this leads us to date at the beginning of autumn the meeting of Picasso and Sabartés. Sabartés obviously has in mind the style that we have analyzed already in the works which we place during the stay in Barcelona. Parenthetically, we note that it would have been characteristic for Picasso not to have shown his friends in Barcelona a change of style. Sabartés' surprise stems from this. But to return to this "playing card" style, Sabartés went into more detail in contrasting it to the "blue style": "I was no longer shocked by the loud colors of the earlier canvases. If I couldn't get used to them, it was because I was away when he began to paint them. I was receptive to the blue style from its outset. It does not depart from drawing as much as the previous one." This previous style, which we call the Vollard style, Sabartés exemplifies with the *Portrait of Gustave Coquiot* (v. 64) in the Musée National d'Art Moderne in Paris. If one compares this work to the Madrid paintings such as *Woman in Blue* (III. 5) or the *Woman with a Plumed Hat* (III. 4), we are struck, in fact, by the shock of colors applied in broken or broad strokes, always confident, a treatment separate from drawing, as Sabartés justly observed. The end of the Vollard style was marked by the disappearance of divisionist brush strokes and the appearance of sharp outlines often circled with blue. At first, blue is only the most prominent among the other colors, hardly less bright than in the Vollard style. This is the style of the *Portrait of Sabartés* (VI. 19) or of the first *Portrait of Mateu F. de Soto* (VI. 21). The distinctly blue, monochrome paintings did not appear until later, in the last weeks of Picasso's stay in Paris. The blue portraits of Sabartés and of Mateu F. de Soto (VI. 34, 33) are typical examples of the monochrome style.

Contrary to what is generally written, the Vollard Exhibition was a success. The pictures listed in the catalogue as sold certainly were sold, and to the owners who are cited. "It went very well," Picasso comments. "It pleased a lot of people. It was only later when I set about to do blue paintings that things went really badly. This lasted for years. It's always been like this with me. Very good and then suddenly very bad. The acrobats again pleased. And what I did after that didn't please any more."

Seven paintings in the Vollard catalogue can be identified accurately (cf. pp. 156-159): *Portrait de M. Mañach ; Iris ; Morphinomane ; L'Absinthe ; La Folle aux chats ; Les Toits ; Boulevard de Clichy*. We are also certain that *Little Girls Dancing* was

BLUE ROOFS, PARIS, 1901, OIL. THE ASHMOLEAN MUSEUM, OXFORD (V. 21).

there, which more likely corresponds to *Blondes Chevelures* than to *Danseuses*. The identifications of *Eglise d'Espagne* with *In Front of the Church*; *L'Enfant blanc* with *Le Gourmand*; *Jeanneton* with *Reclining Nude*; *Au Bord de l'eau* with *Women and Children on the Beach* (v. 54), are extremely probable. This makes a total of twelve paintings. We cannot distinguish precisely the groups of "mother and child" subjects, "flowers," "children in parks," "portraits of prostitutes," "bullfight scenes," but still we have here another dozen works which give us a fair over-all picture even if we cannot be sure which ones were actually in this exhibition. Among them we can safely

conclude that one of the paintings of *Longchamp* or *Auteuil* was present, because of the review by Fagus (Documents, p. 333), "The multicolored swarming of crowds at the race track." This makes up over half the items. The rest remain conjectural, but it is fitting to remark that, even granting that Picasso might have brought a large number of works from Barcelona, he could hardly, in the space of a month and a half, have exceeded the production known to us, however great his capacity for work at twenty. Of course, it is always possible that works now forgotten might reappear, but there could not be many.

TITLES OF WORKS BY PICASSO AS THEY APPEARED
IN THE CATALOGUE

1. Portrait de l'artiste

2. Portrait de M. Iturrino

3. Portrait de M. Mañach
4. Toledo
5. Femme nue
6. Iris
7. Portrait
8. La Mère

9. Morphinomane
10. L'Absinthe
11. Moulin-Rouge
12. La Buveuse
13. La Fille du roi d'Egypte
14. Le Soir
15. Une Fille

16. Les Blondes chevelures
17. La Folle aux chats
18. Le Jardin enchanté
19. Germaine
20. Etude
21. Jardin de rêve
22. Le Square (appartient à Mme Besnard)

23. Les Toits
24. Le Roi Soleil (appartient à M. Fabre)

25. Portrait

26. La Cruche verte (appartient à M. Ackermann)
27. Fleurs (appartient à Mme Besnard)
28. Fleurs (appartient à Mme Besnard)
29. Le Pot blanc

1. There are three self-portraits done in Paris in 1901. *Self-portrait* (VI. 35) must be dated from the end of the year, just before Picasso's return to Barcelona; the style agrees with the other evidence. That leaves then: V. 1, V. 2 and V. 3.

2. As far as we have been able to discover, this has disappeared. The subject is the painter who exhibited at the same time as Picasso at Vollard's.

3. *Portrait of Pedro Mañach*, V. 4.
4. Unidentified.
5. This might be *Nude in Stockings*, V. 5, or *Seated Nude*, V. 6.
6. *Yellow Irises*, V. 25.
7. See No. 25.
8. *La Mère*, and also *La Mère et l'enfant* (Vollard 64) might correspond to *Mother and Child with Flowers*, V. 7; *Mother and Child*, V. 8; *The Mother*, V. 9; *Mother and Child*, V. 10.
9. *Harlot with Hand on her Shoulder*, V. 11.
10. *The Absinthe Drinker*, V. 12.
11. *Au Moulin-Rouge*, V. 13.
12. *Woman Seated on a Café Terrace*, V. 14.
13. Unidentified.
14. Unidentified.
15. See *Courtesan with a Hat*, V. 47; and *Woman with a Jeweled Collar*, V. 48.
16. *Little Girls Dancing*, V. 15.
17. *Nude with Cats*, V. 16.
18. See Nos. 21 and 22.
19. Unidentified.
20. Unidentified.
21. Perhaps: *Woman Seated in a Garden*, V. 17.
22. *Le Square*, or also *Les Gosses* (Vollard 31) might correspond to *In the Public Garden (1)*, V. 18; *Public Garden (2)*, V. 19; or *The Tuileries*, V. 20. *Le Square* (Vollard 22) is mentioned in the Vollard catalogue as the property of Madame Besnard. The *Reclining Nude* in the collection of Mrs. Aldus C. Higgins, done in 1903 (X. 8), has the following inscription on the back: *Toiles Couleurs Fines—Panneaux—L. Besnard, 68, rue de La Rochefoucauld, Paris.*
Madame Besnard was no doubt the wife of Picasso's art materials supplier. Rue de La Rochefoucauld is not far from 130 Boulevard de Clichy, where Picasso then had his studio. Besides, it was L. Besnard's wife who bought a *Mother and Child* from Picasso at the end of 1902, which gave him the funds to make the trip to Spain.

23. *Blue Roofs*, V. 21.
24. This is mentioned as belonging to M. Fabre. We have not identified either the owner or the work.
25. (See also Vollard 7 and Vollard 62): it does not seem that this could be a *Head of a Woman* which might rather have been designated as *Madrilena* (Vollard 53), *Chanteuse* (Vollard 54), etc. There is no proof that the first *Portrait of Gustave Coquiot* (V. 64) was in the Vollard Exhibition. However, it may be the artist's sister or a portrait like *Woman with a Cape* (V. 76).
26. *La Cruche verte, Fleurs* (Vollard 27), *Fleurs* (Vollard 28), *Le Pot blanc* (Vollard 29), *Les Roses* (Vollard 60): there are seven pictures known which may correspond to these titles: *Vase of Flowers*, V. 22; *Vase of Flowers*, V. 24; *Peonies*, V. 23; *Flowers*, V. 26; *Vase of Flowers*, V. 27; *Vase of Flowers*, V. 28; *Chrysanthemums*, V. 29.

THE ABSINTHE DRINKER, PARIS, 1901, OIL. COLLECTION MR. AND MRS. WILLIAM B. JAFFE, NEW YORK (V.12).

30. Boulevard de Clichy (appartient à Mme Besnard)
31. Les Gosses
32. Les Courses

33. Le Matador
34. Les Victimes
35. L'Arène

36. Café-Concert
37. Brasserie

38. La Femme jaune (appartient à M. Personnas)

39. Le Divan japonais (appartient à M. Virenca)

40. El Tango

41. La Bête (appartient à Mme K. Kollwitz, artiste peintre à Berlin)

42. Montjuich

43. Courses de village

---

30. *Boulevard de Clichy*, v. 30.
31. See No. 22.
32. We have considered four pictures for this title : *Les Courses*. Two versions show elegant women at the enclosure, the two others show the race track in general. We have kept the traditional titles of *Auteuil Races*, v. 33, and of *Longchamp*, v. 34, for the two general race track views. We call v. 31 *At the Races*; this work seems to be the one in the Vollard Exhibition. The other race track subject we call *Enclosure at Auteuil*, v. 32.
33. *Le Matador* (Vollard 33), *Les Victimes* (Vollard 34), and *L'Arène* (Vollard 35) : see Catalogue IV, Barcelona, Spring 1901, numbers IV. 5 and IV. 6. It seems certain that *Bullfight*, IV. 5, was one of these in the Vollard Exhibition, since it belonged to Vollard.
36. *Café-Concert, Brasserie* (Vollard 37), *Buveurs* (Vollard 46), *Buveuses* (Vollard 51) : it is possible that these titles indicate works done in 1900 (see Catalogues I and II), which Picasso either left in Paris or brought from Spain. However, this would not agree with the striking unity of style in the Vollard Exhibition. One or two of the these titles might have designated *The Diners*, v. 66; *In the Restaurant*, v. 67; *In the Café*, v. 44; *Women in a Café*, v. 46; *The Café de La Rotonde*, v. 45; *Women Seated on the Terrace of a Café*, v. 80; or *Café in Montmartre*, Addenda No. A. 4.
38. *La Femme jaune* is mentioned in the Vollard catalogue as belonging to M. Personnas. Picasso remembers a collector by that name.
39. This title is a puzzle. The reference to the Lautrec poster for Jane Avril seems clear, but we know that this café-concert, *Le Divan japonais*, was "shut before it was opened." According to the Vollard catalogue, the owner of this work was M. Virenca (M. Virenque). The present heirs of M. Virenque possess no work that could answer to this title. We see nothing either which could evoke the bold design of Lautrec, with a decapitated Yvette Guilbert rising from the footlights behind the violins in the orchestra. One might think of *Woman at the Theater*, v. 71, but this beautiful work, which has *The Absinthe Drinker* (VI. 25) painted by Picasso on the back, is unsigned and has probably never been exhibited.
40. Even admitting that this title might correspond only remotely to the real subject, it does not seem possible to identify it with *The Spanish Dancer*, IV. 3.
41. *La Bête*, mentioned as belonging to the artist Käthe Kollwitz in Berlin. Käthe Kollwitz, who was then thirty-three, divided her time between Berlin where she lived with her husband, and Paris, where she was to study at the Académie Julian in 1904. This encounter at Vollard's between the woman who would become the leading German engraver of the period and a painting by the twenty-year old Picasso, should be stressed. It is unfortunate that we are ignorant of the subsequent history of *La Bête*. Käthe Kollwitz died in 1945. Her son, Dr. Hans Kollwitz, who now lives in West Berlin, replied in such a way as to end our inquiries : "I am not aware that a Picasso belonged to my mother, but if it did, it would have been lost in the fire that destroyed her house in the winter of 1944."
42. The title *Montjuich* does not seem to apply to the three views of Barcelona : *Barcelona at Night*, IX. 3, *Roofs of Barcelona*, IX. 2 and *Street in Barcelona and the Palace of Fine Arts*, IX. 1, which are later and which we can date from 1903.
43. See *Village Corrida, hors catalogue*, page 340.

44. Eglise d'Espagne
45. Village d'Espagne
46. Buveurs
47. L'Enfant blanc
48. Jeanneton
49. La Méditerranée
50. Rochers

51. Les Buveuses (appartient à M. Ackermann)
52. Danseuses (appartient à M. Sainsère)

53. Madrilena (appartient à M. Sainsère)

54. Chanteuse (appartient à M. Blot)
55. L'Amoureuse (appartient à M. Blot)

56. Au Bord de l'eau (appartient à M. Coll)

57. Femme de nuit
58. Vieille fille

59. La Foire
60. Les Roses
61. Carmen

62. Portraits
63. Don Tancredo
64. La Mère et l'enfant
65. Dessins

44. *In Front of the Church*, v. 49.
45. Perhaps *Castilian Village*, v. 51.
46. See No. 36.
47. *Le Gourmand*, v. 53.
48. *Reclining Nude (Jeanne)*, v. 52.
49. Probably *Women and Children on the Beach*, v. 54.
50. Undoubtedly this designates the small work which is seen on the wall of the studio of 130 Boulevard de Clichy, in *The Blue Room*, vi. 15, and which we have not been able to identify.
51. See No. 36.
52. *Danseuses* (Vollard 52) and *Madrilena* (Vollard 53) are mentioned in the Vollard catalogue as the property of M. Sainsère. Olivier Sainsère was a state councilor. He had aided Picasso greatly since his first visits to Paris. He not only bought his works—he owned a portrait of Lola besides the paintings in question here—but also, Picasso recalls, he provided a sort of legal protection against the police, who suspected virtually all the rather Bohemian young Spaniards of anarchism. See *French Cancan*, v. 55.
53. See *Portrait of the Artist's Sister*, v. 56, and *La Madrilène (Woman from Madrid)*, v. 57. See also *Head of a Woman*, v. 58, and *Head of a Woman* (2), v. 59.
54. *Chanteuse* (Vollard 54) and *L'Amoureuse* (Vollard 55) belonged to a M. Blot who, Picasso says, was a picture-dealer. There is another work related to the preceding: *Young Girl with a Red Flower*, v. 60.
56. There is a picture in the style of this period which could correspond to this title: *Women and Children on the Beach*, v. 54.
57. See No. 15.
58. If one takes this title in the sense of an old prostitute, a pun which the spirit of the general choice of titles of the Vollard Exhibition could allow, then two pictures come to mind: *Woman with Jewels*, iv. 4, also called *Old Woman*, which we have related to the *Dwarf Dancer*, iv. 2, and the *Woman with Blue Stockings*, v. 62.
59. *Booth at the Fair*, v. 63.
60. See No. 26.
61. Perhaps this corresponds to one of the titles mentioned in Nos. 53 and 54.
62. See No. 25.
63. Unidentified.
64. See No. 8.
65. Unidentified.

STUDY FOR THE SELF-PORTRAIT: YO PICASSO, PARIS, 1901, PASTEL AND CHARCOAL. PRIVATE COLLECTION, FRANCE. UNPUBLISHED (V.3).

V. 1
SELF-PORTRAIT
Paris, 1901.
Oil on cardboard mounted on wood.
Size : 54 x 31.8 cm.
Signed bottom right : Picasso.
Inscribed top left : Yo.

Exh. Galeries Durand-Ruel, Paris, 1949, No. 12, repr. in cat. Museum of Modern Art, New York, June–September 1951 : *New York Private Collections.* Museum of Modern Art, New York, May–September 1955 : *Paintings from Private Collections,* cat. p. 16. Museum of Modern Art, New York, and The Art Institute of Chicago, 1957 : *Picasso, 75th Anniversary Exhibition,* repr. in cat. p. 17. Philadelphia Museum of Art, 1958 : idem. Yale University Art Gallery, May–June 1960 : *Yale Alumni Collections,* No. 87, repr. in cat. p. 84. Tate Gallery, London, December 16, 1960–January 29, 1961 : *The John Hay Whitney Collection,* No. 41, repr. in cat.

Bibl. Z. I. 113. Lieberman, 1954, pl. 9 (color). Sabartés, *Picasso, documents iconographiques,* No. 63. John Rewald, *French Paintings in the Collection of Mr. and Mrs. John Hay Whitney* in *Connoisseur,* March–April 1957, p. 137. Barr, *75th Anniversary,* p. 17. Lieberman, 1961, pl. 9 (color). Blunt and Pool, No. 42.

Coll. Private collection, Nice ;

Collection Mr. and Mrs. John Hay Whitney, New York.

Sabartés *(Documents iconographiques)* says of this self-portrait that it is the first one done in Paris in 1901, but he did not know the one which follows (V. 2). The younger and less determined look and the more direct handling must indicate an earlier date. This is also Barr's opinion. He puts our No. 2 before No. 1 in the 75th anniversary catalogue.

V. 2
SELF-PORTRAIT : YO PICASSO
Paris, 1901.
Oil on canvas.
Size : 73.5 x 60 cm.
Signed top left : Yo Picasso.

Exh. Museum of Modern Art, New York, and The Art Institute of Chicago, 1957 : *Picasso, 75th Anniversary Exhibition,* repr. in cat. p. 13.

Bibl. Not in Z. Barr, *Picasso, 75th Anniversary Exhibition,* New York, 1957, p. 13.

Coll. Purchased by Hugo von Hofmannsthal with the royalties from his libretto for *Der Rosenkavalier,* at the Thannhauser Gallery, Munich, in 1911 ;

Private collection, New York.

There is a very interesting reference which lets us date this work before the Vollard exhibition : see the following entry, V. 3.

V. 3
SKETCH FOR SELF-PORTRAIT : YO PICASSO
Paris, 1901.
Pastel and charcoal on cardboard.
Size : 67 x 52 cm.
Signed bottom third, right : Picasso.
Recto : At the Races (V. 31).

Exh. Never exhibited.

Bibl. Unpublished.

Coll. Bought directly from the artist by Emmanuel Virenque in 1901 ;

Private collection, France.

Sketched in pastel and charcoal, this is exactly the pose of the artist in the preceding work (V. 2). The oil on the back (V. 31) is probably *Les Courses* shown at Vollard's. We are certain that this sketch and the painting taken from it (V. 2) date before the Vollard exhibition and could have appeared in it.

Color plate, page 160.

V. 4
PORTRAIT OF PEDRO MAÑACH
Paris, 1901.
Oil on canvas.
Size : 100.5 x 67.5 cm.
Signed bottom right : Picasso.
Inscribed top left : Petrus Mañach.

Exh. Galerie A. Vollard, Paris, 1901 :
F. Iturrino et P. R. Picasso, No. 3
(Portrait de M. Mañach). Norton
Gallery, West Palm Beach (Florida),
1953 : *French Painting, David to
Cézanne.*

Bibl. Z. VI. 1459. *Twentieth Century
Paintings and Sculpture of the French
School in the Chester Dale Collection,*
Washington, D.C. 1965, repr. p. 68.
Palau i Fabre, No. 69 (repr. in color).

Coll. Señora Mañach, Barcelona ;
Pierre Matisse, New York ; Chester
Dale, New York ;

*National Gallery of Art, Washington,
D.C., Chester Dale Collection.*

Mañach, whom Picasso met at the
beginning of his stay in Paris, was his
first dealer. They separated at the end
of 1901, but Mañach continued to
show Picassos in the exhibitions he
organized for Berthe Weill.

Color plate, page 39.

V. 5
NUDE IN STOCKINGS
Paris, 1901.
Oil on canvas.
Size : 66.5 x 52 cm.
Signed top right : Picasso.

Bibl. Z. I. 48. Sabartés and Boeck,
p. 458, No. 14.

Coll. Paul Guillaume, Paris ;

*Collection M. Knoedler & Co., New
York.*

V. 6
SEATED NUDE (Nude in the Studio)
Paris, 1901.
Oil on wood panel.
Size : 50.5 x 36.5 cm.
Signed bottom right : Picasso.

Exh. Kunsthaus, Zurich, September 11–
October 30, 1932 : *Picasso,* No. 4,
entitled *Nude in the Studio* (lent by
Herr Alex Vömel, Düsseldorf).

Bibl. Z. I. 50.

Sale : Galerie G. et L. Bollag, Zurich,
November 11, 1933, No. 77, price :
1,000 fr. (unsold).

*Formerly collection Alex Vömel, Düs-
seldorf.*

V. 7
MOTHER AND CHILD
WITH FLOWERS
Paris, 1901.
Oil on cardboard.
Size : 54 x 65 cm.
Signed bottom left : Picasso.

Bibl. Z. I. 77. André Level, *Picasso,*
Paris, 1928, pl. 3 (cited by André
Level as typical of the works in the
Vollard exhibition). C.-P. No. 45.

Coll. Max Pellequer, Paris ;

Private collection, Paris.

V. 8
MOTHER AND CHILD
(On the Bench)
Paris, 1901.
Pastel.
Size : 66 x 51 cm.
Signed bottom right : Picasso.

Bibl. Z. I. 111. Blunt and Pool, No. 83.

Present location unknown.

V. 9
THE MOTHER
Paris, 1901.
Oil on cardboard mounted on wood
panel.
Size : 74.8 x 50.8 cm.
Signed bottom left : Picasso.

Exh. Wildenstein and Co., New York,
October 1928 : *The Chester Dale
Collection,* No. 33. Fogg Art Museum,
Harvard University, March 1929,
No. 70. Museum of French Art, New
York, February 1931, No. 1. Detroit
Institute of Art, 1931, No. 90.
Walker Art Center, 1955: *Expression-
ism in Art.* Wildenstein Gallery, New
York, 1958 : *50 Masterpieces from
the City Art Museum of St. Louis,*
No. 50. St. Louis Artists' Guild,
1960. Des Moines Art Center, 1960.

Bibl. Not in Z. Catalogue of the Sale
of La Peau de l'Ours, Paris, 1914,
No. 62. City Art Museum Bulletin,
XXIV. 2. 1939. Lieberman, *Picasso,
Blue and Rose Periods,* New York,
1961, pl. 8. Helen Kay, *Picasso's
World of Children,* New York, 1965,
repr. in color, p. 41.

Coll. La Peau de l'Ours, Paris, Sale,
March 2, 1914, No. 62, sold for
1,100 fr. to M. Druet, appraiser ; Van
der Velde, The Hague ; Chester Dale,
New York ;

*The City Art Museum of St. Louis,
Missouri.*

V. 10
MOTHER AND CHILD
Paris, 1901.
Oil on cardboard.
Size : 68 x 52 cm.
Signed top left : Picasso.

Bibl. Not in Z. Unpublished.

Private collection, on deposit at the Kunstmuseum, Bern.

This *Mother and Child* is very close to the *Mother* (V. 9) in the City Art Museum of St. Louis (see preceding entry), with its sweeping, blended brush work and its similar subject. The child wears the same blue rompers with white stars as the one in V. 7 and V. 9. Unfortunately, we know nothing of the history of this painting, but it is certainly contemporary with the preceding work. Clearly evident is Picasso's tendency to abandon pointillist technique for a style more strongly sculptural.

V. 11
HARLOT WITH HAND ON HER SHOULDER
Paris, 1901.
Oil on cardboard.
Size : 69.5 x 57 cm.
Signed bottom left : Picasso.

Exh. Musée de Lyon, 1953 : *Picasso,* No. 3 (entitled *The Wait*), repr. in color in cat. pl. I. III Bienal Hispano-americana de Arte, Barcelona, 1955 : *Precursores y maestros del arte Español contemporáneo,* No. 14.

Bibl. Z. I. 63. C.-P. No. 60 *(Woman with heavy Make-up).* A. Vallentin, 1957, pl. III.

Coll. L. Plandiura, Barcelona ; Museo de Arte Moderno, Barcelona ;

Picasso Museum, Barcelona.

Color plate, page 31.

V. 12
THE ABSINTHE DRINKER
Paris, 1901.
Oil on cardboard.
Size : 65.5 x 50.8 cm.
Signed top left : Picasso.

Exh. Knoedler & Co., New York, October 15–November 8, 1947 : *Picasso before 1907,* No. 9. Yale University Art Gallery, New Haven, May 8–June 18, 1956 : *Pictures Collected by Yale Alumni,* No. 132. Knoedler & Co., New York, 1962 : *Picasso, an American Tribute,* No. 8, repr. in cat.

Bibl. Z. I. 62. Lieberman, 1961, pl. 10 (repr. in color). Boudaille, 1964, pl. I (repr. in color).

Coll. Paul Guillaume, Paris ; George Gershwin, New York ; John Hay Whitney, New York ; Sold by Wildenstein & Co., New York, in 1958, to the present owners :

Collection Mr. and Mrs. William B. Jaffe, New York.

This painting seems to belong to an earlier style, comparable to the *Woman with a Plumed Hat* (III. 4) of the Madrid period, or even to the Parisian paintings of 1900. But this does not mean that it was signed at a later date. The title *The Absinthe Drinker* is better than the one used by Zervos *(Drinker resting on her Elbows).* The green liquid in the glass insists on that.

Color plate, page 157.

V. 13
AU MOULIN-ROUGE
Paris, 1901.
Oil on panel.
Size : 70 x 53.4 cm.
Signed bottom right : Picasso.

Exh. Gallery of Modern Art, New York, January 3—March 12, 1967, and Philadelphia Museum of Art, April 6—May 28, 1967 : *The Collection of Dr. and Mrs. T. Edward Hanley,* repr. in color in cat. (frontispiece).

Bibl. Z. I. 69.

Coll. We have information from the family of Emmanuel Virenque that this painting first belonged to him. The subject matter shocked his friends, and he exchanged it for *At the Races* (V. 31) ; M. Knoedler & Co., New York ;

Collection Dr. and Mrs. T. Edward Hanley, Bradford, Pennsylvania.

V. 14
WOMAN SEATED ON A CAFÉ TERRACE
Paris, 1901.
Oil on paper mounted on wood.
Size : 53.5 x 35 cm.
Signed top left : Picasso.

Exh. Boymans Museum, Rotterdam, 1935. Musée de Lyon, June 1953, No. 6. Musée des Arts décoratifs, Paris, 1955 : *Picasso, peintures 1900–1955,* No. 3, repr. in cat. Munich-Hamburg-Cologne, 1955–1956 : *Picasso,* Traveling exhibition, No. 6, repr. in cat. Musée des Beaux-Arts, Liège, 1964, No. 53, repr. in cat. Singer Museum, 1964, *Peintures de la belle époque,* No. 56, repr. in cat. p. 43.

Bibl. Not in Z. Annual report of the Boymans Museum, 1935, p. 20. Catalogue of the Boymans-van Beuningen Museum, No. 1688. Pierre Cabanne, *The Great Collectors* (Cassell, London), 1963, p. 75.

Coll. D. G. van Beuningen, Rotterdam, who gave it to the Boymans Museum in 1935 :

Boymans-van Beuningen Museum, Rotterdam.

Stylistically, all the other figures drinking of 1901, with the exception of this one and V. 12, are clearly later than the Vollard exhibition. This oil is characteristic of this period in brushwork and handling of color.

V. 15
LITTLE GIRLS DANCING
Paris, 1901.
Oil on cardboard.
Size : 56.5 x 38 cm.
Signed top right : Picasso.

Exh. Galerie A. Vollard, Paris, 1901 : *F. Iturrino et P. R. Picasso,* No. 16, entitled *Les Blondes Chevelures.* Galerie Charpentier, Paris, 1951 : *Plaisir de France.*

Bibl. Félicien Fagus, *Revue blanche,* XXV, July 15, 1901 : "Some lucky finds here ; three little girls dancing, the malachite green skirt against the white underclothing, the stiff white, boyish, very starched underclothing of little girls !..." Not in Z. Helen Kay, *Picasso's World of Children,* New York, 1965, repr. in color, p. 38–39.

Coll. Given by the artist to the young critic, Félicien Fagus (pseudonym of Georges Faillet), Paris ; Pierre Lièvre, Paris ;

Private collection, Paris.

Color plate, page 152.

V. 16
NUDE WITH CATS
Paris, 1901.
Oil on cardboard.
Size : 44.5 x 40.6 cm.
Signed bottom right : Picasso.

Exh. Reinhardt Galleries, New York, October–November 1929 : *Drawings, Paintings and Watercolors by Picasso, Matisse, Derain,* No. 3. The Art Institute of Chicago, July–October 1935 : *Summer Loan Exhibition of Paintings and Sculpture,* No. 32. The Arts Club of Chicago, November 1938 : *Loan Exhibition of Modern Paintings and Drawings from Private Collections in Chicago,* No. 108. Palm Beach, Florida, Society of the Four Arts, January–February 1952 : *Spanish Painting,* No. 35. Denver Art Museum, January 7–February 11, 1954 : *Ten Directions by Ten Artists,* No. 60. Joe and Emily Lowe Art Gallery, University of Miami, February 8–March 10, 1963 : *Renoir to Picasso.* The Art Gallery of Toronto and The Montreal Museum of Fine Arts, 1964 : *Picasso and Man,* No. 8, repr. in cat. p. 29.

Bibl. Z. I. 93. "Reinhardt Galleries show paintings recently brought from Europe," in *Art News,* vol. 28, p. 1. The Art Institute of Chicago, 1961, *Catalogue of Paintings,* p. 356, No. 42.464.

Coll. Paul Guillaume, Paris ; Reinhardt Galleries, New York ; Since 1942 :

The Art Institute of Chicago, The Amy McCormick Memorial Collection.

V. 17
WOMAN SEATED IN A GARDEN
Paris, 1901.
Oil on cardboard.
Size : 65 x 95 cm.
Signed bottom right : Picasso.
Verso : The Death of Harlequin, 1905 (XII. 27).

Exh. Galerie Thannhauser, Munich, 1913. National Gallery of Art, Washington, D.C., 1966 : *25th Anniversary Exhibition : French Paintings from the Collections of Mr. and Mrs. Paul Mellon and Mrs. Mellon Bruce,* No. 194, repr. in cat.

Bibl. Z. VI. 332 (wrong dimensions and medium indicated). W.C.A. XIV, 1962.

Coll. Bought directly from the artist by Wilhelm Uhde, in 1905 or 1906 ; lent by Uhde to Rainer Maria Rilke ; Private collection, Westphalia ; J. K. Thannhauser, New York ; Somerset Maugham, St. Jean-Cap Ferrat ; Sale of the Somerset Maugham collection, Sotheby & Co., London, April 10, 1962, No. 26, repr. in color in cat. p. 44, sold (recto and verso) for £80,000 ;

Collection Mr. and Mrs. Paul Mellon, Upperville, Virginia.

In 1905, on the back of this panel, Picasso painted his famous gouache *The Death of Harlequin* (XII. 27). We conclude from this that if the *Woman Seated in a Garden* was exhibited at Vollard's, it remained unsold. Closely related in subject and pose, but not style, to the *Woman in Green* (V. 37).

V. 18
IN THE PUBLIC GARDEN (1)
Paris, 1901.
Oil.
Size : 33 x 55 cm.
Signed bottom right : Picasso.

Bibl. Z. I. 78.

Present location unknown.

This work is known to us only through Zervos.

V. 19
PUBLIC GARDEN (2)
Paris, 1901.
Oil on cardboard.
Size : 32 x 47 cm.
Signed bottom right : Picasso.

Exh. Galerie A. Gattlen, Lausanne, May 6–July 8, 1963 : *De Monet à Picasso,* No. 14. Musée de l'Athénée, Geneva, July 11–September 21, 1963 : *Picasso,* No. 4 (entitled *Le Jardin du Luxembourg*), repr. in color in cat.

Bibl. Not in Z.

Coll. Paul Pétridès, Paris ; Galerie Charpentier, Paris, Sale, December 1, 1959 ;

Collection M. and Mme Silvan Kocher, Solothurn.

As he does often at this time, Picasso uses the same subject twice, experimenting with different settings (see V. 18). Authenticated by the artist, July 28, 1964.

V. 20
THE TUILERIES
Paris, 1901.
Oil on canvas.
Size : 50 x 65 cm.
Signed bottom right : Picasso.

Bibl. Z. VI. 333.

Coll. Mrs. Ralph H. Booth, Detroit ;

Private collection, Grosse Pointe, Michigan.

V. 21
BLUE ROOFS
Paris, 1901.
Oil on cardboard.
Size : 40 x 60 cm.
Signed bottom left : Picasso.

Exh. The Arts Council of Great Britain, Tate Gallery, London, 1960 : *Picasso,* No. 11, repr. in cat. pl. 4 h.

Bibl. Z. I. 82. Cassou, 1940, p. 38. C.-P. No. 146 (*Toitures bleues de Paris,* dated 1903). *Catalogue of the Paintings in the Ashmolean Museum,* 1961, p. 114.

Coll. F. Hindley Smith ; Since 1939 (bequest F. Hindley Smith) :

The Ashmolean Museum, Oxford.

The word "Blue" in the title should not be misleading. This view from the windows of the studio at 130 Boulevard de Clichy, like the painting of that name (V. 30), was done in the spring of 1901. Probably it corresponds to No. 23 of the Vollard exhibition : *Les Toits.*

Color plate, page 155.

V. 22
VASE OF FLOWERS
Paris, 1901. Oil on canvas.
Size : 65 x 49 cm.
Signed bottom right : Picasso.

Exh. Tate Gallery, London, July–
August 1935 : *Contemporary Art
Society Exhibition,* No. 37. Royal
Scottish Academy, Edinburgh, 1946,
No. 182.

Bibl. Z. I. 61. Ronald Alley : *Tate
Gallery—The Foreign Paintings, Drawings and Sculpture,* London, 1959,
pl. 43 b.

Coll. Le Père Soulier, Paris ; Libaude,
Paris ; Leo Lewin, Breslau ; Alex Reid
and Lefevre, London ; Acquired by the
Tate Gallery in 1933 ;

Tate Gallery, London.

V. 23
PEONIES
Paris, 1901.
Oil.
Size : 57 x 38 cm.
Signed bottom right : Picasso.

Exh. Jacques Seligmann & Co., New
York, November 1936 : *Picasso, Blue
and Rose Periods,* No. 11, repr. in cat.
The Arts Club of Chicago, 1937.

Bibl. Z. I. 60.

Coll. Le marquis de Biron ; Chester
Johnson ; Acquired by Mrs. Charles
B. Goodspeed in 1930 ;

*Collection Mrs. Gilbert W. Chapman,
New York.*

V. 24
VASE OF FLOWERS
Paris, 1901.
Oil.
Size : 55.5 x 70 cm.
Signed top right : Picasso.

Bibl. Z. I. 59. C.-P. No. 44.

Coll. Georges Lévy, Paris ;

Present location unknown.

V. 25
YELLOW IRISES
Paris, 1901.
Oil.
Size : 48.3 x 39 cm.
Signed bottom left : Picasso.

Exh. Galerie Vollard, Paris, June 25–July 14, 1901 : *Exposition de tableaux de F. Iturrino et de P. R. Picasso,* No. 6 *(Iris).*

Bibl. Z. I. 58 (entitled *Fleurs*). C.-P. No. 43 (entitled *Fleurs*).

Coll. Alex Reid and Lefevre Gallery, London ; Acquired in 1935 by Captain

S. W. Sykes, Cambridge ; On loan to the Fitzwilliam Museum, Cambridge, England, from 1939 to April 1966 ; Sotheby & Co., London, Sale, June 22, 1966, No. 13, sold for £15,900 ;

Private collection.

This is unquestionably the painting exhibited at Vollard's as No. 6 : *Iris.* Of all the flowers painted by Picasso at this time, it is the only painting of irises.

V. 26
FLOWERS (Flowers in a Vase)
Paris, 1901.
Oil.
Size : 65.5 x 46.5 cm.
Signed bottom right : Picasso.

Exh. Galerie Georges Petit, Paris, summer, 1932 : *Picasso,* No. 22. Kunsthaus, Zurich, autumn, 1932 : *Picasso,* No. 23 (lent by the Duchess of Roxburgh).

Bibl. Z. I. 242 (dated 1904).

Coll. Duchess of Roxburgh ;

Private collection, England.

Zervos dates this painting 1904, relating it to a gouache surely done later. Actually, the handling, the shape and the rather thick brush stroke of the signature, and also the treatment of the subject, close to Renoir or Van Gogh, lead us to date it 1901.

V. 27
VASE OF FLOWERS
Paris, 1901.
Oil on canvas.
Size : 65 x 50 cm.
Signed bottom right : Picasso.

Exh. Never exhibited.

Bibl. Unpublished.

Coll. Olivier Sainsère, Paris ;

Private collection, Switzerland.

This painting, although similar in color and in compositional style to the other flower-pieces of this period, differs from them in handling. The impasto is much thinner. The softening of the vase and the background seems to foreshadow the flat tints of the works painted in the autumn, 1901.

v

V. 28
VASE OF FLOWERS
Paris, 1901.
Oil on cardboard.
Size : 52 x 34.3 cm.
Signed bottom right : Picasso.

Exh. El Paso Museum of Art, 1965 : *French Paintings and Sculpture from the Phoenix Art Museum Collection*, No. 38, repr. in cat.

Bibl. Not in Z.

Coll. Wilhelm Uhde ; Oscar Huldschinsky, Berlin ; M. Knoedler & Co., New York ; Mr. and Mrs. R. Barclay Scull, Villanova, who donated it to the Phoenix Art Museum in 1963 ;

Phoenix Art Museum, Arizona, Gift of Mr. and Mrs. R. Barclay Scull, 1963.

This painting was dated 1901 by Knoedler, which corrects the previously accepted date of 1903. Possibly it corresponds to No. 60 of the Vollard exhibition catalogue, *Roses*, since the two large flowers in the center are roses. On the other hand, there exists a painting of roses by Picasso, and known under that title, but clearly in an earlier style (Z. I. 9, dated 1897 by Z.). Nothing excludes the possibility that this earlier work could have been shown in the Vollard exhibition, but this conjecture does not seem to accord with the spirit of the exhibition of 1901.

V. 29
CHRYSANTHEMUMS
Paris, 1901.
Oil on canvas.
Size : 81.2 x 65.3 cm.
Signed bottom right : Picasso.

Exh. Museum of Modern Art, New York, 1939 : *Picasso, Forty Years of his Art*, No. 11, repr. in cat. p. 26. The Art Institute of Chicago, City Art Museum of St. Louis and Museum of Fine Arts, Boston, 1940 : idem. Virginia Museum of Fine Arts and Philadelphia Museum of Art, 1941 : *Collection of Walter P. Chrysler, Jr.*, No. 150, repr. in cat. Knoedler & Co., New York, 1962 : *Picasso, an American Tribute*, No. 17, repr. in cat. Philadel-phia Museum of Art, 1963 : *World of Flowers*, repr. in color in cat. p. 165.

Bibl. Z. VI. 647 (dated 1904). Barr, *Forty Years*, p. 26 (dated Paris, 1901). Cassou, 1940, p. 44. Joan Merli, Buenos Aires, 1948, No. 40. John Richardson, *An American Tribute*, No. 17 (dated Barcelona, 1903).

Coll. Madame R., Paris ; Perls Galleries, New York ; Walter P. Chrysler, Jr., New York ; Knoedler & Co., New York ; Mrs. John Wintersteen, Villanova (price in February 1962 : $75.000) ;

Philadelphia Museum of Art, Gift of Mrs. John Wintersteen.

V. 30
BOULEVARD DE CLICHY
Paris, 1901.
Oil on canvas.
Size : 61.5 x 46.5 cm.
Signed bottom right : Picasso.

Exh. Galerie Vollard, Paris, 1901 : *F. Iturrino et P. R. Picasso*, No. 30. Contemporary Art Museum, Houston, Texas, January 14—February 20, 1955 : *Picasso*, No. 2. Knoedler & Co., New York, 1962 ; *Picasso, an American Tribute*, No. 9, repr. in cat.

Bibl. Z. I. 72. Cassou, 1940, p. 39. C.-P., 1946, No. 74. Joan Merli, Buenos Aires, 1948, No. 41. C.-P., 1950, No. 69. Sabartés and Boeck, p. 458, No. 13.

Coll. Madame Besnard, Paris ; Max Pellequer, Paris ; Galerie Baläy et Carré, Paris ; M. Knoedler & Co., New York ; Valentine Gallery, New York ; Mrs. Aline Barnsdall, Los Angeles ; M. Knoedler & Co., New York ;

Private collection, Houston, Texas.

This is the street seen from the windows of No. 130 Boulevard de Clichy, where Picasso had his studio.

V. 31
AT THE RACES
Paris, 1901.
Oil on cardboard.
Size : 52 x 67 cm.
Signed bottom left : Picasso.
Verso : sketch for the self-portrait *Yo Picasso* (V. 3).

Exh. Galerie Charpentier, Paris, 1943 : *Paris, mon cœur,* repr. in cat. (withdrawn by order of German authorities during the Occupation).

Bibl. Not in Z. Florent Fels, *L'Art vivant de 1900 à nos jours,* Geneva, 1950, p. 243.

Coll. Bought directly from the artist by Emmanuel Virenque in 1901 ;

Private collection, France.

Color plate, page 35.

V. 32
ENCLOSURE AT AUTEUIL
Paris, 1901.
Oil on cardboard.
Size : 46 x 61 cm.
Signed bottom right : Picasso.

Exh. Knoedler & Co., New York, 1962 : *Picasso, an American Tribute,* No. 10, repr. in cat. (entitled *Women at Auteuil Races*).

Bibl. Z. I. 71.

Coll. Leigh B. Block, Chicago ;

Collection Mr. and Mrs. Joseph H. Hazen, New York.

A painting very similar to the preceding work, but a little less searching, especially in the handling of the faces which are only suggested. No. 20 at the Berthe Weill exhibition (November 15—December 15, 1902) was entitled *Pelouse à Auteuil* (see note in following entry).

V. 33
AUTEUIL RACES
Paris, 1901.
Oil on wood panel.
Size : 45.4 x 71 cm.
Signed bottom left : Picasso.

Exh. Galerie Berthe Weill, Paris, 1902 (?) [see note]. The Arts Council of Great Britain, Tate Gallery, London, 1960 : *Picasso,* No. 7, repr. in cat. pl. 4 j.

Bibl. Not in Z.

Coll. Paul Rosenberg, Paris ; Acquired in April 1937 by the present owner from A. Tooth & Sons, London ;

Collection Lee Hardy, London.

The Berthe Weill Gallery, in its group exhibition of June 2—15, 1902, exhibited as No. 24 a *Grand Prix d'Auteuil* by Picasso. Apparently it was not sold, since in the *Girieud, Launay, Picasso, Pichot* exhibition at the same gallery, November 15—December 15, 1902, there was a *Pelouse à Auteuil* (No. 20) which seems to designate the same work. The first title fits this general view of the racetrack. It corresponds also to *Longchamp* (V. 34), which is very similar but handled perhaps more delicately. As Raynal puts it, *des tachages d'un raffinement et d'une rareté de tons que nul n'a surpassés.*

V. 34
LONGCHAMP
Paris, 1901.
Oil on cardboard.
Size : 53 x 67 cm.
Signed bottom right : Picasso.

Bibl. Z. VI. 301 (dated Paris 1900). Maurice Raynal, Geneva, 1959, p. 22 (repr. in color).

Coll. Lederlin, Berlin ; Blum, Paris ;

Private collection, Paris.

V. 35
WOMAN IN AN EVENING CLOAK
(The Comedienne)
Paris, 1901.
Pastel.
Size : 51 x 39 cm.
Signed bottom right : Picasso.

Bibl. Z. VI. 350.

Present location unknown.

Undeniably close in style to *Au Moulin-Rouge* (V. 36). The wings and the footlights are in exactly the same positions as they are in *The Comedienne* (IV. 9).

V. 36
AU MOULIN-ROUGE
Paris, 1901.
Watercolor on paper.
Size : 64.8 x 49.5 cm.
Signed and dated, bottom right : Picasso 1901.

Exh. Perls Galleries, New York, March–April 1939 : *Picasso before 1910,* No. 16, repr. in cat. M. H. de Young Memorial Museum, San Francisco, December 29, 1939–January 28, 1940 ; *Seven Centuries of Painting,* No. 190. The Virginia Museum of Fine Arts, January 16–March 4, 1941, and The Philadelphia Museum of Art, March 29–May 11, 1941 : *The Collection of Walter P. Chrysler, Jr.,* No. 148, repr. in cat.

Bibl. Z. VI. 351. W.C.A., vol. XIII.

Coll. Walter P. Chrysler, Jr., New York ; Ira Hotchkiss, New York ; Parke-Bernet, New York, Sale, April 26, 1961, sold for $47.500 ; bought by The French Art Gallery, New York ;

Private collection, New York.

V. 37
WOMAN IN GREEN
Paris, 1901.
Watercolor and India ink on paper.
Size : 17.5 x 11.5 cm.
Signed top left : Picasso.

Exh. Musée d'Art et d'Histoire, Geneva, 1956 : *Sélection de la IIIe Biennale Hispano-Américaine : Picasso, Nonell, Manolo,* No. 36.

Bibl. Z. VI. 349. C.-P. No. 91.

Coll. L. Plandiura, Barcelona ; Museo de Arte Moderno, Barcelona ;

Picasso Museum, Barcelona.

The pose recalls *Woman Seated in a Garden* (V. 17). This watercolor is also called *Seated Woman with a Hat.*

V. 38
WOMAN IN THE STREET (The Promenade)
Paris, 1901.
Watercolor and India ink on paper.
Size : 17.5 x 9.5 cm.
Signed bottom right : Picasso.

Exh. Musée d'Art et d'Histoire, Geneva, 1956 : *Sélection de la IIIe Biennale Hispano-Américaine : Picasso, Nonell, Manolo,* No. 36 b.

Bibl. Z. VI. 314. C.-P. No. 92.

Coll. L. Plandiura, Barcelona ; Museo de Arte Moderno, Barcelona ;

Picasso Museum, Barcelona.

V. 39
THE HEDONISTS
Paris, 1901.
Watercolor and India ink on paper.
Size : 18 x 11.5 cm.
Signed bottom left : Picasso.

Exh. Musée d'Art et d'Histoire, Geneva, 1956 : *Sélection de la IIIe Biennale Hispano-Américaine : Picasso, Nonell, Manolo,* No. 37.

Bibl. Z. VI. 322. C.-P. No. 93.

Coll. L. Plandiura, Barcelona ; Museo de Arte Moderno, Barcelona ;

Picasso Museum, Barcelona.

Picasso sent this watercolor from Paris to Barcelona, where it was published in *Pèl y Ploma,* No. 80, September 1901, p. 110. On the same page was a French text by Lorenzo de Bradi : *Les Fleurettes.* The author dedicated his article "To the unknown one, the one I am waiting for, to lighten the despair of my ravaged soul." As Cirici-Pellicer (French edition, 1950, p. 125) points out : "We realize the advance Picasso shows in relation to his symbolist contemporaries if we compare this drawing with the Bradi article."

V. 40
SILHOUETTE OF A WOMAN (Spanish Woman)
Paris, 1901.
Watercolor on cloth (see note).
Size : 15.5 x 9.5 cm.
Signed bottom right : Picasso.
(Signed by the artist in 1961.)
Verso : written inscription : *Femme Espagnole, Picasso, 1901, Berthe Weill.*

Exh. Umelecka Beseda, Prague, 1931 : *Picasso.* Frankfurt and Hamburg, 1965 : *Picasso, 150 Handzeichnungen aus sieben Jahrzehnten,* No. 10, repr. in color in cat.

Bibl. Not in Z.

Coll. Berthe Weill, Paris (1901) ; G. and L. Bollag, Zurich ; B. Roepke, Geneva ;

Collection Max G. Bollag, Zurich.

This small watercolor is a good example, perhaps a parody, of what Picasso made of Art Nouveau. The inscription on the back : "Femme Espagnole, Picasso 1901, Berthe Weill," neither confirms nor denies its presence at the Vollard exhibition. Perhaps Berthe Weill acquired it for her gallery in the second half of the year. On the other hand, it might have been shown at one of the exhibitions organized at Berthe Weill's in 1902 (see introduction to Catalogue VIII). Picasso remembers having painted this watercolor on the fine linen cover of a sketch pad.

V. 41
PICASSO IN A TOP HAT
Paris, 1901.
Oil on paper.
Size : 50 x 33 cm.
Signed bottom left : Picasso.

Exh. Svensk-Franska Konstgalleriet, Stockholm, 1959 : *Picasso.* Kiruna, Sweden, September 1965 : *Picasso i Kiruna,* No. 1, repr. in color in cat.

Bibl. Not in Z. Sabartés, *Picasso, documents iconographiques,* No. 66 (medium incorrectly given as drawing in India ink).

Coll. Göran Bergengren, Lund ; Svensk-Franska Konstgalleriet, Stockholm ;

Collection Herr and Fru Sven Salén, Stockholm.

V. 42
LADY WITH A DOG
Paris, 1901.
Watercolor on paper.
Size : 30.5 x 24.1 cm.
Signed top right : Picasso.
Inscribed on the back : Al amigo Torrez, Picasso.

Exh. Art Center, La Jolla, California 1957 : *Exhibition of French Impressionists.* Fine Arts Gallery, San Diego, California, 1959 : *Exhibition of French Impressionists.*

Bibl. Z. VI. 408. Catalogue of the Sale

Emile Laffon, Zurich, 1938, pl. X, No. 73. W.C.A., vol. XIV.

Coll. Emile Laffon, Paris ; Sale of the collection Emile Laffon (under the direction of W. S. Kundig, Geneva), Zurich, April 7–8, 1938, No. 73 ; Galerie Rosengart, Lucerne ; M. Knoedler & Co., New York ; Oliver B. James, Phoenix, Arizona ; Parke-Bernet, New York, Sale, December 5, 1962, bought by the present owner :

Collection Byron Goldman, New York.

V. 43
COUPLE IN EVENING DRESS
Paris, 1901.
Watercolor and ink on paper.
Size : 17.3 x 13 cm.
Signed top right : Picasso.
(Signature not authentic.)

Bibl. Not in Z.

Collection Miguel Gaspar, Barcelona.

V. 44
IN THE CAFÉ
Paris, 1901.
Watercolor.
Dimensions not known.
Signed bottom left : Picasso.

Bibl. Z. I. 382.

*Formerly Georges Lévy collection,
Paris.*

Known to us only through Zervos.

V. 45
AT THE CAFÉ DE LA ROTONDE
Paris, 1901.
Oil on canvas.
Size : 47 x 82.5 cm.
Signed right : Picasso.

Exh. Galerie Bernheim-Jeune, Paris, 1911. Galerie Bernheim-Jeune, Paris, 1922 : *L'époque bleue de Picasso.* Kunsthaus, Zurich, 1932, No. 2 (entitled *Au Restaurant Duval,* and dated 1901). Alex Reid and Lefevre Gallery, London, 1945 : *Twentieth Century Masterpieces.* Fine Art Associates, New York, 1953 : *French Art around 1900,* No. 16. The Corcoran Gallery of Art, Washington, D.C., February 19–March 28, 1965, and The Baltimore Museum of Art, April 6–May 23, 1965 : *Paintings and Sculpture from the Collection of Mr. and Mrs. David Lloyd Kreeger,* No. 17, repr. in color in cat. p. 10. Knoedler & Co., New York, 1966 : *Seven Decades of Art.* Dallas Museum of Fine Arts, February 8–March 26, 1967 : *Picasso,* No. 6, repr. in cat. p. 12.

Bibl. Z. VI. 1466. W.C.A., Vol. XIII.

Coll. Jules Straus, Paris ; Richard Peto, London ; Sam Kaye, London ; Sam Salz, New York ; Mr. and Mrs. Adolphe A. Juviler, New York ; Sale of the Mr. and Mrs. Adolphe A. Juviler collection, Parke-Bernet, New York (Sale No. 2056), October 25, 1961, No. 35, repr. in color in cat. p. 77 ;

Collection Mr. and Mrs. David Lloyd Kreeger, Washington, D.C.

When Pierre Daix showed a photograph of this painting to Picasso, the artist said, "It's the café on the Boulevard de Clichy where Casagemas committed suicide." At the same time he supplied geographical information which enabled us to discover in the police archives of the 9th *arrondissement* the report written at the time of Casagemas' death (see *Documents,* p. 338). This café has no resemblance to *La Rotonde* in Montparnasse, and the title is certainly wrong. According to the present café owner, at the time of Casagemas' suicide, this café at 128 Boulevard de Clichy was called *L'Hippodrome.* It was frequented by

Lautrec. Usually dated 1900, this painting is one of the most characteristic of Picasso's coloristic dash. The boldness of placement, which decapi-

tates the waiter, unites with extraordinary decisiveness of design. Vigorous touches of pure color substitute for draughtsmanship.

Color plate, page 41.

V. 46
WOMEN IN A CAFÉ
Paris, 1901.
Pastel on paper.
Size : 54.5 x 75 cm.
Signed bottom right : Picasso.

Exh. Lowe Art Gallery, Coral Gables, Florida.

Bibl. Z. VI. 336. Cassou, 1940, p. 37.

Coll. Madame Rabb, Paris ; M. Knoedler & Co., New York ; Acquired by the Norton collection, December 29, 1941 :

Norton Gallery and School of Art, West Palm Beach, Florida.

This large pastel shows a setting and costumes that one imagines more easily at Montmartre than in Spain.

V. 47
COURTESAN WITH A HAT
Paris, 1901.
Oil on canvas.
Size : 66 x 50.8 cm.
Signed bottom right : Picasso.

Exh. Knoedler & Co., New York, 1947 : *Picasso before 1907,* No. 14. The Metropolitan Museum of Art, New York, November 2–December 2, 1951 : *The Lewisohn Collection,* No. 60 (entitled *The Dancer*).

Bibl. Z. I. 65. Stephan Bourgeois, *Catalogue of the Adolph Lewisohn Collection of Modern French Paintings and Sculpture,* New York, 1928 (repr. as *The Dancer*). Joan Merli, 1948, No. 39.

Coll. Mr. and Mrs. Sam A. Lewisohn, New York ;

Private collection, New York.

V. 48
WOMAN WITH A JEWELED COLLAR
Paris, 1901.
Oil on cardboard.
Size : 43.7 x 36.1 cm.
Signed top left : Picasso.

Exh. Fogg Art Museum, Cambridge, 1929 : *French Painting of the 19th and 20th Centuries,* No. 71, repr. in cat. pl. 1. Wadsworth Atheneum, Hartford, 1934 : *Picasso,* No. 3. Jacques Seligmann & Co., New York, 1936 : *Picasso, Blue and Rose,* No. 1, repr. in cat. Museums Associated, Israël, spring, 1955 : *Travelling exhibition,* No. 61. Art Gallery of Toronto, 1957, No. 85. The National Gallery of Canada, Ottawa, 1962 : *European Paintings in Canadian Collections, Corot to Picasso,* No. 68. Toronto and Montreal, 1964 : *Picasso and Man,* No. 10, repr. in cat. p. 31. Museum of Tel-Aviv, Helena Rubinstein Pavilion, February 1966 : *Picasso,* No. 1, repr. in cat.

Bibl. Z. VI. 385. C. J. Bulliet, *The Significant Moderns,* 1936, pl. 100.

Coll. Mr. and Mrs. Q. A. Shaw McKean, Boston ; Cambridge Gallery, Mass. Carstairs Gallery, New York ;

Collection Ayala and Sam Zacks, Toronto.

This is the first version of a subject that Picasso will paint again in the autumn of 1901 (see *Courtesan with a Jeweled Collar,* VI. 17). Both versions are reminiscent of *Woman with a Plumed Hat* (III. 4).

Color plate, page 43.

V. 49
IN FRONT OF THE CHURCH
1901 (see note).
Oil on canvas.
Size : 45.5 x 54 cm.
Signed bottom right : P. R. Picasso.

Exh. Galerie Kaganovitch, Paris, May–July 1951 : *Œuvres choisies du XXᵉ siècle.* Munich-Cologne-Hamburg, October, 1955–April 1956 : *Picasso 1900–1955,* No. 3, repr. in cat. Kunsthaus, Zurich, June 7–September 30, 1958 : *Collection Emil G. Bührle,* No. 302. Berlin, Schloss Charlottenburg, October 5–November 23, 1958 : *Sammlung Emil G. Bührle,* No. 72. Munich, Haus der Kunst, December 5, 1958–February 15, 1959 : *Hauptwerke der Sammlung Emil Georg Bührle,* No. 117. Kunstmuseum, Lucerne, August 11–October 27, 1963 : *Sammlung E. G. Bührle,* No. 69, repr. in cat.

Bibl. Not in Z.

Coll. Private collection, Paris ; Private collection, New York ; Emil G. Bührle, Zurich (acquired in 1953) ;

Emil G. Bührle Foundation, Zurich.

This painting, showing a church in a Spanish village, was probably done at the beginning of 1901 ; the signature is from the Madrid period. We have catalogued it here because it might correspond to the *Spanish Church,* No. 44 in the Vollard exhibition catalogue.

Color plate, page 19.

V. 50
THE TRAMP
Madrid, 1901 (see note).
Watercolor and pencil on paper.
Size : 20.4 x 12.4 cm.
Signed, dated and inscribed, bottom right : Picasso, à Mlle Weill,
Paris, 3 juin 1901.

Exh. Musée de l'Orangerie, Paris, April–May 1941 :
Exposition de la Donation Paul Jamot.

Bibl. Not in Z.

Coll. Paul Jamot, Paris ;

Musée des Beaux-Arts, Reims.

Done in Madrid in 1901, this drawing with touches of watercolor was brought by Picasso to Paris. In the foreground is the
same figure as the one in the following pastel (V. 51). We
relate these two works ; the similarity is obvious.

V. 51
CASTILIAN VILLAGE
Madrid, 1901 (see note).
Pastel.
Size : 36 x 32 cm.
Signed bottom right : P. Ruiz Picasso.

Bibl. Z. VI. 363. C.-P. No. 41.

Coll. Salvio Masoliver, Barcelona ;

Collection Dr. Barbaralee D. Diamonstein, New York.

This pastel, done in the Madrid style, may correspond to
No. 45 of the Vollard exhibition catalogue : *Village d'Espagne.*
It should be remembered that this exhibition was held June 25–
July 14 and that it included a certain number of works brought
by Picasso from Spain. A drawing similar to this one, with the
same countryside in the background, was printed in *Arte
Joven* in 1901 (C.-P. No. 35).

V. 52
RECLINING NUDE (Jeanne)
Paris, 1901.
Oil on canvas.
Size : 70.5 x 90.2 cm.
Signed top right : Picasso.

Exh. Galerie Georges Petit, Paris, summer, 1932 : *Picasso,*
No. 13. Kunsthaus, Zurich, autumn, 1932 : *Picasso,* No. 9 (lent
by Baron Napoléon Gourgaud).

Bibl. Z. I. 106. *Cahiers d'Art,* 1932, No. 5. Cassou, 1940,
No. 38. C.-P. No. 67.

Coll. Baron Napoléon Gourgaud, Paris ;

*Musée National d'Art Moderne, Paris, Gift of Baron Gourgaud
(1965).*

Jeanne is one of the very few professional models Picasso ever
used. Picasso said that Jeanne also posed for *Woman with a
Cape* (V. 76).

V. 53
LE GOURMAND (Le Gourmet)
Paris, 1901.
Oil on canvas.
Size : 90.2 x 68.3 cm.
Signed top left : Picasso.

Exh. Museum of Modern Art, New York, 1930 : *Painting in Paris,* No. 65. The Art Institute of Chicago, 1933 : *A Century of Progress,* No. 401. The Art Institute of Chicago, 1943 : *Twentieth Century French Paintings from the Chester Dale Collection.*

Bibl. Z. I. 51. M. Dale, *Picasso,* New York, 1930, pl. 7. R. Flint, *The Private Collection of Josef Stransky,* "Art News," May 16, 1931, p. 112. R. Wilenski, *Modern French Painters,* London, 1944, p. 166. C.-P. No. 135.

Lieberman, New York, 1952, p. 5. Lieberman, New York, 1954, pl. 14 (repr. in color). *Twentieth Century Paintings and Sculpture of the French School in the Chester Dale Collection,* National Gallery of Art, Washington, D.C., 1965, p. 67. Helen Kay, *Picasso's World of Children,* 1965, p. 31 (repr. in color).

Coll. Dr. Alexandre, Paris ; Josef Stransky, New York ; Chester Dale, Washington, D.C. ;

The National Gallery of Art, Washington, D.C., Collection Chester Dale.

Probably corresponds to No. 47 in the Vollard exhibition catalogue : *Child in White.*

V. 54
WOMEN AND CHILDREN ON THE BEACH
Barcelona (?), 1901 (see note).
Oil.
Size : 28.3 x 35.5 cm.
Signed bottom left : Picasso.

Exh. The National Gallery of Art, Washington, D.C., 1966 : *25th Anniversary Exhibition, French Paintings from the Collections of Mr. and Mrs. Paul Mellon and Mrs. Mellon Bruce,* No. 193, repr. in cat. (as *Beach Scene*).

Bibl. Not in Z.

Collection Mr. and Mrs. Paul Mellon, Upperville, Virginia.

To our knowledge this painting remained unpublished until it was reproduced in the 1966 catalogue of the Paul Mellon collection. Obviously it belongs to the series of scenes of children playing under their mothers' supervision (see *In the Public Garden,* V. 19). If not done from memory, this sandy beach scene with the sea in the background is probably located in Barcelona. Since the Vollard exhibition catalogue emphasized the Spanish character of the subjects, it is possible that this work was No. 49 in the exhibition : *La Méditerranée,* unless it was No. 56 : *By the Sea.*

V. 55
FRENCH CANCAN
Paris, 1901.
Oil on canvas.
Size : 46 x 61 cm.
Signed bottom left : Picasso.

Exh. Musée Rath, Geneva, 1954 : *Trésors des collections romandes,* No. 181. Musée de l'Athénée, Geneva, 1962 : *Soixante ans de peinture française,* No. 107, repr. in cat. Palais de Beaulieu, Lausanne, 1964 : *Chefs-d'œuvre des collections suisses,* No. 224, repr. in cat.

Bibl. Not in Z.

Coll. Durand-Ruel, Paris ;

Collection Raymond Barbey, Geneva.

Color plate, page 179.

FRENCH CANCAN, PARIS, 1901, OIL. COLLECTION RAYMOND BARBEY, GENEVA. UNPUBLISHED IN COLOR (V. 55).

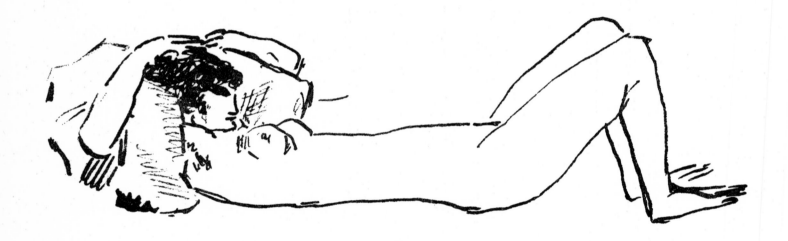

Reclining Nude, Paris, 1910, pen drawing.

V. 56
PORTRAIT OF THE ARTIST'S SISTER
Barcelona, 1901 (see note).
Oil on wood.
Size : 35.3 x 22.2 cm.
Signed bottom left : Picasso.

Exh. The National Gallery of Art, Washington, D.C., 1966 : *25th Anniversary Exhibition, French Paintings from the Collections of Mr. and Mrs. Paul Mellon and Mrs. Mellon Bruce,* No. 196, repr. in cat.

Bibl. Not in Z. Merli, 1942, No. 22. W.C.A., Vol. XV. *Ivory Hammer,* Vol. 2, p. 50. *Studio International,* No. 858, London, October 1964, p. 160.

Coll. Olivier Sainsère, Paris ; Durand-Ruel, Paris ; Henry Zimet Foundation, New York ; Sotheby & Co., London, Sale, October 23, 1963, No. 9, sold for £32,000, bought by the present owners :

Collection Mr. and Mrs. Paul Mellon, Upperville, Virginia.

Possibly *Madrilena,* No. 53 of the Vollard exhibition (property of O. Sainsère). This portrait was painted in Barcelona and brought to Paris before the exhibition.

V. 57
LA MADRILÈNE
(Head of a Young Woman)
Madrid or Paris, 1901 (see note).
Oil on wood.
Size : 52 x 33 cm.
Signed bottom left : Picasso.

Exh. Musée de Lyon, June 1953 : *Picasso,* No. 2. Kunstnernes Hus, Oslo, November–December 1956 : *Picasso,* No. 1.

Bibl. Z. I. 64. *L'Art Vivant,* Paris, October 1930. C.-P. No. 66. Maurice Raynal and Jacques Lassaigne, *Histoire de la peinture moderne, de Picasso au surréalisme,* Geneva, 1950,

p. 17 (repr. in color). *Jardin des Arts,* No. 4, Paris, February 1955, p. 232 (repr. in color).

Coll. Atami Fukushima, Japan ; Etienne Bignou, Paris ; Hôtel Drouot, Paris, Sale, June 14, 1930, No. 38, acquired by Madame Kröller ;

Rijksmuseum Kröller-Müller, Otterlo.

Possibly *Madrilena,* No. 53 of the Vollard exhibition (see note V. 56).

V. 58
HEAD OF A WOMAN
Paris, 1901.
Oil on cardboard.
Size : 47 x 30.5 cm.
Signed bottom left : Picasso.

Exh. Museum of Modern Art, Boston, 1938 : *Picasso and Matisse,* No. 1. Philadelphia Museum of Art, 1947 : *Masterpieces of Private Collections.* Philadelphia Museum of Art, 1958 :

Picasso, No. 6, repr. in cat.

Bibl. Z. I. 73. Joan Merli, Buenos Aires, 1942, p. 140.

Coll. José Viñes, Paris and The Hague ; Lisa Norris Elkins, Philadelphia ;

Philadelphia Museum of Art.

Related to *La Madrilène* (V. 57).

V. 59
HEAD OF A WOMAN
Paris, 1901.
Oil on cardboard. Size : 46 x 33 cm.
Signed bottom right : Picasso.

Bibl. Z. I. 74. C.-P. No. 65. Joan

Merli, Buenos Aires, 1942, pl. IV (repr. in color).

Coll. José Viñes, Paris ;

Present location unknown.

V

V. 60
YOUNG GIRL WITH A RED FLOWER
Paris, 1901.
Oil on cardboard.
Size : 55.9 x 35.6 cm.
Signed bottom left : Picasso.

Exh. Galerie Charpentier, Paris, 1950 : *Cent portraits de femmes,* No. 79. Knoedler & Co., New York, April 25– May 12, 1962 : *Picasso, an American Tribute,* No. 5, repr. in cat. The National Museum of Modern Art, Tokyo, May 23–July 5, 1964 : *Picasso,* No. 3, repr. in cat. p. 28. Same exhibition : Kyoto, July 10–August 3, 1964. Same exhibition : Nagoya, August 7– 18, 1964.

Bibl. Z. VI. 1461.

Collection M. and Mme Jacques Gelmann, Mexico.

V. 61
ON THE UPPER DECK (The Omnibus)
Paris, 1901.
Oil on cardboard mounted on panel.
Size : 49.2 x 64.2 cm.
Signed bottom right : Picasso.

Exh. Chicago, 1932 : *Coburn Collection,* No. 27, repr. Chicago, 1933 : *Century of Progress,* No. 403. Idem, 1934, No. 359. New York, Chicago, Boston, 1939– 1940 : *Picasso, Forty Years of his Art,* No. 9, repr. Denver, 1945 : *Picasso.* Knoedler, New York, 1947 : *Picasso before 1907,* No. 4, repr. Tate Gallery, London, 1960 : *Picasso,* No. 10, repr. pl. 4 j.

Bibl. Not in Z. Barr, *Forty Years,* p. 25. Barr, *Fifty Years,* p. 19–20. Lieberman, 1961, pl. 7. Art Institute of Chicago, 1961, *Catalogue of Paintings,* p. 356, No. 33.448.

Coll. Howard Young, New York ; Mrs. A. S. Coburn ;

The Art Institute of Chicago, Mr. and Mrs. Lewis L. Coburn Collection.

The title of this painting, *On the Upper Deck,* has often been incorrectly interpreted. Picasso himself specified that it is the top deck of a horse-drawn bus, going over a bridge of the Seine. The likeness to the prow of a boat is simply a matter of perspective. One can see the head of the driver in front. In 1902, Berthe Weill sold for 160 fr. a painting by Picasso entitled *The Omnibus,* possibly the work reproduced here.

V. 62
WOMAN WITH BLUE STOCKINGS
Paris, 1901.
Oil.
Size : 65 x 48.3 cm.
Signed bottom right : Picasso.

Bibl. Not in Z. Cassou, 1940, No. 33.

Coll. Galerie Mouradian et Valloton, Paris ; Frank Perls, Los Angeles ; James Vigereno, Los Angeles ; Cronyn, New York ; Sale of the Cronyn collection, Parke-Bernet, New York, January, 1958, sold for $ 21.000, bought by Niveau Galleries, New York ;

Private collection, New York.

This painting might have been shown in the Vollard exhibition as No. 58 (*Vieille Fille*), if that title is taken to mean an old prostitute.

V. 63
BOOTH AT THE FAIR
Paris, 1900 or 1901 (see note).
Oil on canvas.
Size : 36.5 x 44.5 cm.
Signed top right : Picasso.

Exh. Munich-Cologne-Hamburg, 1955–1956 : *Picasso 1900–1955*, No. 2.

Bibl. Not in Z.

Coll. Carl-August Jung, Wuppertal-Elberfeld ;

Collection Fritz Andreae, Sen., Cologne.

This work was dated 1900 by the organizers of the Munich-Cologne-Hamburg exhibition. Its handling bears this out. On the other hand, the signature certainly is not from 1900 ; in shape, it is close to signatures toward the end of 1901, or 1902. This is a booth at the fair like the ones traditionally put up on the Boulevard de Clichy, either for Christmas and New Year festivities, or at the beginning of the summer.

Reproduced in color, at the artist's request, page 23.

V. 64
PORTRAIT OF GUSTAVE COQUIOT
Paris, 1901.
Oil on canvas.
Size : 100 x 80 cm.
Signed bottom right : Picasso.

Exh. Prague, 1931 : *L'Ecole de Paris.* Galerie Georges Petit, Paris, summer, 1932 : *Picasso,* No. 5. Kunsthaus, Zurich, autumn, 1932 : *Picasso,* No. 7 (for sale ; remained unsold). Musée du Jeu de Paume, Paris, February 1936 : *L'Art Espagnol contemporain,* No. 188. Musée de Lyon, 1953 : *Picasso,* No. 5, repr. in cat. fig. 1. Musée Galliera, Paris, 1954 : *Peintres témoins de leur temps.* Musée Calvet, Avignon, July 1954 : *L'Homme dans la Ville.* Recklinghausen, Berlin, 1956. Musée Cantini, Marseilles, 1959 : *Picasso,* No. 3, repr. in cat. Arts Council of Great Britain, Tate Gallery, London, 1960 : *Picasso,* No. 12, repr. in cat. pl. 4 i.

Bibl. Z. I. 84. Catalogue of the Musée National d'Art Moderne, Paris, 1954, p. 126. Elgar and Maillard, 1955 (catalogue).

Coll. Gustave Coquiot, Paris ; Musée du Jeu de Paume, Paris ;

Musée National d'Art Moderne, Paris.

This is the first of the two portraits of Coquiot done by Picasso. It was painted during the summer of 1901, at the time of the encounter between the artist and this art critic for the Vollard exhibition (the second portrait is catalogued as No. VI. 16).

V. 65
THE FLOWER SELLER
Paris, 1901.
Oil on cardboard.
Size : 33.7 x 52.1 cm.
Signed bottom left : Picasso.

Exh. Perhaps : Galerie Berthe Weill, Paris, October 2– November 20, 1904, No. 31 *(Marchande des quatre saisons).* Royal Academy, London, winter, 1962 : *Primitives to Picasso,* No. 256, repr. in cat.

Bibl. Not in Z. Gaston Diehl, *Picasso,* 1960, p. 5 (repr. in color).

Coll. Tanner, Zurich ; William McInnes, Glasgow, who bequeathed it to the Glasgow Art Gallery in 1944 ;

Glasgow Art Gallery and Museum, Glasgow.

At the far left there are two figures closely related to *Little Girls Dancing* (V. 15).

Color plate, page 185.

V. 66
THE DINERS (Les Soupeurs)
Paris, 1901.
Oil on cardboard.
Size : 47 x 62.2 cm.
Signed bottom right : Picasso.

Bibl. Z. I. 67. Cassou, 1940, No. 37. Joan Merli, Buenos Aires, 1948, No. 27. C.-P. No. 50. Elgar and Maillard, 1955 (catalogue). Robert L. Delevoy, *Dimensions du XXᵉ siècle,* Geneva, 1965, p. 21 (repr. in color).

Coll. André Lefèvre, Paris ; Galerie Baläy et Carré, Paris ;

Museum of Art, Rhode Island School of Design, Providence.

V. 67
IN THE RESTAURANT
Paris, 1901.
Watercolor.
Size : 29 x 39 cm.
Signed bottom left : Picasso.

Bibl. Z. I. 68. Joan Merli, Buenos Aires, 1948, No. 25. C.-P. No. 52.

Coll. Galerie Gleizes, Paris ;

Present location unknown.

V. 68
LITTLE GIRL WITH A PENDANT
Paris, 1901.
Oil.
Dimensions not known.
Signed top left : Picasso.

Bibl. Z. I. 75. C.-P. No. 47.

Coll. Hugo Perls, Berlin ; Mrs. Ralph Harmon Booth, Detroit ;

Private collection, Grosse Pointe, Michigan.

It is not impossible that this work, always closely related to the following one (V. 69) because of the similar subject, is slightly later. It might correspond to the *Young Girl* shown in the Berthe Weill exhibition in April 1902.

THE FLOWER SELLER, PARIS, 1901, OIL. GLASGOW ART GALLERY AND MUSEUM, GLASGOW (V. 65).

WOMAN AT THE THEATER, PARIS, 1901, OIL. COLLECTION CHARLES IM OBERSTEG, GENEVA. UNPUBLISHED (V. 71).

V. 69
LITTLE GIRL WITH A HAT
Paris, 1901.
Oil on canvas.
Size : 75 x 51 cm.
Signed top left : Picasso.
Verso : Woman with a Chignon
(VI. 23).

Exh. Museum of Modern Art, New York, 1933. Wadsworth Atheneum, Hartford, February–March 1934 : *Pablo Picasso,* No. 7. Jacques Seligmann & Co., New York, 1936 : *Picasso, Blue and Rose Periods,* No. 7, repr. in cat. Fogg Art Museum, June–September 1946 : *French Painting since 1870,* repr. in cat. p. 47. Musée de la Province de Québec, July–August 1949 : *The Maurice Wertheim Collection,* No. 18, repr. in cat. p. 52. The National Gallery of Art, Washington,

D.C., June–September 1953. Philadelphia Museum of Art, June–September 1957. Minneapolis Institute of Arts, June–August 1958. North Carolina Museum of Art, June–September 1960 : *Modern French Art, Monet to Picasso,* repr. in cat. p. 33. Houston Museum of Fine Arts, June–September 1962 : *The Maurice Wertheim Collection,* repr. in cat. pl. 12.

Bibl. Z. I. 76. C.-P. No. 46. Helen Kay, *Picasso's World of Children,* 1965, p. 22 (repr. in color).

Coll. John Quinn, New York ; Dr. and Mrs. Harry Bakwin, New York ; Mr. and Mrs. Maurice Wertheim, New York ;

Fogg Art Museum, Harvard University, Bequest of Maurice Wertheim.

V. 70
THE FOURTEENTH OF JULY
Paris, 1901.
Oil on board mounted on canvas.
Size : 48.3 x 63.2 cm.
Signed top right : Picasso.

Exh. Galerie Berthe Weill, Paris, April 1–15, 1902, No. 5. Santa Barbara Museum of Art, 1953 : *Fiesta Exhibition, Picasso, Gris, Miró, Dali,* No. 2. The Solomon R. Guggenheim Museum, New York, April-September 1965 : *First Showing of Masterpieces of Modern Art from the Thannhauser Foundation,* No. 33, repr. in color in cat. p. 41.

Bibl. Adrien Farge, preface to the catalogue of the Berthe Weill exhibition, April 1902 : "a brilliant, clamorous *14 Juillet* brings together in the most dazzling colors all the superabundant motion and intense life of a popular holiday." Z. VI. 334.

Coll. Galerie Thannhauser, Berlin ; Mr. and Mrs. Justin K. Thannhauser, New York ;

The Solomon R. Guggenheim Museum, New York, Justin K. Thannhauser Foundation.

V. 71
WOMAN AT THE THEATER
Paris, 1901.
Oil on canvas.
Size : 77 x 61 cm.
Unsigned. Signed verso.
Verso : Absinthe Drinker (VI. 25).

Exh. Never exhibited.

Bibl. Unpublished.

Coll. Galerie G. and L. Bollag, Zurich ; For more than thirty years the property of the present owner :

Property of Charles Im Obersteg, Geneva.

This superb unfinished work has never been reproduced or catalogued. The *Absinthe Drinker* (VI. 25) on the back is, however, known. Zervos pointed out the existence of a work on the back of *Absinthe Drinker,* but he cited it incorrectly as a portrait of Picasso.

Color plate, page 186.

V

V. 72
STILL LIFE (La Desserte)
Paris, 1901.
Oil on canvas. Size : 60 x 80.5 cm.
Signed bottom left : Picasso.

Exh. Barcelona, 1919 : *Exposició d'Art,* No. 515. Galeries Dalmau, Barcelona, October 25–November 15, 1920 : *Exposició d'art francès d'avant-guarda,* No. 68. III Bienal Hispanoamericana de arte, Barcelona, 1955 : *Precursores y maestros del arte Español contemporáneo,* No. 16. Musée d'Art et d'Histoire, Geneva, 1956 : *Sélection de la IIIe Biennale Hispano-Américaine : Picasso, Nonell, Manolo,* No. 4. Musée Cantini, Marseilles, 1959 : *Picasso,* No. 2, repr. in cat. Dallas Museum of Fine Arts, 1967 : *Picasso,* No. 5.

Bibl. Z. I. 70. *Cahiers d'art,* 1928, p. 207. Bulletin of the art museums of Barcelona, vol. 7, No. 77, October, 1937, p. 296–334. C.-P. No. 62. J. C. Aznar, *Picasso y el Cubismo,* Madrid, 1956, p. 340.

Coll. L. Plandiura, Barcelona ; Museo de Arte Moderno, Barcelona ;

Picasso Museum, Barcelona.

This painting is probably the *Still Life,* No. 1, of the Berthe Weill exhibition in April, 1902. (Cf. Adrien Farge in the preface to the catalogue : "Sometimes Picasso is carried away by his passion for color, and then he gives us this luxurious still life.") The style of outlining and the palette foreshadow the paintings which lead to the Blue Period.

V. 73
GIRL IN A CAFÉ
Paris, 1901.
Pastel.
Size : 67 x 52 cm.
Signed bottom right : Picasso.

Bibl. Z. I. 81 (dated Paris, 1901).
C.-P. No. 172 (entitled *Absinthe Drinker,* and dated 1903). Blunt and Pool, No. 19 (dated Paris, 1901).

Coll. Krenz, Holzdorf-Weimar ;

Private collection, Berlin.

V. 74
BIBI LA PURÉE
Paris, 1901.
Oil on wood.
Size : 49 x 39 cm.
Signed bottom right : Picasso.

Exh. Musée de Lyon, 1953 : *Picasso,* No. 4. Palazzo Reale, Milan, 1953 : *Picasso,* No. 1, repr. in cat. Musée des Arts Décoratifs, Paris, 1955 : *Picasso,* No. 4, repr. in cat.

Bibl. Z. VI. 360. Sabartés and Boeck, p. 111 (repr. in color). Gaston Diehl, 1960, p. 24 (repr. in color).

Coll. Gompel (the uncle of Max Jacob), Paris ; Max Pellequer, Paris ;

Private collection, Paris.

Bibi la Purée was an eccentric old actor who frequented the Latin Quarter. There are two known drawings of him, both catalogued by Zervos : Z. VI. 355 and Z. VI. 1460.

V. 75
PARK SCENE
Paris, 1901.
Pastel.
Size : 47.7 x 65.5 cm.
Signed bottom right : Picasso.

Bibl. Z. VI. 331.

Coll. Galerie Thannhauser, Munich ;
Parke-Bernet, New York, Sale, March 27,
1963 ; sold for $11.000 ; bought at this
sale by Mr. W. C. Kennedy ;

Private collection, U.S.A.

If it is contemporary with the work, the
smallness and shape of the signature date
this painting in the autumn of 1901.

V. 76
WOMAN WITH A CAPE
Paris, 1901.
Oil on canvas.
Size : 73 x 50 cm.
Signed top left : Picasso.

Exh. Galerie La Nouvelle Renaissance,
Paris, 1929. Galerie Demotte, Paris,
1931 : *Picasso,* No. 2, repr. in cat. Rein-
hardt Galleries, New York, October 1936 :
*Exhibition of 19th and 20th Century
Paintings.* Jacques Seligmann & Co.,
New York, 1937, No. 1, repr. in cat.
Courvoisier Galleries, San Francisco,
1937 : *French Paintings, 19th and 20th
Centuries,* No. 12, repr. on the cover of
catalogue. Knoedler & Co., New York,
1947 : *Picasso before 1907,* No. 10.
Bordeaux, 1966 : *La peinture française
dans les collections américaines,* No. 109.

Bibl. Z. VI. 542. The Cleveland Museum
of Art, 1958, *In Memoriam Leonard
C. Hanna, Jr.,* No. 27.

Coll. John Quinn, New York ; Libaude,
Paris ; Madame Demotte, Paris ; Robert
Lebel, Paris (1935) ; Reinhardt Galleries,
New York (1936) ; Courvoisier Galleries,
San Francisco ; Leonard C. Hanna, Jr. ;

*The Cleveland Museum of Art, Leonard
C. Hanna, Jr. Collection.*

Picasso told us that this is a portrait of
Jeanne, the model for *Reclining Nude*
(V. 52).

V. 77
WOMAN AT THE THEATER
Paris, 1901.
Watercolor (according to Zervos).
Size : 39 x 51 cm.
Signed bottom left : Picasso.

Bibl. Z. VI. 338.

Present location unknown.

We have not been able to identify either
the original work or the present owner.

V. 78
PORTRAIT OF A YOUNG GIRL
Paris, 1901.
Watercolor.
Size : 20 x 15.5 cm.
Signed top right : Picasso.

Bibl. Z. I. 95. C.-P. No. 76.

Coll. G. Swarzenski, Boston ; Hanns
Swarzenski, Boston ;

Private collection, U.S.A.

V. 79
RECLINING NUDE
Paris, 1901.
India ink and color wash.
Size : 25.5 x 35.5 cm.
Signed (?) top left : Picasso.

Bibl. Z. VI. 353.

Present location unknown.

We know this work only through its
reproduction in the Zervos catalogue.
The woman's hard face might be
compared with those of the *demi-
mondaines* in the series V. 35, V. 36,
V. 37, V. 38, and V. 39.

V. 80
WOMAN SEATED ON THE
TERRACE OF A CAFÉ
Paris, 1901.
Watercolor.
Size : 48 x 64 cm.
Signed and dated, bottom left : Pi-
casso 1901.

Bibl. Z. VI. 391. Sabartés and Boeck,
p. 458, No. 12 (entitled *In the Café*).

Present location unknown.

V. 81
SELF-PORTRAIT
Paris, 1901.
Crayon and wash on paper.
Size : 30.5 x 24 cm.
Signed top right : Picasso (the signa-
ture is probably later).

Exh. California Palace of the Legion of
Honor, San Francisco, June 15–
July 30, 1961: *French Paintings from
the Collection of Mrs. Mellon Bruce,*
No. 34, repr. in cat. National Gallery
of Art, Washington, D.C., 1966 : *25th
Anniversary Exhibition, French Paint-
ings from the Collections of Mr. and*

*Mrs. Paul Mellon and Mrs. Mellon
Bruce,* No. 246, repr. in cat.

Bibl. Not in Z.

*Collection Mrs. Mellon Bruce, Upper-
ville, Virginia.*

This self-portrait has the same intensity
as the oil in the Whitney collection
(V. 1). But it seems to us that it must
belong to the time when Picasso's
work becomes more somber, after the
Vollard exhibition.

PORTRAIT OF SABARTÉS, PARIS, WINTER 1901-1902, OIL. COLLECTION OF THE ARTIST. UNPUBLISHED IN COLOR (VI. 34).

PORTRAIT OF MATEU F. DE SOTO, PARIS, WINTER 1901-1902, OIL. COLLECTION OF THE ARTIST. UNPUBLISHED IN COLOR (VI. 33).

Toward the Blue Period, Paris 1901

We can fix the chronology for this period by the second *Portrait of Gustave Coquiot* (VI. 16), the portraits of Sabartés and of Mateu F. de Soto (VI. 34, 33) (which were begun probably in October and finished after an interval at the very end of the stay in Paris), and *Evocation* (VI. 4) which, according to Sabartés, was at the studio on the Boulevard de Clichy a short while after his arrival in Paris. Finally, the catalogue of the Berthe Weill Exhibition, April 1-15, 1902, the preface by Adrien Farge, and

Despite all our research, we are unsuccessful in identifying Number 6 of the catalogue of the Berthe Weill Exhibition, *The Virgin with Golden Hair*. Adrien Farge described it as "a suggestive and disturbing sphinx, with a sinuous body, a lustful mouth, curled hair, painted nails like petals on long, supple hands, the female quivering voluptuously within the innocent virgin, longing with vague desire for the unknown. What an eloquent symbol is this strange figure!" And there is a description by Félicien Fagus, who after discussing *The Courtesan* proceeds: "This quasi-hieratic quality is more defined in the

CASAGEMAS IN HIS COFFIN, PARIS, 1901, OIL. COLLECTION OF THE ARTIST. UNPUBLISHED (VI. 6).

THE DEATH OF CASAGEMAS, PARIS, 1901, OIL. COLLECTION OF THE ARTIST. UNPUBLISHED (VI. 5).

the article in *La Revue Blanche* by Félicien Fagus are all extremely valuable in placing the fifteen pictures remaining in Mañach's possession and exhibited under his auspices after Picasso's return to Barcelona.

As far as we can determine, none of these canvases appeared in the Vollard Exhibition. Félicien Fagus wrote: "Picasso, only lately the positive reveler in color, concentrates himself on displays of energy." The accompanying descriptions convince us that a different general tonality did appear in this new exhibition. More and more Picasso abandoned the impressionist brush stroke in favor of flat tones in which blues came to dominate, while outlines stressed the precision of the drawing. The vivid colors became more subdued. Félicien Fagus saw in this new style a "look of stained glass."

Virgin with Golden Hair (the same woman or her sister?)—this very young girl, lying on her stomach, head raised, staring out at nothing, inhaling and sniffing suspiciously with her animal-like snub nose; here is the stupefied beast who would attain divinity; here is the sphinx. All this conveyed in vivid but mat flat tints enclosed by carefully elaborated, prominently marked outlines. . . ."

Unfortunately, this work that excited the viewers' most interesting reactions has completely disappeared. We do not know whether Picasso painted another picture over it. This seems unlikely since it was on the art market and Picasso himself was in Barcelona. Perhaps it was destroyed or, ever since the Berthe Weill Exhibition, has remained in the collection of the original purchaser or his heirs.

VI. 1
THE FUGITIVES
Paris, 1901.
Gouache on cardboard.
Size : 56 x 73 cm.
Unsigned.

Bibl. Z. I. 53. Raynal, 1922, pl. 6 (incorrectly dated 1903). C.-P. No. 173 (dated 1903). Sutton, 1955, No. 6. Blunt and Pool, No. 97.

Coll. M. Pellequer, Paris ; Parke-Bernet, New York, sold in 1948, for $3.090 ;

Private collection, U.S.A.

Phoebe Pool relates this gouache to the Daumier sculpture *Les Emigrants* which Picasso might have seen at the Daumier exhibition at the Palais de l'Ecole des Beaux-Arts in Paris during the summer of 1901. The similarity of overall movement is indeed striking. This work is the turning point for a break with the Impressionist brush stroke. It shows a new interest in composing by stressed outlines, omitting details. This is not without analogy to Cézanne.

VI. 2
THE MOURNERS
Paris, 1901.
Oil on canvas.
Size : 100 x 90.2 cm.
Signed bottom right : Picasso.

Exh. Galerie Georges Petit, summer, 1932: *Picasso,* No. 6 *(La Mise au tombeau).* Kunsthaus, Zurich, autumn, 1932 : *Picasso,* No. 5 (for sale ; remained unsold). Jacques Seligmann & Co., New York, 1936 : *Picasso, Blue and Rose Periods,* No. 2, repr. in cat. Los Angeles County Museum of Art, June-July 1941 : *The E. G. Robinson Collection.* Museum of Modern Art, New York, March 4–April 12, 1953, and The National Gallery of Art, Washington, D.C., May 10–June 24, 1953 : *Forty Paintings from the Edward G. Robinson Collection,* No. 20. Los Angeles County Museum of Art, September 11–November 11, 1956, and The California Palace of the Legion of Honor, November 30, 1956–January 13, 1957 : *The Gladys Lloyd Robinson and Edward G. Robinson Collection,* No. 37. Knoedler & Co., New York, December 3, 1957– January 10, 1958, and The National Gallery of Canada, Ottawa, February

1958 : *Loan Exhibition from the Niarchos Collection,* No. 38. Arts Council of Great Britain, Tate Gallery, London, 1960 : *Picasso,* No. 8, repr. in cat. pl. 2 a. U.C.L.A., Los Angeles, 1961 : *Bonne Fête Monsieur Picasso.*

Bibl. Z. I. 52. *Cahiers d'Art,* Vol. III, No. 5-6, 1928, p. 227. Merli, 1948, No. 22. C.-P. No. 59. Maurice Gieure, *Initiation à l'œuvre de Picasso,* 1951, No. 5 *(Mise au tombeau).*

Coll. Ambroise Vollard, Paris ; Pierre Loeb, Paris ; Pierre Matisse, New York ; Edward G. Robinson, Beverly Hills ; Stavros S. Niarchos, Paris (bought from the sale of the Edward G. Robinson collection, 1957) ; Re-purchased by the present owner in 1958–1959 :

Collection Edward G. Robinson, Beverly Hills.

There are two studies for this painting, one in pencil (Z. VI. 328) and the other in pencil with touches of watercolor (Z. VI. 330). The latter is in the collection of Walter P. Chrysler, Jr.

VI. 3
CHILDREN IN THE LUXEMBOURG GARDENS
Paris, 1901.
Oil.
Size : 33 x 41 cm.
Signed bottom right : Picasso.

Exh. Galerie Berthe Weill, Paris, April 1–15, 1902, No. 4 (entitled *Luxembourg*).

Bibl. Z. I. 54. C.-P. No. 63 (called oil on paper, 25 x 35 cm). Blunt and Pool, No. 102.

Coll. Domingo Carles, Barcelona (according to Zervos and Blunt and Pool) ; Barbey, Barcelona (according to C.-P.) ;

Private collection, Barcelona.

EVOCATION
(The Burial of Casagemas)
Paris, 1901.
Oil on canvas.
Size : 150 x 90 cm.
Signed bottom right : Picasso.

Exh. Galerie Berthe Weill, Paris, October 24–November 20, 1904, No. 30. Galerie Georges Petit, Paris, summer, 1932 : *Picasso,* No. 7. Kunsthaus, Zurich, autumn, 1932 : *Picasso,* No. 6, repr. in cat. pl. II (lent by Ambroise Vollard). Musée Galliera, Paris, 1955 : *Regards sur la peinture contemporaine.* Ire Biennale de Paris, 1959. Grand Palais, Paris, November 1966–February 1967 : *Hommage à Pablo Picasso,* No. 8, repr. in cat.

Bibl. Z. I. 55. C.-P. No. 58. Maurice Gieure, 1951, No. 6. Elgar and Mail-lard, 1955 (catalogue). *Connaissance des Arts,* September 1957, p. 44. Penrose, *Picasso, his Life and Work,* 1958, pl. I, No. 9. Blunt and Pool, No. 100. Boudaille, 1964, p. 5.

Coll. Ambroise Vollard ; The Ambroise Vollard Estate (1950) ;

Musée d'Art Moderne de la Ville de Paris.

This large painting, also called *The Burial of Casagemas,* is dedicated to Picasso's companion on his first trip to Paris, who committed suicide February 17, 1901. It is related to *The Mourners* (VI. 2), *The Death of Casagemas* (VI. 5) and *Casagemas in his Coffin* (VI. 6).

VI. 5
THE DEATH OF CASAGEMAS
Paris, 1901.
Oil on wood (a wooden lid with, on the back, a semi-visible stamp : *couleurs*).
Size : 26.9 x 34.8 cm.
Unsigned.

Exh. Never exhibited.

Bibl. Unpublished.

Owned by the artist.

Color plate, page 192.

VI. 6
CASAGEMAS IN HIS COFFIN
Paris, 1901.
Oil on cardboard.
Size : 72.5 x 57.8 cm.
Unsigned.

Exh. Never exhibited.

Bibl. Unpublished.

Owned by the artist.

Color plate, page 192.

PIERROT
Paris, 1901.
Gouache.
Size : 33 x 19 cm.
Signed top left : Picasso.

Exh. Galerie Berthe Weill, Paris, April 1–15, 1902, No. 10. Galerie Georges Petit, Paris, 1932.

Bibl. Adrien Farge, preface to catalogue of Berthe Weill exhibition. Z. I. 56. Joan Merli, Buenos Aires, 1948, No. 30. C.-P. No. 57.

Coll. Etienne Bignou, Paris ;

Private collection, Paris.

VI. 8
CLOWN WITH A MONKEY
Paris, 1901.
Oil.
Dimensions not known.
Signed top right : Picasso.

Exh. Galerie Berthe Weill, Paris, April 1–15, 1902, No. 9.

Bibl. Adrien Farge, preface to catalogue of Berthe Weill exhibition : "A clown in glittering yellows…" Z. I. 57. Joan Merli, Buenos Aires, 1948, No. 31. C.-P. No. 56.

Formerly Pierre Loeb Collection, Paris.

VI. 9
MOTHER AND CHILD BY A FOUNTAIN
Paris, 1901.
Oil on canvas.
Size : 40.8 x 32.8 cm.
Signed bottom right : Picasso.

Exh. Montross Gallery, New York, 1924 : *Living Art,* No. 29. Worcester Art Museum, March 5–30, 1924 : *Exhibition of the Dial Collection.* Hillyer Gallery, Smith College, Northampton, Mass., 1924. Jacques Seligmann & Co., New York, November 1936 : *Picasso, Blue and Rose Periods,* No. 6, repr. in cat. Worcester Art Museum, April 30–September 8, 1959 : *The Dial and the Dial Collection,* No. 74, repr. in cat. p. 84.

Bibl. Z. I. 107. Raynal, 1921, pl. 2. *The Dial,* LXXX, May 1926, p. 357. *Worcester Art Museum Bulletin,* XXII, January 1932, p. 70. C.-P. No. 48. Sutton, 1955, No. 2. Blunt and Pool, No. 107. Helen Kay, *Picasso's World of Children,* 1965, p. 48.

Coll. Baron Napoléon Gourgaud, Paris ;

The Dial Collection, on loan since 1931 to the Worcester Art Museum, Massachusetts.

In the Kahnweiler archives, this work is dated autumn, 1901, Paris.

VI. 10
WOMEN AT THE FOUNTAIN
Paris, 1901.
Oil.
Size : 81 x 65 cm.
Signed top right : Picasso.

Bibl. Z. I. 80.

Coll. Potter Palmer, Jr., Chicago ;

Private collection, U.S.A.

We relate these two paintings (VI. 9

and VI. 10) because of their common subject matter, though the second one is in a rather different style. They might be used as landmarks to explain Picasso's experiments during the autumn of 1901. The first one belongs to the series of works with heavy outlines, the second introduces the exactness of detail which characterizes the works leading to the blue monochromes. The cap worn by the two women in VI. 10 is the same as the one in *Woman with a Cap* (VI. 12).

VI. 11
MOTHER AND CHILD *(Maternité)*
Paris, 1901.
Oil on canvas.
Size : 46 x 33 cm.
Signed on the back : Picasso.

Exh. Der Rheinischer Kunstsalon, Cologne, March–April 1913 : *Pablo Picasso* (53 paintings, 13 drawings), No. 1. Galerie Kate Perls, Paris, 1937, No. 14. The Virginia Museum of Fine Arts, January 16–March 4, 1941, and The Philadelphia Museum of Art, March 29–May 11, 1941 : *The Collection of Walter P. Chrysler, Jr.,* No. 149, repr. in cat.

Bibl. Z. I. 108. Raynal, 1922, pl. 5. Sutton, 1955, repr. No. 1 (as *Virgin and Child*).

Coll. Thannhauser, Munich (1902) ; Alfred Flechtheim, Düsseldorf (1913) ; Hugo Perls, Berlin (1932) ; Galerie Kate Perls, Paris (1937) ; Paul Rosenberg, Paris ; Walter P. Chrysler, New York (1941–1945) ; Parke-Bernet, New York, Sale, March 22, 1945, No. 90 ; Mr. and Mrs. Alfred Romney, New York (1945–1964) ;

The Metropolitan Museum of Art, New York, Gift of Mr. and Mrs. Alfred Romney, 1964.

In the Kahnweiler archives, this painting is dated in the autumn of 1901, Paris.

VI. 12
WOMAN WITH A CAP
Paris, 1901.
Oil on canvas.
Size : 41.3 x 33 cm.
Signed top right : Picasso.

Bibl. Z. I. 101. Cassou, 1940, No. 42.

Owned by the artist.

Color plate, page 47.

VI. 13
WOMAN IN A BATHROBE
Paris, 1901.
Oil on canvas. Size : 46.3 x 33 cm.
Signed top right : Picasso.

Bibl. Z. I. 102. Joan Merli, Buenos Aires, 1948, No. 52.

Owned by the artist.

The blonde model for this *Woman in a Bathrobe* is the same as the one in *The Blue Room* (VI. 15). Is she also the one in the lost painting, *Virgin with Golden Hair* ? (See the foreword to Catalogue VI.)

Color plate, page 47.

VI. 14
CHILD HOLDING A DOVE
Paris, 1901.
Oil on canvas.
Size : 73 x 54 cm.
Signed left center : Picasso.

Exh. Glasgow Art Gallery, 1924. London, 1924. New York, 1928. Musée de l'Orangerie, Paris, 1955, No. 36. Arts Council of Great Britain, Tate Gallery, London, 1960 : *Picasso,* No. 14, repr. in cat., pl. 4 g. The Art Gallery of Toronto and The Montreal Museum of Fine Arts, 1964 : *Picasso and Man,* No. 12, repr. in cat. p. 32. Grand Palais, Paris, November 1966– February 1967 : *Hommage à Pablo Picasso,* No. 9, repr. in cat.

Bibl. Z. I. 83. André Level, 1928, pl. 2. Maurice Raynal and Jacques Lassaigne, *Histoire de la peinture moderne ; de Picasso au surréalisme,* p. 19 (repr. in color). C.-P. No. 61. Douglas Cooper, *The Courtauld Collection,* London, 1954, pl. 67. Elgar and Maillard, 1955 (catalogue). Sutton, 1955, No. 8. Sabartés and Boeck, p. 362. Cassou, 1959, p. 14 and cover (repr. in color). Helen Kay, 1965, p. 29 and cover (repr. in color).

Coll. Paul Rosenberg, Paris ; Alex Reid, Glasgow ; Reid & Lefevre, London ; Mrs. R. A. Workman, London ; Samuel Courtauld, London (1928) ; Acquired by the present owner in 1947 :

Collection The Dowager Lady Aberconway, London.

This famous painting shows Picasso's search for a new direction at the end of the summer of 1901. He turns away from Parisian life to deal with more intimate subjects : the death of his friend Casagemas, or scenes of mothers and children. He also shows sympathy and unusual feeling for his subjects. It is as if in giving up impressionist brushwork and heavy outlines, with their precedence in Manet, Gauguin, or Maurice Denis, he expresses his need for a different plastic language to show the change in his attitude. The palette is highly colored, though blue predominates. It is close to *Woman with a Cap* (VI. 12) and to VI. 13 and VI. 15.

VI. 15
THE BLUE ROOM
Paris, 1901. Oil on canvas.
Size : 51 x 62.5 cm.
Signed bottom left : Picasso.

Exh. Galerie Berthe Weill, Paris, April 1902, No. 14. The Art Institute of Chicago, 1933 : *Century of Progress,* No. 399, repr. Jacques Seligmann, New York, 1936, No. 4, repr. Museum of Modern Art, New York, 1939, and The Art Institute of Chicago, 1940 : *Picasso, Forty Years of his Art,* No. 15, repr. Knoedler, New York, 1947 : *Picasso before 1907,* No. 6, repr. Knoedler, New York, 1962 : *Picasso, an American Tribute,* No. 11, repr.

Bibl. Z. I. 103. Barr, *Forty Years,* p. 29. Barr, *Fifty Years,* p. 22. C.-P. No. 68. The Phillips Collection, Washington, D.C., *Catalogue,* 1952, pl. 162. Elgar and Maillard, 1955 (catalogue). Sabartés and Boeck, p. 365. Penrose, 1958, pl. II, No. 2. Raynal, 1959, pl. 23 (color). Lieberman, 1961, pl. 15 and 16 (color).

Coll. Wilhelm Uhde, Paris (cf. W. Uhde, *Picasso et la tradition française. Notes sur la peinture actuelle,* Paris, 1928, p. 19 : "... a painting I bought more than twenty years ago. The first work by an unknown artist that I owned, a nude woman with blonde hair taking a bath in a blue room. I bought it for ten francs at a mattress-maker's in Montmartre. On the inside of his shop he carried on his business in bedding. Outside he was an art dealer for young and unknown painters") ; Etienne Bignou, Paris ; Reid, London ;

The Phillips Collection, Washington, D.C.

This painting shows Picasso's studio at 130, Boulevard de Clichy. On the wall, the Lautrec poster for May Milton. The small painting next to the poster is a seascape. Could this be *Les Rochers* or *La Méditerranée* of the Vollard exhibition ?

PORTRAIT OF GUSTAVE COQUIOT
Paris, 1901.
Oil on cardboard.
Size : 46 x 38 cm.
Signed bottom left : Picasso.

Exh. Jacques Seligmann & Co., New York, November 1936 : *Picasso, Blue and Rose Periods,* No. 5, repr. in cat. Marlborough Fine Art, London, 1950 : *French Masters of the XIXth and XXth Centuries,* No. 32. Galerie Kaganovitch, Paris, May–July 1951 : *Œuvres choisies du XXᵉ siècle.* Galerie Charpentier, Paris, 1952 : *Cent portraits d'homme,* No. 726. Kunstmuseum, Winterthur, June–July 1955 : *Maîtres européens, 1790–1910,* No. 152. Munich - Cologne - Hamburg, 1955–1956 : *Picasso 1900–1955,* No. 5. Kunsthaus, Zurich, June 7– September 30, 1958 : *Sammlung Emil G. Bührle,* No. 303. Berlin, 1958, No. 73. Haus der Kunst, Munich, December 5, 1958–February 15, 1959: *Hauptwerke der Sammlung Emil G. Bührle,* No. 118.

Bibl. Z. I. 85. Merli, 1948, No. 44. C.-P. No. 82. Sabartés and Boeck, p. 458, No. 15. Florent Fels, *L'Art Vivant, de 1900 à nos jours,* Geneva, 1950, p. 65. Sutton, 1955, repr. No. 3. Raymond Cogniat, *Picasso-Figures,* Lausanne, 1959, p. 11 (repr. in color).

Coll. Pierre Loeb, Paris ; Alphonse Bellier, Paris ; Acquired in 1953 by Emil G. Bührle ;

Emil G. Bührle Foundation, Zurich.

Color plate, page 11.

VI. 17
COURTESAN WITH A JEWELED COLLAR
Paris, 1901.
Oil on canvas.
Size : 65.3 x 54.5 cm.
Signed top left : Picasso.

Exh. Galerie Berthe Weill, Paris, April 1902, No. 2. Knoedler & Co., New York, 1947 : *Picasso before 1907,* No. 8. Santa Barbara Museum of Fine Arts, August 1953 : *Fiesta Exhibition.* Marion Koogler McNay Art Institute, San Antonio, Texas, November 1954 : *Inaugural exhibition,* No. 5. Denver Art Museum, October 1–November 18, 1956 : *Turn of the Century Paintings, 1880–1920.* Museum of Modern Art, New York, June 8–September 6, 1960 : *Art Nouveau Exhibition.* University of California, Los Angeles, October 25–November 12, 1961 : *Picasso,* No. 1. Art Gallery of Toronto and Montreal Museum of Fine Arts, 1964 : *Picasso and Man,* No. 11, repr. in cat. p. 31. Dallas Museum of Fine Arts, February 8–March 26, 1967 : *Picasso,* No. 4, repr. in cat. p. 13.

Bibl. Adrien Farge : Preface to the catalogue of the Berthe Weill exhibition, 1902. Félicien Fagus, *Revue blanche,* September 1, 1902 : "The strong outlines against dull blue, the unconscious dignity, the feline contortion of the shoulders and the hands, the fixity of the stare under a hair style like that of an idol with an enormous dark blue feathered hat, makes something hieratic out of her..." Z. I. 42. C.-P. No. 73. Penrose, 1958, pl. II, No. 9. *Los Angeles County Museum of Art Bulletin,* vol. XV, 1963, p. 5.

Coll. Ricardo Viñes, Paris ; Mr. and Mrs. George Gard de Sylva, Los Angeles ; (Price in 1946, $19.500) ;

The Los Angeles County Museum of Art, Collection of Mr. and Mrs. George Gard de Sylva.

Color plate, page 43.

VI. 18
LA GOMMEUSE
Paris, 1901.
Oil.
Size : 81.3 x 54 cm.
Signed top left : Picasso.

Bibl. Z. I. 104. W.C.A., XII. No. 4187.

Coll. Ambroise Vollard, Paris ; Joseph von Sternberg, Hollywood ; Parke-Bernet, New York, sold in 1949 for $3.500 ; Jacques Sarlie, New York ; Sale of the Jacques Sarlie collection, Sotheby & Co., London, October 12, 1960, No. 5, sold for £30,000 ; bought by Alex Maguy, Paris ;

Private collection, Paris.

This nude figure, unnaturally squat, might be the same model as *Woman with a Jeweled Collar* (V. 48) and *Courtesan with a Jeweled Collar* (VI. 17). Through her we can imagine the strange *Virgin with Golden Hair.* Note the relative smallness of the signature, like that in VI. 17 and *Women at the Fountain* (VI. 10). This signature characterizes most of the works of this period.

VI. 19
PORTRAIT OF SABARTÉS
(The Glass of Beer)
Paris, 1901.
Oil on canvas.
Size : 82 x 66 cm.
Signed top left : Picasso.

Exh. Maison de la Pensée française, Paris, June 1954 : *Picasso,* No. 3. Pushkin Museum, Moscow, 1955 : *L'Art français du XVᵉ au XXᵉ siècle,* repr. in cat. pl. 50. The Hermitage Museum, Leningrad, 1956 : *L'Art français du XVᵉ au XXᵉ siècle,* repr. in cat. p. 46. Grand Palais, Paris, 1966–1967 : *Hommage à Pablo Picasso,* No. 10, repr. in cat.

Bibl. Z. I.97. Catalogue of paintings in the collection of S. I. Tschukin, Moscow, 1913, No. 158. Tougueuhold, *La collection française de S. I. Chtchoukine* in "Apollon," St. Petersburg, 1914, No. 1-2, p. 31. Raynal, Munich, 1921, p. 3. Touguenhold, *Le premier musée de la peinture moderne occidentale, ancienne collection Chtchoukine,* Moscow-Petrograd, 1923, p. 116. Catalogue of Museum of Modern Western Art, Moscow, 1928, p. 78, No. 408. Réau, *L'Art français dans les musées russes,* 1929, No. 998. Paul Eluard, *A Pablo Picasso,* 1944, p. 143. Sabartés, *Picasso, Portraits et Souvenirs,* 1946, No. 2. C.-P. No. 85. Kahnweiler and Parmelin, *Picasso, Œuvres des musées de Leningrad et de Moscou,* 1955, pl. 15 (color). Sabartés and Boeck, p. 364. Penrose, 1958, pl. II, No. 1. Catalogue of paintings, Pushkin Museum, 1961, p. 147. Daix, 1964, p. 32 (color).

Coll. Galerie Kahnweiler, Paris, inv. No. 1063 ; S. I. Tschukin, Moscow (until 1918) ; Museum of Modern Western Art, Moscow (1918–1948) ;

The Pushkin Museum, Moscow.

VI. 20
THE TWO SALTIMBANQUES
(Harlequin and his Companion)
Paris, 1901.
Oil on canvas.
Size : 73 x 60 cm.
Signed top left : Picasso.

Exh. Maison de la Pensée française, Paris, June 1954 : *Picasso,* No. 1. Pushkin Museum, Moscow, 1955 : *L'Art français du XVᵉ au XXᵉ siècle.* Hermitage Museum, Leningrad, 1956 : *L'Art français du XVᵉ au XXᵉ siècle,* repr. p. 47.

Bibl. Z. I. 92. Makovski, *Les peintres français de la collection Morosov,* in "Apollon," St. Petersburg, 1912, p. 49. Catalogue of Museum of Modern Western Art, Moscow, 1928, p. 83. Réau, *L'Art français dans les musées russes,* 1929, No. 1045. Raynal, *Picasso, Œuvres des musées de Leningrad et de Moscou,* Paris, 1954. Kahnweiler and Parmelin, *Picasso, Œuvres des musées de Leningrad et de Moscou,* 1955, pl. 13 (color). Sutton, 1955, pl. I (color). Catalogue of the Pushkin Museum, Moscow, 1957, p. 109. Idem, 1961, p. 147. Sterling, 1957, pl. 152 (color). Diehl, 1960, p. 12 (color). Daix, 1964, p. 33 (color).

Coll. Galerie Vollard, Paris, until 1908 ; I. A. Morosov, Moscow (1908–1918) ; Museum of Modern Western Art, Moscow (1918–1948) ;

The Pushkin Museum, Moscow.

This painting is one of the most famous of the entire year 1901, but it did not find a buyer until later. It was bought by Morosov for 300 francs in 1908.

VI. 21
PORTRAIT OF MATEU F. DE SOTO
Paris, 1901.
Oil on canvas.
Size : 63 x 46 cm.
Signed top left : Picasso.

Exh. Winterthur Museum, 1955 : *La Collection privée d'Oskar Reinhart,* No. 105.

Bibl. Z. I. 94. C.-P. No. 77. Sutton, 1955, pl. III (repr. in color).

Coll. Private collection, Hamburg ; *Collection Oskar Reinhart, Winterthur.*

Like VI. 19, a work painted upon Picasso's arrival in Paris, in October 1901. These portraits of Picasso's two friends were done within the space of a few days. In the top right corner one sees the bottom of *The Mourners* in the Edward G. Robinson collection (VI. 2), which provides a good chronological reference.

VI. 22
HARLEQUIN
Paris, 1901.
Oil on canvas.
Size: 80 x 60.3 cm.
Signed and dated, bottom left: Picasso 1901.
Signature added in 1927, according to Douglas Cooper (Marseilles catalogue, 1959).

Exh. Cologne, 1912, No. 209 (entitled *Harlekin*, 1903). Cologne, March–April 1913 (entitled *Sitzender Pierrot*, 1903). Galerie Thannhauser, Munich, 1913. Brooklyn Museum, New York, 1926. Museum of Modern Art, New York, 1930, No. 77. Jacques Seligmann & Co., New York, 1936, No. 3, repr. Harvard University, 1936: *Harvard Tercentenary.* Boston Museum of Modern Art, 1938: *Picasso and Matisse,* No. 2. Museum of Modern Art, New York and The Art Institute of Chicago, 1939: *Picasso, Forty Years of his Art,* No. 12, repr. p. 27. Sociedad de Arte Moderno, Mexico, 1944: *Picasso,* cat. p. 41. Philadelphia Museum of Art, 1947: *Masterpieces of Philadelphia Private Collections,* No. 50. Knoedler, New York, 1947: *Picasso before 1907,* No. 5, repr. Philadelphia Museum of Art, 1947: *The Collection of Mr. and Mrs. Henry Clifford.* Idem, 1958: *Picasso,* No. 10. Musée Cantini, Marseilles, 1959: *Picasso,* No. 4, repr. Knoedler, New York, 1962: *Picasso, an American Tribute,* No. 15, repr. in color.

Bibl. Z. I. 79. M. K. Rohe, *Die Kunst für Alle,* XXVIII (1912–1913), with the title *Sitzender Pierrot,* 1903. C. Einstein, *Die Kunst des 20. Jahrhunderts,* 1926, p. 265 (dated 1906). Cat. collection John Quinn, 1926, p. 86. G. Stein, *Picasso,* London, 1938, pl. 4. Barr, *Forty Years,* p. 27. R. H. Wilenski, *Modern French Painters,* 1940, p. 138. R. Gómez de la Serna, *Picasso,* Turin, 1944, pl. III. Barr, *Fifty Years,* p. 21. Merli, 1948, pl. 64. Lieberman, 1954, pl. 13 (in color). C.-P. No. 71. W. Hess, *Das Kunstwerk, IX* (1955–1956), No. 3. Elgar and Maillard, p. 271. A. Vallentin, 1957, p. 66. Penrose, 1958, p. 81. Cogniat, 1959, p. 9 (in color).

Coll. Edwin Suermondt, Aix-la-Chapelle, until 1912 (?); Der neue Kunstsalon, Munich (1912–1913); John Quinn, New York, until 1924; Julia Quinn Anderson (1924–1930); Mary Anderson, New York, until 1936; Henry P. McIlhenny, Philadelphia (1936–1937); Mr. and Mrs. Henry Clifford, Radnor, Pennsylvania (1937–1960); Mr. and Mrs. John L. Loeb;

The Metropolitan Museum of Art, New York, Gift of Mr. and Mrs. John L. Loeb, 1960.

Color plate, page 49.

VI. 23
WOMAN WITH A CHIGNON
Paris, 1901.
Oil on canvas.
Size: 75 x 51 cm.
Signed top left: Picasso.
Recto: Little Girl with a Hat (V. 69).

Exh. Metropolitan Museum of Art, New York, May–September 1921: *Loan Exhibition of Impressionist and Post-Impressionist Paintings,* No. 79, repr. in cat. Museum of Modern Art, New York, 1933. Wadsworth Atheneum, Hartford, February–March 1934: *Picasso,* No. 6, repr. in cat. Jacques Seligmann & Co., New York, 1936: *Picasso, Blue and Rose Periods,* No. 8, repr. in cat. Fogg Art Museum, June–September 1946: *French Painting since 1870,* repr. in cat. p. 49. Musée de la Province de Québec, July–August 1949: *Maurice Wertheim Collection,* No. 19, repr. in cat. National Gallery of Art, Washington, D.C., June–September 1953. Philadelphia Museum of Art, June–September 1957. Minneapolis Institute of Fine Arts, June–August 1958. North Carolina Museum of Art, June–September 1960: *Modern French Art, Monet to Picasso,* repr. in cat. p. 35. Houston Museum of Fine Arts, June–September 1962: *Maurice Wertheim Collection,* repr. in cat. pl. 13.

Bibl. Z. I. 96. Huntington, *John Quinn Collection of Paintings, Watercolors, Drawings and Sculpture,* New York, 1926, p. 100. Zervos, *Picasso, œuvres inédites anciennes, Cahiers d'Art,* vol. III, 1920, p. 220. C.-P. No. 70. F. Deknatel, *Harvard Alumni Bulletin,* July 1951.

Coll. John Quinn, New York; Dr. and Mrs. Harry Bakwin, New York; Mr. and Mrs. Maurice Wertheim, New York;

Fogg Art Museum, Harvard University, Maurice Wertheim Bequest.

VI. 24
L'APÉRITIF
Paris, 1901.
Oil on canvas.   Size : 73 x 54 cm.
Signed top right : Picasso.

Bibl. Z. I. 98. Catalogue of The Hermitage Museum, Leningrad,
No. 90.45. C.-P. No. 86 *(Femme au café).* Sutton, 1955,
No. 11. Kahnweiler and Parmelin, 1955, pl. 45 (color). Ster-
ling, 1957, pl. 153 (color).

Coll. S. I. Tschukin, Moscow (1911–1918) ;   Museum of
Modern Western Art, Moscow (1918–1948) ;

The Hermitage Museum, Leningrad.

This work is often confused with the following one, *Absinthe
Drinker* (VI. 25). In the Kahnweiler archives it is entitled *La
Femme au verre d'absinthe* and dated autumn, 1901. We use
the title Zervos gives it, which is justified by the siphon of
soda water.

VI. 25
THE ABSINTHE DRINKER (Girl with Folded Arms)
Paris, 1901.
Oil on canvas.
Size : 77 x 61 cm.
Signed top right : Picasso.
Recto : *Woman at the Theater* (V. 71).

Exh. Never exhibited.

Bibl. Z. I. 100. Cassou, 1940, No. 40. C.-P. No. 124 (dated
1902). Walter Erben, 1947, pl. 2.

Coll. Galerie G. and L. Bollag, Zurich ;   For more than thirty
years :

Collection Charles Im Obersteg, Geneva.

On the other side of this canvas Picasso painted the astonishing
Woman at the Theater (V. 71), an unpublished work. Zervos
indicates incorrectly that a *Portrait of the Artist* is on the back.

VI. 26
WOMAN WITH A CIGARETTE
Paris, 1901.
Oil.
Size : 73 x 49.5 cm.
Signed top left : Picasso.

Bibl. Z. I. 99. Albert C. Barnes, *The Art in Painting,* New York,
1937, repr. p. 475. Paul Eluard, *A Pablo Picasso,* Geneva and
Paris, 1944, p. 142. Barnes Foundation, Inventory, No. 318.

Barnes Foundation, Merion, Pennsylvania.

VI. 27
GIRL IRONING
Paris, 1901.
Oil on canvas mounted on board.
Size : 49.5 x 25.7 cm.
Signed and inscribed, top right : a
Jacobus Sabartés Picasso.

Exh. Philadelphia Museum of Art,
1944 : *History of an American, Alfred
Stieglitz,* No. 89. Museum of Modern
Art, New York, 1947 : *Alfred Stieglitz
Exhibition : his collection,* No. 89.
The Art Institute of Chicago, 1948 :
*Alfred Stieglitz — his photographs and
his collection,* No. 11.

Bibl. Not in Z. J. Sabartés : *Picasso,
Retratos y recuerdos,* 1953. Elgar and
Maillard, Paris, 1955 (catalogue).

Coll. Jaime Sabartés, Barcelona, until
1912 ; Alfred Stieglitz, New York
(1912–1946) ; Estate of Alfred Stieglitz (1946–1949) ;

*The Metropolitan Museum of Art, New
York, Alfred Stieglitz Collection, 1949.*

According to Sabartés, this painting
dates from the end of Picasso's stay
in Paris. It belongs to the series of
studies of crouching and bent-over
postures which typify the women at
the beginning of the Blue Period,
especially *Mother and Child* (VI. 30).
La Soupe (VII. 11) and *The Two
Sisters (The Meeting)* (VII. 22). This
theme repeats itself in the *Woman
Ironing* of 1904 in the Thannhauser
Collection (XI. 6). Picasso signed a
certificate of authenticity for us
(September 3, 1965) authorizing the
Metropolitan Museum to permit us to
reproduce this work.

VI. 28
MOTHER AND CHILD
Paris, 1901.
Oil on canvas.
Size : 91.5 x 60 cm.
Signed center left : Picasso.

Exh. Bernheim-Jeune, Paris, 1926 :
Les Chefs-d'œuvre de Picasso. Ga-
lerie Georges Petit, Paris, 1932, No. 4.
Kunsthaus, Zurich, 1932, No. 12.
Bernheim-Jeune, Paris, 1936 : *Por-
traits de femmes et d'enfants,* No. 27.
Bernheim-Jeune, Paris, 1948 : *La
Femme dans la peinture française,*
No. 67. The Arts Council of Great
Britain, Tate Gallery, London, 1960 :
Picasso, No. 15, repr. in cat. pl. 5 a.
University of California Art Gallery,
Los Angeles, 1961 : *Bonne Fête Mon-
sieur Picasso,* No. 3.

Bibl. Z. I. 109. *L'Art moderne et
quelques aspects de l'Art d'autrefois,*

Bernheim-Jeune, Paris, 1919, Vol. 2,
pl. 48. *Cahiers d'Art,* 1932, 3-5.
Raymond Escholier, *La Peinture fran-
çaise, XXe siècle,* Paris, 1937, p. 75.
Maurice Gieure, *Initiation à l'œuvre de
Picasso,* 1951, pl. 9. Sabartés and
Boeck, p. 363. C.-P. No. 49. Sutton,
1955, pl. IV (repr. in color). Elgar and
Maillard, 1955 (catalogue). Helen
Kay, *Picasso's World of Children,*
New York, 1965, p. 47.

Coll. Ambroise Vollard, Paris, until
1911 ; Gaston Bernheim de Villiers,
Paris ; Sam Salz, New York ;

*Collection Mr. and Mrs. William Goetz,
Los Angeles.*

An engraving of this work, made by
Jacques Villon in 1930, was printed
in an edition of 200 (Bernheim-Jeune,
Paris).

VI. 29
MOTHER AND CHILD
Paris, 1901.
Pastel on paper mounted on canvas.
Size : 46.5 x 31 cm.
Signed bottom right : Picasso.

Exh. Kunsthaus, Zurich, autumn, 1932 :
Picasso, No. 11 (lent by Georg Reinhart).

Bibl. Z. I. 110. C.-P. No. 127.

Coll. La Peau de l'Ours, Paris, Sale,
March 2, 1914, No. 124, sold for
1,350 fr. to the Galerie Thannhauser,
Munich ; François Laya, Geneva ;

Georg Reinhart, Winterthur (1920–
1955) ;

Private collection, Küsnacht, Zurich.

This pastel is described as follows in
the sale catalogue of *La Peau de l'Ours,*
Paris, March 2, 1914, No. 124 :
"Woman and child. Seated, facing
left, dressed in a red skirt and a blue
cape, holding tightly in her arms her
sleeping child. Background pale
blue." This description fits perfectly
the subject and colors of this painting,
now in a private collection in Switzerland.

VI. 30
MOTHER AND CHILD
(Seated Woman and Child)
Paris, 1901.
Oil on canvas.
Size : 110.5 x 96.5 cm.
Signed top right : Picasso.

Exh. Wadsworth Atheneum, Hartford, February–March 1934 : *Picasso,* No. 8. Museum of Modern Art, New York, November 1939–January 1940 : *Picasso, Forty Years of his Art,* No. 17, repr. in cat. p. 31. Same exhibition : The Art Institute of Chicago, Museum of Fine Arts, Boston, San Francisco Museum of Fine Arts, City Art Museum of St. Louis, 1940. Fogg Art Museum, June–September 1946 :

French Painting since 1870, No. 50, repr. in cat. p. 51. Musée de la Province de Québec, July–August 1949 : *Maurice Wertheim Collection,* No. 20. National Gallery of Art, Washington, D.C., June–September 1953. Philadelphia Museum of Art, June–September 1957. Minneapolis Institute of Arts, June–August 1958. North Carolina Museum of Art, June–September 1960, repr. in cat. p. 37. Houston Museum of Fine Arts, June–September 1962 : *Manet to Picasso,* repr. in cat. pl. 14.

Bibl. Z. I. 115. Eugenio d'Ors, *Pablo Picasso,* Paris and New York, 1930, pl. 3. Barr, *Forty Years,* p. 31. Barr,

Fifty Years, p. 25. Sabartés and Boeck, p. 458, No. 17. C.-P. No. 121. Penrose, 1958, pl. II, No. 6. George A. Flanagan, *Understand and Enjoy Modern Art,* New York, 1960, p. 199. Blunt and Pool, No. 105. Helen Kay, 1965, p. 48.

Coll. John Quinn, New York ; Baron Otto Fukushima, Paris ; Mr. and Mrs. Maurice Wertheim, New York ;

Fogg Art Museum, Harvard University, Bequest of Maurice Wertheim.

VI. 31
MOTHER AND CHILD
Paris, 1901.
Oil on canvas.
Size : 92 x 65 cm.
Signed bottom right : Picasso.

Bibl. Z. I. 117.

Formerly Oppenheim Collection, Paris.

VI. 32
CHILD SEATED IN A CHAIR
Paris, 1901.
Oil.
Size : 65 x 54.5 cm.
Signed bottom right : Picasso.

Exh. Galerie Berthe Weill, Paris, April 1902, No. 3.

Bibl. Z. I. 116. Adrien Farge writes in the preface to the catalogue of the Berthe Weill exhibition : "How much soulfulness also in the pensive head of the child, even now heavy with all that innocence foresees of life's cruelty. Seated in a high chair, in a magnificent dress of royal blue, the child already is

thoughtful beyond her years ..." Félicien Fagus in *La Revue blanche,* September 1, 1902 : "A small, serious child, almost stiff, with a stubborn chin, heavy forehead, suffering, suspicious, pitiless eyes, painted all in blue, posing like an historic personage ..." Helen Kay, *Picasso's World of Children,* New York, 1965, p. 42. Barnes Foundation, Inventory, No. 128.

Barnes Foundation, Merion, Pa.

Picasso told us that this painting portrays the daughter of one of his Spanish friends at that time. Later on the little girl became blind.

VI. 33
PORTRAIT OF MATEU F. DE SOTO
Paris, winter, 1901.
Oil on canvas.
Size : 45 x 37 cm.
Unsigned.

Bibl. Z. I. 86. C.-P. No. 72.

Owned by the artist.

See the earlier portrait of Mateu F. de Soto (VI. 21).

Color plate, page 191.

VI. 34
PORTRAIT OF SABARTÉS
Paris, winter, 1901 (see note).
Oil on canvas.
Size : 44.5 x 36.8 cm.
Signed and dated, top left : Jaime Sabartés Picasso fecit 1902.

Bibl. Z. I. 87. Joan Merli, Buenos Aires, 1948, No. 42. Sabartés, *Picasso, Portraits et souvenirs,* Paris, 1946, No. 3.

Owned by the artist.

Done in Paris in the winter of 1901–1902, this painting was probably signed and dated just before Picasso's departure for Barcelona in January, 1902.

Color plate, page 191.

VI. 35
SELF-PORTRAIT
Paris, winter, 1901.
Oil on canvas.
Size : 81 x 60 cm.
Unsigned.

Exh. Galerie Georges Petit, Paris, summer, 1932 : *Picasso,* No. 3. Kunsthaus, Zurich, autumn, 1932 : *Picasso,* No. 19, repr. in cat. pl. 1. The Arts Council of Great Britain, Tate Gallery, London, 1960 : *Picasso,* No. 13, repr. in cat. pl. 1 a. Grand Palais, Paris, November 1966–February 1967 : *Hommage à Pablo Picasso,* No. 11, repr. in cat.

Bibl. Z. I. 91. Barr, *Fifty Years,* p. 23. C.-P. No. 150. Maurice Gieure, *Ini-*

tiation à l'œuvre de Picasso, 1951, pl. 1 (as *Portrait of a Man*). Sabartés, *Picasso, documents iconographiques,* 1954, No. 64. Elgar and Maillard, 1955 (catalogue). Penrose, 1958, pl. II, No. 3. Duncan, *Les Picasso de Picasso,* 1961, p. 204. Blunt and Pool, No. 80. Boudaille, 1964, p. 2. John Berger, *Success and Failure of Picasso,* London, 1965, p. 41.

Owned by the artist.

This work is the last self-portrait done in Paris in 1901. Picasso painted it during the winter before his departure for Barcelona in January 1902.

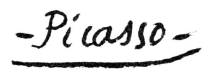

PORTRAIT OF CORINA PERE ROMEU, BARCELONA, 1902, OIL. COLLECTION OF THE ARTIST. UNPUBLISHED IN COLOR (VII. 15).

From the Blue of Paris to the Blues of Barcelona, 1902

The years 1902-1904 constitute basically a Barcelona period. In twenty-eight months, from January 1902, to April 1904, when he finally settled in Paris, Picasso left Barcelona only for one short stay in Paris, from October 1902, to January 1903. The rest of the time he lived in Calle de la Merced with his parents and took a studio on Calle Conde del Asalto with his friend, Mateu F. de Soto.

While Picasso was working in Barcelona, Mañach organized at Berthe Weill's Picasso's first show there, April 1-15, 1902, and arranged for another work to appear in a group show, June 2-15, 1902. The canvases were not new works, but from 1900-1901. These works are discussed in earlier catalogues.

There are several explanations for the apparent unproductivity of 1902 compared with 1901. To keep warm, Picasso burned a large number of drawings before he left Paris at the start of 1903. Perhaps among these works on paper were watercolors and gouaches. Also, to avoid transportation, he stored a number of rolled canvases with Pichot in Montmartre and only claimed them much later. Some were probably lost or else badly damaged.

In compiling this catalogue, we have respected the established classification of the works done in Paris or in Barcelona. But the problems of chronology discussed in Chapter III show that the development of the Blue Period was probably less contingent on the stay in Barcelona than is generally conceded. We know that the origins of the Blue Period were Parisian. It is more consistent with the pattern of Picasso's motivations that his decision to return to Barcelona was brought about by the stylistic change in his work, which was already apparent at the end of 1901.

The insufficiency of biographical landmarks handicaps chronological precision for this period. It is only by comparing attentively the works themselves that we can follow their development. From what we know today it seems that the Barcelona period could be characterized as being the intellectual phase of the Blue Period, in contrast with the works of 1903 which are based on the observation of reality.

Paris, October 1902 — January 1903

Picasso was dissatisfied by the lack of opportunity in Barcelona. He wanted to make another attempt at Paris, and prevailed on his friend Junyer to accompany him. They got to Paris in October and occupied rooms successively at the Hôtel des Ecoles, Rue Champollion, which proved too expensive, and the Hôtel du Maroc, 57 Rue de Seine (now the Hôtel Louis XV). He shared a garret room with a Spanish sculptor named Sisket, whose name Picasso later made his byword for disorder. There was no room to work. He looked up Max Jacob again and Jacob suggested they share a room he had rented on Boulevard Voltaire, near the department store Paris-France where he was working for his uncle, Gompel. Gompel eventually bought some of Picasso's works. How hard this time was for them shows up in their letters and in Max Jacob's accounts. When Picasso and Max Jacob were often without

the means to buy potatoes, the purchase of canvas was highly unlikely. For these several months Picasso had to limit himself to drawing.

During this stay, Picasso participated in his second show of the year, November 15 - December 15, at Berthe Weill's. There were four painters exhibiting: Girieud, Launay, Pichot and Picasso. He may have decided to leave Barcelona for Paris because of the hopes he put in this show. If so, he was disappointed with the results.

The list of Picasso's works in the catalogue is as follows:

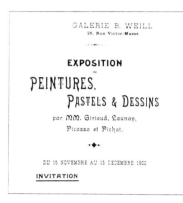

14. *Grand Portrait de Femme.*
15. *Grand Portrait de Femme devant la mer.*
16. *Petit Portrait de Femme.*
17. *Maison à Barcelone.*
18. *Scènes de Concerts (trois pastels).*
19. *La Misère : Mère et enfant.*
20. *Pelouse à Auteuil.*
21. *Etudes (dessins).*

It would be almost impossible to identify the works from these vague titles. There are, fortunately, clearer indications in the preface by Harlor and in a review in the *Mercure de France* by Charles Morice (See Documents, p. 334). They enable us to tell that Picasso was exhibiting several works recently brought from Barcelona. *La Maison à Barcelone* is surely *The Blue House* (VII. 1). It is likewise safe to assume on the basis of the descriptions that the show included *Crouching Woman* (VII. 5) and *Seated Woman in a Hood* (VII. 2). The *Café Scene* (VII. 12) was surely one of the "*scènes de concert*" since it is a pastel and the subject fits Charles Morice's description in the *Mercure de France* (see Documents, pp. 334-335). *La Misère : Mère et Enfant* may correspond to *Woman and Child on the Shore* (VII. 21) or to *Mother and Child in Profile* (VII. 20).

La Pelouse à Auteuil is, no doubt, one of the race course pictures of 1901 discussed in Catalogue V (31, 32, 33, 34). *La Femme nue accroupie* which made Charles Morice so rapturous, even to writing that it "gives you the feeling of a near-miracle," is perhaps the *Nude from the Back* (VII. 17), but more likely *Crouching Nude with Green Stocking* (VII. 16). However, we are advised by Harlor's preface that Berthe Weill augmented the show with older works that were not listed. All these "girls on the night streets, whose faces, under hats too big for them, have an impudent touch of rouge" must be canvases from 1901.

These accounts also corroborate 1902 as the date for all the works in Catalogue VII.

During this stay also, Picasso added marginal drawings to the *Noa-Noa* of Gauguin which Charles Morice had given him. This copy is in Picasso's possession and has never been reproduced.

As for the problem of dating Picasso's return to Barcelona, it must have been at the end of January. For one thing, he drew "The clear and simple story of Max Jacob" for his friend on January 13, 1903, in Paris. He could only afford a train ticket to Barcelona after he had sold the pastel *Woman and Child on the Shore* to a Madame Besnard. This pastel was done in Barcelona, and for this reason is in Catalogue VII.

VII. 1
THE BLUE HOUSE
Barcelona, 1902.
Oil.
Size : 50.5 x 40.5 cm.
Signed bottom right : Picasso.

Exh. Galerie Berthe Weill, Paris, November 15—December 15, 1902, No. 17 (entitled *Maison à Barcelone*). La Peau de l'Ours, March 2, 1914, No. 66, sold for 550 francs. Galerie Georges Petit, Paris, summer, 1932 : *Picasso,*

No. 9. Kunsthaus, Zurich, autumn, 1932 : *Picasso,* No. 14 (loaned by Miss Gertrude Stein, Paris).

Bibl. Not in Z. Sutton, 1955, pl. V (repr. in color).

Coll. Gertrude Stein, Paris ;

Collection of the Heirs of Miss Gertrude Stein.

VII. 2
SEATED WOMAN IN A HOOD
Barcelona, 1902.
Oil on canvas. Size : 88 x 69.5 cm.
Signed top right : Picasso.
Verso : Mother and Child, 1905 (XII. 8).

Exh. Haus der Kunst, Munich, October—December 1955 ; Rheinisches Museum, Cologne, December 1955—February 1956 ; Kunsthalle, Hamburg, March—April 1956 : *Picasso 1900—1955,* No. 8, repr. in cat.

Bibl. Z. I. 119. C.-P. No. 159 (*Femme accroupie près de la mer,* dated 1903). Sutton, 1955, No. 4. Blunt and Pool, No. 72.

Coll. Gertrude Stein, Paris ; Galerie Gaspari, Munich ; Dr. Fritz Nathan, Zurich ;

Staatsgalerie, Stuttgart.

VII. 3
DOZING ABSINTHE DRINKER
Barcelona, 1902.
Oil on canvas. Size : 80 x 62 cm.
Signed top right : Picasso.

Exh. "Entartete Kunst," Munich, 1937. Palazzo Reale, Milan, 1953, *Picasso,* No. 2, repr. in cat. Galerie Beyeler, Basel, 1966—1967 : *Picasso,* No. 3, repr. in color in cat.

Bibl. Z. I. 120. C.-P. No. 128. Elgar and Maillard, 1955 (catalogue). DU, No. 248, October 1961 : *80e Anniversaire de Picasso,* p. 22 (in color). Palau i Fabre, No. 74 (in color).

Coll. Gertrude Stein, Paris (1906) ; Dr. Troplowitz, Hamburg ; Kunsthalle, Hamburg ; Confiscated by the Nazi regime in 1937 ; Galerie Fischer, Lucerne, June 30, 1939, Sale of *Paintings and Sculpture by Modern Masters from German Museums,* No. 116, repr. in cat. p. 63, sold for 80,000 Swiss francs ;
Collection Othmar Huber, Glarus.

Here Picasso returns to the Parisian theme of the absinthe drinker. The expression has completely changed and become oddly painful. His model wears clothing typical of the Blue Period.

VII. 4
CROUCHING WOMAN
Barcelona, 1902.
Oil on canvas. Size : 63.5 x 50 cm.
Signed top right : Picasso.

Exh. Museum of Modern Art, New York, summer, 1932. Jacques Seligmann & Co., New York, November 1936 : *Picasso, Blue and Rose Periods,* No. 14, repr. in cat.

Bibl. Z. I. 160. Stephan Bourgeois, *The Adolph Lewisohn Collection of*

Modern French Paintings and Sculpture, 1928, p. 215. C.-P. No. 125. Maurice Raynal, 1959, p. 25 (repr. in color). W.C.A. XII.

Coll. Ambroise Vollard, Paris ; Sam A. Lewisohn, New York ; Jacques Sarlie, New York ; Sale of the Jacques Sarlie Collection, Sotheby & Co., London, October 12, 1960, No. 4, sold for £48,000 ;

Collection C. B. Nathhorst, Stockholm.

VII. 5
CROUCHING WOMAN
Barcelona, 1902.
Oil on canvas.
Size : 101.2 x 66 cm.
Signed top left : Picasso.

Exh. The Art Gallery of Toronto and
The Montreal Museum of Fine Arts,
January–March 1964 : *Picasso and
Man,* No. 13, repr. in cat. p. 33 and
frontispiece in color. Vancouver Art
Gallery, February 4–March 31, 1966 :

*Treasures from the Art Gallery of
Toronto* (no catalogue).

Bibl. Z. I. 121. Blunt and Pool, No. 71.
Daix, 1964, p. 36 (repr. in color).

Coll. Justin K. Thannhauser, Munich ;
Professor and Mrs. Bruno Mendel ;

*The Art Gallery of Toronto, Anonymous
Gift, 1963.*

Color plate, page 53.

VII. 6
SEATED WOMAN WITH A FICHU
Barcelona, 1902.
Oil on canvas.   Size : 100 x 69 cm.
Signed top left : Picasso.

Exh. Galerie Georges Petit, Paris,
summer, 1932 : *Picasso,* No. 25.
Kunsthaus, Zurich, autumn, 1932 :
Picasso, No. 13 (with the title : *La
Mélancolie).* Jacques Seligmann &
Co., New York, 1936 : *Picasso, Blue
and Rose Periods,* No. 13, repr. in cat.

Bibl. Z. I. 133. Waldemar George : *La
grande peinture contemporaine à la*

Collection Paul Guillaume, Paris, 1929,
p. 117. *Histoire de l'Art Contemporain,*
Paris, 1935, pl. 267. C.-P. No. 166
(dated 1903, medium incorrectly
given as : colored crayons). Sutton,
1955, repr. No. 16.

Coll. Paul Guillaume, Paris ;

Private collection, Detroit.

This painting is traditionally dated
Barcelona, 1902, but, according to
Sabartés *(Picasso, Portraits et Souvenirs),* it was done in Paris during the
winter of 1901–1902.

VII. 7
WOMAN WITH FOLDED ARMS
Barcelona, 1902.
Oil on canvas.
Size : 81 x 60 cm.
Signed top left : Picasso.

Exh. Der Rheinische Kunstsalon, Co-
logne 1913 (with the title : *Sitzende
Frau,* 1903). Kunsthaus, Zurich, 1932 :
Picasso, No. 10 (dated 1901, lent by
Baron G., Berlin). Jacques Selig-
mann & Co., New York, 1936 :
Picasso, Blue and Rose Periods, No. 9
(entitled *Elégie* and dated 1901), repr.
in cat. The Museum of Modern Art,
New York, 1939–1940, and The Art
Institute of Chicago, 1940 : *Picasso,
Forty Years of his Art,* No. 16, repr.
in cat.

Bibl. Z. I. 105 and Z. VI. 543 (catalogued twice). Raynal, 1922, pl. 9.
Barr, *Forty Years,* p. 30. Barr, *Fifty
Years,* p. 25. C.-P. No. 158 (dated
1903). Sutton, 1955, repr. No. 10.

Coll. Baron G., Berlin ; Mr. and Mrs.
Chauncey McCormick, Chicago ;

*Collection the Family of Chauncey
McCormick, Chicago.*

Dated 1901 by Zervos (Vol. I, No. 105),
Seligmann and Barr, and 1903 by
Zervos (Vol. VI, No. 543) and Cirici-
Pellicer, this painting probably belongs
to the series of crouched and seated
women done in Barcelona at the
beginning of 1902.

VII. 8
WOMAN WITH A SHAWL
(Portrait of Germaine Pichot)
Barcelona, 1902.
Oil on canvas.
Size : 46 x 40.8 cm.
Signed top right : Picasso.

Exh. Never exhibited.

Bibl. Unpublished.

Coll. Mme Paul Guillaume, Paris ; Acquired by the present owner in 1932 :

Collection Mrs. Harris Jonas, New York.

Picasso identified this unpublished work for us : A portrait, done in 1902, of Germaine Pichot, wife of the Catalan artist Ramón Pichot.

VII. 9
WOMAN WITH A BLUE SCARF
Barcelona, 1902.
Oil on canvas.
Size : 63 x 52.4 cm.
Signed top left : Picasso.

Exh. Galerie Georges Petit, Paris, summer, 1932 : *Picasso,* No. 11. Kunsthaus, Zurich, autumn, 1932 :

Picasso, No. 17 (entitled *Buste de femme,* loaned by M. Picasso, Paris). Grand Palais, Paris, November 1966– February 1967 : *Hommage à Pablo Picasso,* No. 12, repr. in cat.

Bibl. Z. I. 155.

Owned by the artist.

VII. 10
WOMAN WITH FRINGED HAIR
Barcelona, 1902.
Oil on canvas. Size : 60 x 49 cm.
Signed top left : Picasso.

Exh. The Baltimore Museum of Art, May–October 1930 : *The Cone Collection,* No. 43, repr. in cat. p. 2. The Baltimore Museum of Art, 1941 : *A Century of Baltimore Collecting,* cat. p. 85. The Baltimore Museum of Art, October–November 1954 : *Man and his Years,* cat. p. 122. Knoedler & Co., New York, January–February 1955 : *The Cone Collection.*

Bibl. Z. I. 118. Raynal, 1921, pl. 15 (titled *Portrait*). The Cone Collection of Baltimore, Maryland : *Catalogue of Paintings, Drawings and Sculpture of the 19th and 20th Centuries,* Baltimore, 1934, pl. 58. *Handbook of the Cone Collection,* The Baltimore Museum of Art, 1955, No. 83, repr. p. 33. Sutton, 1955, No. 13 *(Tête de femme).*

Coll. Gertrude Stein, Paris ; Dr. Claribel and Miss Etta Cone, Baltimore ;

The Baltimore Museum of Art, Cone Collection.

VII. 11
LA SOUPE
Barcelona, 1902.
Oil on canvas.
Size : 37 x 45 cm.
Signed two-thirds down, right : Picasso.

Exh. Knoedler & Co., New York, 1947 : *Picasso before 1907,* No. 13. The Art Gallery of Toronto and The Montreal Museum of Fine Arts, 1964 : *Picasso and Man,* No. 14, repr. in cat. p. 34.

Bibl. Z. I. 131. Gertrude Stein, *Picasso,* Paris, 1938, pl. 7 *(La Mère et l'enfant).* Paul Eluard, *A Pablo Picasso,* 1944,

p. 65. C.-P. No. 122. Sutton, 1955, No. 5 *(La Mère et l'enfant).* Helen Kay, 1965, p. 49.

Coll. Gertrude Stein, Paris ; Klaus Sternheim, Paris ; von Ripper ; Knoedler & Co., New York ;

Collection Mrs. Harold Crang, Toronto.

Compare the curve of the woman's back to those of the two women in *The Two Sisters* (VII. 22). A study for this painting is catalogued as D. VII. 1. Cf. also Z. VI. 418 and 420.

VII. 12
CAFÉ SCENE
Barcelona, 1902.
Pastel on cardboard.
Size : 30.5 x 38.7 cm.
Signed bottom right : Picasso.

Exh. Galerie Berthe Weill, Paris, November 15–December 15, 1902, No. 18 (see note). Knoedler & Co., New York, April–May, 1962 : *Picasso, an American Tribute,* No. 12, repr. in cat. Fort Worth Art Center Museum, February 8–March 26, 1967 : *Picasso,* No. 143.

Bibl. Not in Z. *Art in America,* No. 1, 1962, p. 97.

Coll. Theodore Schempp ;

Collection Mr. and Mrs. Lee A. Ault, New York.

Statement of authenticity signed for us by Picasso, September 3, 1965. This pastel was described by Charles Morice in his article on the exhibition at Berthe Weill's gallery (see *Mercure de France,* December 1902, p. 804, reproduced in this book, pages 334–335).

VII. 13
TWO WOMEN AT A BAR
Barcelona, 1902.
Oil on canvas.
Size : 80 x 91.4 cm.
Signed top left : Picasso.

Exh. Boston Museum of Modern Art, 1938 : *Picasso and Matisse,* No. 3. Perls Galleries, New York, 1939 : *Picasso before 1910,* No. 16, repr. on the cover. Museum of Modern Art, New York, 1939–1940, Art Institute of Chicago and St. Louis Museum, 1940 : *Picasso, Forty Years of his Art,* No. 18, repr. in cat. p. 32. Virginia Museum of Fine Arts and Philadelphia Museum of Art, January–May 1941 : *The Collection of Walter P. Chrysler, Jr.,* No. 151, repr. in cat. The Arts Council of Great Britain, Tate Gallery, London, 1960 : *Picasso,* No. 16, repr. in cat. pl. 5 b. Grand Palais, Paris, November 1966–February 1967 : *Hommage à Pablo Picasso,* No. 281, repr. in cat.

Bibl. Z. I. 132. Gertrude Stein, *Picasso,* 1938, p. 138 (in color). Barr, *Forty Years,* p. 32. Barr, *Fifty Years,* p. 26. C.-P. No. 130. Sutton, 1955, No. 9. Elgar and Maillard, 1955 (catalogue). Blunt and Pool, No. 74.

Coll. Gertrude Stein, Paris ;

Collection Walter P. Chrysler, Jr., New York.

VII. 14
SEATED COUPLE FROM THE BACK
Barcelona, 1902.
Gouache on paper.
Size : 43 x 33 cm.
Unsigned.

Exh. Musée des Arts Décoratifs, Paris, June–October 1955 : *Picasso,* No. 7, repr. in cat. (entitled *Femmes assises vues de dos*). Munich, Cologne and Hamburg, 1955–1956 : *Picasso 1900–1955,* No. 10.

Bibl. Not in Z. Maurice Jardot : Catalogue of the Exhibition, Musée des Arts Décoratifs, Paris, 1955, No. 7, repr.

Coll. Bought from Clovis Sagot, in 1913, by the Marquis de Ganay ;

Collection André de Ganay, Buenos Aires.

This gouache is dated 1902 or 1903 by Maurice Jardot. We catalogue it here because of its relative similarity to the previous work (VII. 13). Statement of authenticity signed for us by Picasso, September 3, 1965.

VII. 15
CORINA PERE ROMEU
Barcelona, 1902.
Oil on canvas.
Size : 59 x 48.8 cm.
Signed left, shoulder level : Picasso.

Exh. Galerie Georges Petit, Paris, summer, 1932 : *Picasso,* No. 10. Kunsthaus, Zurich, autumn, 1932 : *Picasso,* No. 15. Grand Palais, Paris, November 1966 – February 1967 : *Hommage à Pablo Picasso,* No. 13, repr. in cat.

Bibl. Z. I. 130. C.-P. No. 157. Maurice Gieure, *Initiation à l'œuvre de Picasso,* Paris 1951, pl. 4 *(Jeune femme espagnole).* Elgar and Maillard, 1955 (catalogue).

Owned by the artist.

This is a portrait of Corina, the wife of Pere Romeu, owner of the *Quatre Gats.* Picasso designed the card announcing the birth of their son, May 12, 1902.

Color plate, page 205.

VII. 16
CROUCHING NUDE WITH GREEN STOCKING
Barcelona, 1902.
Watercolor on beige paper.
Size : 27.7 x 20 cm.
Signed bottom left : Picasso.

Bibl. Not in Z. Sabartés and Boeck, p. 459, No. 19. Elgar and Maillard, 1955, p. 29 (repr. in color).

Coll. Gertrude Stein, Paris ; André Schoeller, Paris ; Madame L., Paris ;

Private collection, Paris.

VII. 17
NUDE FROM THE BACK
Barcelona, 1902.
Oil on canvas. Size : 46 x 40 cm.
Signed top left : Picasso.

Exh. Lyons, 1953 : *Picasso,* No. 7. Musée des Arts Décoratifs, Paris, 1955 : *Picasso,* No. 5, repr. in cat.

Bibl. Z. VI. 449. C.-P. No. 131. Elgar and Maillard, 1955, p. 19 (repr. in color). Diehl, Paris, 1960, p. 9 (repr.

in color). Boudaille, 1964, p. 3. Palau i Fabre, No. 76 (repr. in color).

Coll. Robert de Rothschild, Paris ; Mlle Cécile de Rothschild, Paris ;

Private collection, Paris.

Completely blue, this beautiful study is handled very differently from the preceding nude (VII. 16).

VII. 18
MOTHER AND CHILD
Barcelona, 1902.
Oil on canvas.
Size : 40.7 x 33 cm.
Signed bottom left : Picasso.

Bibl. Not in Z. National Gallery of Scotland, 1960, catalogue of the Maitland Gift, repr. p. 49. Catalogue of reproductions, UNESCO, 1963, p. 358, No. 997.

Coll. René Gaffé, Brussels ; Galerie Berggruen, Paris ; Arthur Tooth & Sons, London (1950–1954) ; Acquired by Mr. and Mrs. Alexander Maitland in 1954 ; Sir Alexander Maitland, who gave it to the National Gallery of Scotland in 1960 ;

The National Gallery of Scotland, Edinburgh, Maitland Gift, 1960.

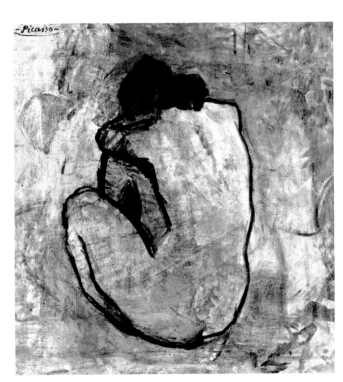

VII. 19
THE FISHERMAN'S GOODBYE
Barcelona, 1902.
Oil on canvas.
Size : 46.3 x 38 cm.
Signed bottom left : Picasso.

Exh. Kunstmuseum, Basel, June 9–July 8, 1956 : *Collection Richard Doetsch-Benziger,* No. 39, repr. in cat. p. 12.

Bibl. Not in Z.

Coll. Richard Doetsch-Benziger, Basel ;

Private collection, Küsnacht, Zurich.

We catalogue this painting with the somewhat fanciful title given it in the Doetsch-Benziger catalogue. Actually it pictures a mother and child by the sea, with a fisherman in his boat at the left. The dominant tones are rather sharply contrasted blues and yellows.

VII. 20
MOTHER AND CHILD IN PROFILE
(Mother and Child by the Sea)
Barcelona, 1902.
Oil on canvas. Size: 83 x 60 cm.
Signed top left: Picasso.
Inscribed in another hand : « à el Dr. Fontbona ».

Exh. Knoedler & Co., New York, 1962 : *Picasso, an American Tribute,* No. 14, repr. in cat.

Bibl. Z. VI. 478. C.-P. No. 126. Helen Kay, *Picasso's World of Children,* p. 51 (repr. in color).

Coll. Dr. Fontbona, Barcelona : Private collection, New York : Sotheby & Co., London, Sale, April 26, 1967, sold for £190,000 (bought by David Mann, head of the Bodley Gallery, New York) ;
Private collection, U.S.A.

Related to *Mother and Child* (VI. 30). The models are similar ; however, the treatment of this work is stylistically more fluid and more typical of the works of the Blue Period in Barcelona.
Color plate, page 57.

VII. 21
WOMAN AND CHILD ON THE SHORE
Barcelona, 1902 or 1903.
Pastel.
Size : 46 x 31 cm.
Signed bottom left : Picasso.

Exh. Kunsthaus, Zurich, 1932 : *Picasso,* No. 272 (*Mère et enfant,* dated 1903, for sale).

Bibl. Z. I. 381. C.-P. No. 161.

Coll. Madame Besnard (?), Paris ; Paul Rosenberg, Paris ;

Present location unknown.

This is probably the pastel with which Picasso paid for his return ticket to Barcelona by selling it to Madame Besnard, the wife of an art supply dealer in Paris. If it is, it could be dated January 1903, but it was done more likely in 1902. The drapery is similar in handling to work of 1902, but the subject relates to *The Tragedy,* 1903 (IX. 6).

VII. 22
THE TWO SISTERS (The Meeting)
Barcelona, 1902.
Oil on canvas.
Size : 152 x 100 cm.
Signed and dated, top right : Picasso 1902.

Exh. Tokyo, 1964 : *Picasso,* No. 4.

Bibl. Z. I. 163. Catalogue of paintings in the Hermitage Museum, 1949, No. 9071. C.-P. No. 129 (entitled *Confidences*). Sterling, 1957, fig. 70. Penrose, 1958, pl. II, No. 5 *(Two Sisters).*

Coll. S. I. Tschukin, Moscow, until 1918 ; Museum of Modern Western Art, Moscow (1918–1948) ;

The Hermitage Museum, Leningrad.

This oil is also called *The Meeting* and *Confidences.* It is one of the most famous paintings of this period.
Picasso decided on the subject after he saw women in the Saint-Lazare prison hospital for venereal diseases (cf. three studies : D. VII. 4 and 6, and Addenda, A. 14).

D. VII. 1
THE OFFERING
Barcelona, 1902.
India ink.
Size : 25 x 26 cm.
Signed and dated, bottom left : Picasso 1902.

Bibl. Not in Z. Sabartés and Boeck, p. 459, No. 20. Blunt and Pool, No. 124. Berggruen Archives No. 82.

Collection Galerie Berggruen, Paris.

This drawing is part of a series of studies for *La Soupe* (VII. 11). Cf. also Z. I. 192, Z. VI. 418 and 420.

D. VII. 2
RECLINING NUDE
Barcelona, 1902.
Ink and colored pencils, on back of a Junyer business card.
Size : 9 x 14 cm.
Unauthentic signature, top left. Re-signed by the artist, top left : Picasso.

Bibl. Unpublished.

Coll. Junyer Vidal, Barcelona ;

Collection Mr. and Mrs. Alex M. Lewyt, New York.

D. VII. 3
NUDE WITH LEFT ARM RAISED
Barcelona, 1902.
Ink and colored pencils.
Dimensions not known.
Unauthentic signature, bottom right : Picasso.

Bibl. Z. I. 153.

Formerly Junyer Vidal collection, Barcelona.

D. VII. 4
THE TWO SISTERS (Study)
Barcelona, 1902.
Sepia drawing.
Size : 20.8 x 13.4 cm.
Inscribed, top right : *Les deux sœurs.*

Bibl. Z. VI. 436.

Formerly Galerie Rosengart collection, Lucerne.

Study for *The Two Sisters* (VII. 22). See also D. VII. 6. A third, hitherto unknown study for the same painting is reproduced in the Addenda, No. A. 14.

D. VII. 5
SLEEPING NUDE AND SKETCHES OF NUDES
Barcelona, 1902.
Pen drawing on paper. Size : 37 x 53 cm.
Signed top right : Picasso.

Exh. Galerie G. and L. Bollag, Zurich, March 31– April 3, 1925 : Exhibition-Sale, No. 162, repr. in cat. pl. 58. Frankfurt and Hamburg, 1965 : *Picasso,* No. 13, repr. in cat. (detail).

Bibl. Not in Z. Ponge and Chessex, 1960, p. 3 (detail).

Coll. Mme B. Bollag, Zurich ;

Collection Max G. Bollag, Zurich.

The bottom left corner of this sketch sheet is missing (torn). The drawings of the nudes are similar to the ones in *The Painter Junyer and his Vision of Majorca* (D. VII. 7) and of *Caridad* (D. IX. 22).

D. VII. 6
STUDY FOR THE TWO SISTERS
Barcelona, 1902.
Graphite drawing.
Size : 16 x 11 cm.
Unsigned.

Bibl. Z. VI. 435. Blunt and Pool, No. 109.

Present location unknown.

Study for *The Two Sisters* (VII. 22). In these two studies (D. VII. 4 and D. VII. 6) and in Addenda No. A. 14, the woman on the left wears the Phrygian cap of the inmates of St. Lazare (see note, VII. 22).

D. VII. 7
THE PAINTER JUNYER AND HIS VISION OF MAJORCA
Barcelona, 1902.
India ink and colored pencils on paper.
Size : 16 x 22 cm.
Signed bottom right : Picasso (later signature).

Bibl. Z. VI. 495 (dated 1902 or 1903). C.-P. No. 101 (dated 1901).

Coll. Junyer Vidal, Barcelona ;

Private collection, Belgium.

This title is the one that Sabartés and Cirici-Pellicer give to the drawing.

D. VII. 8
SELF-PORTRAIT ON THE BEACH
Barcelona, 1902.
Ink and colored pencils, on the back of a Junyer business card.
Size : 9 x 14 cm.
Unauthentic signature, bottom right. Re-signed by the artist, bottom right : Picasso.

Bibl. Z. I. 129. C.-P. No. 102 (dated 1901). Sabartés, *Picasso, documents iconographiques,* No. 73. Sabartés and Boeck, p. 458, No. 18.

Formerly collection Junyer Vidal, Barcelona.

Zervos and Sabartés place this drawing at Barcelona in 1902. The unauthentic signature on the drawing as reproduced above has been removed and replaced by an authentic one.

D. VII. 9
WOMAN ON THE SHORE
Barcelona, 1902.
Ink and colored pencils, on the back of a Junyer business card.
Size : 14 x 9 cm.
Signed bottom left : Picasso.
(Later signature. The unauthentic signature, bottom left, has been effaced.)

Bibl. Z. I. 151. C.-P. No. 108 (entitled *Mendiante à la plage* and dated 1901).

Coll. Junyer Vidal, Barcelona ; O'Hana Gallery, London ;

Collection Gustave Kahnweiler, England.

Related to the two scenes of a mother and child by the sea (VII. 20 and VII. 21).

D. VII. 10
SEATED WOMAN WITH ARMS CROSSED
Barcelona, 1902.
Colored crayons and wash, on the back of a Junyer business card.
Size : 14 x 9 cm.
Signed top left : Picasso.
(Later signature. The unauthentic signature, bottom left, has been effaced.)

Exh. Sidney Janis Gallery, New York ; O'Hana Gallery, London ; Stoneleigh Abbey, Warwickshire ; Galerie Motte, Geneva, 1960 : *Picasso, his Blue Period,* No. 25, repr. in cat. (dated 1901). The New Gallery, New York, 1962 : *Picasso, an American Tribute,* No. 3, repr. in cat.

Bibl. Z. I. 114. C.-P. No. 113 (dated 1901).

Coll. Junyer Vidal, Barcelona ;

Private collection, New York.

Erroneously dated 1901 by Cirici-Pellicer and Jacques O'Hana, this drawing was done in Barcelona in 1902. Zervos and John Richardson *(American Tribute)* correctly date it 1902.

D. VII. 11
HEAD OF A WOMAN IN PROFILE
Barcelona, 1902–1903.
Conté crayon.
Size : 16.5 x 11 cm.
Signed top right : Picasso.

Exh. Buchholz Gallery, N. Y., 1945 : *Picasso, drawings and watercolors,* No. 5. Cranbrook, 1947 : *Collection John S. Newberry, Jr.* Detroit, 1947 : *Modern Drawings from Detroit Collections.* Fogg Art Museum, Buchholz Gallery, N.Y. and University of Michigan, 1948 : *Drawings and watercolors, Collection John S. Newberry, Jr.* San Francisco, 1948 : *The Newberry Collection.* Toronto, 1949 : *Picasso,* No. 35. Detroit, 1949 : *50 Drawings from the Newberry Collection,* No. 36. Princeton, 1949 : *Picasso, drawings,* No. 2. Fogg Art Museum, 1958 : *Collections of Members of Class 1933,* No. 67. Boston, 1962 : *51 Watercolors and Drawings, the Newberry Collection.*

Bibl. Not in Z. *Bulletin of the Detroit Institute of Arts,* vol. 44, No. 4, 1965, p. 68 and on cover.

Coll. G. Bernheim, Paris ; Lucie Weill, Paris ; John S. Newberry, Jr., Detroit ;

The Detroit Institute of Arts.

VIII. 1
MAN IN BLUE
Paris-Barcelona, winter, 1902–1903.
Oil on canvas.
Size : 88.5 x 76.5 cm.
Signed top right : Picasso.

Exh. Galerie Georges Petit, Paris, summer, 1932 : *Picasso,*
No. 12. Kunsthaus, Zurich, autumn, 1932 : *Picasso,*
No. 16 (entitled *Portrait d'homme* ; lent by M. Picasso,
Paris).

Bibl. Z. I. 142. André Level, 1928, pl. 6. Cassou,
1940, p. 45. C.-P. No. 134. Maurice Gieure, *Initiation
à l'œuvre de Picasso,* 1951, pl. 2 *(Portrait d'homme).*

Owned by the artist.

The paint has flaked off the bottom part of this work,
showing the canvas underneath. Commenting on the
subject matter, Picasso said, "He was a kind of madman
who roamed the streets. Everyone knew him in Barcelona." "Then you painted him in Barcelona ?"
"Models stay, but artists travel."

VIII. 2
THE POET CORNUTY *(Absinthe)*
Paris, winter, 1902–1903.
Watercolor.
Size : 31 x 23.5 cm.
Signed top right : Picasso.
On the back : note by Max Jacob on Cornuty.

Exh. Musée National d'Art Moderne, Paris, March–
April 1964 : *Collection André Lefèvre,* No. 239.

Bibl. Z. I. 182. C.-P. No. 147 (dated 1903).

Coll. La Peau de l'Ours, Paris, Hôtel Drouot, Sale,
March 2, 1914, No. 122, sold for 400 francs ;
André Lefèvre, Paris ; Sale of the André Lefèvre
collection (Part 3 : watercolors and drawings),
Palais Galliera, Paris, November 29, 1966, No. 37,
repr. in color in cat., sold for 160,000 F. ;

Private collection, Paris.

VIII. 3
INTIMACY (Women and Children)
Paris, winter, 1902–1903.
Pastel on paper.
Size : 37 x 46 cm.
Signed top right : Picasso.

Exh. (See note): Galerie Berthe Weill, Paris, October 24–
November 20, 1904, No. 37 (entitled *Scène d'intérieur,*
pastel). Musée des Arts Décoratifs, Paris, 1955 :
Picasso, No. 6, repr.

Bibl. Z. I. 180. André Level, 1928, pl. 7. C.-P. No. 144.
Cassou, 1959, p. 15 (repr. in color).

Coll. La Peau de l'Ours, Paris, Hôtel Drouot, Sale,
March 2, 1914, sold for 700 francs ; E. Level, Paris ;

Private collection, Paris.

Picasso's commentary on this work : "I was living in
the Rue Champollion. I wanted to do something to
make some money. I'm a little ashamed to admit it, but
that's how it was. So I did this pastel. I rolled it up and
carried it to Berthe Weill. She lived in Montmartre, at the
other end of Paris. It was snowing. And me with my
pastel under my arm.... She had no money.... So I
went away... and left her the pastel."

VIII. 4
THE MISTLETOE SELLER
Paris, winter, 1902–1903.
Gouache on paper.
Size : 55 x 38 cm.
Signed bottom right : Picasso.

Exh. Musée des Arts Décoratifs, Paris, 1955 :
Picasso, No. 8, repr. in cat.

Bibl. Z. I. 123. C.-P. No. 156. Sabartés and Boeck,
p. 459, No. 21.

Coll. Max Pellequer, Paris ;

Private collection, Paris.

VIII. 5
STUDY FOR THE MISTLETOE SELLER
Paris, winter, 1902–1903.
Ink and watercolor on paper.
Size : 37.5 x 27 cm.
Signed bottom left : Picasso.

Bibl. Not in Z. Berggruen archives, No. 1944.

Collection Galerie Berggruen, Paris.

Another sketch, on a piece of cardboard, for *The Mistletoe Seller* was partially blocked out when Picasso painted over it the gouache *Head of a Boy* in 1905 (D. XIII. 11).

D. VIII. 1
STUDY OF MALE NUDE WITH ARMS RAISED
Paris, winter, 1902–1903.
Pencil on paper.
Size : 46 x 24 cm.
Unsigned.

Exh. Petit Palais, Paris, 1935 : *Chefs-d'œuvre du Musée de Grenoble,* No. 337. Kunsthaus, Zurich, 1946 : *Musée et Bibliothèque de Grenoble,* No. 188.

Bibl. Not in Z. Gabrielle Kueny and Germain Viat, *Catalogue des dessins modernes du Musée de Grenoble,* Editions des Musées Nationaux, Paris, 1963, p. 195.

Coll. Galerie Zack, Paris ; Purchased in 1934 from the Galerie Zack by Musée des Beaux-Arts, Grenoble ;

Musée des Beaux-Arts, Grenoble.

This drawing is a variation of the one catalogued by Zervos (Z. VI. 515) with the inscription "*Paris, rue de Seine.*" Thus this study can be dated in the winter of 1902–1903.

FIGURES BY THE SEA (LES MISÉRABLES AU BORD DE LA MER), BARCELONA, 1903, OIL. SMITH COLLEGE MUSEUM OF ART, NORTHAMPTON, MASSACHUSETTS, GIFT OF JERE ABBOTT, 1966 (IX. 5).

ROOFS OF BARCELONA, BARCELONA, 1903, OIL. COLLECTION OF THE ARTIST. UNPUBLISHED IN COLOR (IX. 2).

Barcelona 1903

Picasso ended his stay in Paris in complete poverty. He returned to Barcelona, without money, sometime after the middle of January. He went to live with his parents again on Calle de la Merced, but almost immediately rented a studio, or rather a large room to use as a studio, with Angel de Soto on Calle Riera de San Juan (Sant Joan) until the beginning of 1904.

His work became finer and stronger. His blues deepened, the figures went through stages of undress to stand revealed in all their expressive nudity. Unlike 1900 and 1901, the year 1903 is short of facts with which to arrive at an exact chronology of the important series of major canvases which bear this date. Hence we have classified them by subjects : scenes of Barcelona; portraits of friends and acquaintances; the wonderful series of *pauvres* and *miséreux*, at first clothed and with a very Spanish character, then gradually disrobed until they achieve the state of *The Embrace* (IX. 12) and the highly symbolic synthesis of *La Vie* (IX. 13); works of various subjects, particularly studies of nudes; and finally, study drawings for known pictures or more often, random sketches and anecdotal jottings. Also in the course of 1903, Picasso lavishly decorated the walls of Jaime Sabartés' lodgings on Calle Consulado in Barcelona. There is no documentation of these mural paintings beyond the descrip-

tion Sabartés provided in his *Picasso, Portraits et Souvenirs* (pp. 103-106); they were destroyed when the next tenant moved in.

Beginning of a Transition : Barcelona, Winter, 1903-1904

In the last months of 1903 and the first of 1904 Picasso produced several watercolors in a new manner. He evolved a flowing treatment which is more than the result of the medium; it predicts the direction he would follow. However, this change is not immediate and Picasso continued to work in the same spirit as that of 1903. It was not until 1905 that he fully developed these experimental or spontaneous notations. The last works from Barcelona in the first months of 1904 could just as well have been from 1903.

From the first of the year, Picasso had a studio to himself on Calle del Commercio and he left his parents' home for a small room of his own on the same street.

The number of works of these last months in Barcelona is comparatively unimportant. This is not surprising, inasmuch as the long-considered plan for leaving again engrossed Picasso and soon he was involved in the actual preparations. In March 1904 he packed up canvases of the year before and sent them to Paris. Some of these were exhibited at Berthe Weill's in October.

IX. 1
STREET IN BARCELONA
AND THE PALACE OF FINE ARTS
Barcelona, 1903.
Oil on canvas.
Size : 60 x 40 cm.
Signed bottom left : Picasso.

Exh. The Arts Council of Great Britain,
Tate Gallery, London, 1960 : *Picasso,*
No. 17, repr. in cat. pl. 5 e (lent by
the Hon. Michael Astor, London).

Bibl. Z. I. 122.

Coll. Josef Stransky, New York ; The
Hon. Michael Astor, London ;

Private collection, London.

The Palace of Fine Arts in Barcelona
was built for the Universal Exhibition
in 1888. It was pulled down in 1940,
after severe damage from bombings
during the Spanish Civil War. It was
located east of the old quarter of
Barcelona, quite far from Picasso's
studios.

IX. 2
ROOFS OF BARCELONA
Barcelona, 1903.
Oil on canvas.
Size : 69.5 x 109.6 cm.
Unsigned.

Exh. Galerie Georges Petit, Paris,
summer, 1932 : *Picasso,* No. 14,
Kunsthaus, Zurich, autumn, 1932 :
Picasso, No. 20 (lent by M. Picasso,
Paris). Grand Palais, Paris, November
1966–February 1967 : *Hommage à
Pablo Picasso,* No. 14, repr. in cat.

Bibl. Z. I. 207. André Level, 1928,
pl. 5. C.-P. No. 145.

Owned by the artist.

This landscape of roofs in Barcelona
is a view from Picasso's studio in the
Calle Riera de Sant Joan (in Catalan :
Sant Joan ; in Spanish : San Juan).
See the note to the following entry.

Color plate, page 218.

IX. 3
BARCELONA AT NIGHT
Barcelona, 1903.
Oil on canvas.
Size : 54 x 45.5 cm.
Signed bottom right : Picasso.

Exh. City Art Museum of St. Louis,
1931 : *Paintings and Prints by Masters
of Post-Impressionism,* No. 25. Haus
der Kunst, Munich, October-December 1955 ; Köln-Deutz Rheinisches
Museum, December 1955–February
1956 ; Kunstverein Hamburg, March–
April 1956 : *Picasso 1900-1955,*
No. 4. Kunsthaus, Zurich, 1958 :
Sammlung Emil G. Bührle, No. 305,
repr. in cat. p. 242, pl. 75. The Royal
Scottish Academy, Edinburgh, August
19–September 17, 1961 : *Masterpieces
of French Painting from the Bührle
Collection,* No. 75. Kunstmuseum
Lucerne, August 11–October 27, 1963 :
Sammlung Emil G. Bührle, No. 70.

Bibl. Not in Z. Palau i Fabre, No. 81
(repr. in color).

Coll. Georges Wildenstein, Paris and
New York ; Mrs. Charles H. Schweppe,
New York ; Emil G. Bührle, Zurich ;

*Collection of the family of E.G. Bührle,
Zurich.*

We owe the following details to information supplied us by Señor Ainaud
de Lasarte, general director of the art
museums of Barcelona : " The painting
is a view from Picasso's studio in the
Riera de Sant Joan. The street and the
district as a whole were demolished
between 1907 and 1913... The scene
was painted from the northwest side
of the Riera de Sant Joan, looking
toward the south. At the left, one sees
the roof and facade of the baroque
church of Santa Marta (18th century)... Today, the site corresponds to
the block of houses located between
the Via Layetana and the Via Tapineria,
northeast of the cathedral."

IX. 4
POVERTY *(Les Misérables)*
Barcelona, 1903
Ink and blue wash.
Size : 37.5 x 26.7 cm.
Signed bottom right : Picasso.

Exh. Arts Council of Great Britain, 1952–1953 : *Drawings and Watercolours from the Whitworth Art Gallery, Manchester,* No. 33. Idem, 1960, No. 94, repr. in cat. pl. 11. Norwich Castle Museum, 1961 : *Continental Drawings from the Whitworth Art Gallery.* Royal Academy, London, winter, 1962 : *Primitives to Picasso,* No. 421, repr. in cat. p. 61.

Bibl. Not in Z.

Coll. A. E. Anderson, who gave it to the Whitworth Art Gallery in 1928 ;

Whitworth Art Gallery, University of Manchester.

Not included in previous monographs on Picasso's work, this watercolor is a study closely related to the following entry (IX. 5). In the drawing catalogue IX, we have a variant of the same subject : D. IX. 1.

IX. 5
FIGURES BY THE SEA
(Les Misérables au Bord de la Mer)
Barcelona, 1903.
Oil on canvas.
Size : 59.7 x 49.5 cm.
Signed top right : Picasso.

Exh. Hamburg, 1927 : *Art européen d'aujourd'hui.* Wadsworth Atheneum, Hartford, January 24–February 14, 1933 : *Literature and Poetry in Painting since 1850* (entitled *Au bord de la mer*). Smith College Museum of Art, Northampton : at various times between 1932 and 1947.

Bibl. Z. I. 197.

Coll. Josef Stransky, New York ; Purchased for $3.000, in 1933, by Jere Abbott, Dexter, Maine ;

Smith College Museum of Art, Northampton, Massachusetts, Gift of Jere Abbott, 1966.

In the collection of Josef Stransky, this work was called *Saltimbanques by the Sea.* We have eliminated the word *saltimbanques* because it is obviously incorrect and causes confusion with the works of 1905. See the study above : *Poverty* (IX. 4).

Color plate, page 217.

IX. 6
THE TRAGEDY
Barcelona, 1903.
Oil on wood panel.
Size : 105.4 x 69 cm.
Signed bottom right : Picasso.
Dated top right : 1903.

Exh. Museum of French Art, New York, 1931 : *Picasso, Braque, Léger,* No. 2. The Art Institute of Chicago, 1943 : *20th Century French Paintings from the Chester Dale Collection.*

Bibl. Z. I. 208. M. Dale, *Picasso,* New York, 1930, pl. 5. R. Flint in *Art News,* February 21, 1931, p. 14. Gertrude Stein, *Picasso,* Paris, 1938, pl. 8. Gertrude Stein, *Picasso,* London, 1939, pl. 9. Cassou, 1940, p. 50. C.-P. No. 162. Maurice Gieure, *Initiation à l'œuvre de Picasso,* 1951, pl. 8 *(Les Parias).* Elgar and Maillard, 1955 (catalogue). Sutton, 1955, No. 17.

National Gallery of Art, Washington, D.C., 1965, *Twentieth Century Paintings and Sculpture of the French School in the Chester Dale Collection,* p. 69 (also in 1952 and 1960 editions). Helen Kay, 1965, p. 50.

Coll. Schubert, Bochum ; Mr. and Mrs. Chester Dale, New York ;

The National Gallery of Art, Washington, D.C., Chester Dale Collection.

Here Picasso returns to a theme painted in Barcelona in 1902 (cf. VII. 21). However, in this famous work he conveys a more tragic mood of solitude and intensifies the modeling of the figures and the monochrome blue of the palette.

Color plate, page 59.

X. 7
MOTHER AND CHILD
(The Sick Child)
Barcelona, 1903.
Pastel on paper.   Size : 47.5 x 41 cm.
Signed and dated, top right : Picasso
1903.

Exh. Galeries Dalmau, Barcelona,
October 25–November 15, 1920 : *Art
Francès d'avantguarda,* No. 66. III
Bienal Hispanoamericana de Arte,
Barcelona, 1955 : *Precursores y maes-
tros del arte Español contemporáneo,*
No. 12.

Bibl. Z. I. 169.   C.-P. p. 144 (color).
Florent Fels, 1950, p. 249 (color).
Jacques Lassaigne, 1952, p. 119
(color).   Diehl, 1960, p. 13 (color).
Blunt and Pool, No. 92. Sabartés,
Picasso, les bleus de Barcelone, 1963,
pl. 7 (color).   Helen Kay, 1965, p. 53.
Palau i Fabre, No. 75 (color).

Coll. L. Plandiura, Barcelona ; Museo
de Arte Moderno, Barcelona ;

Picasso Museum, Barcelona.

IX. 8
HEAD OF A WOMAN
Barcelona, 1903.
Pastel.
Size : 29 x 28.3 cm.
Signed top right : Picasso.

Exh. The Solomon R. Guggenheim
Museum, New York, April-September
1965 : *First Showing of Masterpieces
of Modern Art from the Thannhauser
Foundation,* No. 38, repr. in color in
cat. p. 43.

Bibl. Z. I. 206.   C.-P. No. 175. Sutton,

1955, repr. No. 29.

Coll. Justin K. Thannhauser, New
York ;

*The Solomon R. Guggenheim Mu-
seum, New York, Justin K. Thannhauser Foundation.*

IX. 9
MÉNAGE DE PAUVRES
(Man and Woman in a Café)
Barcelona, April, 1903.
Oil on canvas.
Size : 81.5 x 65.5 cm.
Signed and dated, top right : Picasso
1903, avril.

Exh. Fransk Genombrottskonst, Stockholm - Oslo - Göteborg - Copenhagen,
1931, No. 120. Kunstnernes Hus, Oslo,
1956 : *Picasso,* No. 4.

Bibl. Z. I. 167. Paul Jamot, *L'Art fran-

çais en Norvège* in *La Renaissance,*
No. 2, February, 1929, p. 93. *Kunst og
Kultur,* 1938, p. 46. *Franske malerei i
Nasjonalgalleriet,* p. 51. Sutton, 1955,
No. 15.

Coll. Bilbao (Vilaro ?), Barcelona ;
Alfred Flechtheim, Düsseldorf (1912) ;
Dr. Alfred Gold, Copenhagen ; Dona-
tion Nasjonalgalleriets Venner (1917) ;

Nasjonalgalleriet, Oslo.

Cf. a sketch for this work : Addenda
No. A. 16.

IX. 10
CROUCHING WOMAN
Barcelona, 1903.
Gouache and watercolor on paper
mounted on canvas.
Size : 55 x 38 cm.
Signed top right : Picasso.

Exh. Kunsthaus, Zurich 1932 : *Picasso,*
No. 274.   Palais de Beaulieu, Lausanne, 1964 : *Chefs-d'œuvre des collections suisses,* No. 226, repr. in cat.

Bibl. Z. VI. 476.   Paul Eluard, *A Pablo

Picasso,* 1944, p. 70 (incorrectly dated
1905).

Coll. G. and L. Bollag, Zurich (bought
directly from the artist) ;

Collection Max G. Bollag, Zurich.

Color plate, page 61.

IX. 11
THE EMBRACE
Barcelona, 1903.
Gouache.
Dimensions not known.
Signed and dated, bottom right :
Picasso 1903.

Bibl. Z. I. 162. Blunt and Pool, No. 89.

Formerly Galerie Thannhauser Collection, Paris.

Study for *The Embrace* (IX. 12) in the Jean Walter-Paul Guillaume collection. Since this version, with the couple standing out against a plain background is dated, it confirms that both works were done in Barcelona in 1903.

IX. 12
THE EMBRACE
Barcelona, 1903.
Pastel.
Size : 98 x 57 cm.
Signed top right : Picasso.

Exh. Galerie Charpentier, Paris, 1946 : *Cent Chefs-d'œuvre de l'Ecole de Paris.* Paris, 1960 : *Les sources du XXᵉ siècle,* No. 551. Musée de l'Orangerie des Tuileries, Paris, 1966 : *Collection Jean Walter-Paul Guillaume,* No. 92, repr. in cat. p. 194. Grand Palais, Paris, November 1966–February 1967 : *Hommage à Pablo Picasso,* No. 16, repr. in cat.

Bibl. Z. I. 161. *Les Arts à Paris,* No. 17, May, 1930, p. 6 (entitled *La joie pure*). C.-P. No. 170 (entitled *L'Embrassement*). Elgar and Maillard, 1955 (catalogue). Sutton, 1955, pl. VI (repr. in color). Palau i Fabre, No. 96 (repr. in color).

Coll. Ambroise Vollard, Paris ; Paul Guillaume, Paris ; Madame Domenica Walter, Paris ; since 1966 :

Musée de l'Orangerie des Tuileries, Paris, Collection Jean Walter-Paul Guillaume.

IX. 13
LA VIE
Barcelona, 1903.
Oil on canvas.
Size : 197 x 127.3 cm.
Signed top left : Picasso.

Exh. Galerie Thannhauser, Berlin, 1927 : *Erste Sonderausstellung in Berlin,* No. 175, repr. cat. p. 117. Alex Reid & Lefevre Gallery, London, 1931. Galerie Georges Petit, Paris, 1932 : *Picasso,* No. 17. Kunsthaus, Zurich, 1932 : *Picasso,* No. 18, repr. cat. pl. III. MMA, New York and AIC, Chicago, 1939-1940 : *Picasso, Forty Years of his Art,* No. 19, repr. cat. p. 33. Knoedler, New York, 1947 : *Picasso before 1907.* Tate Gallery, London, 1960 : *Picasso,* No. 20, repr. cat. pl. 3 a. Musée des Augustins, Toulouse, 1965 : *Picasso et le théâtre.* Grand Palais, Paris, 1966–1967 : *Hommage à Picasso,* No. 15, repr. in cat.

Bibl. Z. I. 179. Eugenio d'Ors, 1930, pl. 11. Barr, *Forty Years,* p. 33. Cassou, 1940, p. 51. Barr, *Fifty Years,* p. 26. Sutton, 1948, p. 2. Maurice Gieure, 1951, pl. 7. C.-P. No. 179.

Elgar and Maillard, 1955 (catalogue). Sabartés and Boeck, p. 366. Penrose, 1958, pl. II, No. 4. Jan Runnqvist, *Minotauros - Picassos Konst 1900–1937,* Stockholm, 1959, p. 13. Lieberman, 1961, pl. 17 (in color). Germain Seligman, *Merchants of Art, 1880–1960, 80 Years of Professional Collecting,* New York, 1961, pl. 69. Blunt and Pool, No. 115. Palau i Fabre, No. 105 (in color).

Coll. Ambroise Vollard, Paris ; Etienne Bignou, Paris ; J. K. Thannhauser, Lucerne ; Rhode Island School of Design, Providence ;

The Cleveland Museum of Art, Gift of Hanna Fund, 1945.

A major work in which Picasso synthesizes several themes. We discuss it in Chapter III. One of the studies for *La Vie* (cf. D. IX. 5), dated Barcelona, May 2, 1903, is an important point of reference in dating this large canvas.

Color plate, page 223.

LA VIE, BARCELONA, 1903, OIL. THE CLEVELAND MUSEUM OF ART, GIFT OF HANNA FUND, 1945 (IX. 13).

IX. 14
WOMAN WITH A NECK SCARF
Barcelona, 1903.
Oil on canvas backed with cardboard.
Size : 50 x 36 cm.
Unsigned.

Exh. The Hermitage Museum, Leningrad, 1956 : *L'Art français du XVe au XXe siècle.*

Bibl. Z. I. 66. Catalogue of paintings in the collection of S. I. Tschukin, Moscow, 1913. Sterling, 1957, fig. 69. Catalogue of the Hermitage Museum, No. 6573. Blunt and Pool, No. 79. Boudaille, 1964, pl. 45.

Coll. S. I. Tschukin, Moscow (until 1918) ; Museum of Modern Western Art, Moscow (1918–1931) ;

The Hermitage Museum, Leningrad.

IX. 15
WOMAN WITH A LOCK OF HAIR
Barcelona, 1903.
Watercolor on paper.
Size : 50 x 37 cm.
Signed and dated, top left : Picasso 1903.

Exh. III Bienal Hispanoamericana de Arte, Barcelone, 1955 : *Precursores y maestros del arte Español contemporáneo,* No. 32. Musée d'Art Moderne, Paris, 1960 : *Les Sources du XXe siècle,* No. 549.

Bibl. Z. I. 165. C.-P. p. 112 (repr. in color). Sabartés, *Picasso, les bleus de Barcelone,* 1963, pl. 3 (repr. in color). Palau i Fabre, No. 80 (repr. in color).

Coll. L. Plandiura, Barcelona ; Museo de Arte Moderno, Barcelona ;

Picasso Museum, Barcelona.

IX. 16
HEAD OF A WOMAN
Barcelona, 1903.
Oil on canvas.
Size : 40.3 x 35.6 cm.
Signed top left : Picasso.

Exh. Perls Gallery, New York, 1958. Columbus Gallery of Fine Arts, Ohio, 1959.

Bibl. Z. VI. 548.

Coll. Baron Fukushima, Paris ; Miss Adelaide Milton de Groot, New York ;

The Metropolitan Museum of Art, New York, Collection Miss Adelaide Milton de Groot, on loan since 1936.

IX. 17
HEAD OF A WOMAN
Barcelona, summer, 1903.
Gouache on canvas.
Size : 36 x 27 cm.
Signed top right : Picasso.

Bibl. Z. I. 205. C.-P. No. 174. Sutton, No. 12. Pierre Cailler, *Guillaume Apollinaire,* Geneva, 1965, No. 107.

Coll. Guillaume Apollinaire, Paris ;

Collection Mme Jacqueline Apollinaire, Paris.

Dated summer, 1903 in the Kahnweiler archives. There is an uneasy poetry about this work, overtones of symbolism close to that of Odilon Redon.

IX. 18
BUST OF A WOMAN (Genoveva)
Barcelona, 1903.
Pastel.
Dimensions not known.
Unsigned ? (see note).

Bibl. Z. VI. 462. C.-P. No. 148 (entitled *Genoveva*).

Formerly collection Junyent, Barcelona.

We were not able to identify the original work and know it only through the reproduction published by Zervos and Cirici-Pellicer. No signature is visible on the photograph reproduced here.

IX. 19
NUDE WITH CROSSED LEGS
Barcelona, 1903.
Gouache on cardboard.
Size : 58 x 44 cm.
Signed and dated, top left : Picasso 1903.

Bibl. Z. I. 181. C.-P. No. 178.

Present location unknown.

The medium and dimensions above are those from the Kahnweiler archives. Zervos and Cirici-Pellicer call it a pastel on cardboard, 60 x 46 cm. We were not able to identify the original work and cannot verify this data.

IX. 20
ANGEL FERNÁNDEZ DE SOTO
Barcelona, 1903.
Oil on canvas.
Size : 69.7 x 55.2 cm.
Signed and dated, top right : Picasso 1903.

Exh. Knoedler, New York, 1947 : *Picasso before 1907,* No. 15. Knoedler, New York, 1962 : *Picasso, an American Tribute,* No. 18, repr. in cat. Toronto and Montreal, 1964 : *Picasso and Man,* No. 17, repr. in cat. p. 37. Dallas Museum of Fine Arts, 1967 : *Picasso,* No. 7, repr. in cat. p. 14.

Bibl. Z. I. 201. Elgar and Maillard, 1955 (catalogue). Sutton, 1955, No. 24.

Coll. Paul von Mendelssohn, Germany ; Justin K. Thannhauser, Lucerne ; William H. Taylor, West Chester ; Acquired by the present owners in 1946 :

Collection Mr. and Mrs. Donald S. Stralem, New York.

IX. 21
THE PAINTER SEBASTIÁN JUNYER
Barcelona, 1903.
Oil on canvas.
Size : 125.5 x 91.5 cm.
Signed, dated and inscribed, bottom right : A Sebastián Juñer, Picasso, Junio 1903.

Exh. The Museum of Modern Art, New York and The Art Institute of Chicago, 1957 : *Picasso, 75th Anniversary Exhibition,* repr. in cat. p. 18. Grand Palais, Paris, November 1966—February 1967 : *Hommage à Pablo Picasso,* No. 17, repr. in cat.

Bibl. Z. I. 174. C.-P. p. 80 (repr. in color). Palau i Fabre, No. 97.

Coll. Sebastián Junyer Vidal, Barcelona ; Mr. and Mrs. David Edward Bright, Los Angeles ;

Collection Mrs. Dolly Bright Capen, Los Angeles.

IX. 22
PORTRAIT OF THE TAILOR SOLER
Barcelona, summer, 1903.
Oil on canvas.
Size : 100 x 70 cm.
Signed and dated, top left : Picasso
1903.

Exh. The Hermitage Museum, Leningrad, 1956 : *L'Art français du XVe au XXe siècle.*

Bibl. Z. I. 199. C.-P. No. 151. Sutton, 1955, No. 7. Catalogue of the Hermitage Museum, No. 6528. Sterling, 1957, pl. 151. Boudaille, 1964, p. 14. Palau i Fabre, No. 88 (repr. in color).

Coll. M. Soler, Barcelona; S. I. Tschukin, Moscow (until 1918); Museum of Modern Western Art, Moscow (1918–1930);

The Hermitage Museum, Leningrad.

IX. 23
THE SOLER FAMILY
Barcelona, summer, 1903.
Oil on canvas.
Size : 150 x 200 cm.
Signed top left : Picasso.

Exh. Munich, 1937 : *Entartete Kunst,* No. 134. Lyons, 1953 : *Picasso,* No. 8, repr. fig. 2. Tate Gallery, London, 1960 : *Picasso,* No. 19, cat. pl. 6 a. Paris, 1966–1967 : *Hommage à Picasso,* No. 18, repr.

Bibl. Z. I. 203 and 204. *Catalogue des peintures françaises,* Musée des Beaux-Arts, Liège, ed. 1950, pl. X; ed. 1963, pl. XVI. C.-P. No. 152. Elgar and Maillard, 1955 (catalogue). Penrose, 1958, pl. III, No. 5. Helen Kay, 1965, p. 30. Palau i Fabre, No. 87 (color).

Coll. M. Soler, Barcelona; D. H. Kahnweiler, Paris; Wallraf-Richartz Museum, Cologne (1913–1937); Confiscated by the Nazi regime in 1937; Galerie Fischer, Lucerne, June 30, 1939 : *Sale of Paintings and Sculpture by Modern Masters from German Museums,* No. 114, p. 38, repr. p. 59;

Musée des Beaux-Arts, Liège.

Originally this painting had a uniform background. At Soler's request, Picasso authorized his friend, the painter Sebastián Junyer, to surround the family with a wooded landscape (cf. Z. 1. 204). In 1913 Picasso restored the plain background. Our photograph shows its present state.

IX. 24
PORTRAIT OF MADAME SOLER
Barcelona, 1903.
Oil on canvas. Size : 100 x 73 cm.
Signed bottom left : Picasso.

Exh. Galerie Thannhauser, Munich, 1909. New York, Chicago and Boston, 1913 : *The Armory Show, International Exhibition of Modern Art,* New York, No. 348; Chicago No. 291; Boston, No. 148 (price listed : $1,350). Galerie Thannhauser, Berlin, 1930 : *Moderner Deutscher, Französischer und Spanischer Künstler.* Buenos Aires, 1934 : *First Picasso exhibition in South America.* Museum of Modern Art, New York, 1943 : *20th Century Portraits.* Santa Barbara Museum of Art, 1953 : *Fiesta Exhibition.* Marion Koogler McNay Art Institute, San Antonio, 1961. Knoedler & Co., New York, 1962 : *Picasso, an American Tribute,* No. 19, repr. in cat. New York and Utica, 1963 : *The Armory Show in Retrospect.*

Bibl. Z. I. 200. Cassou, 1940, p. 46. Sutton, 1955, No. 33. Palau i Fabre, No. 86 (repr. in color).

Coll. M. Soler, Barcelona; D. H. Kahnweiler, Paris; Justin K. Thannhauser, New York; Purchased from J. K. Thannhauser in 1964 for the Bavarian State Collections, at the equivalent of $285,700;

Neue Pinakothek, Munich.

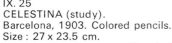

IX. 25
CELESTINA (study).
Barcelona, 1903. Colored pencils.
Size : 27 x 23.5 cm.
Unauthentic signature effaced, bottom left ;
Re-signed by the artist, bottom left : Picasso.

Exh. Sidney Janis Gallery, New York ; O'Hana Gallery, London ; Stoneleigh Abbey, Warwickshire ; Galerie Motte, Geneva, 1960 : *Picasso, his Blue Period,* No. 40, repr. in color in cat. Musée Jenisch, Vevey, 1962 : *De Cézanne à Picasso,* No. 185. Musée de l'Athénée, Geneva, 1963 : *Picasso,* No. 8, repr. in color in cat.

Palais de Beaulieu, Lausanne, 1964 : *Chefs-d'œuvre des collections suisses,* No. 225, repr. in cat.

Bibl. Z. I. 191. C.-P. No. 153. Bouret, 1950, p. 23. Palau i Fabre, No. 89 (color).

Coll. Junyer Vidal, Barcelona ;

Collection Mme M. Motte, Geneva.

The sketch of the man on Celestina's right is a burlesque portrait of Sebastián Junyer. It is almost identical to the caricature of Junyer in the drawing *Junyer the Satyr* (Gattlen collection, Lausanne).

IX. 26
CELESTINA
Barcelona, 1903.
Oil on canvas.
Size : 81 x 60 cm.
Signed top left : Picasso.

Exh. Galerie Georges Petit, Paris, summer, 1932 : *Picasso,* No. 23. Kunsthaus, Zurich, autumn, 1932 : *Picasso,* No. 21. Paris, 1966–1967 : *Hommage à Picasso,* No. 19, repr.

Bibl. Z. I. 183. C.-P. No. 154. Maurice Gieure, 1951, pl. 3. Jacques Lassaigne, Geneva, 1952, p. 118 (repr. in color). Sabartés and Boeck, p. 121 (repr. in color). Elgar and Maillard,

1955 (catalogue). Kahnweiler and Parmelin, 1955, pl. 1 (color). Champris, 1960, p. 16. Jaffé, New York, 1964. p. 12. Daix, 1964, p. 38 (color). Palau i Fabre, No. 90 (color).

Coll. Max Pellequer, Paris (often listed as owned by the artist) ;

Private collection, Paris.

On the stretcher of this painting is the inscription : *Carlota Valdivia, calle Conde Asalto, 12–4°, 1a Escalera interior.* Also the date : March, 1904. This might be a registration date before Picasso's departure for Paris in April, 1904. Experts unanimously date the work 1903.

IX. 27
OLD WOMAN
Barcelona, 1903.
Oil on canvas.
Size : 32 x 18 cm.
Signed bottom right : Picasso.
(Also signed on back of canvas.)

Bibl. Z. I. 230. Sutton, 1955, repr. No. 18.

Coll. Saidenberg Gallery, New York ; Kornfeld & Klipstein, Bern, Sale No. 123, June 14–17, 1967, No. 1203, repr. in color in cat. pl. 3, sold for 60.000 Swiss francs ;

Private collection, U.S.A.

IX. 28
OLD WOMAN WITH A HAT
Barcelona, 1903.
Ink and sepia wash on paper.
Size : 32.4 x 24.1 cm.
Signed and dated, bottom right : Picasso 1903.

Exh. College Art Association Traveling Exhibition, 1933–1934. Fort Worth, Texas, 1935. Jacques Seligmann & Co., New York, 1936 : *Picasso, Blue*

and Rose Periods, No. 12. Albright Knox Art Gallery, Buffalo, April 30– June 6, 1966 : *A. Conger Goodyear Collection,* No. 88.

Bibl. Z. VI. 600. C.-P. No. 160. Elgar and Maillard, 1955, p. 21. Palau i Fabre, No. 95.

Coll. Junyent, Barcelona ; A. Conger Goodyear, New York ;

Collection Mrs. Theodore G. Kenefick, Buffalo.

IX. 29
OLD MAN AND CHILD
Barcelona, 1903.
Colored pencils.
Size : 35 x 26 cm.
Unauthentic signature effaced, bottom left ;
Re-signed by the artist, bottom left : Picasso.

Exh. Sidney Janis Gallery, New York ; O'Hana Gallery, London ; Stoneleigh Abbey, Warwickshire ; Galerie Motte, Geneva, 1960 : *Picasso, his Blue Period,* No. 41, repr. in color in cat.

Musée Jenisch, Vevey, 1962 : *De Cézanne à Picasso,* No. 186.

Bibl. Z. I. 170. C.-P. No. 165.

Coll. Junyer Vidal, Barcelona ; Mme Marguerite Motte, Geneva ;

Private collection, Switzerland.

This study for the following painting is made up of only two colors : a pervasive blue and, standing out against it, the pink of the child's cloak.

IX. 30
THE OLD JEW (Old Man and Child)
Barcelona, 1903.
Oil on canvas.
Size : 125 x 92 cm.
Signed top right : Picasso.

Exh. Maison de la Pensée Française, Paris, June, 1954 : *Picasso.* The Pushkin Museum, Moscow, 1955 : *Art français du XVᵉ au XXᵉ siècle,* p. 50. The Hermitage Museum, Leningrad, 1956, same exhibition, p. 46. Tate Gallery, London, 1960: *Picasso,* No. 272.

Bibl. Z. I. 175. Catalogue of the collection of S. I. Tschukin, Moscow, 1913, No. 160. Touguenhold, Moscow-Petrograd, 1923, p. 117. Cat.

Museum of Modern Western Art, Moscow, 1928, No. 419. Level, 1928, p. 4. Réau, 1929, No. 1000. Javorskaïa, Moscow, 1933, p. 10. Ternowietz, Moscow, 1935, pl. XXX. C.-P. No. 164. Kahnweiler and Parmelin, 1955, pl. 16. Elgar and Maillard, 1955 (catalogue). Sterling, 1957, pl. 156 (in color). Penrose, 1958, pl. II, No. 7. Prokofiev, 1962, No. 192.

Coll. S. I. Tschukin, Moscow (until 1918) ; Museum of Modern Western Art, Moscow (1918–1948) ;

The Pushkin Museum of Fine Arts, Moscow.

Inscribed on the stretcher : Picasso, calle de la Merced 3 piso 2°, Barcelona.

IX. 31
THE BLIND MAN
Barcelona, 1903.
Gouache on canvas.
Size : 51.5 x 34.3 cm.
Signed bottom right : Picasso.

Exh. Jean Aron, Paris (date unknown). Fogg Art Museum, summer, 1946 : *French Painting since 1870,* repr. in cat. p. 53. Musée de la Province de Québec, summer, 1949, same exhibition, No. 21, repr. in cat. p. 59. The National Gallery of Art, Washington, D. C., June–September 1953. Philadelphia Museum of Art, June–September 1957. Minneapolis Institute of Arts, June–August 1958. North Carolina Museum of Art, June–September 1960 : *Manet to Picasso,* repr. in cat. p. 39. Houston Museum of Fine Arts, June–September 1962 : *Maurice Wertheim Collection,* repr. in cat. pl. 15.

Bibl. Z. I. 172. Raynal, Munich, 1921, pl. II. *Documents,* 2ᵉ année, Paris, 1930, p. 303. Merli, Buenos Aires, 1942, p. 42.

Coll. D. H. Kahnweiler, Paris ; The Toledo Museum of Art, Ohio ; Mr. and Mrs. Maurice Wertheim, New York ;

Fogg Art Museum, Harvard University, Maurice Wertheim Bequest.

There are several studies for this work. We have catalogued one of them (D. IX. 23). A drawing of the same subject, catalogued by Zervos (Z. VI. 533), was taken from a sketchbook dated Barcelona, October 1903. Hence the present work can be dated from the same period.

X. 32
THE BLIND MAN'S MEAL
Barcelona, 1903.
Oil on canvas.
Size : 95.3 x 94.6 cm.
Signed top right : Picasso.

Exh. Moderne Galerie (Heinrich Thann-hauser), Munich, 1913 : *Picasso*, No. 10. Der Rheinischer Kunstsalon, Cologne, 1913, No. 7 (?). Buenos Aires, 1934 : *Picasso*. Galerie Thannhauser, Paris, 1938. Museum of Modern Art, New York and The Art Institute of Chicago, 1957 : *Picasso, 75th Anniversary Exhibition*, cat. p. 19. Philadelphia Museum of Art, 1958 : *Picasso*, No. 12. Tate Gallery, London, 1960 : *Picasso*, No. 18, repr. in cat. pl. 6 b. Knoedler, New York, 1962 : *Picasso, an American Tribute*, No. 13, repr. in cat.

Bibl. Z. I. 168. *Cahiers d'Art*, VII, 1932, p. 91 (dated 1902). C.-P. No. 123 (dated 1902). Lieberman, 1954, pl. 19 (repr. in color). A. Vallentin, 1957, p. 87. Penrose,

1958, pl. II, No. 8. Lieberman, 1961, pl. 19 (color). Palau i Fabre, No. 91 (color).

Coll. Ambroise Vollard, Paris ; Heinrich Thannhauser, Munich ; Private collection, Westphalia ; J. K. Thannhauser, New York, (1934–1950) ; Mr. and Mrs. Ira Haupt, New York (1950) ;

The Metropolitan Museum of Art, New York, Gift of Mr. and Mrs. Ira Haupt, 1950.

The Barnes Foundation has a letter written by Picasso while he was working on *The Blind Man's Meal,* with a sketch for it on one page : "I'm painting a blind man at a table. He holds some bread in his left hand and gropes with his right for a jug of wine. At his side a dog looks at him. I'm quite satisfied. It's not yet finished." The dog seen in the sketch was not included in the final composition.

IX. 33
THE ASCETIC
Barcelona, 1903.
Oil on canvas.
Size : 130 x 97 cm.
Signed top left : Picasso.

Bibl. Z. I. 187. C.-P. No. 155. Barnes Foundation Inventory No. 115.

Coll. Paul Guillaume, Paris (according to Zervos, but the Paul Guillaume archives contain no reference to this work) ;

Barnes Foundation, Merion, Pa.

The model is the same as the one who appears in *The Old Guitarist* (IX. 34). This work shows the change in Picasso's style, already apparent in *The Old Jew* (IX. 30). His use of mannerism reaches its peak in the dramatic treatment of *The Old Guitarist* and in the paintings of 1904 : *The Couple* (XI. 5), *Woman Ironing* (XI. 6), *Woman with a Helmet of Hair* (XI. 7), and *Woman with a Crow* (XI. 10).

IX. 34
THE OLD GUITARIST
Barcelona, 1903.
Oil on panel.
Size : 122.3 x 82.5 cm.
Signed bottom right : Picasso.

Exh. Arts Club of Chicago, March-April, 1930 : *Picasso*. Art Institute of Chicago, 1933 : *Century of Progress*, No. 402. Idem, 1934, No. 358. Wadsworth Athen-eum, February–March 1934 : *Picasso*, No. 11, repr. in cat. Jacques Seligmann & Co., New York, 1936 : *Picasso, Blue and Rose Periods*, No. 15, repr. in cat. Museum of Modern Art, New York, Art Institute of Chicago and Museum of Fine Arts, Boston, 1939–1940 : *Picasso, Forty Years of his Art*, No. 20, repr. in cat. p. 34.

Bibl. Z. I. 202. *Art Institute of Chicago Bulletin*, 1926, No. 20 : 64. Idem, 1931, No. 25 : 68. *Catalogue John Quinn Col-lection*, New York, 1926, No. 96. *Cahiers d'Art*, 5–6, 1928, p. 213. Idem, 3–5, 1932, p. 88. Idem, 8–10, 1932, p. 334. Barr, *Forty Years*, p. 34. R. H. Wilenski, *Modern*

French Painters, 1940, p. 199. *Catalogue Birch Bartlett Collection*, Chicago, 1946, p. 38. Barr, *Fifty Years*, p. 29. C.-P. No. 163. A. Bertram, 1951, pl. 4. Pen-rose, 1958, pl. III, No. 6. Lieberman, 1961, pl. 18 (color). Art Institute of Chicago, *Catalogue of Paintings*, 1961, ref. p. 356. Blunt and Pool, No. 111. Boudaille, 1964, pl. IV (color). Palau i Fabre, No. 92 (color).

Coll. Ambroise Vollard, Paris ; John Quinn, New York ; Frederick C. Bartlett, Chicago ;

The Art Institute of Chicago, Helen Birch Bartlett Memorial Collection.

Usually compared in style to El Greco, this famous work evokes 16th century mannerism. Here Picasso returns to the theme of the blind man. There are several other variants in 1903 (IX. 30, 31, 32, and the drawing, page 62).

Color plate, page 63.

D. IX. 1
LES PAUVRES
Barcelona, 1903.
Brush drawing, blue wash on buff paper.
Size : 46.8 x 36 cm.
Signed bottom right : Picasso.

Bibl. Not in Z.

Coll. Baron Eduard von der Heydt, Ascona, who gave it to the Museum :

Von der Heydt-Museum der Stadt Wuppertal.

Related to the series IX. 4, IX. 5 and IX. 6.

D. IX. 2
MOTHER AND CHILD
Barcelona, 1903.
Pen drawing, brown ink on paper.
Size : 37 x 26.5 cm.
Signed bottom right : Picasso.

Bibl. Not in Z.

Collection Galerie Rosengart, Lucerne.

There is a statement by the artist, signed and dated, confirming the authenticity of this work : Picasso, le 15. 10. 64.

D. IX. 3
PORTRAIT OF A CHILD
Barcelona, 1903.
Graphite pencil on paper.
Size : 32 x 26 cm.
Signed and dated, bottom right : Picasso 1903.

Bibl. Not in Z. Helen Kay, 1965, p. 32.

Coll. Private collection, France ; Anonymous gift to the Musée Goya :

Musée Goya, Castres.

D. IX. 4
STUDY FOR *LA VIE*
Barcelona, 1903.
Pen drawing.
Size : 15.7 x 11 cm.
Unsigned.

Bibl. Z. VI. 534. Blunt and Pool, No. 116. Palau i Fabre, No. 103.

Present location unknown.

See *La Vie* (IX. 13) and the following study (D. IX. 5).

D. IX. 5
STUDY FOR *LA VIE*
Barcelona, May, 1903.
Pencil drawing on paper.
Size : 26.7 x 19.7 cm.
Unsigned.
Dated on back : Barcelona 2 Mayo 1903.

Exh. Knokke-le-Zoute, 1950 : *Picasso,* No. 6.

Bibl. Not in Z. Penrose, 1956, p. 34. Blunt and Pool, No. 117. Palau i Fabre, No. 104.

Coll. Hugh Walpole, London ;

Collection Sir Roland Penrose, London.

Picasso did this drawing on the back of an official letter (an announcement of a memorial service). The letter is dated Barcelona, April 30, 1903. At the bottom of the letter is the written inscription : *Director de la Escuela Oficial de Bellas Artes.* In the left margin, in the artist's handwriting : *Barcelona, 2 mayo 1903.* This document permits us to date the first studies for *La Vie* (IX. 13) May, 1903.

D. IX. 6
BLIND WOMAN
Barcelona, May 23, 1903.
India ink and wash on paper.
Size : 23.5 x 17 cm.
Signed top left : Picasso.
Dated on verso, bottom left : 23 Mayo 1903.

Exh. Museum Boymans, Rotterdam. Almelo 1956 : *De Daumier à Picasso,* No. 109, repr. in cat. p. 56.

Bibl. Not in Z. H. P. Bremmer, *Breldende Kunst,* 1931, No. 40. D. Hannema, *Kunst in Oude Sfeer,* 1952, p. 104, repr. 73. Evelyne Schlumberger in *Connaissance des Arts,* Paris, April 1961, p. 77, repr. p. 24.

Coll. Kunsthandel Huinck en Scherjon, Utrecht (1928) ; Purchased for 600 florins in 1928 by Dr. D. Hannema, Heino ;

Hannema-de Stuers Foundation, Heino.

Zervos catalogues a pen drawing of the same model (Z. VI. 451), with the same treatment of the figure.

D. IX. 7
SOLER IN RIDING CLOTHES
Barcelona, 1903.
India ink and watercolor.
Size : 21 x 15 cm.
Signed top right : Picasso.

Bibl. Not in Z. Palau i Fabre, No. 49 (dated 1900).

Coll. Soler, Barcelona ; Galerie Berggruen, Paris ;

Collection Mr. and Mrs. Henry John Heinz II, Pittsburgh.

The signature does not seem authentic.

D. IX. 8
MAN WITH A DOG
Barcelona, 1903.
Ink drawing with watercolor, on paper.
Size : 21.5 x 14 cm.
Unsigned.

Exh. Sidney Janis Gallery, New York ; O'Hana Gallery, London ; Stoneleigh Abbey, Warwickshire ; Galerie Motte, Geneva, 1960 : *Picasso,* No. 32, repr. in cat.

Bibl. Z. I. 194. C.-P. p. 177.

Formerly collection Junyer Vidal, Barcelona.

D. IX. 9
ANGEL DE SOTO IN A CAFÉ
Barcelona, 1903.
India ink, watercolor and colored pencil on paper.
Size : 26.9 x 20 cm.
Unauthentic signature, bottom right ;
Re-signed by the artist, bottom left : Picasso.

Bibl. Not in Z. Ponge and Chessex, 1960, p. 70. Arthur Millier ; *The Drawings of Picasso,* Los Angeles, 1961.

Coll. Junyent, Barcelona ; Galerie Rosengart, Lucerne ;

Collection Forberg, Düsseldorf.

There is a statement of authenticity for this work : "Este dibujo es mio ó mas hacho por mi, Picasso, Cannes el 10. 11. 55." (See IX. 20.)

D. IX. 10
HEAD OF A WOMAN IN PROFILE AND FOUR SKETCHES
Barcelona, 1903.
Head : brush drawing. Sketches : pen drawings.
Size : 18 x 16 cm.
Signed bottom right : Picasso.

Bibl. Unpublished.

Coll. L. Garriga Roig, Paris ;

Picasso Museum, Barcelona.

On this sheet of sketches, which date probably from 1902, Picasso has superimposed a head of a woman with the same profile as the one taken from a sketchbook of October 1903. Cf. also Zervos I. 195.

D. IX. 11
OLD WOMAN AND TWO NUDES
Barcelona, 1903.
Watercolor and ink on paper.
Size : 55 x 37 cm.
Signed bottom right : Picasso.

Bibl. Z. VI. 578.

Coll. G. and L. Bollag, Zurich ;

Collection M. et Mme F. Kirchheimer, Küsnacht.

D. IX. 12
HEAD OF AN OLD WOMAN AND SKETCH OF A HEAD
Barcelona, 1903.
Pen drawing in India ink.
Size : 11.5 x 9 cm.
Unsigned.

Bibl. Not in Z. Ponge and Chessex, 1960, p. 1 (dated 1904).

Coll. G. and L. Bollag, Zurich (bought directly from the artist in 1918) ;

Private collection, Zurich.

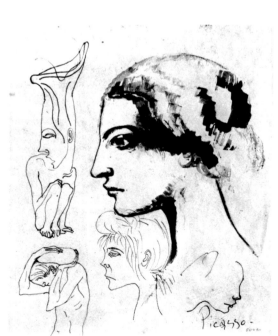

D. IX. 13
FAMILY AT DINNER (Evocation of Horta de Ebro)
Barcelona, 1903.
Ink and watercolor on paper. Size : 31.7 x 43.2 cm.
Signed bottom right : Picasso.

Exh. Yale University Art Gallery, February–March 1951 : *Pictures for a Picture of Gertrude Stein.* Baltimore Museum of Art, March–April 1951 : same exhibition, No. 26. Milwaukee Art Institute, 1957, No. 82.

Bibl. Z. VI. 563. *Magazine of Art,* vol. 34, No. 7, 1941, p. 384. C.-P. No. 143 *(Le Repas des laboureurs).* Helen Kay, 1965, p. 52. Palau i Fabre, No. 94.

Coll. Gertrude Stein, Paris ; Galerie Kate Perls, Paris ; Peter Watson, London ; French Art Galleries, New York ;

Albright-Knox Art Gallery, Buffalo.

D. IX. 14
THE SHEPHERD
Barcelona, 1903.
Charcoal and pencil on Ingres paper.
Size : 45.7 x 59 cm.
Signed bottom left : Picasso.

Exh. Kunstmuseum, Basel, May 13–June 17, 1956 : *Collection Rodolphe Staechelin,* No. 50. Musée National d'Art Moderne, Paris, April 10–June 28, 1964 : *Fondation Rodolphe Staechelin,* No. 47, repr. in cat.

Bibl. Not in Z. *DU,* No. 248, October, 1961 : *80ᵉ Anniversaire de Picasso,* p. 23.

Rodolphe Staechelin Foundation, Basel.

D. IX. 15
GUITAR PLAYER
Barcelona, 1903.
Watercolor on paper.
Size : 31 x 22 cm.
Signed and dated, bottom right : Picasso 1903.

Exh. Galerie G. and L. Bollag, Zurich, March 31–April 2, 1925, No. 151, repr. in cat. pl. 59 (exhibition preceding sale, April 3, 1925).

Bibl. Z. VI. 481.

Coll. G. and L. Bollag, Zurich ; Max G. Bollag, Zurich ; Hermann Lion, Steckborn ;

Private collection, Thurgau.

D. IX. 16
CATALAN PEASANTS (see note)
Barcelona, 1903.
Watercolor on paper.
Size : 31.7 x 22.5 cm.
Signed and dated, bottom right : Picasso 1903.

Bibl. Z. I. 376.

Coll. Etienne Bignou, Paris ; Quest Art Galleries, Chicago ;

The Marion Koogler McNay Art Institute, San Antonio.

Incorrectly entitled *The Sailors* by Zervos, this watercolor actually shows three peasants in Catalan costume. This correction is made by request of the artist.

D. IX. 17
EL TONTO (The Idiot)
Barcelona, 1903.
Watercolor and ink on paper.
Size : 31.5 x 22 cm.
Signed and dated, bottom right : Picasso 1903.

Exh. Galerie G. and L. Bollag, Zurich, November 11, 1933 : Exhibition-Sale, No. 78.

Bibl. Z. VI. 482.

Coll. G. and L. Bollag, Zurich (bought directly from the artist in 1918) ;

Private collection, Zurich.

D. IX. 18
THE GUITARIST
Barcelona, 1903.
Pen drawing and colored pencils on cardboard.
Size : 26 x 35 cm.
Unauthentic signature effaced, bottom left ;
Re-signed by the artist, bottom right : Picasso.

Exh. Kunsthaus, Zurich, June 7–September 30, 1958:
Sammlung Emil G. Bührle, No. 304.

Bibl. Z. I. 178. C.-P. No. 167.

Coll. Carlos Junyer, Barcelona ; Gabriel Dereppe,
Lugano ; Acquired in 1956 by Emil G. Bührle ;

Emil G. Bührle Foundation, Zurich.

D. IX. 19
SPANISH PEASANTS
Barcelona, 1903.
Ink and sepia wash on yellow cardboard.
Size : 37.2 x 26.8 cm.
Signed bottom left : Picasso.

Bibl. Not in Z.

Coll. André Lefèvre, Paris ; D. Bernados, Geneva ;
Baron Eduard von der Heydt, Ascona, who gave it
to the Museum :

Von der Heydt-Museum der Stadt Wuppertal.

On the back of this piece of cardboard, Picasso has
drawn a nude and some figure sketches. The
museum is not able to photograph this drawing,
since it cannot unframe *Spanish Peasants* without
damaging it.

D. IX. 20
LA JOTA
Barcelona, 1903.
Watercolor.
Size : 26 x 35 cm.
Signed bottom left : Picasso.

Bibl. Z. I. 186.

Formerly collection Ricardo Viñes, Paris.

In this depiction of folk-dancing *(La Jota)* in a
Catalan village, one finds some of the people
sketched in *Spanish Peasants* (D. IX. 19), especially
the dancing couple at the far left.

D. IX. 21
STUDY FOR LA JOTA
Barcelona, 1903.
Pen drawing.
Size : 28 x 12 cm.
Unsigned.

Bibl. Not in Z. Ponge and Chessex, 1960, p. 6.

Coll. Mme Françoise Mermod, Lausanne ;

Private collection, Lausanne.

A drawing related to the previous work (D. IX. 20).

D. IX. 22
CARIDAD (Charity)
Barcelona, 1903.
India ink and colored crayons on paper.
Size : 26 x 36 cm.
Unauthentic signature effaced, bottom right ;
Re-signed by the artist, top right : Picasso.

Exh. Sidney Janis Gallery, New York ; O'Hana Gallery, London ; Stoneleigh Abbey, Warwickshire ;
Galerie Motte, Geneva, 1960 : *Picasso,* No. 22, repr.
in cat.

Bibl. Z. VI. 438. C.-P. No. 99.

Coll. Junyer Vidal, Barcelona ;

Collection Marcel Mabille, Brussels.

Drawings of various periods are superimposed on
this page of sketches, dated 1902 by Zervos.
However, the presence, at the right, of the "madman
with a dog" (see *El Loco,* X. 5), the latest drawing
on this sheet, induces us to place *Caridad* among
the works from Barcelona, 1903. The man with the
headdress, in the left hand corner, is Picasso himself.

D. IX. 23
THE BLIND MAN
Barcelona, 1903.
Drawing with pastel.
Size : 36 x 26 cm.
Signed bottom right : Picasso.
(The signature is recent.)

Bibl. Not in Z.

Collection Alex Maguy, Paris.

This drawing belongs to a series of sketches for
The Blind Man (IX. 31.) A variant of the same
subject, catalogued by Zervos (VI. 533), appears in
a sketchbook dated Barcelona, October 1903.

X. 1
POOR MAN'S MEAL
Barcelona, 1903–1904.
Watercolor.
Size : 24 x 33 cm.
Signed top left : Picasso.

Exh. Musée National d'Art Moderne, Paris, March—April 1964 : *Collection André Lefèvre,* No. 241.

Bibl. Z. I. 209. Helen Kay, 1965, p. 20.

Coll. André Level, Paris ; Hôtel Drouot, Paris, Sale, March 3, 1927, No. 58 ; André Lefèvre, Paris ; Sale of the André Lefèvre collection (Part 3 : watercolors and drawings), Palais Galliera, Paris, November 29, 1966, No. 38, repr. in color in cat., sold for 120,000 F. ;

Collection Galerie Beyeler, Basel.

X. 2
THE TRAMP'S MEAL
(Le Repas du Gueux)
Barcelona, 1903–1904.
Watercolor an dink. Size : 27 x 35 cm.
Signed top right : Picasso.

Bibl. Z. I. 210. André Level, 1928, p. 12 (entitled *Le Repas*).

Coll. Raoul Pellequer, Paris ;

Private collection, Detroit.

X. 3
THE BEGGAR'S MEAL
Barcelona, 1903–1904.
Watercolor.
Size : 24.5 x 34.5 cm.
Signed bottom right : Picasso
(later signature).

Bibl. Z. VI. 684. Gertrude Stein,

Picasso, Paris 1938, pl. 17 (repr. in color and titled *Les Pauvres*).

Coll. Gertrude Stein, Paris ; Jacques Seligmann, New York ; Arthur Sachs, Paris ;

Private collection, Paris.

X. 4
HEAD OF A BEGGAR
Barcelona, 1903–1904.
Watercolor.
Dimensions not known.
Signed top right : Picasso.

Bibl. Z. VI. 544.

Present location unknown.

X. 5
EL LOCO (Madman with a Dog)
Barcelona, 1903–1904.
Watercolor on paper.
Size : 29.2 x 21 cm.
Inscribed top right : El Loco.

Exh. The Solomon R. Guggenheim Museum, New York, April–September 1965 : *First Showing of Masterpieces of Modern Art from the Thannhauser*

Foundation, No. 36, repr. in color in cat. p. 43.

Bibl. Z. I. 184.

Coll. Ricardo Viñes, Paris ; Justin K. Thannhauser, New York ;

The Solomon R. Guggenheim Museum, New York, Justin K. Thannhauser Foundation.

X. 6
THE MADMAN
Barcelona, 1904.
Watercolor on paper.
Size : 86 x 36 cm.
Signed and dated, top left : Picasso 1904.
Inscribed center left : A mi buen amigo Sebastian Junyent, Picasso.

Exh. III Bienal Hispanoamericana de Arte, Barcelona, 1955 : *Precursores y maestros del arte Español contemporáneo,* No. 15. Musée d'Art et d'Histoire, Geneva, 1956 : *Sélection de la IIIe Biennale Hispano-Américaine : Picasso, Nonell, Manolo,* No. 29. Musée Réattu, Arles, 1957 : *Picasso, dessins, gouaches, aquarelles 1898–1957,* No. 8. Musée National d'Art Moderne Paris, 1960 : *Les sources du XXe siècle,* No. 550.

Bibl. Z. I. 232. C.-P. p. 176 (repr. in color). Sabartés and Boeck, p. 367. Sabartés, *Picasso, les bleus de Barcelone,* 1963, pl. 12 (repr. in color). Daix, 1964, p. 24. Palau i Fabre, No. 101 (repr. in color).

Coll. Sebastián Junyent, Barcelona ; L. Plandiura, Barcelona ; Museo de Arte Moderno, Barcelona ;

Picasso Museum, Barcelona.

This is a work in monochrome, done with blue wash on two pieces of yellow paper glued together.

X. 7
NUDE LYING ON HER STOMACH
Barcelona, 1903–1904 (?).
Oil.
Dimensions not known.
Signed top right : Picasso.

Bibl. Z. VI. 413.

Coll. Roger Dutilleul, Paris ; Sold in Paris (Maître Oury), December 9, 1960, for 95,000 francs.

Present location unknown.

We were not able to analyze this oil. It is hard to date precisely. Zervos dates it 1902 or 1903, but we believe it might be even later than 1903.

X. 8
RECLINING NUDE
Barcelona, 1903–1904 (?).
Oil on canvas.
Size : 45.7 x 55 cm.
Signed bottom left : Picasso.

Bibl. Z. VI. 479.

Coll. Mme Jeanne Bucher, Paris ; Acquired by Aldus C. Higgins (from Mme Jeanne Bucher) July 2, 1935 ;

Collection Mrs. Aldus C. Higgins, Worcester, Massachusetts.

Picasso repainted the top part of this

painting in May, 1935. In its first state, the background showed a head of a woman, done by another artist, above the reclining nude. The owner of the painting sent us a photograph on which Picasso had written : *"Partie reprise par moi en mai 1935, Picasso."* On the back of the canvas is the following inscription, in Picasso's hand : *"Bien entendu ce tableau est de moi, Picasso, Paris le 17 novembre XXXIV."* Our photograph shows the present condition of the painting, which was cleaned by the Worcester Art Museum in February, 1965.

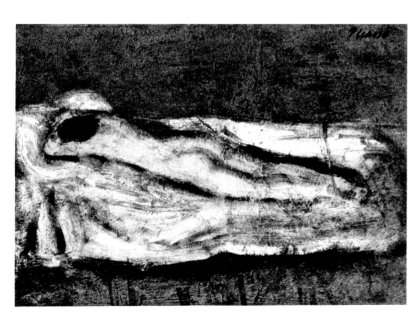

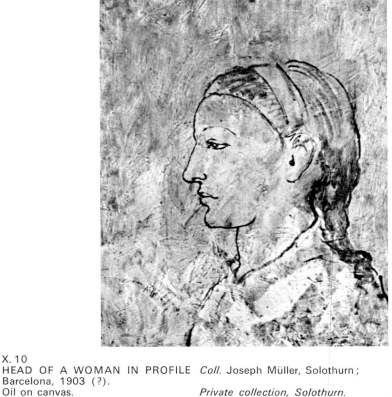

X. 9
MOTHER AND CHILD
Paris, 1901 (cf. note).
Oil on wood. Size : 100 x 73 cm.
Signed bottom right : Picasso.
Verso : Charcoal sketch : *Study of a Nude* (D. XVI. 5).

Exh. Galerie Charpentier, Paris, 1962 : *Chefs-d'œuvre des collections françaises.*

Bibl. Not in Z. Helen Kay, *Picasso's World of Children*, 1965, p. 54 (color).

Coll. Galerie Vollard, Paris ; Frau Julius Schmits, Wuppertal-Elberfeld ;

J. K. Thannhauser, New York ; Arnold Kirkeby, New York ; Parke-Bernet, New York, Sale of the Arnold Kirkeby collection, 1958 ; bought by the present owner :

Collection Stavros S. Niarchos, Paris.

This work is catalogued here by mistake. Usually dated 1903–1904, it is actually contemporary with the mother and child scenes of 1901 (correction at the artist's request).

X. 10
HEAD OF A WOMAN IN PROFILE
Barcelona, 1903 (?).
Oil on canvas.
Size : 46 x 38 cm.
Signed on the stretcher : Picasso.

Exh. Galerie Georges Petit, Paris, summer, 1932 : *Picasso,* No. 38. Kunsthaus, Zurich, autumn, 1932 : *Picasso,* No. 29 (lent by Joseph Müller, Solothurn).

Bibl. Z. VI. 467. Raymond Cogniat, *Picasso, Figures,* Lausanne, 1959, p. 13 (repr. in color).

Coll. Joseph Müller, Solothurn ;

Private collection, Solothurn.

Zervos dates this work 1902 or 1903. It was dated 1905 by C. Vranken, author of the exhibition catalogues for the Georges Petit Gallery and the Kunsthaus in Zurich (1932). Since it is impossible to relate it to other works similar in handling, and we lack the necessary proof to place it chronologically, we favor the most recent Zervos dating : 1903.

X. 11
PORTRAIT OF JAIME SABARTÉS
Barcelona, 1904.
Oil.
Size : 49.5 x 38 cm.
Signed, dated and inscribed, top left : Al amigo Sabartés, Picasso 1904.

Exh. Petit Palais, Paris, June–October 1937 : *Les Maîtres de l'art indépendant 1895–1937.* Kunstnernes Hus, Oslo, 1956 : *Picasso,* No. 6.

Bibl. Z. VI. 653. Sabartés, *Picasso, Portraits et Souvenirs,* Paris, 1946,

No. 4. Sabartés and Boeck, p. 481, No. 247. Elgar and Maillard, 1955 (catalogue).

Coll. Jaime Sabartés, Paris ;

Private collection, Oslo.

In the chronology of Sabartés portraits by Picasso (according to Sabartés himself), this one is the fourth, and the third in oil. Sabartés wears the same glasses in the 1901 portrait with long hair (VI. 34), but he has grown thinner and his features are harder.

X. 12
PORTRAIT OF LUIS VILARO
Barcelona, 1904.
Oil on wood .
Size : 45 x 24.5 cm.
Signed top left : Picasso.
Dated and inscribed, on the back : Al amigo recuerdo de Picasso, 15 Mz 1904.

Bibl. Z. I. 164 (dated 1903). Sutton, 1955, repr., No. 22.

Coll. Luis Vilaro, Barcelona ; Private collection, Switzerland, on loan to

the Kunsthaus, Zurich, until summer, 1965 ;

Private collection, Switzerland.

If the inscription on the back of this panel is contemporary with the work itself (perhaps done during the winter of 1903–1904), then this is one of the last paintings Picasso did in Barcelona, before his departure for Paris in April 1904.

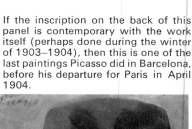

WOMAN WITH A HELMET OF HAIR (HEAD OF THE ACROBAT'S WIFE), PARIS, 1904, GOUACHE. THE ART INSTITUTE OF CHICAGO, GIFT OF KATE L. BREWSTER (XI. 7).

Paris 1904

Picasso arrived in Paris with Sebastián Junyer Vidal in April of 1904. Through his friend, the sculptor Paco Durio, who already lived there, Picasso settled immediately in a somewhat squalid but spacious studio at 12 Rue Ravignan (now Place Emile-Goudeau). This was the strange building known as the Bateau-Lavoir (see the description of Picasso's studio by Fernande Olivier, p. 336). Between spring and the end of the year Picasso completed an altogether remarkable series of works.

From October 24 to November 20 he exhibited at the Berthe Weill Gallery with six other artists : Charbonnier, Clary-Baroux, Raoul Dufy, Girieud, Picabia and Thiesson. Berthe Weill's catalogue, in small format as always, includes a poem and text by Maurice Le Sieutre for its preface. We deal immediately with this exhibition because it includes only early work, at least earlier than 1904. Were these the works in Mañach's possession or those stored at Pichot's ? Le Sieutre in his preface devotes a paragraph to each artist. Of Picasso : "And he also is a good image-maker. A fine enameler, if one may express it that way. In his pastels, one finds oxide tones, acidulated, with a trace of the chemical, carefully intentional. Their line is elegant, outlining the splashes of pinks and particularly blues which are flowers, draperies, dresses, the shawls of lively Spanish women. There is a woman dressed in pastel yellow, a music-hall performer, bony, over-taxing her consumptive form. Moreover, one senses the painter is interested in the tone which modern misery strikes in the suburbs of Paris. Here on the ramparts are vulgar couples; at the crossroads of crowded streets there are idlers, workers, women, all unfortunates, abject and weary, rough, indistinct, worn down, tossed by life like pebbles by the sea."

Here is the list of works by Picasso, as they appear in the catalogue :

29. *Au Pesage (peinture)*.
30. *L'Enterrement (peinture)*.
31. *Marchande des quatre-saisons (peinture)*.
32. *Idylle aux boulevards extérieurs (peinture)*.
33. *Scène de rue (peinture)*.
34. *Dans une Loge (Espagne)* [*pastel*].
35. *Romancière de Music-Hall (pastel)*.
36. *La Misère (pastel)*.
37. *Scène d'intérieur (pastel)*.
38. *Tête de femme (gouache)*.
39. *Le Fou (dessin)*.
40. *Croquis rehaussés d'aquarelle*.

Some of these works are identifiable, but not all. *Au Pesage* probably corresponds to *Enclosure at Auteuil* which had been in the Weill exhibition in June 1902 (v. 32). *L'Enterrement* is *The Mourners* or *Evocation (The Death of Casagemas)*, v. 2 or 4. The *Marchande des quatre-saisons* may have been *The Flower Seller* (v. 65); it dates from 1901. *Idylle aux boulevards extérieurs* certainly corresponds to one of the works entitled *The Embrace*, with the street as a background, ii. 12 or 13; it is probably the second, now titled *Lovers in the Street*, a work of 1900. *Scène de Rue* could have been *Rue Lepic* (Addenda No. A. 5), according to Le Sieutre's description : ". . . at the crossroads of crowded streets there are idlers, workers, women. . . ." *Dans une Loge (Espagne)* might correspond to *At the Theater (The Courtesan)* (iii. 3).

Romancière de Music-Hall "dressed in pastel yellow" certainly corresponds to the pastel *The End of the Number* (iv. 11) in the Picasso Museum in Barcelona. *La Misère* is specified as a pastel; it could be *Woman and Child on the Shore* (vii. 21), 1902. *Scène d'intérieur* (see the note, viii. 3) is the pastel *Intimacy* (viii. 3) of 1902. *Tête de femme*, because of the imprecision of the title, leads to more hypotheses than we can consider.

The drawing titled *Le Fou* is, on the other hand, certainly a more recent work, one of the bearded individuals which Picasso treated rather romantically in the period just before he returned to Paris : *El Loco* or *The Madman* (x. 5 and 6). He was perhaps disappointed to see Berthe Weill exhibit only his older works, and we can imagine that he suggested including some newer ones like *The Madman*, and the sketches heightened with watercolor (Weill catalogue No. 40), about which we have no information.

All in all, this catalogue tells us nothing new and it only confirms the chronology of the earlier works. Picasso, finally settled in Paris, had already moved away from the iridescent style of some of the works at the Berthe Weill exhibition. Temporarily anyway, he had turned against coloristic effects in favor of a melancholy poetry, increasingly dense and touching.

GALERIE B. WEILL

25, Rue Victor-Massé

EXPOSITION DE PEINTURES

Aquarelles, Pastels & Dessins

par

MM. Charbonnier

Clary-Baroux

Dufy (Raoul)

Girieud

Picabia

Picasso

Thiesson

Du 24 Octobre au 20 Novembre 1904

De 10 à 7 heures, sauf dimanches et fêtes

INVITATION

XI. 1
BOY WITH A MILK CAN
Paris, 1904.
Gouache on paper.
Dimensions not known.
Unsigned (see note).

Bibl. Z. I. 227 (dated 1905). Sutton, 1955, repr. No. 45.

Coll. Gertrude Stein, Paris ;

Collection of the Heirs of Miss Gertrude Stein.

Our photograph comes from the Kahnweiler archives. It was taken before the work bore a signature, but it could have been signed later.

XI. 2
THREE CHILDREN
(Petits Gueux)
Paris, 1904.
Watercolor and ink.
Dimensions not known.
Signed and dated, top left : Picasso 1904.

Bibl. Z. I. 219.

Coll. Vömel, Düsseldorf (according to Zervos, but M. Alex Vömel informs us that he does not know this work) ;

Present location unknown.

This is a work contemporary with the following one (XI. 3). It is impossible to say which is earlier.

XI. 3
THREE CHILDREN
(Petits Gueux)
Paris, 1904.
Watercolor on paper.
Size : 36.8 x 27 cm.
Signed bottom left : Picasso.
Verso : Brooding Woman (XI. 4).

Exh. Museum of Modern Art, New York, January 29–February 24, 1957 : *Drawings recently acquired for the Museum's collections* (recto only shown : *Three Children*).

Bibl. Z. I. 218. André Level, 1928, p. 15 (entitled *Enfants*). The Museum of Modern Art Bulletin, vol. XXIV, No. 4 : *Painting and Sculpture Acquisitions,* p. 11. Helen Kay, 1965, p. 21.

Coll. See *Brooding Woman* (XI. 4) ;

The Museum of Modern Art, New York, Gift of Mr. and Mrs. Werner E. Josten.

XI. 4
BROODING WOMAN
Paris, 1904.
Blue watercolor on paper.
Size : 27 x 36.8 cm.
Unsigned (signed on recto).
Recto : Three Children (XI. 3).

Exh. Museum of Modern Art, New York, November 28, 1956–January 20, 1957 : *Recent European Acquisitions* (verso shown). Museum of Modern Art, New York, The Art Institute of Chicago and Philadelphia Museum of Art, 1957–1958 : *Picasso, 75th Anniversary Exhibition,* repr. in cat. p. 19. Museum of Modern Art, New York 1962 : *Picasso, 80th Birthday Exhibition.*

Bibl. Z. I. 231. André Level, 1928, p. 16. Barr, *75th Anniversary,* p. 19.

Coll. André Level, Paris ; Leperrier, Paris ; M. Pellequer, Paris ; George Eumorphopoulos, London ; Sotheby & Co., London, 1940, Sale of the Eumorphopoulos Collection, sold for £210 (recto and verso) ; Justin K. Thannhauser, New York ; Knoedler & Co., New York (1944) ; Mr. and Mrs. Werner E. Josten, New York ;

The Museum of Modern Art, New York, Gift of Mr. and Mrs. Werner E. Josten.

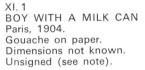

XI. 5
THE COUPLE *(Les Misérables)*
Paris, 1904.
Oil on canvas.
Size : 100 x 81 cm.
Signed bottom left : Picasso.

Exh. Galerie Thannhauser, Munich, 1909 : *Picasso.* Kunsthaus, Zurich, 1932 : *Picasso,* No. 224. Palazzo Reale, Milan, 1953 : *Picasso,* No. 4, repr. in cat. Palais de Beaulieu, Lausanne, 1964 : *Chefs-d'œuvre des collections suisses,* No. 228, repr. in cat.

Bibl. Z. I. 224. Level, 1928, pl. 8. Cassou, 1940, pl. 48. Raynal, *Histoire de la peinture moderne, de Picasso au surréalisme,* 1950, p. 21 (repr. in color).

Raynal, 1953, p. 27 (repr. in color). Elgar and Maillard, 1955 (catalogue). Sutton, 1955, repr. No. 20.

Coll. Thannhauser, Munich; Bernard Mayer, Zurich;

Private collection, Ascona.

In this painting and the following one (XI. 6), Picasso returns to the angular outline characteristic of the "mannerist" works done in Barcelona in 1903 (see IX. 32, 33, and 34). We reproduce an unpublished study for this oil : cf. Addenda No. A. 17.

Color plate, page 241.

XI. 6
WOMAN IRONING
Paris, 1904.
Oil on canvas.
Size : 116.2 x 72.7 cm.
Signed bottom right : Picasso.

Exh. Museum of Modern Art, New York, and the Art Institute of Chicago, 1939–1940 : *Picasso, Forty Years of his Art,* No. 27, repr. in cat. p. 38. Museum of Modern Art, New York, 1946 : *Picasso, Fifty Years of his Art,* repr. in cat. p. 20. Museum of Modern Art, New York, 1957 : *Picasso, 75th Anniversary Exhibition,* repr. in cat. p. 20 (shown only in New York). The Solomon R. Guggenheim Museum New York, April–September 1965 : *First Showing of Masterpieces of Modern Art from the Thannhauser Foundation,* No. 39, repr. in color in cat. p. 45.

Bibl. Z. I. 247. Level, 1928, pl. 9. Barr, *Forty Years,* p. 38. Barr, *Fifty Years,* p. 20. C.-P. No. 180. Lieberman, 1961, pl. 20 (color). Boudaille, 1964, pl. V (color). Daix, 1964, p. 39 (color). Daulte in *Connaissance des Arts,* May 1966, p. 66 (color).

Coll. Galerie Thannhauser, Munich; Mr. and Mrs. Justin K. Thannhauser, New York;

The Solomon R. Guggenheim Museum, New York, Justin K. Thannhauser Foundation.

This painting is closely related to *The Old Guitarist* of 1903 (IX. 34). Picasso returns here to a previously handled subject (*Girl Ironing,* 1901, VI. 27).

XI. 7
WOMAN WITH A HELMET OF HAIR
(Head of the Acrobat's Wife)
Paris, 1904.
Gouache on paperboard.
Size : 42.9 x 31.2 cm.
Signed and dated, top left : Picasso 1904.

Exh. Galerie Alfred Gold, Berlin, 1930 : *French Impressionists,* No. 8. The Arts Club of Chicago, April 1930 : *Picasso.* Art Institute of Chicago, 1933 : *Collection Brewster,* No. 21. Jacques Seligmann & Co., New York, 1936 : *Picasso 1901–1906,* No. 16, repr. Art Institute of Chicago, 1937 : *International Watercolor Exhibition,* No. 117. Museum of Modern Art, New York, Art Institute of Chicago and Boston Museum of Fine Arts, 1939–1940 : *Picasso, Forty Years of his Art,* No. 24, repr. Art Institute of Chicago, September 1950 : *Collection Brewster.* Marion Koogler McNay Art Institute, November 4–December 5, 1954 : *Picasso,* No. 7, repr. Museum of

Modern Art, New York, and Art Institute of Chicago, 1957 : *Picasso, 75th Anniversary Exhibition,* repr. p. 24.

Bibl. Z. I. 233. Raynal, 1922, pl. 13. C. J. Bulliet, 1936, pl. 101. Barr, *Forty Years,* p. 36. Barr, *Fifty Years,* p. 30. Cassou 1947, pl. 16. AIC Bulletin, vol. 44, No. 3, 1950, p. 54. C.-P. No. 181. Sabartés and Boeck, p. 459, No. 24. Elgar and Maillard, 1955 (catalogue). Sutton, 1955, No. 30. Art Institute of Chicago, *Catalogue of Paintings,* 1961, p. 427.

Coll. Alfred Gold, Berlin (1930); Chester H. Johnson, Chicago; Mr. and Mrs. Walter S. Brewster, Chicago;

The Art Institute of Chicago, Gift of Kate L. Brewster.

Color plate, page 237.

THE COUPLE, PARIS, 1904, OIL. PRIVATE COLLECTION, ASCONA (XI. 5).

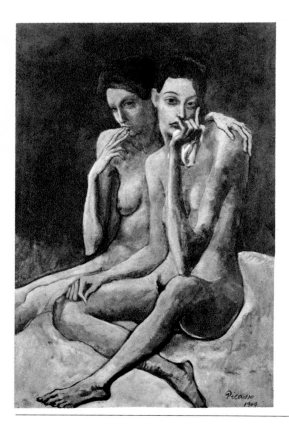

XI. 8
THE TWO FRIENDS
(Les Deux Amies)
Paris, 1904.
Gouache on paper.
Size : 55 x 38 cm.
Signed and dated, bottom right :
Picasso 1904.

Exh. Musée des Arts Décoratifs, Paris,
1955 : *Picasso,* No. 9 (reproduction in
the catalogue of this exhibition was
not authorized). Galerie Charpentier,
Paris, 1962 : *Chefs-d'œuvre des collections françaises.*

Bibl. Z. VI. 652. Guillaume Apollinaire
in *La Plume,* May 15, 1905, repr.
p. 481. Paul Eluard, *A Pablo Picasso,*
1944, p. 68. *Cahiers d'Art,* 1950,
p. 320. Elgar and Maillard, 1955,
p. 23 (repr. in color). Sutton, 1955,
pl. VIII (repr. in color).

Coll. Madame Richet, Paris ;

Private collection, Paris.

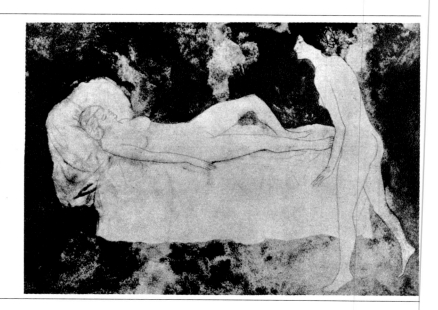

XI. 9
THE TWO FRIENDS
Paris, 1904.
Watercolor.
Dimensions not known.
Signed bottom left : Picasso.

Bibl. Not in Z. Raymond Escholier,
La peinture française, XXᵉ siècle, Paris
1937, p. 74.

Present location unknown.

XI. 10
WOMAN WITH A CROW
Paris, 1904.
Gouache and pastel on paper mounted
on board.
Size : 65 x 49.5 cm.
Signed and dated, bottom right :
Picasso 1904.

Exh. Galeries Serrurier, Paris, 1905,
No. 21. Galerie Georges Petit, Paris,
1932, No. 24, repr. pl. IV. Kunsthaus,
Zurich, 1932, No. 22, repr. pl. IV.
Petit Palais, Paris, 1935. Jacques
Seligmann & Co., New York, 1936,
No. 17, repr. Art Institute of Chicago,
1937. San Francisco, 1939 : *Golden
Gate Exhibition,* No. 40, repr. p. 5.
Museum of Modern Art, New York,
and Art Institute of Chicago, 1939–
1940 : *Forty Years,* No. 25, repr. p. 36.
Sociedad de Arte Moderno, Mexico,
1944. Musée des Beaux-Arts, Lyons,
1953, No. 11, repr. fig. 3. Palazzo
Reale, Milan, 1953, No. 3, repr.
Museum of Modern Art, New York,
Art Institute of Chicago and Phila-
delphia Museum of Art, 1957–1958 :
75th Anniversary, No. 15, repr. p. 24.

Bibl. Z. I. 240. Guillaume Apollinaire
in *La Plume,* May 15, 1905, repr.

p. 479. Waldemar George, *La grande
peinture contemporaine à la collection
Paul Guillaume,* p. 116. *Cahiers d'Art,*
1927, No. 1. Henri Mahaut, 1930,
pl. 12. Barr, *Forty Years,* p. 36. Paul
Eluard, 1944, p. 66. Barr, *Fifty Years,*
p. 30. C.-P. No. 185. Elgar and
Maillard, 1955, p. 22 (color).

Coll. Paul Guillaume, Paris ; Edward
Drummond Libbey ;

*The Toledo Museum of Art, Gift of
Edward Drummond Libbey, 1936.*

The *Woman with a Crow* is a portrait
of Margot, the daughter of Frédé,
owner of the *Lapin Agile.* She had
tamed a crow which became a
curiosity to her father's customers.
Margot married the writer Pierre Mac
Orlan ; she died in 1963. See in the
Addenda (No. A. 7) a second,
hitherto unknown version of the same
portrait.

Color plate, page 243.

WOMAN WITH A CROW, PARIS, 1904, GOUACHE AND PASTEL. THE TOLEDO MUSEUM OF ART, GIFT OF EDWARD DRUMMOND LIBBEY, 1936 (XI. 10).

Self-Portrait, Barcelona or Paris, 1904, pencil on paper, 20.9 × 13.1 cm., signed and inscribed : à Max Jacob, Picasso. Nationalmuseum, Stockholm.

XI. 11
SLEEPING NUDE
Paris, 1904.
Watercolor and pen.
Size : 36 x 26 cm.
Signed top right : Picasso.
(Signed in 1924.)

Bibl. Z. I. 234. Ponge and Chessex, *Dessins de Picasso, époques bleue et rose,* Lausanne, 1960, p. 15.

Collection Jacques Helft, Paris.

XI. 12
MEDITATION (Contemplation)
Paris, 1904.
Watercolor and pen.
Size : 36.8 x 27 cm.
Signed bottom right : Picasso.

Exh. Jacques Seligmann & Co., New York, 1936 : *Picasso, Blue and Rose Periods,* No. 18. Museum of Modern Art, New York, and The Art Institute of Chicago, 1957 : *Picasso, 75th Anniversary Exhibition,* repr. in cat. p. 23.

Philadelphia Museum of Art. 1958 : *Picasso,* No. 16. Knoedler & Co. New York, 1962 : *Picasso, an American Tribute,* No. 20, repr. in cat. The Art Gallery of Toronto and The Montreal Museum of Fine Arts, 1964 : *Picasso and Man,* No. 18, repr. in cat. p. 9.

Bibl. Z. I. 235 *(Le Nu endormi).* Level, 1928, frontispiece in color. C.-P. No. 184 *(La Femme endormie).* Penrose, 1958, pl. III, No. 3.

Coll. Raoul Pellequer, Paris ; Jules Furthman, New York ;

Collection Mrs. Bertram Smith, New York.

The thoughtful onlooker is Picasso himself.

XI. 13
FLOWERS IN A BLUE VASE
Paris, 1904.
Gouache and watercolor on paper mounted on panel.
Size : 61.5 x 47 cm.
Signed bottom right : Picasso.

Bibl. Z. I. 241.

Coll. Paul Guillaume, Paris ; Josef Stransky, New York ; Acquired in 1923 by Mr. and Mrs. James Sibley Watson, Rochester, N.Y. ;

Memorial Art Gallery of the University of Rochester, Gift of Mrs. James Sibley Watson.

XI. 14
VASE OF FLOWERS
Paris, 1904 (see note).
Gouache on paper.
Size : 61.5 x 47 cm.
Signed bottom left : Picasso.

Bibl. Not in Z.

Coll. Owned by the artist ; Sam Salz Inc., New York ;

Collection Mr. and Mrs. William Goetz, Los Angeles.

The owners of this gouache inform us that there is a written inscription on the back of the sheet : *Collection privée de l'artiste.* They date it probably 1905. But Picasso did not deal with this subject in 1905. We catalogue it here because of its similarity with *Flowers in a Blue Vase* (XI. 13). It is identical in medium and dimensions. Its fluid and supple handling is typically transitional to the Rose period.

XI. 15
PORTRAIT OF SEBASTIÁN JUNYER
Paris, 1904.
Oil on paper.
Size : 58 x 47 cm.
Unauthentic signature, bottom right :
Picasso.

Exh. Barcelona, 1919 : *Exposició d'Art,*
No. 521. Galeries Dalmau, Barcelona,
October 26–November 15, 1920 : *Art
Francés d'avantguarda,* No. 67. Lyons,
1953 : *Picasso,* No. 10. III Bienal
Hispanoamericana de Arte, Barcelona,
1955 : *Precursores y maestros del arte
Español contemporáneo,* No. 9. Musée

d'Art et d'Histoire, Geneva, 1956 :
*Sélection de la IIIᵉ Biennale Hispano-
américaine : Picasso, Nonell, Manolo,*
No. 6.

Bibl. Z.I.214 (entitled *Figure d'homme*).
Merli, Buenos Aires, 1948, No. 103.
C.-P. No. 149. Sabartés, *Picasso, les
bleus de Barcelone,* Paris, 1963, pl. 5
(color). Palau i Fabre, No. 100 (color).

Coll. L. Plandiura, Barcelona ; Museo
de Arte Moderno, Barcelona ;

Picasso Museum, Barcelona.

XI. 16
PORTRAIT OF SUZANNE BLOCH
Paris, 1904.
India ink and sepia wash.
Size : 14.3 x 13.3 cm.
Signed and dated, bottom center :
Picasso 1904.

Exh. Frankfurt and Hamburg, summer,
1965 : *Picasso, 150 Handzeichnungen
aus sieben Jahrzehnten,* No. 23, repr.
in cat. (incorrectly titled *Portrait de
Colette*).

Bibl. Not in Z.

*Collection Mme Trudi Neuburg-Coray,
Ascona.*

This watercolor was previously incorrectly called *Portrait of Colette.* It is
actually a portrait of Suzanne Bloch
(cf. XI. 18). Picasso himself pointed
out the error to us.

XI. 17
PORTRAIT OF GABY
Paris, 1904.
Tempera on cardboard.
Size : 101.6 x 75.5 cm.
Unauthentic signature, bottom right :
Picasso.

Exh. Arts Council of Great Britain, Tate
Gallery, London, 1960 : *Picasso,*
No. 21, repr. in cat. pl. 5 d (entitled
Portrait of a Woman).

Bibl. Z. I. 215 (entitled *Gaby*). C.-P.
No. 183 (entitled *Portrait d'une femme
sur carton*).

Coll. Junyer, Barcelona ; Matthiesen
Gallery, London ; Acquired in 1963
by the present owner :

Private collection, Paris.

Gaby was the wife of the actor Harry
Baur.

XI. 18
PORTRAIT OF SUZANNE BLOCH
Paris, autumn, 1904.
Oil on canvas. Size : 65 x 54 cm.
Signed top left : Picasso.

Exh. Galerie Thannhauser, Munich,
1913. Buenos Aires, 1939. San Francisco, 1940. Los Angeles, 1941 : *From
Cézanne to Picasso,* No. 36. National
Gallery of Art, Washington, D.C.,
1942. Paris, 1953 ; Brussels, London,
Düsseldorf, Bern, 1954 (No. 60) ;
Milan, 1955 ; New York, Toledo,
1956 : *Masterpieces from the Museum
of Art, Sao Paulo.*

Bibl. Z. I. 217. Eugenio d'Ors, 1930,
pl. VII. Sutton, 1955, No. 14. Cassou,
1958, p. 21 (*Portrait d'une femme,*
repr. in color). Cogniat, Lausanne,
1959, p. 15 (color).

Coll. Sichowski, London ; Bieber,
Lugano ;

Museu de Arte, Sao Paulo.

Suzanne Bloch, sister of the violinist
Henri Bloch, became a famous
Wagnerian singer.

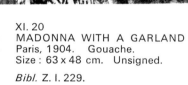

XI. 19
THE KISS
Paris, September 7, 1904.
Watercolor on paper.
Size : 37.5 x 26.7 cm.
Signed and dated, bottom right :
7 Septiembre 1904, Picasso.

Exh. Kiruna, Sweden, September,

1965 : *Picasso i Kiruna,* No. 32
(entitled *The Embrace*).

Bibl. Not in Z.

Coll. H. G. Turitz, Göteborg, who gave
it to the Museum in 1937 :

Göteborgs Konstmuseum, Göteborg.

In the drawing catalogue XI, see
Mother and Child (D. XI. 25), done
the same day.

XI. 20
MADONNA WITH A GARLAND
Paris, 1904.   Gouache.
Size : 63 x 48 cm.   Unsigned.

Bibl. Z. I. 229.

Coll. Max Pellequer, Paris ;

Private collection, Paris.

XI. 21
MOTHER AND CHILD
Paris, 1904.
Watercolor and India ink on paper.
Size : 35.3 x 25.3 cm.
Signed bottom left : Picasso.

Exh. Musée des Beaux-Arts, Budapest :
Régi és modern rajzok, 1922 ; *Francia
rajzok,* 1933 ; *Rajzoló eljárások,* 1934 ;
Legszebb Külföldi rajzok, 1936 ; *Em-
lékkiállítás a Magyar Tanácsköztársa-
ság 40. Évfordulója Alkamából,* 1959.

Bibl. Not in Z. D. Rózsaffy, in *Le
Bulletin de l'Art ancien et moderne,*
Budapest, 1933, p. 383. E. Hajós,

Francia Rajzok in *Magyar Müvészet,*
Budapest, 1933, p. 331. D. Pataky,
De Delacroix à Picasso, Paris, 1960,
No. 81.

Coll. François Hatvany, Budapest,
who gave it to the Museum :

Szépmüvészeti Múzeum, Budapest.

We have a statement of authenticity
signed by the artist February 11, 1965.
This work is related to the sheet of
studies (D. XI. 26) and to *Mother and
Child* (XII. 4).

XI. 22
PIERRETTE'S WEDDING
(Les Noces de Pierrette)
Paris, 1904.
Oil on canvas.
Size : 95 x 145 cm.
Signed bottom left : Picasso.

Bibl. Z. I. 212. Blunt and Pool, No.136.

Coll. Josef Stransky, New York ;
Georges Renand, Paris ;

Present location : see note.

The last owner of this painting gave us
the following information : it was sold
to a Parisian dealer, who sold it to a
private owner. At his death, after a
quarrel between the heirs, the painting
was destroyed. *We give this information very cautiously.* One can see
in this work the first harlequin, foreshadowing those of 1905, and also,
in the center, a woman who resembles the *Madonna with a Garland*
(XI. 20).

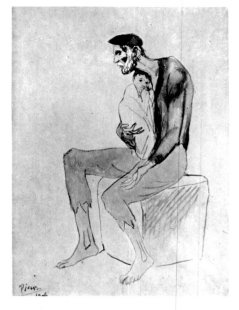

D. XI. 1
STREET URCHINS
Barcelona or Paris, 1904.
Colored crayons.
Size : 36 x 26.5 cm.
Signed bottom right : Picasso.

Exh. Kunsthaus, Zurich, 1932 : *Picasso,* No. 269.
Museum of Modern Art, New York, and The Art
Institute of Chicago, 1939–1940 : *Picasso, Forty
Years of his Art,* No. 21 (not reproduced in cat.).

Bibl. Z. I. 185. Helen Kay, 1965, p. 37.

Coll. Galerie Thannhauser, Lucerne ;

Thannhauser Foundation, New York.

D. XI. 2
SOLITUDE
Barcelona or Paris, 1904.
Watercolor.   Size : 36 x 26 cm.
Signed bottom right : Picasso.

Exh. Perls Galleries, New York, September-October
1938 : *The School of Paris,* No. 2. Arts Club of
Chicago. January 3–27, 1939 : *Drawings by Picasso
loaned by Walter P. Chrysler, Jr.,* No. 25. Perls Galleries, New York, March, 1939 : *Picasso before 1910.*
Virginia Museum of Fine Arts, January 16–March 4,
and Philadelphia Museum of Art, March 29–May 11,
1941 : *Collection Walter P. Chrysler, Jr.,* No. 199,
repr. cat.

Bibl. Not in Z.

Coll. Perls Galleries, New York ;

Collection Walter P. Chrysler, Jr., New York.

D. XI. 3
OLD MAN WITH A CHILD *(Le Mendiant)*
Paris, 1904.
Watercolor.
Size : 36 x 26 cm.
Signed and dated, bottom left : Picasso 1904.

Exh. Musée National d'Art Moderne, Paris, March–
April 1964 : *Collection André Lefèvre,* No. 243.

Bibl. Z. I. 237. Ponge and Chessex, 1960, p. 11.

Coll. André Lefèvre, Paris ; Sale of the André Lefèvre
collection (Part 3 : watercolors and drawings),
Palais Galliera, Paris, November 29, 1966, No. 40,
repr. in cat., sold for 126,000 F. ;

Private collection, Paris.

D. XI. 4
MATERNITY (Couple with a Child)
Paris, 1904.
Pen drawing and watercolor.
Size : 34.5 x 23.5 cm.
Signed top left : Picasso.

Exh. Musée National d'Art Moderne, Paris, March–
April 1964 : *Collection André Lefèvre,* No. 242.

Bibl. Z. I. 238.

Coll. André Lefèvre, Paris ; Sale of the André Lefèvre
collection (Part 3 : watercolors and drawings),
Palais Galliera, Paris, November 29, 1966, No. 39,
repr. in cat., sold for 80,000 F. ;

Private collection.

D. XI. 5
COUPLE WITH A CHILD
Paris, 1904.
Pen drawing and watercolor.
Size : 37 x 26 cm.
Signed and dated, top left : Picasso 1904.

Bibl. Z. VI. 615.

Formerly Roger Dutilleul collection, Paris.

D. XI. 6
FAMILY WITH A CHILD
Paris, 1904.
Crayon and watercolor on paper.
Size : 35.5 x 26 cm.
Signed bottom right : Picasso.

Exh. Musée Cantini, Marseilles, May 11–July 31,
1959 : *Picasso,* No. 5, repr. in cat.

Bibl. Z. VI. 704.

Private collection, Marseilles.

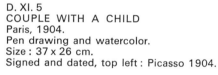

D. XI. 7
THE SEIZURE
Paris, 1904.
Pen and gouache on cardboard.
Dimensions not known.
Signed top right : Picasso.

Bibl. Not in Z. Ponge and Chessex, 1960, p. 33.
Catalogue of reproductions, UNESCO, Paris, 1963,
p. 359, No. 1000.

Coll. Sam A. Lewisohn, New York ;

Private collection, Paris.

D. XI. 8
MAN AND STANDING FEMALE NUDE
Paris, 1904.
Brush drawing.
Dimensions not known.
Signed and dated, bottom right : Picasso 1904.

Bibl. Not in Z. Ponge and Chessex, Lausanne, 1960,
p. 10.

Present location unknown.

D. XI. 9
THE CHRIST OF MONTMARTRE (The Suicide)
Paris, 1904.
Pen and watercolor.   Size : 36 x 26 cm.
Signed and dated, bottom left : Picasso 1904.

Exh. Galerie Serrurier, Paris, 1905, No. 16. Galerie
Suzanne Bollag, Zurich, 1959 : *Contrastes*, repr. p. 2.
Lausanne, 1964 : *Chefs-d'œuvre des collections
suisses*, No. 229, repr. Frankfurt and Hamburg, 1965,
No. 15, repr.

Bibl. Z. VI. 617. *Cahiers d'Art*, Paris, 1950, No. II,
p. 322.

Coll. G. and L. Bollag, Zurich (bought from the
artist in 1918) ;

Collection Mlle Suzanne Bollag, Zurich.

See Addenda No. A. 18.

D. XI. 10
PORTRAIT OF THE SCULPTOR MANOLO
Paris, 1904.
Pen drawing and watercolor.
Size : 37.3 x 26.8 cm.
Unsigned.

Exh. Petit Palais, Paris, 1966–1967 : *Hommage à
Pablo Picasso,* No. 14, repr. in cat.

Bibl. Z. I. 211. Level, 1928, p. 9. C.-P. No. 186.
Florent Fels, 1950, p. 241. Ponge and Chessex,
1960, p. 14. Duncan, 1961, p. 204.

Owned by the artist.

The Spanish sculptor Manolo (Manuel Hugué) also
lived in Montmartre.

D. XI. 11
WOMAN IRONING
Paris, 1904.
Pastel.
Size : 37 x 51.5 cm.
Signed bottom left : Picasso.

Exh. Arts Club of Chicago, January 1939 : *Drawings
by Picasso loaned by Walter P. Chrysler, Jr.,* No. 3.
Perls Galleries, New York, 1939 : *Picasso before
1910,* No. 13. Virginia Museum of Fine Arts,
January 16–March 4, and Philadelphia Museum of
Art, March 29–May 11, 1941 : *Collection Walter P.
Chrysler, Jr.,* No. 152, repr.

Bibl. Z. I. 248.

Coll. Hessel, Paris ;

Collection Walter P. Chrysler, Jr., New York.

See *Woman Ironing* (XI. 6).

D. XI. 12
PROFILE OF WOMAN WITH A CHIGNON
Paris, 1904.
Drawing with touches of pastel.
Size : 36 x 26 cm.
Signed bottom left : Picasso.

Bibl. Z. I. 221

Coll. René Gaffé, Brussels ;

Present location unknown.

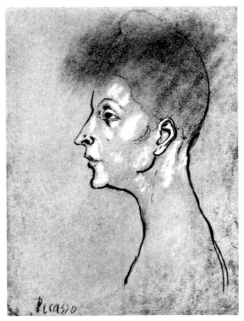

D. XI. 13
THE LOVERS
Paris, 1904.
Pen drawing.
Size : 34 x 25 cm.
Signed bottom left : Picasso.
Dated top right : Agosto 1904.

Bibl. Not in Z. Duncan, 1961, p. 204.

Owned by the artist.

D. XI. 14
THE STRANGLER *(Sainte Roulette)*
Paris, 1904.
Watercolor.
Size : 73 x 60 cm.
Signed left : Picasso.

Bibl. Z. VI. 616.

Coll. Perls Galleries, New York ;

Private collection, U.S.A.

Study for a poster (see D. XI. 15).

D. XI. 15
SKETCH FOR A POSTER *(Sainte Roulette)*
Paris, 1904. Gouache.
Signed bottom left : Picasso.

Bibl. Not in Z.

Present location unknown.

A sketch for a four-act play by Gustave Coquiot and Jean Lorrain : *Sainte Roulette* (first performed at the Théâtre Molière, Paris, October 10, 1904). The poster was never printed because the director of the theater rejected the sketch.

D. XI. 16
SKETCH FOR HÔTEL DE L'OUEST,
CHAMBRE 22 Paris, 1904.
Watercolor on paper. Size : 54.5 x 43.8 cm.
Signed bottom left : Picasso.
Inscribed bottom left : Esquisse pour Hôtel de l'Ouest, Chambre 22.
Exh. Arts Club of Chicago, 1937, No. 35. Detroit Institute of Arts, 1937, No. 118. New York and Chicago, 1939–1940 : *Forty Years*, No. 28. Virginia and Philadelphia, 1941 : *Collection Walter P. Chrysler, Jr.,* No. 201.
Bibl. Z. I. 213.
Coll. Libaude, Paris ; Kate Perls, Paris ; Walter P. Chrysler, Jr., New York ; Parke-Bernet, New York, February 16, 1950 : Sale of the Walter P. Chrysler, Jr. collection, No. 34 ;
Collection Mr. and Mrs. William Goetz, Los Angeles.
Sketch for the two-act play by Gustave Coquiot and Jean Lorrain : *Hôtel de l'Ouest, Chambre 22* (first performed at the Grand Guignol, Paris, May 28, 1904).

D. XI. 17
COUPLE IN A TAVERN
Paris, 1904.
Pencil drawing.
Size : 21 x 28 cm.
Signed bottom right : Picasso.

Bibl. Not in Z.

Coll. Bernard Poissonnier, Paris ;

Private collection, Paris.

D. XI. 18
THE APERITIF
Paris, 1904.
Watercolor.
Size : 43.3 x 34.3 cm.
Signed bottom left : Picasso.
(The signature does not seem authentic.)

Exh. Cincinnati Art Museum. Carnegie Institute AFA : *Adventures in Collecting*, September 22, 1958–November 5, 1960 (traveling exhibition).

Bibl. Not in Z.

Coll. Valentine Gallery, New York ; Howald, Ohio ;

The Columbus Gallery of Fine Arts, Ohio.

The man is certainly Angel F. de Soto.

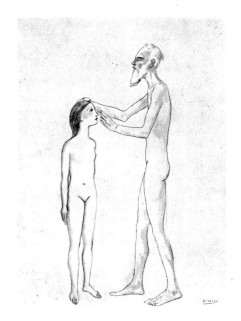

D. XI. 19
MOTHER AND DAUGHTER Paris, 1904.
Blue crayon with touches of red and yellow on white paper. Size : 35 x 26.5 cm.
Signed bottom left : Picasso.

Exh. Fogg Art Museum, summer, 1946, cat. p. 69. Quebec, summer, 1949 : *Maurice Wertheim Collection,* No. 30. Washington, D.C., summer, 1953. Philadelphia, summer, 1957. Minneapolis, summer, 1958. North Carolina, 1960 : *Manet to Picasso,* cat. p. 67. Houston, 1962 : *Maurice Wertheim Collection,* pl. 27.

Bibl. Z. I. 239. Helen Kay, 1965, p. 81.

Coll. Pierre Matisse, New York ; Mr. and Mrs. Maurice Wertheim, New York ;

Fogg Art Museum, Harvard University, Bequest of Maurice Wertheim.

D. XI. 20
OLD MAN AND LITTLE GIRL (The Blind Man)
Paris, 1904.
India ink and watercolor.
Size : 46 x 31 cm.
Signed bottom right : Picasso.

Exh. Lausanne, 1964 : *Chefs-d'œuvre des collections suisses,* No. 227, repr. in cat.

Bibl. Z. VI. 631. Maurice Gieure, 1951, No. 116. Ponge and Chessex, 1960, p. 8.

Coll. G. and L. Bollag, Zurich ; Galerie Bollag, Zurich, Sale, April, 1925, No. 153, repr. pl. 22 (entitled *L'Aveugle*) ;

Collection Curt Burgauer, Küsnacht.

D. XI. 21
KNEELING NUDE
Paris, 1904.
Watercolor and blue crayon on paper.
Size : 34 x 24 cm.
Signed bottom right : Picasso.

Exh. Traveling exhibition of the G. David Thompson Collection : Kunsthaus, Zurich, October 15–November 27, 1960 ; Düsseldorf and The Hague, 1960–1961 ; Galleria Civica d'Arte Moderna, Turin, 1961.

Bibl. Z. VI. 632.

Coll. Bernard Poissonnier, Paris ; G. David Thompson, Pittsburgh ;

Collection Fernand C. Graindorge, Liège.

D. XI. 22
STUDY OF SEATED MAN
Paris, 1904–1905.
Pen drawing in bistre on paper.
Size : 34 x 23 cm.
Signed bottom left : Picasso.

Exh. Frankfurt and Hamburg, 1965, No. 17, repr. in cat. Galerie Knoedler, Paris, November–December 1966 : *Picasso, dessins et aquarelles, 1889–1965,* No. 27, repr. in cat.

Bibl. Not in Z.

Collection Lionel Prejger, Paris.

D. XI. 23
SEATED WOMAN IN PROFILE
Paris, 1904.
Pen drawing.
Size : 32.5 x 24.8 cm.
Signed bottom right : Picasso.

Bibl. Not in Z.

Coll. Léo Bollag, Zurich ; Wurmser, Zurich ; Galerie Obere Zäune, Zurich ; Acquired in 1965 by :

Collection Roland, Browse and Delbanco, London.

This drawing has a statement of authenticity signed by D. H. Kahnweiler.

D. XI. 24
STANDING MALE NUDE
1903–1904 (see note).
Ink on paper. Size : 34.3 x 26.6 cm.
Unsigned. *Verso : Mother and Child* (D. XI. 26).

Bibl. Not in Z. Mongan and Sachs, 1940, No. 741.

Coll. Charles Vignier, Paris ; Paul J. Sachs (bought in Paris, December 10, 1929) ;

Fogg Art Museum, Harvard University, Meta and Paul J. Sachs Collection.

The Fogg Art Museum dates this drawing 1904 because it is on the back of *Mother and Child* (signed and dated 1904). Actually *Standing Male Nude* is probably earlier by several months. The face of the man is the same as the *Self-Portrait* (repr. p. 55). In 1904 Picasso no longer wore a moustache (cf. the two self-portraits with a pipe, D. XI. 28 and 29).

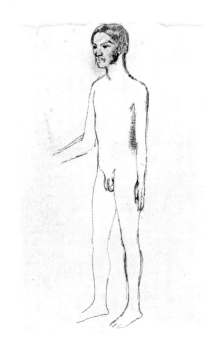

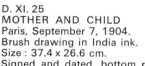

D. XI. 25
MOTHER AND CHILD
Paris, September 7, 1904.
Brush drawing in India ink.
Size : 37.4 x 26.6 cm.
Signed and dated, bottom right : Picasso, 7 Septiembre 1904.

Exh. Kunsthaus, Zurich, 1932 : *Picasso,* No. 273.

Bibl. Unpublished.

Formerly Hahnloser collection, Winterthur.

This drawing was done the same day as *The Kiss* (XI. 19) and *Mother and Child* (Z. VI. 654). The mother's hands are similar to those in the following *Mother and Child* (D. XI. 26).

D. XI. 26
MOTHER AND CHILD AND STUDIES OF HANDS
Paris, 1904.
Conté crayon.   Size : 34.3 x 26.6 cm.
Signed and dated bottom right : Picasso 1904.
Recto : Standing Male Nude (D. XI. 24).

Exh. Wadsworth Atheneum, 1934, No. 82. New York and Chicago, 1939–1940 : *Forty Years,* No. 23, repr. Detroit, 1941, No. 54. San Antonio, 1954, No. 6. Houston, 1955, No. 3. Toronto and Montreal, 1964 : *Picasso and Man,* No. 20, repr.

Bibl. Z. I. 220. Barr, *Forty Years,* p. 35. Mongan and Sachs, 1940, No. 741, fig. 399. Rewald and Wheeler, New York, 1944. Barr, *Fifty Years,* p. 29. C.-P. No. 182. Bouret, 1950, p. 25. Schoolman and

Slatkin, New York, 1950, pl. 143. Elgar and Maillard. 1955, p. 24. Rosenberg, Harvard, 1959, No. 228, Jardot, New York, 1959, No. 8. Ponge and Chessex, 1960, p. 13. Millier, Los Angeles, 1961, p. 15. *Great Drawings of All Time,* New York, 1962, pl. 855. Blunt and Pool, No. 133. *Drawings of the Masters, 20th Century,* vol. I, New York, 1964, pl. 38. Helen Kay, 1965, p. 70.

Coll. See *Standing Male Nude* (D. XI. 24).

Fogg Art Museum, Harvard University, Bequest of Meta and Paul J. Sachs.

Related to XI. 21 and XII. 4. Our list of exhibitions and reproductions of this famous work is made up of the major ones.

D. XI. 27
PORTRAIT OF MAX JACOB   Paris, 1904–1905.
Pen drawing on paper. Size : 25.8 x 20.1 cm.
Signed in pencil, top right : Picasso.

Bibl. Not in Z. Sutton, 1955, last page.

Coll. André Lefèvre, Paris ; Kornfeld & Klipstein, Bern, Sale No. 121, June 10–11, 1966, cat. No. 819 a, repr., estimated price : 8,000 Swiss francs ;
Collection M. L., Paris.
A drawing done on a sheet of writing paper with the heading of the café-restaurant Faurena, 75 *bis,* Boulevard de Clichy, Paris.
On the back : three small sketches of heads and three lines by Max Jacob : "Pas les vieilles anguilles / — Oui, mais les carpes ! les / Carpes sautent...."

D. XI. 28
SELF-PORTRAIT WITH A PIPE
Paris, December, 1904.
Pen drawing and wash on paper.
Dimensions not known.
Signed and inscribed, top center : A Sebastia Junyent, Picasso.
Dated bottom left : Paris Diciembre 1904.
Inscribed bottom left : Mi retrato.

Bibl. Not in Z. Sabartés, *Picasso, documents iconographiques,* 1954, No. 86.

Formerly Junyent collection, Barcelona.

D. XI. 29
SELF-PORTRAIT WITH A PIPE
Paris, winter, 1904–1905.
Watercolor and India ink on paper.
Size : 17 x 10.5 cm.
Unsigned.

Exh. Institute of Contemporary Arts, London, 1956, repr. in color in cat. (frontispiece). Musée Réattu, Arles, 1957 : *Picasso,* No. 9, repr. in cat. pl. 5.

Bibl. Not in Z. John Richardson, Basel, 1956, pl. 4. (repr. in color).

Coll. Mlle Dora Maar, Paris ;

Private collection, Paris.

AT THE LAPIN AGILE, PARIS, 1905, OIL.   COLLECTION MRS. CHARLES S. PAYSON, MANHASSET, N.Y. (XII. 23).

Harlequins, Athletes and Saltimbanques, Paris, 1905

Picasso was living at the Bateau-Lavoir. A lot of people visited him there, and there he met Fernande Olivier.

He exhibited at the Galeries Serrurier on the Boulevard Haussmann from February 25 to March 6. That summer he made a trip to Holland that left its mark on his work (see the introduction to Catalogue XIII).

But the transition from the Blue Period to the Rose Period is the outstanding feature of 1905. The transformation came in stages. At first the blue moved toward a luminous gray increasingly heightened with rose that at the end of the year had deepened to red. This is a simplification of the facts, of course, for Picasso continued the habit of following several leads at once, and also was using bright colors off and on from the beginning of the year. The transformation of the palette was matched by a radical change in Picasso's outlook. Harlequins and circus people replace the beggars and the down-and-out, and the melancholy of the last period retreated before an optimism that grew in proportion as Picasso's living conditions improved.

This was a year of great activity, as productive as the summer of 1901. Picasso also tried his hand at sculpture again and made his first series of prints (sixteen etchings and drypoints).

For a better understanding of Picasso's work, while preserving chronological order as much as possible, we have subdivided this year into two catalogues which point up the development of each of the subjects handled by the artist.

The works of the first half of the year come in the following order :

Transition from Blue to Rose, 1904-1905

The *Seated Nude* (XII. 3) of the Musée National d'Art Moderne in Paris is an example of the development from the end of 1904 through the early months of 1905. The color of this nude, a sort of red-ochre, evolves toward rose in the costume of *The Actor* (XII. 1). *Mother and Child* (XII. 4), which has a preliminary study dated 1904, is blue and rose.

Yet, in spite of being named the "rose" period, it is less the color than the drawing and the subjects that determine the chronological sequence. The drawing technique at the start of the year is still close to that of the Blue Period, sharp and angular. We see it grow increasingly supple, curvilinear, and in the Dutch works of the summer of 1905, marked by an incidental fullness.

Exhibition at the Galeries Serrurier and the First Harlequins

The exhibition held from February 25 to March 6, 1905, at the gallery's premises on Boulevard Haussmann, brought together works by three painters : Trachsel, Gérardin and Picasso. The preface was written by Charles Morice, a Symbolist poet and one of Gauguin's friends (See p. 335 for the preface as well as for articles published on this occasion by Apollinaire in *La Revue Immoraliste*, April, 1905, and in *La Plume*, May 15, and by Charles Morice in the *Mercure de France*). Neither the invitation nor the catalogue preserved by Jacques Doucet, which may be consulted at the Institut d'Art et d'Archéologie in Paris, bears the year of the exhibition. Some biographers have placed this exhibition in 1905, others in 1904; still others posited two exhibitions by Picasso at the Gallery, one in 1904, another in 1905. The reviews published by Apollinaire and Charles Morice prove that this exhibition was held in 1905.

Here is the list of the works exhibited by Picasso :

1-8. *Saltimbanques.*	23. *Portrait de Mlle K.*
9. *Petite Maternité.*	24. *Amies.*
10-14. *Pauvres.*	25. *Paysage de Montjuich (Espagne).*
15. *El Mandigo.*	26. *La Rue Ravignan à Paris.*
16. *Le Pendu.*	27. *Portrait de Mlle S.*
17. *Les Baigneuses.*	28. *Tête (étude).*
18. *La Femme au bas.*	29. *La Femme au bas (estampe).*
19. *Jeune Garçon.*	30. *La Femme au bas (estampe).*
20. *Jeune Garçon.*	31-33. *Trois eaux-fortes.*
21. *La Femme au corbeau.*	1 album de dessins.
22. *Jeune Fille de dos.*	

The presence of eight works with saltimbanque subjects in an exhibition opening February 25, with the catalogue prepared ahead of time, proves that Picasso must have begun these themes in the last part of 1904. The vagueness of numbers 1-8 (group of saltimbanques) makes us think that Picasso wanted his most recent works in the exhibition but that he had not made the final choices at the time the catalogue was sent to the printers. No doubt he wished to feel free to finish some, to withdraw others, selecting only those he thought were best.

Apollinaire's illustrated article in *La Plume*, May 15, 1905, gives us definite information. The works reproduced date from 1904, or at the latest, the beginning of 1905 :

La Femme à la corneille (*Woman with a Crow*, XI. 10).

Les deux Amies (*The Two Friends*, XI. 8).

L'Arlequin assis (*Seated Harlequin with Red Background*, XII. 10).

Acrobate et jeune arlequin (*Acrobat and Young Harlequin*, XII. 9).

Deux Saltimbanques avec chien (*Two Acrobats with a Dog*, XII. 17).

No work can be identified from titles so vague as *Petite Maternité, Pauvres, El Mandigo, Les Baigneuses, Jeune Garçon, Jeune Fille de dos* or *Etude de tête*. However, Apollinaire's article in *La Plume* leads us to believe that several of the "beggars" of 1903-1904 were shown.

Also in *La Plume*, the passage, "In the square room, fatherhood transfigures the harlequin, whose wife bathes with cold water and admires her figure, as slender and frail as her husband, the puppet," is clearly a description of *The Harlequin's Family*, XII. 6.

Le Pendu, described by Apollinaire as a man hanging from a roof in Montmartre, must refer to the watercolor later known as

Circus Family (Les Saltimbanques), Paris, 1905, drypoint (see the watercolor of the same subject, XII. 18).

The Christ of Montmartre (The Suicide) (D. XI. 9). *La Femme à la Corneille* (*Woman with a Crow*) has never changed its title (see Paris 1904 : XI. 10, and Addenda No. A. 7). The painting *Amies* is the one now known as *The Two Friends* (XI. 9).

We cannot place the *Mlle. K. Mlle. S.* is probably Suzanne Bloch (XI. 18). *La Femme au bas* no doubt refers to the *Crouching Nude with Green Stocking* (VII. 16). *La Rue Ravignan à Paris* could well have been *Rue Lepic,* a painting which is also titled *Rue Ravignan* (see Addenda No. A. 5 and note).

Le Paysage de Montjuich is perhaps Number 42 of the Vollard Exhibition in 1901, still unidentified. If this is the case, it would be the only comparatively old work in this show, where the majority are from the year just ended or the first weeks of 1905.

In 1905 Picasso did his first series of etchings and drypoints which Delâtre printed in a limited edition. They were completely unsuccessful until 1913 when Vollard acquired them, steel-faced the plates, and published them with *The Frugal Repast* of 1904 in an edition of 279 for each print. He gave them the title of *The Saltimbanques.* In February 1905, Picasso had probably not yet completed this series and we do not know what prints were shown at Serrurier in addition to *The Frugal Repast.*

Athletes and giants

These figures, who have something in common with *El Tio Pepe Don José* (XII. 30), appeared a little later and are akin to the *Portrait of Guillaume Apollinaire* (D. XII. 24).

Saltimbanques

The great painting *Family of Saltimbanques* (XII. 35) in the National Gallery in Washington, and the preliminary study for it in gouache (XII. 33) in the Pushkin Museum in Moscow were preceded (and sometimes, perhaps, followed) by numerous studies of each the figures in the painting.

Some of the figures are characteristic of works from the beginning of the year, whereas others seem to show the influence of the trip to Holland; hence our opinion that the painting was started before the summer and completed much later, perhaps during the fall.

XII. 1
THE ACTOR
Paris, winter, 1904–1905.
Oil on canvas.
Size : 194 x 112 cm.
Signed bottom right : Picasso.

Exh. Städtische Ausstellungshalle, Cologne, 1912 : *International Kunst Ausstellung,* No. 216. Museum of Modern Art, New York, and Art Institute of Chicago, 1939–1940 : *Picasso, Forty*

Years of his Art, No. 29, repr. in cat. p. 39. *Same exhibition,* 1940 : St. Louis City Art Museum, Boston Museum of Fine Arts, San Francisco Museum of Art. Los Angeles County Museum, 1941 : *Cézanne to Picasso,* No. 31.

Bibl. Z. I. 291. Raynal, 1922, pl. 18. Schürer, 1927, pl. 2. Barr, *Forty Years,* p. 39. Barr, *Fifty Years,* p. 33. J. A

Gaya Nuño, 1950, pl. 12. Lieberman, 1954 and 1961, pl. 21 (color). Elgar and Maillard, 1955 (catalogue). A. Vallentin, 1957, p. 113. Penrose, 1958, pl. III, No. 1. Boudaille, 1964, pl. VI (color).

Coll. P. Leffmann, Cologne (1912) ; Private collection, Germany (1913–1938) ; Hugo Perls, New York (1938); Paul Rosenberg, New York (1938–

1941) ; Knoedler, New York (1941) ; Thelma Chrysler Foy, New York (1941–1952) ;

The Metropolitan Museum of Art, New York, Gift of Thelma Chrysler Foy, 1952.

See the study for *The Actor* : XII. 2.

XII. 2
STUDY FOR THE ACTOR
(and two profiles of Fernande)
Paris, winter, 1904–1905.
Pencil on paper.
Size : 48.3 x 31.7 cm.
Signed bottom left : Picasso.

Exh. Galerie Berggruen, Paris, May–July, 1954 : *Picasso, dessins 1903–1907,* No. 19, repr. in cat. Kunstnernes Hus, Oslo, 1956 : *Picasso.* Museum of Modern Art, New York, and Art Institute of Chicago, 1957 : *Picasso, 75th Anniversary Exhibition,* repr. in cat. p. 24. Philadelphia Museum of Art, 1958 : *Picasso.* Fort Worth Art Center Museum, February 8–March 26, 1967 : *Picasso,* No. 146.

Bibl. Z. VI. 681. Lieberman, 1961, pl. 40. Blunt and Pool, No. 139.

Coll. Gertrude Stein, Paris ; Alice B. Toklas, Paris ; Curt Valentin, New York ; Nelson A. Rockefeller, New York ;

Private collection, New York.

Study for *The Actor* (XII. 1). The two sketches of heads are probably the first portrayals of Fernande in Picasso's work.

XII. 3
SEATED NUDE
Paris, 1905.
Oil on cardboard mounted on panel.
Size : 106 x 76 cm.
Signed bottom right : Picasso.

Exh. Pierre Matisse Gallery, New York, January 1937 : *Masterpieces,* No. 18. Idem, January 1939 : *Early Paintings by French Moderns,* No. 13. M. H. de Young Memorial Museum, San Francisco, December 29, 1939–January 28, 1940 : *Seven Centuries of Painting,* No. 191, repr. in cat. Virginia Museum of Arts, January–March 1941, and Philadelphia Museum of Art, March–May, 1941 : *Collection Walter P. Chrysler, Jr.,* No. 153 (entitled

Nude in Grey), repr. in cat.

Bibl. Z. I. 257. Cassou, 1940, p. 56. Sutton, 1955, No. 49. Cogniat, 1959, p. 19 (repr. in color). Diehl, 1960, p. 16 (color). Bernard Dorival, *L'Ecole de Paris au Musée National d'Art Moderne,* Paris, 1961, p. 163 (color). B. Dorival, *Le Musée National d'Art Moderne,* Kunsten Idag, 1962, No. 3.

Coll. Gertrude Stein, Paris ; Pierre Matisse, New York ; Walter P. Chrysler, Jr., New York ; Purchase of the Musées Nationaux de France, in 1954 ;

Musée National d'Art Moderne, Paris.

XII. 4
MOTHER AND CHILD
Paris, 1905.
Gouache.
Size : 65 x 50.5 cm.
Signed and dated, bottom right : Picasso 1905.

Exh. Grand Palais, Paris, November 1966–February 1967 : *Hommage à Pablo Picasso,* No. 21, repr. in cat.

Bibl. Not in Z. Sabartés and Boeck, p. 371. Sutton, 1955, pl. XI (repr. in color). Boudaille, 1964, pl. XIII (repr. in color). Helen Kay, *Picasso's World of Children,* 1965, p. 71.

Coll. Olivier Sainsère, Paris ; Mme Richet, Paris ;

Private collection, Paris.

See the sheet of studies for *Mother and Child,* dated 1904 (D. XI. 26).

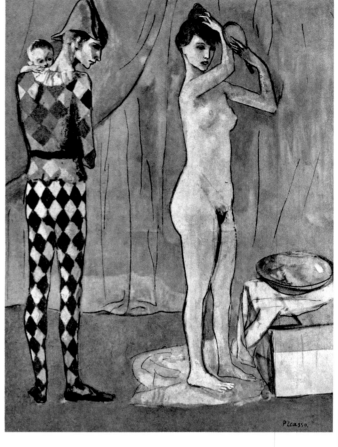

XII. 5
WOMAN IN A CHEMISE
Paris, 1905.
Oil on canvas.
Size : 72.5 x 60 cm.
Signed and dated, bottom left :
Picasso 05.

Exh. Leicester Galleries, London, January, 1921 : *Pablo Picasso,* No. 8. Knoedler, London, Contemporary Art Society, February, 1928 : *Foreign Paintings,* No. 43. Lefevre Gallery, London, June, 1931 : *Thirty Years of Pablo Picasso,* No. 7. Galerie Georges Petit, Paris, summer, 1932 : *Picasso,* No. 31. Kunsthaus, Zurich, autumn, 1932 : *Picasso,* No. 31. Walker Art Gallery, Liverpool, October-December, 1933 : Re-opening exhibition, No. 597, repr. Tate Gallery, London, 1960 : *Picasso,* No. 22, repr. pl. 5 g. Grand Palais, Paris, 1966–1967 : *Hommage à Pablo Picasso,* No. 22, repr.

Bibl. Z. I. 307. Paul Eluard, 1944, p. 69. Maurice Gieure, 1951, pl. 13 *(Femme de profil). Art et Style,* No 27. Paris, 1953 : *The Tate Gallery* (repr. in color). Sutton, 1955, No. 25. Elgar and Maillard, 1955 (catalogue). Cassou, 1958, p. 20 (color). Ronald Alley, *Tate Gallery, The Foreign Paintings, Drawings and Sculpture,* London 1959, pl. 16. *Cinquante Chefs-d'œuvre,* Paris, 1963, p. 189.

Coll. Galerie Kahnweiler, Paris (bought from the artist in 1909); Alfred Flechtheim, Berlin ; C. Frank Stoop, London, who bequeathed it to the Tate Gallery in 1933 ;

Tate Gallery, London.

XII. 6
THE HARLEQUIN'S FAMILY
Paris, 1905.
Gouache and India ink on paper.
Size : 58 x 43.5 cm.
Signed and dated, bottom right :
Picasso 1905.

Exh. Wadsworth Atheneum, 1934 : *Picasso,* No. 15, repr. in cat. Museum of Modern Art, New York, summer, 1935. Society of Four Arts, Palm Beach, 1936. Jacques Seligmann & Co., New York, 1936 : *Picasso, Blue and Rose Periods,* No. 22, repr. in cat. Museum of Modern Art, New York, and Art Institute of Chicago, 1939–1940 : *Picasso, Forty Years of his Art,* No. 47, repr. in cat. p. 46. Knoedler, New York, 1962 : *Picasso, an American Tribute,* No. 22, repr. in cat.

Bibl. Z. I. 298. Henri Mahaut, 1930. pl. 8. Eugenio d'Ors, 1930, pl. 10,

The Lewisohn Collection, "Formes," XXVIII–XXIX, 1932, repr. C. J. Bulliet, 1936, pl. 102. Barr, *Forty Years,* p. 46. Sabartés and Boeck, p. 133 (color). Elgar and Maillard, 1955, p. 35 (color). Ponge and Chessex, 1960, p. 32. Lieberman, 1961, pl. 24 (color). *Nouveau Dictionnaire de la Peinture Moderne,* 1963, p. 280 (color). Helen Kay, 1965, p. 68.

Coll. Mr. and Mrs. Sam A. Lewisohn, New York ;

Collection Mr. and Mrs. Julian C. Eisenstein, Washington, D.C.

In 1905 Picasso did an etching on zinc of this same subject : *The Mother Dressing* (Geiser 15 b, Vollard Suite No. 13).

XII. 7
THE ACROBAT'S FAMILY WITH A MONKEY
Paris, 1905.
Gouache, watercolor, pastel and India ink on cardboard.
Size : 104 x 75 cm.
Signed top right : Picasso.

Exh. Stockholm, 1954 : *Cézanne till Picasso.* Kiruna, Sweden, September, 1965 : *Picasso i Kiruna,* No. 2, repr. in color in cat. Louisiana Konstmuseum, Humlebaek, Denmark, March 26–May 22, 1966 : *Göteborgs Konstmuseum.* Grand Palais, Paris, November 1966–February 1967 : *Hommage à Pablo Picasso,* No. 23, repr. in cat.

Bibl. Z. I. 299. Gertrude Stein, *Picasso,* Paris, 1938, pl. 11. Raynal and Lassaigne, *Histoire de la peinture moderne, de Picasso au surréalisme,* 1950, p. 23 (repr. in color). Elgar and Maillard, 1955 (catalogue). Sutton, 1955, pl. XIII (color). Penrose, 1958, pl. III, No. 7. Blunt and Pool, No. 131. John Berger, *Success and Failure of Picasso,* 1965, p. 46.

Coll. Conrad Pineus, Göteborg ; Acquired by the Museum in 1922 :

Göteborgs Konstmuseum, Göteborg.

Color plate, page 73.

XII. 8
MOTHER AND CHILD
(Saltimbanques)
Paris, 1905.
Gouache on canvas.
Size : 88 x 69.5 cm.
Unsigned (signed, recto).
Recto : Seated Woman with Hood (VII. 2).

Exh. Munich, Cologne and Hamburg, 1955–1956 : *Picasso 1900–1955,* No. 12, repr. in cat.

Bibl. Z. I. 296 (entitled *Baladins*). Sabartés and Boeck, p. 459, No. 28.

Sutton, 1955, No. 51. Helen Kay, 1965 (frontispiece in color). Robert Delevoy, *Dimensions du 20ᵉ siècle,* Geneva, 1965, p. 23 (repr. in color).

Coll. Gertrude Stein, Paris ; Galerie Caspari, Munich ; Dr. Fritz Nathan, Zurich ;

Staatsgalerie, Stuttgart.

Color plate, page 77 and on the cover.

XII. 9
ACROBAT AND YOUNG
HARLEQUIN
Paris, 1905.
Gouache on cardboard.
Size : 105 x 76 cm.
Signed and dated, top right : Picasso 1905.

Exh. Zunfthaus zur Meise, Zurich, May 17–27, 1939, and Lucerne, May 30– June 29, 1939 : *Exhibition before sale,* No. 115 (cf. Sale, Galerie Fischer, below). Knokke-le-Zoute, July–August 1950 : *Picasso,* No. 10. Musée Royal des Beaux-Arts, Antwerp, May–June 1955 : *L'Art contemporain.* Musée National d'Art Moderne, Paris, July, 1959 : *L'Ecole de Paris dans les collections belges.* Grand Palais, Paris November 1966–

February 1967 : *Hommage à Pablo Picasso* : No. 24, repr. in cat.

Bibl. Guillaume Apollinaire in *La Plume,* Paris, May 15, 1905, repr. p. 482. Z. I. 297. Raymond Cogniat, 1959, p. 21 (repr. in color).

Coll. Gift of Museumverein Elberfeld to Städtisches Museum, Wuppertal, in 1911 ; Städtisches Museum, Wuppertal (1911–1937) ; Confiscated by the Nazi regime in 1937 ("Decadent Art") ; Galerie Fischer, Lucerne, June 30, 1939 : *Sale of paintings and sculpture by modern masters from museums in Germany,* No. 115, cat. p. 60, repr. p. 61 ; Acquired by the present owner :

Private collection, Belgium.

XII. 10
SEATED HARLEQUIN
WITH RED BACKGROUND
Paris, 1905.
Watercolor and India ink.
Dimensions not known.
Signed and dated, top left : Picasso 1905.

Bibl. Guillaume Apollinaire in *La Plume,* Paris, May 15, 1905, repr. p. 483. Not in Z. Germain Bazin, *Histoire de l'Art, de la préhistoire à nos jours,* Paris, 1953, pl. XVI (repr. in color). Raynal, Geneva, 1959, p. 33 (color).

Coll. Bignou, Paris ; Mlle Cécile de Rothschild, Paris ;

Private collection, Paris.

The reproduction of this work in *La Plume* of May 15, 1905 proves that it dates from the first months of 1905. The reproduction in the same magazine of *Acrobat and Young Harlequin* (XII. 9) is also an important chronological reference.

XII. 11
THE HARLEQUIN'S FAMILY
Paris, 1905.
Gouache and India ink.
Size : 29.5 x 21 cm.
Signed bottom left : Picasso.

Bibl. Z. I. 244. Blunt and Pool, No. 138.

Coll. Private collection, Cologne ;
Sotheby & Co., London, Sale, November 25, 1959, No. 61, sold for

£12,000 ; Bought at this sale by
M. Knoedler & Co., London and New
York ;

Private collection, U.S.A.

There are many variations on this
theme ; two are drypoints (Geiser 13 b
and 14 b, Vollard Suite No. 11 and
No. 12).

XII. 12
HARLEQUIN MAKING-UP
Paris, 1905.
Gouache on cardboard.
Size : 69 x 54 cm.
Signed bottom left : Picasso.

Exh. Kunsthaus, Zürich, 1932 : *Picasso,*
No. 25 *(Arlequin et femme).*

Bibl. Z. VI. 702. Ponge and Chessex
Lausanne, 1960, p. 34 (entitled *Couple
de Bateleurs*).

Coll. Marcel Fleischmann, Zurich ;

Private collection, U.S.A.

XII. 13
THE ACROBAT'S FAMILY
Paris, 1905.
Gouache.
Size : 22 x 29 cm.
Signed and dated, bottom left :
Picasso 1905.

Bibl. Z. I. 289.

Coll. Georg von Schnitzler, Frankfurt ;

Private collection, Germany.

One can see in this series (XII. 11, 13,
and 14) the same ladder and the same
drum—the accessories of circus people.

XII. 14
THE ACROBAT'S MEAL
Paris, 1905.
Watercolor and gouache.
Size : 31.6 x 23.3 cm.
Signed top left : Picasso.

Exh. Jacques Seligmann & Co., New
York, November 2–26, 1936 : *Picasso,*

Blue and Rose Periods, No. 24, repr.
in cat.

Bibl. Z. I. 292.

Coll. Reber, Lausanne ; Mrs. Frederick
G. Clark, New York ;

Private collection, New York.

XII. 15
YOUNG ACROBAT AND CHILD
Paris, March 1905.
Watercolor and gouache.
Size : 23.5 x 17.8 cm.
Signed and dated, bottom right :
Picasso, Paris 26 mars 05.
Inscribed above the signature :
A Mlle A. Nachmann.

Exh. The Solomon R. Guggenheim
Museum, New York, April–September
1965 : *First Showing of Masterpieces
of Modern Art from the Thannhauser
Foundation,* No. 41 (entitled *Two
Harlequins*), repr. in color in cat. p. 46.

Bibl. Z. VI. 718.   Helen Kay, 1965,
p. 64.

Coll. Justin K. Thannhauser, New
York ;

*The Solomon R. Guggenheim Mu-
seum, New York, Justin K. Thannhauser Foundation.*

We reject the title *Two Harlequins*
given to this work by the Thannhauser
Foundation.   Neither of these two
young boys is dressed in harlequin
costume.

XII. 16
BOY WITH A DOG
Paris, 1905.
Gouache.
Size : 57 x 41 cm.
Signed and dated, top left : Picasso 05.

Bibl. Z. I. 306.   Sterling, *Musée de
l'Ermitage,* 1957, pl. 154.   Boudaille,
Le Musée de l'Ermitage, 1964, pl. 45.
Helen Kay, 1965, p. 63.

Coll. S. I. Tschukin, Moscow ; Museum
of Modern Western Art, Moscow
(1918–1948) ;

The Hermitage Museum, Leningrad.

This work belongs to the series of
studies which leads to the large-scale
composition *Family of Saltimbanques*
(XII. 35).

XII. 17
TWO ACROBATS WITH A DOG
Paris, 1905.
Gouache on cardboard.
Size : 105.5 x 75 cm.
Signed and dated, bottom right : Pi-
casso 1905.

Exh. Museum of Modern Art, New
York, May-September 1939 : *Art in
our Time, 10th Anniversary Exhibition,*
No. 85, repr. in cat. p. 155.   Museum
of Modern Art, New York, and Art
Institute of Chicago, 1939–1940 :
Picasso, Forty Years of his Art, No. 31,
repr. p. 41.   Museum of Modern Art,
New York, 1941 : *138 Masterpieces of
Picasso.*   Museum of Modern Art,
New York, 1957 : *Picasso, 75th Anni-
versary Exhibition,* repr. p. 25.   Museum
of Modern Art, New York, October 8–
November 9, 1958 : *Works of Art,
given or promised.* Wildenstein & Co.,

New York, May 1961 : *In Memory of
Adèle Levy.*

Bibl. Guillaume Apollinaire in *La
Plume,* Paris, May 15, 1905, repr.
p. 477.   Z. I. 300.   Barr, *Forty Years,*
p. 41.   Barr, *Fifty Years,* p. 34 (color).
Lieberman, 1954, pl. 8 (color).   Elgar
and Maillard, 1955 (catalogue).   Lieberman, 1961, pl. 23 (color).   Helen
Kay, 1965, p. 62.

Coll. Galerie Thannhauser, Paris ;
Wright Ludington, Santa Barbara ;

*Collection The Hon. and Mrs. William
A. M. Burden, New York.*

The reproduction of this gouache in
La Plume of May 15, 1905 proves that
it dates from the first months of the
year.

XII. 18
CIRCUS FAMILY
Paris, 1905.
Watercolor and India ink on paper.
Size : 24 x 30.5 cm.
Signed bottom right : Picasso.

Exh. Knoedler, New York, January–February 1955 : *The Cone Collection.* Museum of Modern Art, New York, and Art Institute of Chicago, 1957 : *Picasso, 75th Anniversary Exhibition,* repr. p. 25. Philadelphia Museum of Art, 1958 : *Picasso,* No. 24, repr. Santa Barbara Museum of Art, April 1959, and The California Palace of The Legion of Honor, December 1959 : *The Greatest Show on Earth,* No. 48, repr. on cover. Knoedler, New York, 1962 : *Picasso, an American Tribute,* No. 21, repr.

Bibl. Not in Z. Catalogue : *The Cone Collection,* Baltimore, 1934, pl. 61. Raynal, 1953, p. 31 (color). *Handbook of the Cone Collection,* Baltimore Museum of Art, 1955, No. 87, p. 10 (color). Elgar and Maillard, 1956 (New York edition) p. 14 (color). Ponge and Chessex, p. 28–29. Lieberman, 1961, pl. 12. Helen Kay, 1965, p. 66.

Coll. Miss Etta and Dr. Claribel Cone, Baltimore ;

The Baltimore Museum of Art, The Cone Collection.

In 1905 Picasso made a drypoint of this same subject (Geiser 9 b). We reproduce it on page 255.

XII. 19
YOUNG ACROBAT ON A BALL
Paris, 1905.
Oil on canvas.
Size : 147 x 95 cm.
Signed bottom right : Picasso.

Exh. Maison de la Pensée française, Paris, 1954 : *Picasso.* Pushkin Museum, Moscow, 1955 : *L'art français des XVe-XXe siècles,* p. 50. Hermitage Museum, Leningrad, 1956 : *Same exhibition,* p. 47. Exposition universelle et internationale de Bruxelles, 1958, No. 255. Tate Gallery, London, 1960 : *Picasso,* No. 273, repr. pl. 57 a.

Bibl. Z. I. 290. Raynal, 1921, pl. 22. Ternowietz, *Le Musée d'Art Moderne Occidental de Moscou,* 1925, p. 485. Level, 1928, pl. 16. *Catalogue du Musée d'Art Moderne Occidental de Moscou,* 1928, p. 83. No. 459. Réau, 1929, No. 1046. Javorskaïa, 1933, p. 14. Ternowietz, 1935, pl. XXI. Gertrude Stein, 1938, pl. 9. Eluard, 1944, p. 67. Elgar and Maillard, 1955 (catalogue). Sutton, 1955, pl. XV (color). Kahnweiler and Parmelin, 1955, pl. 17 (color). Sterling, 1957, pl. 157 (color). Penrose, 1958, pl. IV, No. 2. Diehl, 1960, p. 11 (color). Prokofiev, 1962, No. 197 (color). Blunt and Pool, No. 153. Boudaille, 1964, p. 11. Daix, 1964, p. 48 (color). Helen Kay, 1965, p. 67.

Coll. Gertrude Stein, Paris ; Galerie Kahnweiler, Paris (No. 1491) ; I. A. Morosov, Moscow (1913–1918), purchase price in 1913 : 16,000 fr. ; Museum of Modern Western Art, Moscow (1918–1948) ;

The Pushkin Museum, Moscow.

There are several motifs in this large oil which appear in other works of this period : the little girl on a ball, the white horse, a mother and child, in XII. 18 ; the dog, in XII. 16, 17, 31, and 33 ; and the athlete, cf. XII. 20.

Color plate, page 83.

XII. 20
THE ATHLETE
Paris, 1905.
Gouache on cardboard.
Size : 54 x 44 cm.
Signed and inscribed, top left : A Paul Fort, Picasso.

Exh. Musée des Arts Décoratifs, Paris, 1955 : *Picasso 1900–1955,* No. 10, repr. in cat. Grand Palais, Paris, November 1966–February 1967 : *Hommage à Pablo Picasso,* No. 25, repr. in cat.

Bibl. Not in Z. Elgar and Maillard, 1955, p. 43 (repr. in color). John Richardson, Basel, 1964, p. 25 (repr. in color).

Coll. Olivier Sainsère, Paris ; Richet, Paris ;

Private collection, Paris.

A study for this gouache is catalogued in the following Drawings Section (see D. XII. 21).

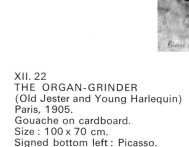

XII. 21
THE KING
Paris, 1905.
Pastel.
Size : 55 x 45 cm.
Signed bottom right : Picasso.

Bibl. Z. I. 245. W. Pfeiderer, *Samm-lung Hugo Borst,* Stuttgart, 1931, p. 43. Blunt and Pool, No. 157.

Coll. Hugo Borst, Stuttgart ;

Staatsgalerie, Stuttgart.

In the Staatsgalerie, Stuttgart, this pastel is catalogued as *Le Roi Dago-bert.* There is a variant of the same subject, a pencil drawing, in the Push-kin Museum, Moscow ; the man wears not a crown but a tiara orna-mented with naked figures (Zervos I. 246).

XII. 22
THE ORGAN-GRINDER
(Old Jester and Young Harlequin)
Paris, 1905.
Gouache on cardboard.
Size : 100 x 70 cm.
Signed bottom left : Picasso.

Exh. Palazzo Reale, Milan, 1953 : *Picasso,* No. 5, repr. in cat. (entitled *Saltimbanco seduto con ragazzo,* dated 1906). Haus der Kunst, Munich, 1955. Musée National d'Art Moderne, Paris, 1960 : *Les sources du XXᵉ siècle,* No. 551 bis. Grand Palais, Paris, November 1966–February 1967 : *Hommage à Pablo Picasso,* No. 31, repr. in cat.

Bibl. Z. VI. 798 (dated 1906). Elgar and Maillard, 1955, p. 38 (repr. in

color). J. de la Encina, *La Pittura Espagnola,* Milan, 1961, pl. XLII. Blunt and Pool, No. 159. Helen Kay, 1965, p. 59 *(Child and Acrobat).*

Coll. Purchase price in 1942 : 10,000 fr.

Kunsthaus, Zurich.

We catalogue this work with the title given it by the Kunsthaus in Zurich. It belongs logically to the series of circus folk and harlequins of 1905, in spite of the fact that it is traditionally dated 1906.

Color plate, page 71.

XII. 23
AT THE LAPIN AGILE
Paris, 1905.
Oil on canvas.
Size : 99 x 100.3 cm.
Unsigned.

Exh. Musée Cantini, Marseilles, May 11–July 31, 1959 : *Picasso,* No. 6 (en-titled *Arlequin et femme dans un café*), repr. in cat. Knoedler & Co., New York, 1962 : *Picasso, an American Tribute,* No. 16 (dated 1904), repr. in color in cat. Dallas Museum of Fine Arts, February 8–March 26, 1967 : *Picasso,* No. 8.

Bibl. Z. I. 275 *(Arlequin au verre).* K. Asplund, *Rolf de Mares Tavelsam-ling,* Stockholm, 1923, pl. 22. Sutton, 1955, No. 38. Penrose, 1958, pl. I, No. 7. Cogniat, 1959, frontispiece

(color). Blunt and Pool, No. 137. John Berger, 1965, p. 44.

Coll. Frédéric Gérard, Paris (1905) ; Alfred Flechtheim, Berlin (1912) ; Rolf de Mare, Stockholm ;

Collection Mrs. Charles S. Payson, Manhasset, N.Y.

This painting used to hang in the famous Montmartre café, the *Lapin Agile.* The artist gave it to Frédé, the owner. The guitar player seated in the background is Frédé himself (cf. the drawing of the same subject, D. XII. 10). The man in the foreground is a self-portrait of Picasso dressed as a harlequin.

Color plate, page 253.

XII. 24
HARLEQUIN ON HORSEBACK
Paris, 1905.
Oil on cardboard.
Size : 100 x 69.2 cm.
Signed bottom left : Picasso.

Exh. Kunsthaus, Zurich, 1932 : *Picasso*, No. 275. Musée Jenisch, Vevey, 1962 : *De Cézanne à Picasso,* No. 184, repr. in cat. National Gallery of Art, Washington, D.C., 1966 : *25th Anniversary Exhibition : French Paintings from the Collections of Mr. and Mrs. Paul Mellon and Mrs. Mellon Bruce,* No. 195, repr. in cat.

Bibl. Z. I. 243 (entitled *Clown à cheval,* dated 1904). Level, 1928, pl. 10.

Sabartés and Boeck, p. 459, No. 25. Sutton, 1955, pl. VII (color). Cogniat, 1959, p. 17 (color). Cassou, 1959, p. 26 (color).

Coll. M. Level, Paris ; H. L. Mermod, Lausanne ;

Collection Mr. and Mrs. Paul Mellon, Upperville, Virginia.

This work is usually dated 1904. We date it 1905, placing it logically among works with similar subjects, which are themselves unmistakably 1905. Cf. the study, D. XII. 11.

Color plate, page 81.

XII. 25
TWO HARLEQUINS
(Jester and Young Harlequin)
Paris, 1905.
Oil.
Size : 190.5 x 108 cm.
Signed bottom right : Picasso.

Bibl. Z. I. 301 (entitled *Comédiens*). Albert C. Barnes, *The Art in Painting,*

New York, 1937, p. 23. Sutton, 1955, repr. No. 39 (entitled *Baladins*). Barnes Foundation Inventory, No. 382.

Barnes Foundation, Merion, Pa.

The model for the young harlequin is probably the same one who posed for *The Organ-Grinder* (XII. 22).

XII. 26
THE JESTER
Paris, 1905.
Gouache on cardboard.
Size : 70 x 54 cm.
Signed top left : Picasso.

Bibl. Z. I. 293.

Coll. Robert de Rothschild, Paris ;

Private collection, Paris.

Picasso modeled the same person in one of his early sculptures : *Head of a Jester,* bronze, H. 41 cm., cast for Ambroise Vollard in 1905 (Z. I. 322).

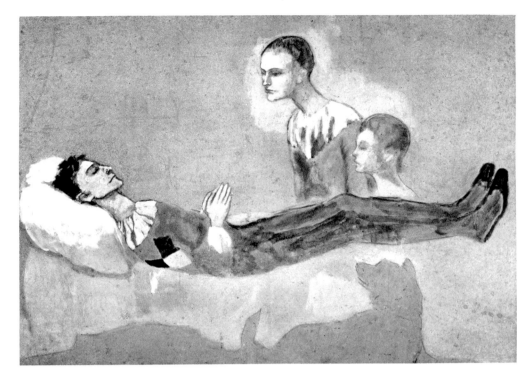

XII. 27
THE DEATH OF HARLEQUIN
Paris, 1905.
Gouache on cardboard.
Size : 65 x 95 cm.
Signed bottom right : Picasso.
Recto : Seated Woman in a Garden
(V. 17).

Exh. Galerie Thannhauser, Munich,
1913. National Gallery of Art, Washington, D.C., 1966 : *25th Anniversary
Exhibition : French Paintings from the
Collections of Mr. and Mrs. Paul*

Mellon and Mrs Mellon Bruce,
No. 194, repr. in cat.

Bibl. Z. I. 302. Elgar and Maillard,
1955 (catalogue). Sutton, 1955,
No. 27. Blunt and Pool, No. 134.
Helen Kay, 1965, p. 72.

Coll. Bought from the artist in 1905–
1906 by Wilhelm Uhde ; Lent by
Uhde to Rainer Maria Rilke ; Private
collection, Westphalia ; J. K. Thannhauser, New York ; Somerset Maug-

ham, St-Jean-Cap Ferrat ; Sotheby
& Co., London, April 10, 1962, Sale of
the Somerset Maugham collection,
No. 26, repr. in color in cat. p. 43, sold
for £80,000 (recto and verso) ;

*Collection Mr. and Mrs. Paul Mellon,
Upperville, Virginia.*

According to the Kahnweiler archives
in the Louise Leiris Gallery, this painting was signed by the artist in 1911.

XII. 28
BUFFOON AND YOUNG ACROBAT
Paris, 1905. Gouache and pastel.
Size : 66 x 56 cm.
Signed bottom right : Picasso.

Exh. Jacques Seligmann, New York,
1936, No. 23, repr.

Bibl. Z. I. 284 (incorrect dimensions).

Coll. Countess Mechtilde Lichnowsky,
Kuchelna ; Perls Galleries, New York ;

Private collection, U.S.A.

XII. 29
BUFFOON AND YOUNG ACROBAT
(Study for *Family of Saltimbanques*)
Paris, 1905.
Watercolor, pastel and charcoal.
Size : 60 x 47 cm.
Signed bottom right : Picasso.

Exh. Virginia Museum of Fine Arts,
1953 : *The Cone Collection*. Knoedler
& Co., New York, 1955 : *The Cone
Collection*. The Woman's College of
the University of North Carolina,
Greensboro, 1955 : *The Cone Collection*.

Bibl. Z. I. 283. *Handbook of the Cone
Collection,* Baltimore Museum of Art,
1955, No. 85, repr. in color p. 32.
Elgar and Maillard, 1955 (catalogue).
Raynal, 1959, p. 32 and cover (color).
Blunt and Pool, No. 151. Helen Kay,
1965, p. 61 (color).

Coll. Galerie Thannhauser, Lucerne ;
Galerie Rosengart, Lucerne ; Miss
Etta and Dr. Claribel Cone, Baltimore ;

*The Baltimore Museum of Art, The
Cone Collection.*

XII. 30
EL TIO PEPE DON JOSÉ
(Buffoon with a Rapier)
Paris, 1905.
Pen drawing.
Size : 25.5 x 21.5 cm.
Signed bottom right : Picasso.
Inscribed top right : El tio Pepe Don
José à 40 años.

Bibl. Not in Z.

*Collection Mr. and Mrs. Lee A. Ault,
New York.*

This beautiful drawing (unpublished,
to our knowledge) shows "Uncle Don
José," the figure who also posed for
the buffoon in *Family of Saltimbanques*
(XII. 33 and 35). Cf. also the series of
studies XII. 28, 29 and D. XII. 18, 19,
20.

XII. 32
BOY WITH A BARREL
(Study for *Family of Saltimbanques*)
Paris, 1905.
Sanguine drawing on paper.
Size : 49.5 x 31.7 cm.
Signed bottom right : Picasso.

Exh. Knoedler, New York, April–May 1957 : *Modern Paintings, Drawings and Sculpture Collected by Louise and Joseph Pulitzer, Jr.* Fogg Art Museum, May–September 1957.

Bibl. Not in Z. Catalogue of the Joseph Pulitzer Jr. Collection, 2 vol., ed. Fogg Art Museum.

Coll. Suermondt, Aix-la-Chapelle (bought from the artist in 1912) ; Fine Arts Associates, New York ;

Collection Mr. and Mrs. Joseph Pulitzer, Jr., St. Louis.

Study for the young acrobat in the center of *Family of Saltimbanques* (XII. 33 and 35).

XII. 31
LITTLE GIRL WITH A DOG
(Study for *Family of Saltimbanques*)
Paris, 1905.
Pastel and gouache on paper.
Size : 70.5 x 47.5 cm.
Signed bottom left : Picasso.

Exh. Kunsthaus, Zurich, 1932 : *Picasso*, No. 278. Lefevre Gallery, London, March 1943 : *Picasso and his contemporaries*, No. 18. National Gallery of Scotland, Edinburgh, 1944 : *A Century of French Art 1840–1940*, No. 233. Lefevre Gallery, London, May–June 1953 : *Picasso 1898–1936*, No. 3, repr. in cat.

Bibl. Z. I. 286 (incorrectly assigned to the Museum of Modern Western Art, Moscow). Helen Kay, 1965, p. 62.

Coll. Galerie Thannhauser, Lucerne ; Captain S. W. Sykes, Cambridge ; Mrs. S. Kaye, London ; Mrs. Chester Beatty, London ; Sam Salz Inc., New York ;

Collection Mr. and Mrs. William Goetz, Los Angeles.

Study for XII. 33 and 35.

XII. 33
FAMILY OF SALTIMBANQUES
(Study for XII. 35)
Paris, 1905.
Gouache on cardboard.
Size : 51.2 x 61.2 cm.
Signed bottom left : Picasso.

Exh. Museum of Modern Western Art, Moscow, 1925 : *Dessins français de la fin du XIXᵉ au XXᵉ siècle.* The Pushkin Museum, Moscow, 1955 : *L'Art français des XVᵉ–XXᵉ siècles*, p. 81. The Pushkin Museum, Moscow, 1959 : *Drawings and Watercolors*, p. 34.

Bibl. Z. I. 287. Touguenhold, *La collection française de S. I. Chtchoukine* in *Apollon*, No. 1–2, Petrograd, 1914, p. 40. Réau, *Catalogue de l'art français dans les musées russes*, 1929, No. 1009.

Coll. S. I. Tschukin, Moscow (until 1918) ; Museum of Modern Western Art, Moscow (1918–1948) ;

The Pushkin Museum, Moscow.

Study for *Family of Saltimbanques* (XII. 35).

XII. 34
WOMAN OF MAJORCA
(Study for XII. 35)
Paris, 1905. Gouache on cardboard.
Size : 67 x 51 cm.
Signed bottom left : Picasso.

Exh. Maison de la Pensée Française, Paris, June 1954 : *Picasso.* The Pushkin Museum, Moscow, 1955 : *L'Art français des XVᵉ–XXᵉ siècles*, p. 50. The Hermitage Museum, Leningrad, 1956 : Same exhibition, p. 46.

Bibl. Z. I. 288. *Catalogue* (paintings) *de la collection S. I. Chtchoukine*, Moscow, 1913, No. 153. Touguenhold, Moscow, 1923, p. 121. Cat. of the Museum of Modern Western Art, Moscow, 1928, No. 417. Réau, 1929, No. 1007. Kahnweiler and Parmelin, 1955, pl. 18 (color). Cat. (paintings) The Pushkin Museum, Moscow, 1957, p. 109. Idem, 1961, p. 147. Sterling, 1957, pl. 158 (color). Prokofiev, 1962, No. 196. *Les Grands Maîtres de la peinture au Musée de Moscou*, 1963, No. 100 (color).

Coll. S. I. Tschukin, Moscow (until 1918) ; Museum of Modern Western Art, Moscow (1918–1948) ;

The Pushkin Museum, Moscow.

XII. 35
FAMILY OF SALTIMBANQUES
Paris, 1905.
Oil on canvas.
Size : 212.8 x 229.6 cm.
Signed bottom right : Picasso.

Exh. Museum of French Art, New York, 1931 : *Picasso, Braque, Léger,* No. 4. Art Institute of Chicago, 1954 : *20th Century Paintings from the Chester Dale Collection.*

Bibl. Z. I. 285. Catalogue, Galerie Heinrich Thannhauser, Munich, 1916, pl. 150. Level, 1928, pl. 17. R. M. Rilke, *Duino Elegies,* New York, 1939, frontispiece. Barr, *Fifty Years,* p. 46. C.-P. No. 188. Maurice Gieure, 1951, pl. 15. Elgar and Maillard, 1955 (catalogue). Sutton, 1955, pl. X (color). Sabartés and Boeck, p. 369. Penrose, 1958, pl. IV, No. 4. Cassou, 1958, p. 18 (color). Ripley, 1959, p. 17. Lieber-man, 1961, pl. 26–27 (color). Blunt and Pool, No. 149. National Gallery of Art, Washington, D.C., *Chester Dale Collection* (1965 edition), p. 72. Helen Kay, 1965, p. 60–61 (color). Berger, 1965, p. 45.

Coll. André Level, Paris ; La Peau de l'Ours, Paris ; Hôtel Drouot, Paris, March 2, 1914, Sale of the collection of La Peau de l'Ours, No. 63 ; Hertha von Koenig, Munich ; Chester Dale, New York ;

The National Gallery of Art, Washington, D.C., Chester Dale Collection.

Compare this final version of *Family of Saltimbanques* with the earlier sketch (XII. 33). This famous painting is treated in Chapter IV, part 3.

D. XII. 1
MONKEY
Paris, 1905.
Pen drawing and watercolor on paper.
Size : 50 x 32 cm.
Unsigned.

Exh. Virginia Museum of Fine Arts, 1953 : *The Cone Collection.* Knoedler, New York, 1955 : *The Cone Collection.* New York and Chicago, 1957 : *Picasso, 75th Anniversary Exhibition,* cat. p. 24. Philadelphia, 1958 : *Picasso,* No. 25, repr. Boymans-van Beuningen Museum, Rotterdam, August 2–September 28, 1958 : *French Drawings from American Collections.* Same exhibi-

tion : Musée de l'Orangerie, Paris, October 2, 1958–January 2, 1959.

Bibl. Not in Z. *Catalogue of the Cone Collection,* Baltimore, 1934, pl. 60. A. D. Breeskin in *Magazine of Art,* March, 1952, p. 107 and cover. *Handbook of the Cone Collection,* Baltimore Museum of Art, 1955, No. 86, repr. p. 22.

Coll. Miss Etta and Dr. Claribel Cone, Baltimore ;

Baltimore Museum of Art, The Cone Collection.

D. XII. 2
CIRCUS FAMILY
Paris, 1905.
India ink and watercolor on Ingres paper.
Size : 9.5 x 9.7 cm.
Unsigned.

Exh. Galerie Flechtheim, Düsseldorf, 1913 : *Beitrage zur Kunst des 19. Jahrhunderts und unserer Zeit,* repr. in cat. p. 150.

Bibl. Z. I. 281 (entitled Study for *Bateleurs*). C.-P. p. 161.

Coll. Alfred Flechtheim, Düsseldorf ; Acquired in 1914 by :

Von der Heydt—Museum der Stadt Wuppertal.

D. XII. 3
HARLEQUIN'S FAMILY WITH A MONKEY
Paris, 1905.
Ink drawing on paper.
Size : 18.7 x 12.4 cm.
Signed bottom left : Picasso.

Bibl. Not in Z. Lieberman, 1961, pl. 41.

Private collection, U.S.A.

This drawing, reversed in printing, is the subject of a drypoint etched by Picasso in 1905 (*Family of Saltimbanques with a Macaque.* Geiser 13/b, No. 11 of the Vollard Suite).

D. XII. 4
JESTER HOLDING A CHILD
Paris, 1905.
Ink and colored pencils on paper.
Signed, dated and inscribed, right : Picasso, à Guillaume Apollinaire, 1905.

Bibl. Not in Z. Pierre Cailler, *Apollinaire,* Geneva, 1965, No. 109.

Coll. Guillaume Apollinaire, Paris ;

Collection Mme Jacqueline Apollinaire, Paris.

D. XII. 5
THE JESTER'S FAMILY
Paris, 1905.
Ink, colored pencils and wash.
Size : 16.5 x 12.4 cm.
Signed and inscribed, top right : Pour Fernande, Pablo.

Bibl. Not in Z.

Coll. Fernande Olivier, Paris ; Sarah S. Stein (1910) ;

Collection Mrs. Robert Woods Bliss, Washington.

The model for the jester is the same one in the preceding drawing (D. XII. 4).

D. XII. 6
HARLEQUIN AND WOMAN WITH AN AMPHORA
Paris, 1905.
Watercolor and ink on paper.
Size : 17.8 x 11.7 cm.
Signed in the margin, right : Picasso.

Exh. Never exhibited.

Bibl. Unpublished.

Coll. Knoedler & Co., New York ;

The Lehman Collection, New York.

Inscription, partially covered with a white wash, in the right margin : "Mon amour mon ange Gaby fut (illegible word). J'aime mon amour (four illegible words) ma vie. Picasso."

D. XII. 7
FAMILY WITH A CROW
Paris, 1905.
Ink and colored crayon on paper.
Size : 32.6 x 24.1 cm.   Signed bottom right : Picasso.
Exh. MMA, New York, December 21, 1960–February 5, 1961 : *Recent Acquisitions, Drawings and Watercolors.* MMA, New York, 1962 : *Picasso, 80th Birthday Exhibition.* Toronto and Montreal, 1964 : *Picasso and Man,* No. 28, repr. p. 44.
Bibl. Z. VI. 703. Sabartés and Boeck, p. 460, No. 31.
Coll. Heinz Berggruen, Paris ; Private collection, Basel ; John S. Newberry ; Since 1960 :
Museum of Modern Art, New York, John S. Newberry Collection.

The same group is seen in the drawing : Zervos I. 279.

D. XII. 8
CIRCUS ARTIST AND CHILD
Paris, 1905.
India ink and watercolor on paper.
Size : 16.5 x 10.2 cm.
Unsigned.

Exh. Wildenstein & Co., London, October–November 1948. Tate Gallery, London, June 1964.

Bibl. Unpublished.

Coll. C. Frank Stoop, London, who gave it to his niece, the present owner, in 1937 ;

Collection Mrs. Anne Kessler, Preston, Rutland.

D. XII. 9
EX-LIBRIS FOR GUILLAUME APOLLINAIRE
Paris, 1905.
Watercolor and ink on paper.   Size : 19 x 12 cm.
Signed bottom right : Picasso Fecit.
Exh. Kunsthaus, Zurich, 1932 : *Picasso,* No. 276. New York, Chicago, St. Louis and Boston, 1939–1940 : *Picasso, Forty Years of his Art.* No. 50. Virginia and Philadelphia, 1941 : *Collection Chrysler,* No. 196.
Bibl. Z. I. 225. Blunt and Pool, No. 160.
Coll. Guillaume Apollinaire, Paris ; Alfred Flechtheim, Berlin ; Douglas Cooper, London ; Buchholz Gallery, New York ; Walter P. Chrysler, Jr., New York ; Sotheby & Co., London, Sale, July 1, 1959, No. 30.

Present location unknown.

D. XII. 10
GUITAR PLAYER
Paris, 1905.
Pen drawing.
Size : 17 x 15.5 cm.
Unsigned.

Bibl. Not in Z. Duncan, p. 204 (incorrectly dated 1901).

Owned by the artist.

This is Frédé, the owner of the *Lapin Agile.* He is also seen with his guitar, wearing the same wooden shoes, in the background of the painting *At the Lapin Agile* (XII. 23).

D. XII. 11
HARLEQUIN ON HORSEBACK
Paris, 1905.
Watercolor.   Size : 22 x 13 cm.
Signed top right : Picasso.

Exh. Musée National d'Art Moderne, Paris, March–April, 1964 : *Collection André Lefèvre,* No. 244.

Bibl. Not in Z.

Coll. Bought at the second Kahnweiler sale, November 17–18, 1921, No. 249, by André Lefèvre, Paris ; Palais Galliera, Paris, November 29, 1966 : Sale of the André Lefèvre collection, No. 41, repr. in cat., sold for 90,000 F. ;

Collection Galerie Alex Maguy, Paris.

Study for *Harlequin on Horseback* (XII. 24).

D. XII. 12
EQUITATION
Paris, 1905.
Pen drawing on paper.
Size : 31.8 x 40.7 cm.
Signed bottom right : Picasso.

Bibl. Not in Z. Ponge and Chessex, 1960, No. 30.

Coll. Gertrude Stein, Paris ; Galerie Rosengart, Lucerne ; J. Westheimer, Cincinnati ;

Private collection, Cincinnati.

D. XII. 13
THE EQUESTRIENNE
Paris, 1905.
Pen drawing on paper.
Size : 23.5 x 30.5 cm.
Signed bottom left : Picasso.

Bibl. Unpublished (to be published in a supplement to the Zervos catalogue).

Coll. Galerie Rosengart, Lucerne ;

Private collection, Switzerland.

Picasso has acknowledged this previously unpublished drawing as authentic : statement signed by D. H. Kahnweiler, November 6, 1953.

D. XII. 14
THE GALLOPING HORSE
Paris, 1905.
Pen drawing.
Dimensions not available.
Signed bottom left : Picasso.

Bibl. Not in Z. *The Cone Collection,* Catalogue, Baltimore, 1934, pl. 100 a.

Coll. Miss Etta and Dr. Claribel Cone, Baltimore ;

Baltimore Museum of Art, The Cone Collection.

See the following entry (D. XII. 15).

D. XII. 15
YOUNG EQUESTRIENNE
Paris, 1905.
Gouache on cardboard.
Size : 60 x 79 cm.
Unsigned.

Exh. Galerie Georges Petit, Paris, summer, 1932 : *Picasso,* No. 26. Kunsthaus, Zurich, autumn, 1932 : *Picasso,* No. 27. Grand Palais, Paris, November 1966–February 1967 : *Hommage à Pablo Picasso,* No. 26, repr. in cat.

Bibl. Not in Z. Maurice Gieure, 1951, pl. 14.

Owned by the artist.

D. XII. 16
LITTLE GIRL STANDING ON A HORSE
Paris, 1905.
Pen drawing.
Dimensions not available.
Signed bottom left : Picasso.

Bibl. Not in Z. *The Cone Collection,* Catalogue, Baltimore, 1934, pl. 100 b. Helen Kay, 1965, p. 57.

Coll. Miss Etta and Dr. Claribel Cone, Baltimore ;

Baltimore Museum of Art, The Cone Collection.

D. XII. 17
EQUESTRIENNE
Paris, 1905.
Pen drawing on paper.
Size : 21.5 x 27.5 cm.
Unsigned (?).

Exh. Kunstnernes Hus, Oslo, 1956 : *Picasso,* No. 10.

Bibl. Unpublished.

Collection Arild Wahlström, Oslo.

D. XII. 18
SEATED BUFFOON (Saltimbanque at Rest)
Paris, 1905.
India ink and watercolor.
Size : 23 x 15 cm.
Signed and dated, top right : Picasso 1905.

Bibl. Z. VI. 734. Sabartés and Boeck, p. 460, No. 29.

Formerly collection Perls Galleries, New York.

In 1905 Picasso etched the same subject in drypoint (*Saltimbanque at Rest,* Geiser 12/b, No. 10 of the Vollard Suite).

D. XII. 19
BUFFOON AND YOUNG GIRL
Paris, 1905.
Watercolor.
Size : 29 x 18.5 cm.
Signed bottom left : Picasso.

Bibl. Z. VI. 697.

Collection Justin K. Thannhauser, New York.

There is a pen drawing of the same subject, catalogued by Zervos (Z. VI. 689).

D. XII. 20
THE BUFFOON (The Saltimbanque)
Paris, 1905.
Pencil drawing on paper.
Size : 14.5 x 11.8 cm.
Signed bottom right : Picasso.

Exh. Kunsthalle, Bremen, 1961, No. 18. Hanover, 1965 : *The Sprengel Collection,* No. 248.

Bibl. Not in Z. Arthur Millier, Los Angeles, 1961.

Coll. L. Bollag, Zurich ; Galerie Rosengart, Lucerne ;

Collection Bernhard Sprengel, Hanover.

Authenticated by the artist, October 17, 1960.

D. XII. 21
THE ACROBAT (The Athlete)
Paris, 1905.
Pen drawing and watercolor.
Size : 31 x 24 cm.
Signed bottom left : Picasso.

Bibl. Not in Z. *The Cone Collection,* Catalogue, Baltimore, 1934, pl. 98 a.

Coll. Miss Etta and Dr. Claribel Cone, Baltimore ;

Baltimore Museum of Art, The Cone Collection.

A study for the gouache, *The Athlete* (see XII. 20).

D. XII. 22
NUDE MAN CARRYING A BURDEN
Paris, 1905.
Pen drawing in India ink.
Size : 16.9 x 10.7 cm.
Unsigned.
Verso : Nude with Arms Raised (D. XVI. 8).

Bibl. Not in Z. Catalogue : Öffentliche Kunstsammlung Basel, 1944, p. 200 (recto and verso).

Coll. Klipstein (Gutekunst & Klipstein), Bern, Sale, June 27, 1944, No. 366, sold for 195 Swiss francs ;

Kupferstichkabinett, Kunstmuseum, Basel.

This figure is not unlike the Atlases on the tiara of the *King* (Z. I. 246).

D. XII. 23
THE TWO GIANTS
Paris, 1905.
Pen drawing in India ink.
Size : 32 x 22 cm.
Signed bottom right : Picasso.

Exh. Frankfurt and Hamburg, 1965, No. 20, repr. in cat.

Bibl. Z. VI. 797.

Coll. Gertrude Stein, Paris ;

Collection Rudolf Springer, Berlin.

This drawing is part of the series of athletes and giants, cf. Z. VI. 658, 659, 664, 666, 668, 671.

D. XII. 24
PORTRAIT OF GUILLAUME APOLLINAIRE
Paris, 1905.
Pen drawing in India ink on paper.
Size : 31 x 23 cm.
Signed bottom right : Picasso.

Exh. Frankfurt and Hamburg, 1965, No. 21, repr. in cat. Galerie Knoedler, Paris, 1966, No. 24, repr. in cat.

Bibl. Not in Z. Gertrude Stein, Paris, 1938, pl. 4.

Coll. Gertrude Stein, Paris ;

Collection Lionel Prejger, Paris.

D. XII. 25
STUDIES : HARLEQUINS WITH A RAPIER, HEAD, AND FEMALE NUDE
Paris, 1905.
Pen drawing on paper.
Dimensions not available.
Signed bottom right : Picasso.

Bibl. Not in Z.

Coll. Galerie Berggruen, Paris, inventory No. 1794 ;

Collection Berggruen, Paris.

D. XII. 26
STUDIES FOR THE JESTER
Paris, 1905.
India ink on white paper mounted on cardboard.
Size : 24.5 x 17 cm.
Signed bottom right : Picasso.

Exh. Musée Réattu, Arles, 1957, No. 6, repr. in cat. pl. 3 *(Le Saltimbanque).* Musée des Augustins, Toulouse, 1965 : *Picasso et le Théâtre,* No. 2. Galerie Knoedler, Paris, 1966, No. 23.

Bibl. Not in Z. Unpublished until 1957.

Coll. Private collection, France ; Kornfeld & Klipstein, Bern, Sale No. 100, June 8, 1961, No. 80, repr. in cat. p. 159 ;

Collection Lionel Prejger, Paris.

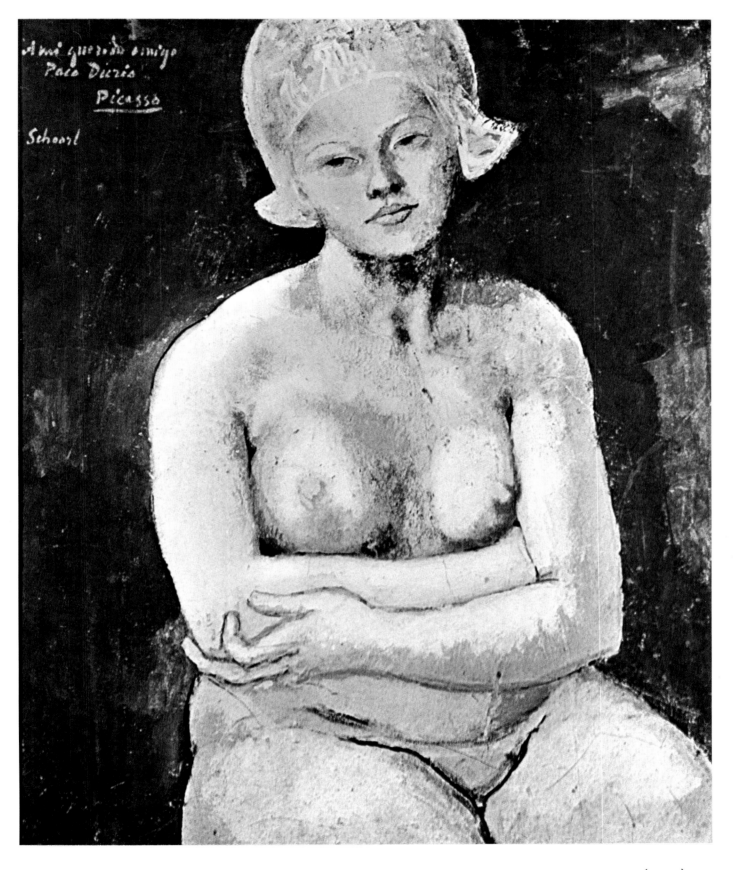

DUTCH GIRL, SCHOORL, SUMMER 1905, OIL, GOUACHE AND CHALK. QUEENSLAND ART GALLERY, BRISBANE (XIII. 1).

Holland and Rose Classicism, 1905

Relatively little evidence remains of the trip Picasso took to Holland in the summer of 1905. A Dutch writer, Tom Schilperoort, made the initial move by inviting Picasso to his native village of Schoorl, near Alkmaar. Fernande Olivier, whom Picasso had met a short while before, did not go along.

Picasso was deeply impressed by the stature, fair coloring, and pearly skin of the women of Holland. The rare works which are

catalogued from this Dutch period confirm this. Apparently Picasso rediscovered in Holland his enjoyment of painting and of looking at female bodies. He renounced the long faces and sharp features full of anguish, sadness, poverty, and despair. A new delight came out in these smooth, round faces, the rosy bodies, the happy expressions. In these works belonging to the final months of 1905, everything is conveyed in delicate curves and bathed in warm light.

Picasso retained his affectation for the rose tonality but intensified it, by deepening it to red, or by constrasting it with equally strong blues. Contours growing ever more rounded lead up to *The Watering Place* and its preliminary studies, where the rose turns into a more ochre tonality which foreshadows the Gosol period, in 1906.

Picasso told us an anecdote about the trip: "Schilperoort came into some money; he inherited 10,000 francs. He'd made up his mind to go to his village in Holland. I didn't have any money. A little, at least, was needed to make the trip. Max Jacob didn't have any more than I did. He went to the concierge and returned with 20 francs. I had a satchel (here Picasso mimed the fitting of the strap over his shoulder) and I'd put my paints in, but the brushes wouldn't go. So I broke them in half and was on my way. I'd left my studio at the Bateau-Lavoir in the hands of Salmon and some friends. Before I went I'd drawn a picture of a lawyer pointing his finger, just like a Daumier, and I'd signed it 'H. Daumier.' When I came back from Holland, I found out they'd sold the drawing as a Daumier. Now whenever I go to a museum, I'm a little nervous about running into my drawing. . . ."

Study for La Coiffure (XIII. 3), *Paris, 1905, Conté crayon.*

XIII. 1
DUTCH GIRL *(La Belle Hollandaise)*
Schoorl, summer, 1905.
Oil, gouache and blue chalk on cardboard, mounted on panel.
Size: 78 x 67.3 cm.
Signed, dated and inscribed, top left: a mi querido amigo / Paco Durio / Picasso / 1905 Schoorl.

Exh. Fitzwilliam Museum, Cambridge, 1938–1939: *Freshfield Loan Exhibition.* Arts Council of Great Britain, Tate Gallery, London, 1960: *Picasso,* No. 25, repr. in cat. pl. 5 h.

Bibl. Z. I. 260. Barr, *Fifty Years,* p. 37. Jack Bilbo, *Famous Nudes by Famous Artists,* 1946, p. 44 (color). Jacques Lassaigne, 1949, pl. 22. Sabartés and Boeck, p. 459, No. 27 *(La Hollandaise).* Sutton, 1955, No. 28.

Coll. Paco Durio, Paris and Barcelona; J. K. Thannhauser; J. B. Stang, Oslo; J. W. Freshfield, England; Oliver Gollancz, London; H. de Vahl Rubin, England; Sotheby & Co., London, May 6, 1959: Sale of the H. de Vahl Rubin collection, No. 17, sold for £55,000;

Queensland Art Gallery, Brisbane.

Picasso did this painting during his stay in Holland in the summer of 1905. He was invited there by the Dutch writer, Tom Schilperoort, who was living in the village of Schoorl, near Alkmaar.

Color plate, page 273.

XIII. 2
THREE DUTCH GIRLS
Schoorl, summer, 1905.
Gouache on paper mounted on cardboard.
Size : 77 x 67 cm.
Signed and dated, bottom left : Picasso 05.
Inscribed on the back : Picasso, Schoorl, 1905.

Exh. La Peau de l'Ours, Paris, 1911, No. 154 (entitled *Les Trois Commères*). Musée National d'Art Moderne, Paris, March–April 1964 : *Collection André Lefèvre*, No. 24, repr. in cat. Grand Palais, Paris, 1966–1967 : *Hommage*

à *Pablo Picasso*, No. 27, repr. in cat.

Bibl. Z. I. 261. Level, 1928, pl. 18. Jérôme Peignot in *Connaissance des Arts*, No. 168, Paris, February 1966, p. 47 (repr. in color).

Coll. Hôtel Drouot, Paris, March 2, 1914 : Sale of the collection of la Peau de l'Ours, No. 123, repr. in cat. p. 68, estimated price 2,000 fr., sold for 5,200 fr. to Emile Level ; Emile Level Paris ; André Lefèvre, Paris ;

Musée National d'Art Moderne, Paris, Gift of M. and Mme André Lefèvre.

XIII. 3
LA COIFFURE
Paris, 1905.
Oil on canvas.
Size : 81 x 65 cm.
Signed bottom right : Picasso.

Exh. Galerie Georges Petit, Paris, summer, 1932 : *Picasso,* No. 34. Kunsthaus, Zurich, autumn, 1932 : *Picasso,* No. 30 (for sale). Baltimore Museum of Art, 1941 : *A Century of Baltimore Collecting,* cat. p. 85. Knoedler, New York, 1955 : *The Cone Collection.*

Bibl. Z. I. 309. Level, 1928, pl 11. Maurice Gieure, 1951, pl. 12. *Handbook of the Cone Collection,* Baltimore Museum of Art, 1955, No. 84, repr. p. 41.

Coll. Saint, Paris ; Paul Rosenberg, Paris (?) ; Miss Etta and Dr. Claribel Cone, Baltimore ;

The Baltimore Museum of Art, The Cone Collection.

XIII. 4
NUDE WITH A CAP
Schoorl, summer, 1905.
Gouache on cardboard.
Size : 75.5 x 60 cm.
Signed bottom left : Picasso.
(The signature does not seem authentic.)

Bibl. Z. I. 255.

Formerly collection Galerie Thannhauser, Paris.

XIII. 5
NUDE WITH HAIR PULLED BACK
Paris, 1905.
Gouache on cardboard.
Size : 55 x 50 cm.
Signed bottom right (?).

Bibl. Z. I. 259. Elgar and Maillard, 1955 (catalogue). Sutton, 1955, No. 46.

Coll. Gertrude Stein, Paris ;

Present location unknown.

XIII. 6
NUDES EMBRACING
Paris, 1905.
Gouache and watercolor on card-
board.
Size : 26.3 x 21 cm.
Signed twice ; top right : Picasso, and
bottom left : Picasso.

Exh. Stockholm, Oslo, Göteborg and
Copenhagen, 1931 : *Fransk Genom-
brottskonst fran Nittonhundratalet,*
No. 132.

Bibl. Z. I. 228. Cat. of the Christian
Tetzen collection, Lund, 1934, No. 38.
Erik Zahle, 1938, p. 18. Leo Zwane in
Kunstmus. Aa., XXVI. 1939, p. 99.
Cat. Statens Museum for Kunst, Co-
penhagen, 1964, No. R. 175.

Coll. Paul Guillaume, Paris ; Christian
Tetzen, Lund ; Viggo Jarl ; Skaenket
Museet (April, 1939) ;

*Statens Museum for Kunst, Copen-
hagen.*

XIII. 7
THE EMBRACE
Paris, 1905.
Oil on canvas.
Signed, dated and inscribed, bottom
right :
A mon cher ami Guillaume Apollinaire,
Picasso 1905.

Bibl. Not in Z. Pierre Cailler, *Guillaume Apollinaire,* 1965, No. 108.

Coll. Guillaume Apollinaire, Paris ;

*Collection Mme Jacqueline Apolli-
naire, Paris.*

Related to the watercolor, *The Lovers*
(D. XIII. 5), and to the etching, *The
Embrace* (Geiser 16/c). Two studies
of the same motif (watercolors, 11.5 x
18 cm., signed) are in the Bernard
Poissonnier collection, Paris. We
received photographs of these two
works after this book was in press.

XIII. 8
GIRL WITH A BASKET OF FLOWERS
Paris, 1905.
Oil on canvas.
Size : 152 x 65 cm.
Signed top right : Picasso.
Inscribed and dated on the back :
Picasso / 13 rue Ravignan / 1905.

Exh. Grafton Galleries, London, November, 1910 : *Manet and the Post-
Impressionists,* No. 30. Galerie Georges Petit, Paris, summer, 1932 : *Picasso,*
No. 37. Kunsthaus, Zurich, autumn,
1932 : *Picasso,* No. 26. Petit Palais,
Paris, June, 1937 : *Les maîtres de l'art
indépendant,* No. 29. Maison de la
Pensée Française, Paris, 1954 : *Picasso*
No. 2. Musée Cantini, Marseilles,
1959 : *Picasso,* No. 7. Tate Gallery,
London, 1960 : *Picasso,* No. 23, repr.
pl. 5 c.

Bibl. Z. I. 256. Raynal, 1922, pl. 20.
Gertrude Stein, 1938, pl. 10. Cassou,
1940, p. 57. Sutton, 1955, pl. XIV
(color). Elgar and Maillard, 1955
(catalogue). Kahnweiler and Parmelin, 1955, pl. 2 (color). J. C. Aznar,
1956, p. 374. Diehl, 1960, p. 15
(color). Daix, 1964, p. 43 (color).

Coll. Leo and Gertrude Stein, Paris
(bought from Clovis Sagot in 1905 for
150 fr.) ; Gertrude Stein, Paris ;

*Collection of the Heirs of Miss Ger-
trude Stein.*

This is the first Picasso painting
bought by the Steins. Shortly afterward the Steins met the artist at the
dealer Clovis Sagot's.

XIII. 9
PORTRAIT OF MADAME CANALS
Paris, 1905.
Oil on canvas.
Size : 90.5 x 70.5 cm.
Signed top right : Picasso.

Exh. Barcelona, 1919 : *Exposició d'Art*,
No. 522. Grand Palais, Paris, November 1966–February 1967 : *Hommage
à Pablo Picasso*, No. 28, repr. in cat.

Bibl. Z. I. 263. Palau i Fabre, No. 158
(repr. in color).

Coll. Ricardo Canals, Barcelona ;
L. Plandiura, Barcelona ; Museo de
Arte Moderno, Barcelona ;

Picasso Museum, Barcelona.

Madame Canals, the beautiful Benedetta from Rome, was the wife of the
Spanish painter Ricardo Canals (1876–
1931). This friend from the *Quatre
Gats* lived in Montmartre and taught
Picasso the technique of etching.

Color plate, page 85.

XIII. 10
BUST OF A LITTLE BOY
Paris, 1905.
Gouache on cardboard.
Size : 51 x 41 cm.
Signed top right : Picasso.

Exh. Baltimore Museum of Art, May–
October, 1930 : *The Cone Collection*,
No. 45, repr. in cat. p. 11. Baltimore
Museum of Art, November–December
1950 : *Behold the Child*, cat. p. 18.
Virginia Museum of Art, October–
November 1953 : *The Cone Collection*.

Bibl. Z. VI. 688. *The Cone Collection*,
Catalogue, Baltimore, 1934, pl. 59.
Cahiers d'Art, II, Paris, 1950, p. 323,
Handbook of the Cone Collection.
Baltimore Museum of Art, 1955,
No. 91. Helen Kay, 1965, p. 61 (color).

Coll. Miss Etta and Dr. Claribel Cone,
Baltimore ;

*Baltimore Museum of Art, The Cone
Collection.*

XIII. 11
STROLLING PLAYER AND CHILD
(Comédien et Enfant)
Paris, 1905.
Pastel on brown paper.
Size : 70.5 x 52 cm.
Signed and dated, bottom right :
Picasso 1905.

Bibl. Z. I. 295. Ponge and Chessex,
1960, pl. 37. Lieberman, 1961, pl. 25

(repr. in color). Boudaille, 1964,
pl. IX (color).

Coll. Stephen C. Clark, New York ;

*Collection Estate of Stephen C. Clark,
New York.*

XIII. 12
BOY WITH A BOUQUET
Paris, 1905.
Gouache on cardboard.
Size : 64.7 x 54.2 cm.
Signed bottom right : Picasso.

Exh. Knoedler & Co., New York, 1947 :
Picasso, No. 20. Philadelphia Museum
of Art, 1958 : *Picasso*, No. 20. Toronto

and Montreal, 1964 : *Picasso and
Man*, No. 27, repr. in cat. p. 43.

Bibl. Z. I. 262.

Coll. Mrs. John D. McIlhenny, Philadelphia ;

*Collection Mrs. John Wintersteen,
Villanova.*

XIII. 13
BOY WITH A PIPE
Paris, 1905.
Oil on canvas.
Size : 100 x 81.3 cm.
Signed bottom left : Picasso.

Exh. Museum of Modern Art, New York, June–September 1951 : *New York Private Collections.* Paul Rosenberg, New York, March–April 1953 : *Collectors' Choice.* Museum of Modern Art, New York, May–September 1955 : *Paintings from Private Collections,* cat. p. 16. Museum of Modern Art, New York, and Art Institute of Chicago, 1957 : *Picasso, 75th Anniversary Exhibition,* repr. in color in cat. p. 21. Philadelphia Museum of Art, 1958 : *Picasso.* Arts Council of Great Britain, Tate Gallery, London, 1960 : *Picasso,* No. 24, repr. in cat. pl. 5 f. Tate Gallery, London, December 16, 1960–January 29, 1961 : *The John Hay Whitney Collection,* No. 42, repr. in cat. Grand Palais, Paris, November 1966–February 1967 : *Hommage à Pablo Picasso,* No. 30, repr. in cat.

Bibl. Z. I. 274. Jean Cocteau, *Picasso,* Paris, 1923, pl. 3. Lassaigne, 1949, pl. 16. Lieberman, 1954 and 1961, pl. 31 (color) and cover (detail). Sutton, 1955, No. 43. Cassou, 1958, p. 23 (color). John Rewald, *Catalogue of the John Hay Whitney Collection,* 1960, No. 42. Lieberman, 1964, pl. XII (color).

Coll. Paul von Mendelssohn, Berlin ;

Collection Mr. and Mrs. John Hay Whitney, New York.

See the sketch for this painting : D. XIII. 10.

XIII. 14
WOMAN WITH A FAN
Paris, 1905.
Oil on canvas.
Size : 99 x 81.3 cm.
Signed and dated, bottom right : Picasso 1905.

Exh. Galerie Georges Petit, Paris, 1932 : *Picasso,* No. 36, repr. Marie Harriman Gallery, New York, 1933. Chicago Art Institute, 1933 : *Century of Progress,* No. 408, repr. pl. XLVIII. Wadsworth Atheneum, 1934 : *Picasso,* No. 17, repr. pl. 17. St. Louis City Art Museum, summer, 1934. Cleveland Museum of Art, June, 1936 : *20th Century Exhibition,* No. 332, repr. Jacques Seligmann, New York, 1936 : *Picasso, Blue and Rose Periods,* No. 21, repr. Phillips Memorial Gallery, Washington, D.C., April, 1938 : *Picasso.* Marie Harriman Gallery, New York, summer, 1939 : *Modern French Masters.* New York, Chicago and Boston, 1939–1940 : *Picasso, Forty Years of his Art,* No. 55, repr. p. 50. Art Institute of Chicago, January–February 1955 : *Chauncey McCormick Memorial Exhibition.* Paul Rosenberg, New York, February 6–March 2, 1957 : *Masterpieces Recalled, Loan Exhibition of 19th and 20th Century Paintings,* No. 39. Yale University Art Gallery, May–June 1960. Tate Gallery, London, 1960 : *Picasso,* No. 26, repr. pl. 3 b. National Gallery of Art, Washington, D.C., April 15–May 14, 1961 : *Collection Marie and Averell Harriman,* repr. p. 27. Knoedler, New York, 1962 : *Picasso, an American Tribute,* No. 25, repr. Grand Palais, Paris, November 1966–February 1967 : *Hommage à Pablo Picasso,* No. 29, repr. in cat.

Bibl. Z. I. 308. Raynal, 1922, pl. 17. R. H. Wilenski, 1931, p. 140. C. J. Bulliet, 1936, p. 104. Barr, *Forty Years,* p. 50. Maurice Gieure, 1951, pl. 10. Sabartés and Boeck, p. 459, No. 26. Elgar and Maillard, 1955, p. 31 (color). Penrose, 1958, pl. IV, No. 6. Lieberman, 1964, pl. XI (color).

Coll. Gertrude Stein, Paris ; Paul Rosenberg, Paris ;

Collection The Hon. and Mrs. W. Averell Harriman, New York.

XIII. 15
HEAD OF A HARLEQUIN
Paris, 1905.
Oil on canvas.
Size : 40.7 x 31.8 cm.
Signed top right : Picasso.

Exh. Galerie Georges Petit, Paris, 1932 : *Picasso,* No. 28, repr. in cat. p. 16. Jacques Seligmann & Co., New York, 1937 : *Twenty Years in the Evolution of Picasso, 1903–1923,* No. 3, repr. in cat. pl. 3. Jacques

Seligmann & Co., New York, 1939 : *The Stage,* No. 33, pl. 33.

Bibl. Z. VI. 686. *Cahiers d'Art,* Paris, 1950, p. 330. Maurice Gieure, 1951, pl. 11.

Coll. Mme J. Doucet, Paris ; Jacques Seligmann, New York ;

Private collection, Detroit.

XIII. 16
HEAD OF A HARLEQUIN
Paris, 1905.
Oil on panel.
Size : 35 x 24 cm.
Signed top left : Picasso.

Exh. Kunsthaus, Zurich, 1932 : *Picasso,* No. 24 (lent by A. Vömel). Munich,

Cologne and Hamburg, 1955–1956 : *Picasso 1900–1955,* No. 11.

Bibl. Z. I. 252. André Level, 1928, pl. 19 (entitled *Jeune arlequin*).

Coll. Alex Vömel, Düsseldorf ;

Private collection, Düsseldorf.

XIII. 17
BOY HOLDING A VASE
Paris, 1905.
Oil on canvas (relined).
Size : 54 x 34 cm.
Signed bottom right : Picasso.

Bibl. Z. I. 272. Sutton, 1955, No. 48.

Coll. Paco Durio, Barcelona (?) (1905) ; Flechtheim, Düsseldorf (1912) ;

Hyde Museum, Glens Falls, N. Y.

XIII. 18
BOY WITH A FRILLED COLLAR
Paris, 1905.
Gouache on cardboard.
Size : 77.5 x 65.5 cm.
Unsigned (?).

Bibl. Z. I. 273.

Coll. Haldsdurk, Berlin ;

Collection Mr. and Mrs. André Meyer, New York.

XIII. 19
BOY WITH A FRILLED COLLAR STANDING IN PROFILE
Paris, 1905.
Gouache on cardboard.
Size : 79.3 x 59.5 cm.
Signed bottom left : Picasso.

Exh. Montross Gallery, New York, 1924, No. 32. Worcester Art Museum, March 5–30, 1924 : *Dial Collection of Paintings, Drawings and Engravings by Contemporary Artists.* Hillyer Art Gallery, 1924. Jacques Seligmann, New York, 1936 : *Picasso,* No. 20, repr. Art Institute of Chicago, 1937 : *16th International Watercolor Exhibition,* No. 114. Wildenstein, New York, March, 1945 : *The Child through Four Centuries,* No. 52. Worcester Art Museum, 1949. Atlanta Art Association Galleries and Birmingham Museum of Art, Alabama, 1955 : *David to Rouault,* No. 47. Worcester Art Museum, April–September 1959: *The Dial Collection,* No. 76 (frontispiece).

Knoedler, New York, 1962 : *Picasso, an American Tribute,* No. 24, repr. p. 26.

Bibl. Z. I. 276 and 277. *Living Art,* New York, 1923. *The Dial,* LXXIX, 1925, No. 445. Worcester Art Museum Bulletin, XXII, January 1932, p. 65. Rafael Benet, *Simbolismo,* Barcelona, 1953, p. 146 and cover (color). Elgar and Maillard, 1955, p. 26 (color). Sutton, 1955, No. 36.

Coll. Paul Guillaume, Paris ; Bought from Paul Guillaume in 1923 for the Dial Collection ;

The Dial Collection, on loan (since 1931) to the Worcester Art Museum.

Our photograph shows the present condition of the painting, after cleaning. Zervos reproduces the work in its original condition (Z. I. 276).

XIII. 20
JUGGLER WITH STILL LIFE
Paris, 1905.
Gouache on cardboard.
Size : 100 x 69.9 cm.
Signed bottom left : Picasso.

Exh. Wildenstein & Co., New York, 1928 : *Modern French Art,* No. 34. Museum of French Art, New York, 1931 : *Picasso, Braque, Léger,* No. 5. Art Institute of Chicago, 1943 : *20th Century French Paintings from the Chester Dale Collection.* National Gallery of Art, Washington, D.C., 1952 : *20th Century French Paintings from the Chester Dale Collection,* repr. p. 51.

Bibl. Z. I. 294. M. Dale in *Art News,* October 13, 1928, p. 10. Maud Dale, *Before Manet to Modigliani,* New York, 1929, p. 77. Maud Dale, *Picasso,* New York, 1930, frontispiece. H. Mc-Bride in *Formes,* April 1931, p. 58. Wilenski, 1940, p. 300. National Gallery of Art, Washington, D.C., 1965, *20th Century Paintings and Sculpture of the French School in the Chester Dale Collection,* p. 70.

Coll. Chester Dale, New York ;

National Gallery of Art, Washington, D.C., Chester Dale Collection.

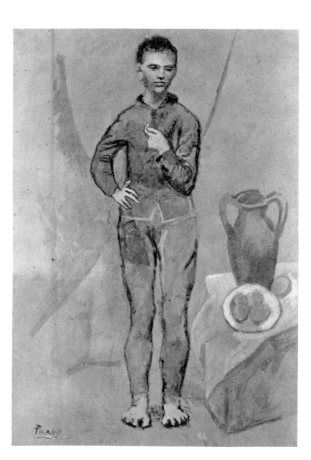

XIII. 21
BLUE BOY
Paris, 1905.
Gouache on cardboard.
Size : 99.5 x 55.4 cm.
Signed bottom left : Picasso.

Exh. Galerie H. Thannhauser, Munich, 1913 : *Picasso.* Galerie Georges Petit, Paris, 1932 : *Picasso,* No. 8. Wadsworth Atheneum, 1934 : *Picasso,* No. 14, repr. Museum of Modern Art, New York, 1934–1935 : *5th Anniversary Exhibition,* No. 123, repr. Jacques Seligmann, New York, 1936 : *Picasso, Blue and Rose Periods,* No. 19, repr. Wildenstein, New York, March 1938 : *Impressionist and Post-Impressionist Portraits,* repr. Boston Museum of Art, 1938 : *Picasso and Matisse,* No. 6. Museum of Modern Art, New York, April–November 1939 : *Art in our Time,* No. 30. MMA, New York, and Art Institute of Chicago, 1939–1940 :

Picasso, Forty Years of his Art, No. 30, repr. p. 40. MMA, New York, summer, 1955 : *Paintings from Private Collections,* No. 106. Metropolitan Museum of Art, New York, 1956. Albright Art Gallery, 1957. Virginia Museum, 1958: *Mr. and Mrs. Edward M. M. Warburg Collection.*

Bibl. Z. I. 271. Barr, *Forty Years,* p. 40. Hobart and Smith, *Literature in Our Time,* New York, 1952. Lieberman, 1953.

Coll. Bought from the artist (1910) by Alfred Flechtheim, Berlin ; Countess Mechtilde Lichnowsky, Kuchelna (1913) ; German Embassy in London (1914) ; On loan to the Kronprinzen Palais, Berlin (1914–1930) ; Curt Valentin, New York ;

Collection Mr. and Mrs. Edward M.M. Warburg, New York.

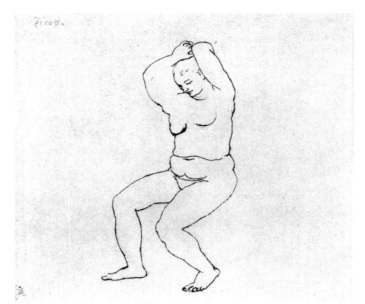

D. XIII. 1
SEATED WOMAN ARRANGING HER HAIR
Paris, 1905.
Brush and rose-red watercolor.
Size : 39.6 x 27.2 cm.
Unsigned.

Exh. Toronto and Montreal, 1964 : *Picasso and Man,*
No. 30, repr. p. 46.

Bibl. Not in Z. *The Cone Collection,* Catalogue,
Baltimore, 1934, pl. 105 a.

Coll. Miss Etta and Dr. Claribel Cone, Baltimore ;
Since 1950 :

Baltimore Museum of Art, The Cone Collection.

D. XIII. 2
NUDE WOMAN ARRANGING HER HAIR
Paris, 1905.
Pen drawing.
Dimensions not available.
Signed top left : Picasso.

Bibl. Not in Z. *The Cone Collection,* Catalogue,
Baltimore, 1934, pl. 103 a.

Coll. Miss Etta and Dr. Claribel Cone, Baltimore ;
Since 1950 :

Baltimore Museum of Art, The Cone Collection.

This drawing, as well as No. D. XIII. 1 and D. XIII. 3,
is related to the gouache *Nude with Hair Pulled
Back* (XIII. 5).

D. XIII. 3
NUDE ARRANGING HER HAIR,
FROM THE FRONT
Paris, 1905.
Brush drawing and wash on paper.
Size : 41 x 27 cm.
Signed bottom right : Picasso.

Exh. Kunstmuseum, Basel, May 13–June 17, 1956 :
Collection R. Staechelin, No. 54. Musée National
d'Art Moderne, Paris, April 10–June 28, 1964 :
Fondation Rodolphe Staechelin, No. 50, repr.

Bibl. Not in Z.

Rodolphe Staechelin Foundation, Basel.

D. XIII. 4
HEAD OF A WOMAN IN PROFILE
Paris, 1905.
Pencil drawing on paper.
Size : 30.5 x 25 cm.
Signed bottom right : Picasso.

Bibl. Not in Z.

Coll. Jacob de Graaff, London (acquired in Paris in
1919) ; Mme L. de Graaff-Bachiene Mazerolles,
London ; Dr. D. Hannema (gift of Mme L. de Graaff
in 1949) ;

Hannema-de Stuers Foundation, Heino.

This profile drawing is reminiscent of the *Woman
with a Fan* (XIII. 14).

D. XIII. 5
THE LOVERS
Paris, 1905.
Blue watercolor on paper.
Size : 12 x 19 cm.
Signed bottom left : Picasso.

Bibl. Not in Z.

Coll. Christian Dior, Paris ; Galerie Dubourg, Paris ;

Collection Mrs. Helen Serger, New York.

Authenticated by Picasso, March 14, 1960. Related
to *The Embrace* (XIII. 7). This is a study for the
etching of 1905, *The Embrace* (Geiser 16/c).

D. XIII. 6
PORTRAIT OF ALICE DERAIN Paris, 1905.
India ink and sepia wash on paper.
Size : 36 x 26.6 cm.
Signed, dated and inscribed, bottom left :
A Alice ! Picasso 1905.

Exh. Kunsthaus, Zurich, 1932 : *Picasso,* No. 280.
Petit Palais, Paris, 1959 : *De Géricault à Matisse,*
No. 179, repr. pl. 63. Kunsthalle, Hamburg, 1959 :
Französische Zeichnungen des XX. Jahrhunderts,
No. 239, repr. No. 25.

Bibl. Z. I. 251. *Le Dessin français au XXᵉ siècle,*
1951, pl. 80. Jardot, Suttgart, 1959, pl. 9. Ponge
and Chessex, No. 23. Diehl, 1960, p. 17. *DU,*
No. 248, 1961, p. 25. Millier, 1961. Boudaille,
1964, p. 16.

Coll. Baron von der Heydt, Ascona ;

Collection Siegfried Rosengart, Lucerne.

D. XIII. 7
THE VIOLINIST (Family with a Monkey)
Paris, 1905.
Pen drawing and watercolor.   Size : 16.2 x 14.2 cm.
Unsigned (?).

Bibl. Not in Z.   *The Cone Collection,* Catalogue,
Baltimore, 1934, pl. 98 b.   *Handbook of the Cone
Collection,* Baltimore Museum of Art, 1955, No. 88.
Ponge and Chessex, No. 35.

Coll. Miss Etta and Dr. Claribel Cone, Baltimore ;

Baltimore Museum of Art, The Cone Collection.

D. XIII. 8
MOTHER AND CHILD
Paris, 1905.
Pen drawing and wash.
Size : 14 x 12 cm.
Unsigned (?).

Bibl. Not in Z.   *The Cone Collection,* Catalogue,
Baltimore, 1934, pl. 102 b.   Ponge and Chessex,
No. 48.   Helen Kay, 1965, p. 85.

Coll. Miss Etta and Dr. Claribel Cone, Baltimore ;

Baltimore Museum of Art, The Cone Collection.

D. XIII. 9
HEAD OF A WOMAN IN PROFILE
Paris, 1905.
India ink and wash.
Dimensions not available.
Unsigned.

Bibl. Not in Z.   *The Cone Collection,* Catalogue,
Baltimore, 1934, pl. 102 d.   Maurice Gieure, 1951,
pl. 115 (dated 1902).

Coll. Miss Etta and Dr. Claribel Cone, Baltimore ;

Baltimore Museum of Art, The Cone Collection.

D. XIII. 10
YOUNG MAN SEATED
Paris, 1905.
Pen drawing.
Size : 30 x 23 cm.
Signed bottom right : Picasso.

Bibl. Not in Z.   *The Cone Collection,* Catalogue,
Baltimore, 1934, pl. 101 b.   Elgar and Maillard, 1955,
p. 36.   Elgar, 1956, p. 3.   Ponge and Chessex, pl. 36.
Lieberman, 1961, pl. 38.

Coll. Miss Etta and Dr. Claribel Cone, Baltimore ;

Baltimore Museum of Art, The Cone Collection.

Study for *Boy with a Pipe* (XIII. 13).

D. XIII. 11
HEAD OF A BOY
Paris, 1905.
Gouache on cardboard.
Size : 45 x 37 cm.
Signed and dated, top left : 1905 Picasso.

Bibl. Z. I. 216.   Sutton, 1955, No. 31.   Duncan,
p. 204.

Owned by the artist.

There are traces of several figure sketches on the
cardboard support for this gouache. One can make
out a woman holding two children by the hand, and
a man wearing a hat, with a child. The man and the
child are a study for *The Mistletoe Seller,* 1903 (cf.
VIII. 4 and 5).

D. XIII. 12
JUGGLER, SKETCHES AND CARICATURES
OF APOLLINAIRE
Paris, December 24, 1905, midnight.
India ink on paper.
Size : 17.6 x 15.3 cm.
Unsigned.
Dated, verso (imprinted with an etching needle on
the paper) : Paris 24 décembre 1905, media noche,
Paris, Paris, Paris.

Exh. Musée des Augustins, Toulouse, 1965 : *Picasso
et le théâtre,* No. 6, repr. in cat.

Bibl. Unpublished until the exhibition in Toulouse,
1965.

Owned by the artist.

A drawing of special importance because of the date
on the back. If the caricatures were done on the
night of December 24, it is likely that Picasso
sketched them on the edge of a recent drawing.
Therefore, the figures of jugglers and boys in blue
are from the end of 1905.

The Watering Place, Paris, 1905, drypoint (see XIV. 14, 15 and 16).

Standing Nude Arranging her Hair, Paris, 1905-1906, pen drawing.
Collection Galerie Louise Leiris, Paris.

The Nudes of The Watering Place and the Portraits of the Stein Family, Paris, Winter 1905-1906

Because of the confusion of dates, for which Picasso himself as well as the Steins and Fernande Olivier are to blame, it is very hard to arrive at a coherent chronology. The majority of the works we have grouped here are dated 1905 by Zervos. The study for the *Nude Boy on Horseback* (D. XIV. 1), dated 1906, confirms our feeling that the project for *The Watering Place* and its preliminary sketches should be dated from the very end of 1905 or the beginning of 1906. We consider the portrait of Leo Stein (XIV. 1) contemporary with that of Allan (XIV. 2). It is possible that it was not considered as finished (delivered) until the autumn, but in no way does it belong to the work that Picasso conceived on his return from Gosol, and it is hardly like Picasso to have broken off his own experimenting to go backward just to please Leo Stein.

Fernande Olivier wrote an interesting account of Gertrude Stein and her brother, Leo : "They made a real pair. He, with a professorial air, bald, wearing gold-rimmed glasses. A long beard with reddish highlights, a shrewd eye, a large, stiff body given to strange positions and unfinished gestures. The exact type for a German-American Jew. She, stout, short, solid, a fine, strong head with noble features, emphatic and regular, and intelligent, clairvoyant, lively eyes. Her voice and her whole behavior were masculine. Picasso met them both at Sagot's and was so taken with the woman's physical personality that he suggested doing her portrait before he actually was acquainted with her. The Steins were both dressed in brown corduroy, wearing sandals like their friend, Raymond Duncan. Much too intelligent to mind ridicule, and too self-confident to bother with what others thought, they were rich, and he wanted to paint. . . ."

If the recollections of Gertrude Stein in the *Autobiography of Alice B. Toklas* are trustworthy as to dates, everything in the portrait, except the face, was done in the winter of 1905-1906. She wrote, "Picasso sat very tight on his chair and very close to his canvas and on a very small palette which was of a uniform brown-gray color, mixed some more brown-gray and the painting began. This was the first of some eighty or ninety sittings. . . All of a sudden one day Picasso painted out the whole head. 'I can't see you any longer when I look,' he said irritably. And so the picture was left like that."

The particulars are important because Gertrude Stein's clothing in the *Portrait* (XVI. 10), and the background, are painted in a way that resembles *La Coiffure* (XIV. 20). The use of muted tones, the handling of folds of material, the modeling of the hands are common to both; and they both present similar mask-like faces. This would seem to support our theory that the two pictures were begun in the winter of 1905-1906 and both were finished in the autumn, after the return from Gosol.

XIV. 1
PORTRAIT OF LEO STEIN
Paris, spring, 1906.
Gouache. Size : 27.7 x 17 cm.
Unsigned.

Exh. Virginia Museum of Fine Arts, 1953 : *The Cone Collection.* Knoedler, New York, January–February 1955 : *The Cone Collection.* MMA, New York, and Art Institute of Chicago, 1957 : *Picasso, 75th Anniversary Exhibition,* repr. in cat. p. 29. Philadelphia, 1958 : *Picasso,* No. 27, repr. Toronto and Montreal, 1964 : *Picasso and Man,* No. 38, repr. p. 53. Greensboro Library, North Carolina, April, 1965 : *The Cone Collection.*

Bibl. Z. I. 250 (dated 1905). *The Cone Collection,* Catalogue, Baltimore, 1934,

pl. 62. Paul J. Sachs, 1954, pl. 88. *Handbook of the Cone Collection,* Baltimore Museum of Art, 1955, No. 94, repr. p. 19. Sutton, 1955, No. 56. Aline B. Saarinen, 1958, No. 41. *Great Drawings of all Time,* vol. III, No. 858 (color).

Coll. Leo and Gertrude Stein, Paris ; Miss Etta and Dr. Claribel Cone, Baltimore ;

The Baltimore Museum of Art, The Cone Collection.

Dated spring, 1906, in the Kahnweiler archives. Technically this portrait belongs to the style of the Rose Period, to which Leo Stein was more sensitive. Cf. introduction to Catalogue XIV.

XIV. 2
PORTRAIT OF ALLAN STEIN
Paris, spring, 1906.
Gouache on cardboard.
Size : 74 x 59.7 cm.
Signed top right : Picasso.

Exh. Baltimore Museum of Art, 1950 : *Behold the Child,* cat. p. 18. Virginia Museum of Fine Arts, October–November 1953 : *The Cone Collection.* Knoedler, New York, January–February 1955 : *The Cone Collection.* Woman's College, University of North Carolina, autumn, 1955 and autumn, 1958 : *The Cone Collection.* Knoedler, New York, 1962 : *Picasso, an American Tribute,* No. 26, repr. in cat.

Bibl. Z. I. 353. *Handbook of the Cone Collection,* Baltimore Museum of Art,

1955, No. 93. Sutton, 1955, No. 61 *(Jeune Homme).* Richardson, 1964, p. 27 (color). Helen Kay, 1965, p. 83

Coll. Michael Stein, Vaucresson ; Miss Etta Cone, Baltimore ;

The Baltimore Museum of Art, The Cone Collection.

Allan Stein was the son of Michael Stein and the nephew of Leo and Gertrude Stein. According to John Richardson, this is the last painting bought by Miss Etta Cone before her death (1949).

XIV. 3
GIRL ON HORSEBACK AND BOY
Paris, 1905–1906.
Watercolor on paper.
Size : 51 x 34.5 cm.
Signed top left : Picasso.

Bibl. Z. I. 269 (dated 1905). Merli, 1948, No. 126. Sabartés and Boeck, p. 460, No. 34 (dated 1906). Sutton,

1955, No. 53 (entitled *Saltimbanques,* dated 1906).

Coll. L. A. Tietz, Cologne ;

Present location unknown.

The boy and his dress are closely related to XIII. 20 and 21, and XIV. 4.

XIV. 4
BOY AND HORSE Paris, 1905–1906.
Watercolor on paper, mounted on panel.   Size : 50 x 32 cm.
Signed top left : Picasso.

Exh. Colnaghi's Galleries, London, June–July, 1924 : *The Contemporary Art Society, Modern Foreign Paintings,* No. 29. Tate Gallery, London, 1960 :

Picasso, No. 28, repr. in cat. pl. 5 j.
Bibl. Z. I. 270. Elgar, 1956, pl. 11. Ronald Alley, *Tate Gallery, The Foreign Paintings, Drawings and Sculpture,* London, 1959, pl. 43 a.

Coll. C. Frank Stoop, London, who bequeathed it to the Tate Gallery in 1933 : *Tate Gallery, London.*

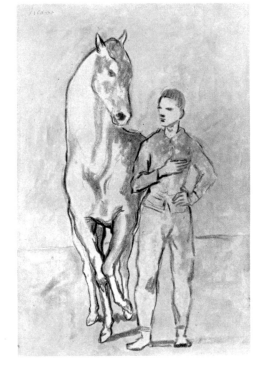

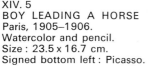

XIV. 5
BOY LEADING A HORSE
Paris, 1905–1906.
Watercolor and pencil.
Size : 23.5 x 16.7 cm.
Signed bottom left : Picasso.

Bibl. Not in Z. *The Cone Collection,* Catalogue, Baltimore, 1934, pl. 109 a (dated 1906). *Handbook of the Cone Collection,* Baltimore Museum of Art, 1955, No. 90.

Coll. Miss Etta and Dr. Claribel Cone, Baltimore ;

The Baltimore Museum of Art, The Cone Collection.

Study for *Boy Leading a Horse* (XIV. 7), and for the central figure in *The Watering Place* (cf. XIV. 14, 15, 16).

XIV. 6
BOY LEADING A HORSE
Paris, 1905–1906.
Brush drawing with sepia wash.
Size : 49 x 32 cm.
Signed bottom right : Picasso.

Bibl. Not in Z. Waldemar George, *Picasso, Dessins,* 1926, pl. 3. *The Cone Collection,* Catalogue, Baltimore, 1934, pl. 109 b. Maurice Gieure, 1951, pl. 118. *Handbook of the Cone Collection,* Baltimore Museum of Art, 1955, No. 89. Ponge and Chessex, 1960, pl. 42. Lieberman, 1961, pl. 43.

Coll. Michael Stein, Vaucresson ; Miss Etta and Dr. Claribel Cone, Baltimore ;

The Baltimore Museum of Art, The Cone Collection.

Study for *Boy Leading a Horse* (XIV. 7), a motif found in the central figure of *The Watering Place* (XIV. 14, 15, 16).

XIV. 7
BOY LEADING A HORSE
Paris, 1905–1906.
Oil on canvas.
Size : 221 x 130 cm.
Signed bottom right : Picasso.

Exh. Museum of Modern Art, New York, Art Institute of Chicago, St. Louis Museum, Boston Museum of Fine Arts, 1939–1940 : *Picasso, Forty Years of his Art,* No. 54, repr. in cat. p. 49. Museum of Modern Art, New York, and The Art Institute of Chicago, 1957 : *Picasso, 75th Anniversary Exhibition,* repr. in cat. p. 27. Knoedler & Co., New York, 1962 : *Picasso, an American Tribute,* No. 23, repr. in cat.

Bibl. Z. I. 264. André Level, 1928, pl. 15. Gertrude Stein, 1938, pl. 12. Barr, *Forty Years,* p. 49. Cassou, 1940, No. 55. Merli, 1948, No. VII. Elgar

and Maillard, 1955 (catalogue). Sutton, 1955, No. 41. Sabartés and Boeck, p. 370. Penrose, 1958, pl. III, No. 9. Blunt and Pool, No. 163. Helen Kay, 1965, p. 79.

Coll. Ambroise Vollard, Paris ; Galerie Thannhauser, Lucerne ; William S. Paley, New York, who gave it to The Museum of Modern Art, New York, in 1964, but retained a life interest ;

Collection William S. Paley, Manhasset, N.Y.

The motif of this large oil occurs in the center of *The Watering Place* (XIV. 14, 15, 16). We cannot say whether this work is the end of this series or a step toward the monumental *Watering Place (L'Abreuvoir),* which never materialized. (See Chapter 5.)

XIV. 8
NUDE BOY
Paris, spring, 1906.
Gouache on cardboard.
Size : 68 x 52 cm.
Signed bottom right : Picasso.

Bibl. Z. I. 268.   Sterling, 1957, pl. 155 (repr. in color).

Coll. Museum of Modern Western Art, Moscow (1918–1948) ;

The Hermitage Museum, Leningrad.

XIV. 9
NUDE BOY ON HORSEBACK
Paris, spring–summer, 1906.
Oil.
Size : 55 x 38 cm.
Signed bottom left : Picasso.

Bibl. Not in Z. Sutton, 1955, pl. IX (repr. in color, incorrectly dated 1904).

Coll. Van Dongen, Monte Carlo ;

Private collection, France.

This is the horseman at the right in *The Watering Place* (XIV. 14, 15, 16).

XIV. 10
THE YOUNG HORSEMAN
Paris, spring–summer, 1906. Watercolor on paper.
Size : 44 x 30 cm.   Signed bottom right : Picasso.

Exh. Kunsthaus, Zurich, 1932 : *Picasso,* No. 277 (incorrectly entitled *Arlequin à cheval*).

Bibl. Z. VI. 683.   Catalogue of the Galerie Bollag, Zurich, April 1925, No. 152, pl. 64.   Ponge and Chessex, pl. 31.

Coll. G. and L. Bollag, Zurich ;   Mme B. Bollag, Zurich ;

Collection M. and Mme F. Kirchheimer, Küsnacht.
Study for *Nude Boy on Horseback* (XIV. 9) and for *The Watering Place* (XIV. 15, 16).

XIV. 11
YOUTH ON HORSEBACK
Paris, spring–summer, 1906.
Charcoal on gray paper.   Size 46.6 x 30.4 cm.
Signed (in 1937) bottom left : Picasso.
Exh. New York and Chicago, 1939–1940 : *Picasso, Forty Years of his Art,* No. 53, repr. p. 48. New York and Chicago, 1957 : *Picasso, 75th Anniversary Exhibition,* repr. p. 27. Philadelphia, 1958 : *Picasso,* No. 19. Toronto and Montreal, 1964 : *Picasso and Man,* No. 29, repr. p. 45.
Bibl. Z. VI. 682. Barr, *Forty Years,* p. 48. Barr, *Fifty Years,* p. 42. Ponge and Chessex, pl. 38. Lieberman, 1961, pl. 39.
Coll. Pierre Matisse, New York ;   Since 1937 :
Collection Mr. and Mrs. John W. Warrington, Cincinnati.
Study for *The Watering Place* (XIV. 14 and 16).

XIV. 12
NUDE BOY SEATED IN A LANDSCAPE
Spring–summer, 1906.
India ink on paper.
Size : 12 x 7.5 cm.
Unsigned.

Bibl. Not in Z. Douglas Cooper, *Picasso, Carnet Catalan,* p. 23.

Owned by the artist.

Page 23 of the notebook that Picasso bought in Paris in 1906 and brought to Gosol. This sketch and the one following are important in dating the studies for *The Watering Place* (XIV. 16).

XIV. 13
SEATED NUDE BOY
Spring–summer, 1906.
India ink on paper.
Size : 12 x 7.5 cm.
Unsigned.

Bibl. Not in Z. Douglas Cooper, *Picasso, Carnet Catalan,* p. 25.

Owned by the artist.

Page 25 of the Catalan notebook (cf. note to No. XIV. 12). Related to the young nude horsemen (XIV. 9, 10, 11).

XIV. 14
STUDY FOR THE WATERING
PLACE
Paris, spring–summer, 1906.
Pencil drawing.
Size : 29.2 x 44.5 cm.
Unsigned.

Exh. Virginia Museum of Fine Arts,
January 16–March 4, and Philadelphia
Museum of Art, March 29–May 11,
1941 : *The Collection of Walter
P. Chrysler, Jr.,* No. 205, repr. in cat.
(entitled *Figures on Horses*).

Bibl. Not in Z. Lieberman, 1961, pl. 2.

Coll. Lewisohn, New York ; Parke–
Bernet, New York, May 17, 1939 :
Sale of the Lewisohn collection,
No. 214, repr. in cat. p. 41 ;

*Collection Walter P. Chrysler, Jr.,
New York.*

Study for *The Watering Place*
(XIV. 16).

XIV. 15
THE WATERING PLACE
Paris, spring–summer, 1906.
Watercolor.
Size : 31 x 49 cm.
Signed bottom left : Picasso.

Bibl. Not in Z. Berggruen Archives,
No. 1768.

Coll. Galerie Berggruen, Paris ;

*Collection Mrs. C. Kavanagh, Buenos
Aires.*

Study for *The Watering Place* (XIV.
16). The details studied in XIV. 6 and
10 have been worked in here. This is
a version slightly different from the
following work.

XIV. 16
THE WATERING PLACE
Paris, spring–summer, 1906.
Gouache on cardboard.
Size : 37.7 x 57.9 cm.
Signed bottom left : Picasso.

Exh. Montross Gallery, New York,
1924. Worcester Art Museum, 1924.
Hillyer Art Gallery, 1924. Wadsworth
Atheneum, 1934 : *Pablo Picasso,*
No. 13. Art Institute of Chicago,
March 18–May 16, 1937 : *16th Inter-
nationalWatercolorExhibition,* No.115.

Museum of Modern Art, New York, and
Art Institute of Chicago, 1939–1940 :
Picasso, Forty Years of his Art, No. 52,
repr. in cat. p. 48. Institute of Modern
Art, Boston, January 24–March 3,
1946 : *Four Spaniards,* No. 44. Worcester Art Museum, April 30–September 8, 1959 : *The Dial Collection,*
No. 75, cat. p. 84.

Bibl. Z. I. 265. *Living Art,* New York,
1923, No. 6. *The Dial,* LXXVIII, 1925,
No. 445. Worcester Art Museum Bulle-

tin, XXII, January 1932, p. 67. Barr,
Forty Years, p. 48. Barr, *Fifty Years,*
p. 42. Elgar and Maillard, 1955, p. 34
(color). Elgar, 1956, pl. 10 (color).

Coll. Galerie Alfred Flechtheim, Berlin ; Acquired in 1923 for the Dial
Collection ;

*The Dial Collection, on loan (since
1931) to the Worcester Art Museum.*

This gouache is the result of several
studies and works catalogued herein
(XIV. 3–15.) They are preliminary
studies for *The Watering Place (L'A-
breuvoir),* a large-scale composition
which was never realized. Picasso
did an etching of the same subject
(*The Watering Place,* Geiser 10/b) :
reproduced page 283.

XIV. 17
STUDY FOR LA COIFFURE
Paris, 1906. Pen drawing.
Signed bottom left : Picasso.

Bibl. Not in Z. *The Cone Collection,* Catalogue, Baltimore, 1934, pl. 105 b. Ponge and Chessex, 1960, cover.

Coll. Miss Etta and Dr. Claribel Cone, Baltimore ;

Baltimore Museum of Art, The Cone Collection.

Study for *La Coiffure* (XIV. 20).

XIV. 18
STUDY FOR LA COIFFURE
Paris, 1906.
Ink and crayon on gray paper.
Size : 18 x 30 cm.
Signed top right : Picasso.

Bibl. Z. VI. 741. Ponge and Chessex, 1960, pl. 18.

Coll. Miss Sally Jarvis, Portland ; Christie's, London, Sale, June 19, 1964, No. 90 ;

Collection Hon. Michael Smith, England.

XIV. 19
STUDY FOR LA COIFFURE
Paris, 1906.
Gouache and crayon.
Size : 25 x 17 cm.
Signed bottom left : Picasso.

Exh. University of Southern California, Los Angeles, 1961 : *Bonne Fête Monsieur Picasso.*

Bibl. Z. VI. 744.

Coll. Rev. James L. McLane, Los Angeles ;

Private collection, Los Angeles.

Preliminary version, reversed, of the two women in *La Coiffure* (XIV. 20).

XIV. 20
LA COIFFURE
Paris or Gosol, 1906 (Cf. note).
Oil on canvas.
Size : 175 x 99.7 cm.
Signed bottom left : Picasso.

Exh. Berlin, 1911 : *XXII Ausstellung der Berliner Secession,* No. 192. Valentine Gallery, New York, 1933. Museum of Modern Art, New York, 1933 : *Modern European Art.* MMA, New York, and Art Institute of Chicago, 1939–1940 : *Picasso, Forty Years of his Art,* No. 51. Traveling exhibition, 1941–1942 : *Picasso, Epochs in his Art ;* Munson-Williams-Proctor Institute, Utica ; Duke University, North Carolina ; William Rockhill Nelson Art Gallery, Kansas City ; Milwaukee Art Institute ; Dartmouth College ; Vassar College. Grand Palais, Paris, November 1966–February 1967 : *Hommage à Pablo Picasso,* No. 32, repr. in cat.

Bibl. Z. I. 313 (dated 1905). Level 1928, pl. 14. Merli, 1942, p. 156. Barr, *Fifty Years,* p. 43. Elgar and Maillard, 1955 (catalogue). Sutton, 1955, No. 54. Vallentin, 1957, p. 128. Blunt and Pool, No. 170. Boudaille, 1964, pl. XIV (color).

Coll. Ambroise Vollard, Paris ; Hugo Perls, Berlin (1924–1930) ; Pierre

Matisse, New York (1930) ; Stephen C. Clark, New York (1930–1937) ; Museum of Modern Art, New York (1937–1951) ;

Metropolitan Museum of Art, New York, Wolfe Fund 1951, Anonymous Gift.

Usually dated 1905, this large scale canvas is dated 1906 by Barr, Antonina Vallentin, and the Metropolitan Museum. Picasso might have begun it in the spring of 1906 and finished it in the autumn, after his return from Gosol (as he did with the portrait of Gertrude Stein). Or he might have done it in Gosol. These conjectures are supported by the style of the work, the colors, the resemblance of the child to the one in *The Two Brothers* (XV. 9), and the profile of the seated woman.

The Barnes Foundation has two studies for *La Coiffure :*

1. Pen and colored crayons, about 30 x 20 cm, with color notations in Spanish, top right ;

2. Pen drawing, about 30 x 20 cm, signed bottom right.

D. XIV. 1
BOY ON HORSEBACK (and other sketches)
Paris, 1906.
Pen on paper.   Size : 40.7 x 32.4 cm.
Signed bottom left : Picasso.
Dated top left : P. 06.

Exh. Galerie Louise Leiris, Paris, May–June 1954 :
Dessins de Picasso. Oslo, 1956 : *Picasso.* Brooklyn
Museum, New York, summer, 1962 : *Masterpieces
from the Collection of Governor Rockefeller.* Atlanta
Art Association, November 1962 : *Nelson A. Rocke-
feller Collection.*

Bibl. Z. VI. 864.

Coll. Gertrude Stein, Paris ;   Curt Valentin, New
York ; Nelson A. Rockefeller, New York ;

Private collection, New York.

An important work in dating the series of nude
horsemen related to *The Watering Place* (XIV. 16).

D. XIV. 2   **D. XIV. 3**
MONSIEUR CUL   MADAME CON
Paris, 1906.
Two drawings, India ink on paper.
Size : 16.5 x 10 cm.
Both signed, top : Picasso.
Inscribed (D. XIV. 2) top : Monsieur Cul.
Inscribed (D. XIV. 3) top : Madame Con.

Bibl. Not in Z.

Coll. Oswaldo de Andrade, Brazil ;

Collection Michel Couturier, Neuilly.

Caricatures related to the ones in the preceding
drawing (D. XIV. 1). Cf. also the grotesque figures
in the drypoint *The Dance* (Geiser 18/b).

D. XIV. 4
SEATED NEGRO
Paris, 1906.
Pen drawing on paper.
Size : 17 x 10.5 cm.
Unsigned.

Exh. Frankfurt and Hamburg, 1965 : *Picasso, 150
Handzeichnungen,* No. 24, repr. in cat.

Bibl. Not in Z.

Coll. G. and L. Bollag, Zurich ;

Collection Max G. Bollag, Zurich.

D. XIV. 5
STUDY FOR THE BLUE VASE
Paris, 1906.
Ink and colored crayons on paper.
Size : 26 x 21 cm.
Signed bottom right : Picasso.

Exh. Galerie G. and L. Bollag, Zurich, March 31–
April 2, 1925 : Exhibition before the Sale, April 3,
1925, No. 164, repr. in cat. pl. 62.

Bibl. Not in Z.

Formerly Collection of G. and L. Bollag, Zurich.

D. XIV. 6
BLUE VASE
Paris, 1906.
Ink and blue crayon on yellow paper.
Size : 31.5 x 24.5 cm.
Signed and dated, bottom right : Picasso 06.

Exh. Frankfurt and Hamburg, 1965 : *Picasso, 150
Handzeichnungen,* No. 22, repr. in color in cat.
Bibl. Not in Z. Catalogue Galerie Bollag, Zurich,
April, 1925, No. 163, pl. 61.
Coll. G. and L. Bollag, Zurich ;

Collection Mlle Suzanne Bollag, Zurich.
This work and the study for it (D. XIV. 5) are preliminary works for a vase which was never realized.

D. XIV. 7
ROSES
Paris (?), 1906.
Yellow and red watercolor.
Size : 62 x 45 cm.
Signed bottom right : Picasso.

Exh. Galerie G. and L. Bollag, Zurich, March 31–
April 2, 1925 : Exhibition before the Sale, April 3,
1925, No. 155, repr. in cat. pl. 60.

Bibl. Not in Z.

Formerly Collection of G. and L. Bollag, Zurich.

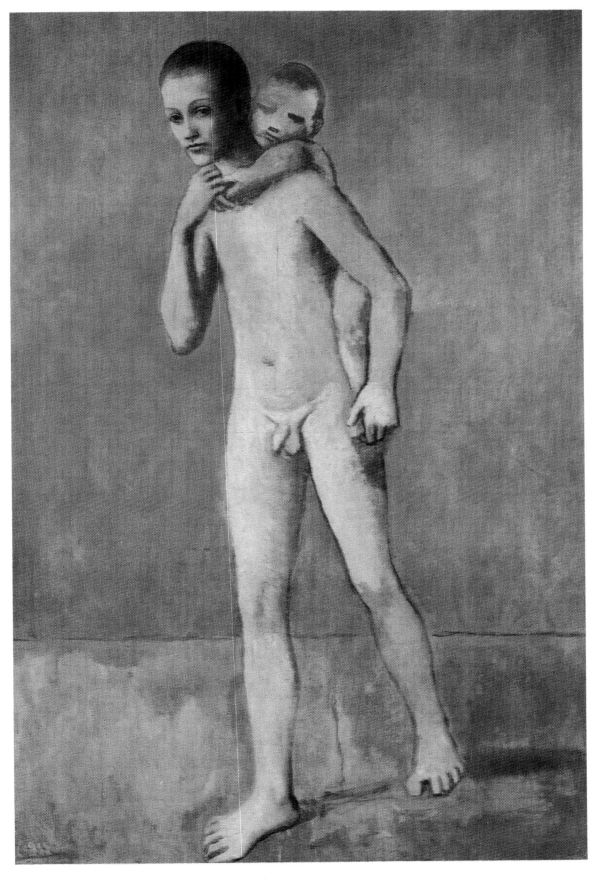

THE TWO BROTHERS, GOSOL, SUMMER 1906, OIL. RODOLPHE STAECHELIN
FOUNDATION, ON LOAN TO THE KUNSTMUSEUM, BASEL (XV.9).

The Flowering of Classicism at Gosol, Summer 1906 (1)

"Each year he used to spend a few months in Spain," wrote Fernande Olivier, "and come back refreshed, with studies new in expression, always in a manner that those of us who were following his work closely could not foresee... Much stronger feeling and sensibility emanated from these studies... In Spain I saw him a different person or, rather, not like the Picasso of Paris, but light-hearted, gentler, more witty and lively, responsive, calm and sure of himself, happy, in other

Peasants from Andorra, Gosol, summer 1906, pen drawing. The Art Institute of Chicago, Gift of Robert Allerton.

words. He radiated happiness—unlike his ordinary outlook and disposition.

"When he was in Spain he never spent much time in cities. He would stay with his family for a few days in Barcelona, then he'd set out for the country. He would live in an isolated part of Aragon, Catalonia, Valencia, or somewhere else. As soon as he'd arrive in a place, he would look for a room or a house where he could settle down and work without any interruption, free to do what he wanted, all day. He enjoyed the company of the peasants and these people liked him. Without restraint he would join them in drinking and their other amusements...

"He lived for several months in the Catalan village of Gosol, above the valley of Andorra, steadily working and building up his health."

They went through Barcelona on the way to Gosol; there is a photograph of Pablo and Fernande taken by Vidal y Ventosa in his studio (see Documents, p. 340).

From there, the train took them to Ripoll where they changed to a coach and finally to mules for the last part of the way to Gosol. The itinerary traced in the *Carnet Catalan* was the one they followed hastily on their way back, when the innkeeper's daughter came down with typhoid fever: by mule from Gosol to Vallvé (Bellver, on the Segre, on the other side of the Sierra del Cadi); by coach to Puixcerda and Ax-les-Thermes, since the railway then did not run through the pass; by train from Ax to Paris. Fernande verifies this in her memoirs: "Picasso wanted to go direct to France. To do so you had to cross the Pyrenees. I recall we left Gosol at 5 a.m. and did not arrive till 5 p.m. at the village where a coach was available."

The stay in Gosol extended over three months, from the middle of May to the middle of August.

When we asked Picasso how he chose Gosol for the trip, his answer was: "I discovered Gosol the usual way—through friends. A sculptor in Barcelona named Casanova and the son of a well-known Greek Prime Minister had been to Gosol and they said it was magnificent..."

The Catalan Experience, Gosol, Summer 1906 (2)

We have catalogued here the material that Picasso derived from Gosol, as opposed to the development of the series of classical nudes begun in Paris. It is obvious, in fact, as Barr has already pointed out, that works such as *Woman with Loaves* (xv. 46) clearly come after the nudes that we have already catalogued.

In this part of the catalogue, our chronological classification in relation to Zervos's dating is never due simply to stylistic analysis, but is based on either the *Carnet Catalan* or drawings unknown to Zervos. We have isolated the works of this transitional period in order to group the works of the end of the summer that reveal the evolution towards *Les Demoiselles d'Avignon.*

As to the dating of the works leading to *Composition: The Peasants* (xv. 62), Picasso's letter to Leo Stein of August 17, 1906 (reproduced p. 339, Documents) is proof that, although the studies for this work were made during the stay in Gosol, he painted the large work in the Barnes Foundation immediately after his return to Paris.

XV. 1
NUDE BOY WITH RAISED ARMS AMONG TREES
Gosol, summer, 1906.
India ink on paper.   Size : 12 x 7.5 cm.
Unsigned.

Bibl. Not in Z.   Douglas Cooper, *Picasso, Carnet Catalan*, p. 16.

Owned by the artist.

Page 16 of the Gosol notebook.   This drawing (reversed) corresponds to the figure at the left in *The Adolescents* (XV. 11).   Cf. also XV. 2, 3, and 4.

XV. 2
NUDE BOY WITH RAISED ARMS
Gosol, summer, 1906.
Watercolor and ink.
Signed bottom right : Picasso.

Bibl. Z. VI. 662 (dated 1905).

Collection Berggruen, Paris.

Study for the figure at the left in *The Adolescents* (XV. 11).   Cf. also XV. 1, 3, and 4 (studies for *The Two Brothers*).

XV. 3
BOY CARRYING A CHILD
Gosol, summer, 1906.
India ink on paper.   Size : 12 x 7.5 cm.
Unsigned.

Bibl. Not in Z.   Douglas Cooper, *Picasso, Carnet Catalan*, p. 27.

Owned by the artist.

Page 27 of the Gosol notebook.   Sketch for *The Two Brothers* (XV. 9) and for the following work (XV. 4).

XV. 4
YOUNG MAN AND CHILDREN
Gosol, summer, 1906.
Watercolor and pencil on ruled paper.
Size : 17.8 x 12 cm.
Signed (Nov. 27, 1948) bottom right : Picasso.

Exh. In 1950 : York City Art Gallery ; Hatton Gallery, Newcastle ; Leicester Art Gallery ; Brighton Art Gallery. In 1952 : Southampton Art Gallery. In 1962 : Manchester City Art Gallery ; Leeds City Art Gallery.

Bibl. Z. VI. 713 (dated 1905).

Coll. Mayor Gallery, London ;   Miss Coltman, London ;

Collection Dr. Henry M. Roland, Surrey, England.

Study for *The Two Brothers* (XV. 9).

XV. 5
BOY CARRYING A CHILD, FROM THE BACK
Gosol, summer, 1906.
India ink on red ground, on paper.
Size : 32.5 x 25.5 cm.
Signed bottom right : Picasso.

Bibl. Unpublished.

Coll. Léo Bollag, Zurich ;   Private collection, Zurich ;

Private collection, Switzerland.

Study for *The Two Brothers* (XV. 9), from the back. Unpublished drawing, authenticated by Picasso ; statement signed by D. H. Kahnweiler.

XV. 6
STUDY FOR THE TWO BROTHERS
Gosol, summer, 1906.
Pen drawing.
Size : 30 x 24 cm.
Signed bottom left : Picasso.

Bibl. Not in Z.   *The Cone Collection*, Catalogue, Baltimore, 1934, pl. 101 a.   Helen Kay, 1965, p. 64.

Coll. Miss Etta and Dr. Claribel Cone, Baltimore ;

Baltimore Museum of Art, The Cone Collection.

Study for *The Two Brothers* (XV. 9).   This is the drawing which appears at the right in *Still Life with a Portrait* (XV. 14).

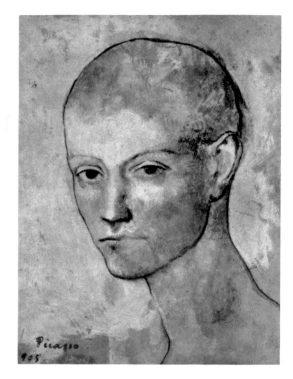

XV. 7
HEAD OF A YOUNG MAN
1905–1906 (see note).
Gouache on cardboard.
Size : 31 x 24 cm.
Signed and dated, bottom left :
Picasso 1905.

Exh. Jacques Seligmann, New York,
1937 : *Picasso 1903–1923,* No. 4.
Cleveland Museum of Art, 1939 :
*Impressionism and Related Move-
ments.* J. B. Speed Memorial Museum,
Louisville, Kentucky, 1944. Knoedler,
New York, 1947 : *Picasso before 1907,*
No. 27.

Bibl. Z. I. 303. Ponge and Chessex,
pl. 25.

Coll. Gertrude Stein, Paris ; Horst
Bohrmann, Berlin ; Jacques Doucet,
Paris ; Leonard C. Hanna, Jr. ;

*The Cleveland Museum of Art, Leonard
C. Hanna, Jr. Collection.*

If the signature and the date of this
work are contemporary, it means that
Picasso initiated the theme of *The
Two Brothers* (XV. 9) in Paris, in 1905.
If they are later, the date might be a
lapse of memory. Picasso has mis-
dated certain works done in 1906.
This head of a young man is similar to
the elder of the *Two Brothers.*

XV. 8
TWO BROTHERS, FROM THE
FRONT
Gosol, summer, 1906.
Gouache on cardboard.
Size : 80.3 x 60.2 cm.
Unsigned.

Exh. Galerie Georges Petit, Paris, 1932 :
Picasso, No. 27. Kunsthaus, Zurich,
1932 : *Picasso,* No. 28 (*Les jeunes
acrobates,* 1905). Grand Palais, Paris,
November 1966–February 1967 : *Hommage à Pablo Picasso,* No. 33, repr. in
color in cat.

Bibl. Z. VI. 720.

Owned by the artist.

Study for *The Two Brothers* (XV. 9).
This gouache has the flavor of the
circus period, but next to the drum
there is the pitcher with flowers, a sign
of works done in Gosol.

XV. 9
THE TWO BROTHERS
Gosol, summer, 1906 (see note).
Oil on canvas.
Size : 142 x 97 cm.
Signed bottom left : Picasso.

Exh. Munich, Cologne, Hamburg,
1955–1956 : *Picasso 1900–1955,*
No. 51. Kunstmuseum, Basel, May 13–
June 17, 1956 : *Collection R. Staeche-
lin,* No. 51. Musée National d'Art
Moderne, Paris, April 10–June 28,
1964 : *Fondation Rodolphe Staechelin,*
No. 45, repr. in cat.

Bibl. Z. I. 304. Merli, 1948, No. 121
and 122. Daix, 1964, p. 49 (repr. in
color). Helen Kay, 1965, p. 65.

*Rodolphe Staechelin Foundation, on
loan to the Kunstmuseum, Basel.*

This large canvas is usually dated
1905. Nonetheless, everything indicates it was done in Gosol, in 1906 :
the sketches in the Catalan notebook,
the study for *The Two Brothers* in the
background of *Still Life with a Portrait* (XV. 14), the red-ochre tonality
(the color of the earth in Gosol)
characteristic of Picasso's palette at
this time, and the monochrome background. It is true that Picasso in this
period was often working from
memory, without a model. So he
could have continued at Gosol a theme
begun in Paris at the end of 1905 or
the beginning of 1906.

Color plate, page 291.

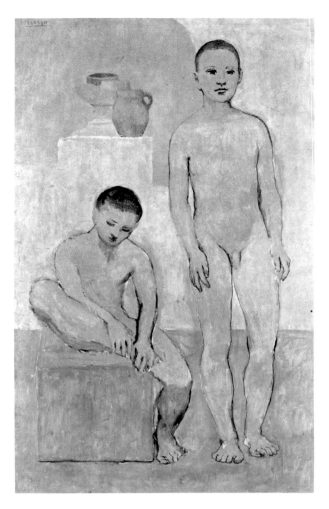

XV. 10
TWO YOUTHS
Gosol, summer, 1906.
Oil on canvas.
Size : 151.5 x 93.7 cm.
Signed top left : Picasso.

Exh. Wildenstein, New York, 1926 : *Tri-National Art : French, British, American,* No. 188. Museum of French Art, New York, 1931 : *Picasso, Braque, Léger,* No. 3. Galerie Georges Petit, Paris, 1932 : *Picasso,* No. 32. Art Institute of Chicago, 1943, and National Gallery of Art, Washington, D.C., 1965 : *20th Century French Paintings from the Chester Dale Collection* (Washington : repr. p. 52).

Bibl. Z. I. 305 and VI. 715. Level, 1928, pl. 20. Maud Dale, 1930, pl. 10. Cassou, 1940, p. 54. Merli, 1948, No. 141. Blunt and Pool, No. 162.

20th Century Paintings and Sculpture of the French School in the Chester Dale Collection, Washington, D.C., 1965 edition, p. 71.

Coll. Ambroise Vollard, Paris ; Helft, Paris ; Chester Dale, New York ;

National Gallery of Art, Washington, D.C., Chester Dale Collection.

Dated 1905 by Zervos, who also wrongly dated 1905 the trip to Gosol. There is a clear similarity between these two nude boys and those in *The Two Brothers* (XV. 9) and *The Adolescents* (XV. 11). (Cf. also the drawings in the Catalan notebook, XIV. 12 and 13.) Here, in addition, the background of Catalan pottery is certainly a sign of the Gosol period.

XV. 11
THE ADOLESCENTS
Gosol, summer, 1906.
Oil on canvas.
Size : 157 x 117 cm.
Signed top right : Picasso.

Exh. Galerie Georges Petit, Paris, summer, 1932 : *Picasso,* No. 42. Kunsthaus, Zurich, autumn, 1932 : *Picasso,* No. 33. Jacques Seligmann, New York, 1936 : *Picasso, Blue and Rose Periods,* No. 30, repr. in cat. Musée de l'Orangerie des Tuileries, Paris, 1966 : *Collection Jean Walter-Paul Guillaume,* No. 93, repr. in cat. p. 196.

Bibl. Z. I. 324. *Les Arts à Paris,* No. 17, May, 1930, p. 19. Merli, 1948, No. 137. Sutton, 1955, pl. XIV (repr. in color). Palau i Fabre, No. 112 (repr. in color).

Coll. Ambroise Vollard, Paris ; Paul Guillaume, Paris ; Mme Jean Walter, Paris ;

Musée de l'Orangerie, Paris, Collection Jean Walter-Paul Guillaume.

Zervos wrongly dates this 1905 (cf. note No. XV. 10). André Level (1928) noticed in this painting, which he dates 1906, and in the nudes painted in Gosol, the beginning of the "flesh stage" and a paler color. The figure at the right carries a piece of Gosol pottery. Cf. No. XV. 2 for the sketch of the young man's pose.

XV. 12
BOWL, PITCHER AND MILK CAN
Gosol, summer, 1906.
Watercolor on paper.
Size : 41.9 x 29 cm.
Signed bottom right : Picasso.

Exh. Kunstmuseum, Basel, May 13–June 17, 1956 : *Collection R. Staechelin,* No. 52. Musée National d'Art Moderne, Paris, April 10–June 28-1964 : *Fondation Rodolph e Staeche, lin,* No. 48, repr. in cat. (dated 1905).

Bibl. Not in Z.

Rodolphe Staechelin Foundation, Basel.

Dated 1905 in the archives of the Staechelin Foundation, but this is certainly Gosol pottery, with a milk can.

XV. 13
STILL LIFE WITH VASES
(The *Porrón*)
Gosol, summer, 1906.
Oil on canvas.
Size : 38.5 x 56 cm.
Signed (in 1911) bottom right :
Picasso.

Bibl. Z. I. 343 (Gosol, but dated 1905).
Sutton, 1955, No. 44. Kahnweiler and
Parmelin, 1955, pl. 19 (color). Cata-

logue of the Hermitage Museum,
No. 8895.

Coll. S. I. Tschukin, Moscow (until
1918) ; Museum of Modern Western
Art, Moscow (1918–1948) ;

The Hermitage Museum, Leningrad.

A *porrón* is a Spanish vessel used for
drinking by pouring the wine from the
spout down one's throat.

XV. 14
STILL LIFE WITH A PORTRAIT
Gosol, summer, 1906.
Oil on canvas.
Size : 82 x 100.3 cm.
Unsigned.

Exh. Knokke-le-Zoute, 1950 : *Picasso,*
No. 11.

Bibl. Z. I. 342 (dated Paris, 1905). Sabartés and Boeck, p. 372.

Coll. Galerie Kahnweiler, Paris (1911);
Dr. Robeyn, Brussels ;

*The Phillips Collection, Washington,
D.C.*

The *porrón* (Spanish wine vessel) is
also seen in XV. 13. Among the
pottery, the chocolate pot is the same
as the one in XV. 16. The drawing on
the wall, at the right, is a study for
The Two Brothers (cf. XV. 6).

XV. 15
PITCHER WITH FLOWERS
Gosol, summer, 1906.
Watercolor on paper.
Dimensions not known.
Signed bottom left : Picasso.

Bibl. Unpublished.

*Collection Mrs. John A. MacAulay,
Winnipeg.*

XV. 16
STILL LIFE : FLOWERS IN A VASE
Gosol, summer, 1906.
Gouache on cardboard.
Size : 70.5 x 54 cm.
Signed bottom left : Picasso.

Exh. The Solomon R. Guggenheim
Museum, New York, April–September
1965 : *First Showing of Masterpieces
from the Thannhauser Foundation,*
No. 43, repr. in color in cat. p. 47.

Bibl. Z. VI. 889 (dated 1905).

Coll. Bought from the artist by Justin
K. Thannhauser, Paris ;

*The Solomon R. Guggenheim Mu-
seum, New York, Justin K. Thannhauser Foundation.*

In the foreground on the right is the
chocolate pot which appears in *Still
Life with a Portrait* (XV. 14).

XV. 17
HEAD OF A YOUNG MAN
Gosol, summer, 1906.
Gouache on cardboard.
Size : 38 x 25.4 cm.
Signed bottom right : Picasso.

Exh. Knoedler, New York, 1962 : *Picasso, an American Tribute,* No. 30, repr. in cat.

Bibl. Z. I. 331 and VI. 781. Sabartés and Boeck, p. 481, No. 248. Blunt and Pool, No. 126.

Coll. A. Saint, Paris ; Valentine Dudensing, New York ;

Collection Mr. and Mrs. Lee A. Ault, New York.

XV. 18
THREE NUDES
Gosol, summer, 1906.
Gouache on paper.
Size : 63 x 48.3 cm.
Signed bottom left : Picasso.

Exh. Marlborough Fine Art, London, February–March 1953 : *Important French Masters,* No. 19, repr. p. 11. Idem, October–November 1954 : *French Masters of 19th and 20th Century,* No. 37, repr. p. 21. MMA, New York, 1956 : *Paintings from Private Collections,* repr. p. 16.

Bibl. Z. I. 340. Merli, 1948, No. 129.

Coll. Max Pellequer, Paris ;

Collection The Alex Hillman Corporation, New York.

On the front of this work are annotations by the artist in Spanish indicating that this is a study. Translation, top to bottom : "Decoration on the walls / flowers / landscape and fruits —a room painted in pink / some white curtains / a sofa, the kind in straw (plaited ?) / on it, mauve bolster / marble (illegible word) / on it, some bowls and a small mirror—maybe some gauze veils—he holds in / his hand / a cigarillo—he holds a porrón in his hand / a fruit dish / here."

XV. 19
STANDING NUDE, HANDS CLASPED
Gosol, summer, 1906. Gouache.
Size : 58 x 37.5 cm. Signed (?).

Exh. Knokke-le-Zoute, 1950 : *Picasso,* No. 12. Fort Worth Art Center Museum, February 8–March 26, 1967 : *Picasso,* No. 149.

Bibl. Z. I. 258. Penrose, 1958, pl. III, No. 8.

Coll. Ambroise Vollard, Paris ; Private collection, London ;

Collection Mr. and Mrs. Eugene McDermott, Dallas.

Related to the standing nude in *Three Nudes* (XV. 18).

XV. 20
HEAD OF A WOMAN WITH A CHIGNON
Gosol, summer, 1906.
Gouache.
Size : 62 x 47 cm.
Unsigned (?).

Bibl. Z. I. 332 (dated 1905).

Formerly collection of A. Vollard, Paris.

Cf. XV. 27.

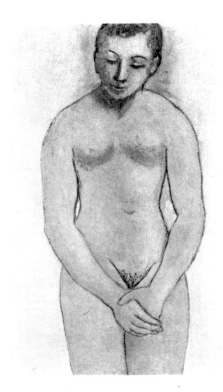

XV. 21
HEAD OF A WOMAN : FERNANDE
Summer, 1906.
Varnished gouache on canvas.
Size : 37.5 x 33 cm.
Signed top right : Picasso.

Exh. Knoedler, New York, 1962 : *Pi-*

casso, an American Tribute, No. 32,
repr. in cat.

Bibl. Z. VI. 749. Sutton, 1955, No. 32.

Private collection, U.S.A.

XV. 22
HEAD OF A WOMAN
Summer, 1906.
Gouache on paper mounted on board.
Size : 63.8 x 48.3 cm.
Signed top right : Picasso.

Exh. San Francisco, 1934. Jacques
Seligmann, New York, 1936 : *Picasso,
Blue and Rose Periods,* No. 25, repr.
Knoedler, New York, 1962 : *Picasso,
an American Tribute,* No. 29, repr.
Fort Worth Art Center Museum,

February 8–March 26, 1967 : *Picasso,*
No. 145.

Bibl. Z. I. 333. Merli, 1948, No. 143.

Coll. Ambroise Vollard, Paris ; The
Toledo Museum of Art, Ohio ; Acquir-
ed in February 1961 by Knoedler &
Co., New York ;

*Collection Mr. and Mrs. Henry Ford II,
Michigan.*

XV. 23
NUDE WITH A PITCHER
Summer, 1906.
Oil on canvas.
Size : 100 x 81 cm.
Signed bottom right : Picasso.

Exh. Tate Gallery, London 1960 :
Picasso, No. 27, repr. in cat. pl. 5 i.

Bibl. Z. I. 330. Merli, 1948, No. 134.

Coll. R. F. Reber, Lausanne ; Richet,
Paris ; Edward James, London ;

*Collection Mr. and Mrs. Leigh B. Block,
Chicago.*

Dated 1905 by Zervos and by Penrose
(London cat., 1960). This painting
belongs more logically to the series of
pre-cubist nudes of 1906 (cf. especially XV. 18, 19, 20, 24, 38).

XV. 24
TORSO OF A YOUNG GIRL
Summer, 1906.
Oil on canvas. Size : 100 x 81 cm.
Unsigned.

Exh. Munich, Cologne, Hamburg,
1955–1956 : *Picasso 1900–1955,*
No. 13.

Bibl. Not in Z.

Coll. Hans Engelhorn, Ziegelhausen
am Neckar ;

Present location unknown.

Related to the *Nude with a Pitcher*
(XV. 23). Here again is the familiar
pottery. Cf. the study, dated '06, of the
same pose (Z. VI. 880).

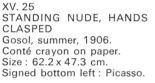

XV. 25
STANDING NUDE, HANDS
CLASPED
Gosol, summer, 1906.
Conté crayon on paper.
Size : 62.2 x 47.3 cm.
Signed bottom left : Picasso.

Exh. Virginia and Philadelphia, 1941 :
Collection Walter P. Chrysler, Jr.,
No. 211. New Gallery, New York,
1962 : *Picasso, an American Tribute,*
No. 6, repr. Art Institute of Chicago,

September 20–November 27, 1963 :
Chicago Collections.

Bibl. Z. VI. 779.

Coll. Gertrude Stein, Paris ; Perls
Galleries, New York ; Walter P.
Chrysler, Jr., New York ;

*Collection Mr. and Mrs. Leigh B.
Block, Chicago.*

Study for *Standing Female Nude*
(XV. 27).

XV. 26
STANDING NUDE IN FRONT
OF A RED ARCH
Summer, 1906.
Oil on canvas.
Size : 26 x 18 cm.
Unsigned.

Bibl. Z. I. 326. Sutton, 1955, No. 34.
Barnes Foundation, Inventory No. 112.

Barnes Foundation, Merion, Pa.

Study in oil for *Standing Female Nude*
(XV. 27). The red arch framing the
woman in this version does not appear
in the following large work.

XV. 27
STANDING FEMALE NUDE
Summer, 1906.
Oil on canvas.
Size : 153 x 94 cm.
Unsigned.

Exh. Maison de la Pensée Française,
Paris, June 1954 : *Picasso 1900–
1914,* No. 3. Idem, July 1954 :
Picasso, Deux Périodes, No. 3. Musée
Cantini, Marseilles, 1959 : *Picasso,*
No. 8, repr.

Bibl. Z. I. 327. Eugenio d'Ors, 1930,
pl. 14. Merli, 1948, No. 138. Kahn-

weiler and Parmelin, 1955, pl. 3
(color). Sutton, 1955, pl. XII (color).
Daix, 1964, p. 55 (color).

Coll. Gertrude Stein, Paris ;

*Collection of the Heirs of Miss Ger-
trude Stein.*

This large nude, with Fernande's eyes,
prefigures the sculptural works of the
autumn of 1906. Cf. study for the
head (XV. 20) and the studies XV. 25,
26.

XV. 28
NUDE WITH HANDS CLASPED
1906 (see note).
Gouache on canvas.
Size : 95.8 x 75.5 cm.
Signed on the back : A mon vrai ami /
Picasso / 1er janvier 1907.

Exh. Toronto, Winnipeg, Vancouver,
Minneapolis, 1956–1957 : *Collection
Ayala and Sam Zacks,* No. 86, repr.
pl. 18. Toronto and Montreal, 1964 :
Picasso and Man, No. 31, repr. p. 47.
Tel-Aviv Museum, February 1966 :
Picasso, No. 2, repr. Dallas, 1967 :
Picasso, No. 9, repr.

Bibl. Z. I. 310. Raynal, 1922, pl. 27.
Merli, 1948, No. 144. Sutton, 1955,
No. 42.

Coll. Galerie Rosengart, Lucerne ;
Since August 14, 1956 :

*Collection Ayala and Sam Zacks, To-
ronto.*

Usually dated 1905, this admirable
portrait of Fernande, with its pale
colors, belongs more naturally to 1906
(cf. XV. 19, 27, and D. XV. 17).

Color plate, page 89.

XV. 29
NUDE HOLDING A MIRROR
Gosol, summer, 1906.
Pen drawing.
Size : 25 x 17 cm.
Signed bottom right : Picasso.

Bibl. Not in Z. Catalogue Galerie Bollag, Zurich, Sale, April 3, 1925, No. 167, pl. 62.

Formerly Collection of G. and L. Bollag, Zurich.

This study for *La Toilette* (XV. 34) is the only one we know of showing the woman with the mirror nude.

XV. 30
STUDY FOR LA TOILETTE
Gosol, summer, 1906.
Charcoal drawing.
Size : 24 x 15 cm.
Signed bottom right : Picasso.

Bibl. Not in Z. Catalogue Galerie Bollag, Zurich, Sale, October 23, 1931, No. 130, pl. IX.

Coll. G. and L. Bollag, Zurich ; Private collection, Basel ;

Private collection, London.

XV. 31
STUDY FOR LA TOILETTE
Gosol, summer 1906.
Watercolor on paper.
Size : 25.5 x 16.5 cm.
Signed bottom left : Picasso.

Exh. Springfield, Mass., 1933, No. 124. Virginia and Philadelphia, 1941 : *Collection Walter P. Chrysler, Jr.,* No. 207, repr. in cat.

Bibl. Not in Z.

Coll. Leo Stein, Paris ; Mrs. Cornelius J. Sullivan, New York ; Parke-Bernet, New York, December, 1939 : Sale of the collection of Mrs. Cornelius J. Sullivan, No. 143, repr. p. 60 ;

Collection Walter P. Chrysler, Jr., New York.

XV. 32
STUDY FOR LA TOILETTE
Gosol, summer, 1906.
Charcoal on beige-colored paper.
Size : 62.2 x 40.7 cm.
Signed and dated, bottom right : Picasso 1906.

Exh. Joe and Emily Lowe Art Gallery, Miami, 1963 : *Renoir to Picasso,* No. 93, repr. p. 60.

Bibl. Not in Z. Lieberman, 1952, pl. 22. Lieberman, 1961, pl. 44.

Coll. Alfred Flechtheim, Berlin ; Hugo Stinnes, Berlin ;

Collection The Alex Hillman Corporation, New York.

A dated work important in the dating of *La Toilette* (XV. 34).

XV. 33
STUDY FOR LA TOILETTE
Gosol, summer, 1906.
Oil on cardboard.
Size : 52 x 31 cm.
Signed bottom left : Picasso.

Exh. Jacques Seligmann, New York, 1936 : *Picasso, Blue and Rose Periods,* No. 32.

Bibl. Z. VI. 736.

Coll. J. B. Stang, Oslo ; James P. Warburg, New York ;

Museu de Arte, Sao Paulo.

A small version, in oil, of *La Toilette* (XV. 34).

XV. 34
LA TOILETTE
Gosol, summer, 1906.
Oil on canvas.   Size : 151 x 99 cm.
Signed top left : Picasso.

Exh. MMA, New York, 1930 : *Painting in Paris,* No. 67, repr. Chicago, 1933 : *Century of Progress,* No. 404. Wadsworth Atheneum, 1934 : *Picasso,* No. 18, repr. Cleveland, 1936, No. 334. Seligmann, New York, 1936 : *Picasso, Blue and Rose,* No. 29, repr. Boston, 1938 : *Picasso and Matisse,* No. 4. New York and Chicago, 1939–1940 : *Picasso, Forty Years of his Art,* No. 57, repr. p. 52. Mexico, 1944. Wadsworth Atheneum, 1946, No. 43. Toronto, 1949, No. 3. Pittsburgh, 1954, No. 88, repr. Wildenstein, New York, 1956,

No. 38. Boston, 1957, No. 113, repr. Tate Gallery, London, 1960 : *Picasso,* No. 29, repr. pl. 7 a. Toronto and Montreal, 1964 : *Picasso and Man,* No. 33, repr. p. 49. Grand Palais, Paris, 1966–1967 : *Hommage à Pablo Picasso,* No. 34, repr. in cat.

Bibl. Z. I. 325. Catalogue, *Collection John Quinn,* New York, 1926, p. 93. Level, 1928, pl. 12. Barr, *Forty Years,* p. 52. Merli, 1948, No. 127. Elgar and Maillard, 1955, p. 46 (color). J. C. Aznar, 1956, fig. 273. Cassou, 1958, p. 27 (color). D. H. Kahnweiler, 1958, pl. 21. Lieberman, 1961, pl. 32 (color). Boudaille, 1964, pl. XV (color). Daix, 1964, p. 27 (color). Palau i Fabre, No. 113 (color).

Coll. John Quinn, New York ; Acquired in 1926 by :

Albright-Knox Art Gallery, Buffalo.

This major work sums up all previous explorations of this period and re-introduces the theme of women arranging their hair (cf. XV. 35, 40, and Catalogue XVI). Formerly dated 1905, *La Toilette* was done at Gosol in 1906 (cf. dated study, XV. 32).

Color plate, page 91.

XV. 35
YOUNG FEMALE NUDE
AND NUDE CHILD, WITH A GOAT
Gosol, summer, 1906.
Oil on canvas.   Size : 146 x 114 cm.
Signed bottom left : Picasso.

Bibl. Z. I. 249 (dated 1905). Level, 1928, pl. 13. Merli, 1948, No. 125. Champris, 1960, No. 11.

Barnes Foundation, Merion, Pa.

The presence of the nude boy relates this work to *The Two Brothers* (XV. 8, 9, and sketches) and to *The Two Youths* (XV. 10) and *The Adolescents* (XV. 11). The young girl arranging her hair is shown here in the same pose as the figure at the left in *The Harem* (XV. 40). Cf. sketch XV. 36.

XV. 36
YOUNG GIRL ARRANGING HER HAIR
Gosol, summer, 1906.
Black crayon on paper.
Size : 12 x 7.5 cm.
Unsigned.

Bibl. Not in Z. Douglas Cooper, *Picasso, Carnet Catalan,* p. 21.

Owned by the artist.

Sketch for the central figure of *Young Female Nude and Nude Child, with a Goat* (XV. 35), and also for the figure at the left in *The Harem* (XV. 40). This page, No. 21, of the Gosol notebook is an important chronological reference.

XV. 37
YOUNG MAN FROM GOSOL
Gosol, summer, 1906.
Gouache and watercolor on paper.
Size : 61.5 x 48 cm.
Signed on the back : Picasso.

Exh. Stockholm, 1954. Tokyo, 1964 :
Picasso, No. 5. Kiruna, Sweden, September 1965 : *Picasso i Kiruna,* No. 34.

Bibl. Z. I. 318. Palau i Fabre, No. 115
(repr. in color).

Coll. Halvorsens Kunsthandel, Oslo ;
Acquired in 1916 by :

Göteborgs Konstmuseum, Göteborg.

The museum in Göteborg calls this
head of a young Spaniard (wearing
the traditional *barretina*) *Portrait of
Fernande Olivier.* The same incorrect
title was used in the Tokyo exhibition
catalogue. Picasso himself drew our
attention to this error.

XV. 38
NUDE, STUDY FOR THE HAREM
Gosol, summer, 1906.
Watercolor on paper.
Size : 64.1 x 49 cm.
Signed bottom right : Picasso.

Exh. Cleveland Museum of Art, 1932 :
9th Exhib. of Watercolors and Pastels.
Wadsworth Atheneum, 1934 : *Picasso,*
No. 91. Cleveland Museum, 1936 :
20th Anniversary, No. 333. Jacques
Seligmann, New York, 1936 : *Picasso,
Blue and Rose,* No. 27, repr. New
York and Chicago, 1939–1940 : *Picasso, Forty Years of his Art,* No. 61,
repr. p. 54.

Bibl. Z. I. 320. C. J. Bulliet, 1936,
pl. 106. Barr, *Forty Years,* p. 54.
Barr, *Fifty Years,* p. 251. Merli, 1948,
No. 123.

Coll. Hinman B. Hurlbut, Cleveland ;

*The Cleveland Museum of Art, Hinman
B. Hurlbut Collection.*

Study for the central figure in *The
Harem* (XV. 40).

XV. 39
SKETCH FOR THE HAREM
Gosol, summer, 1906.
Conté crayon.
Size : 57.5 x 46 cm.
Unsigned.

Bibl. Z. VI. 657. Cassou and Jacottet,
1951, pl. 79. Elgar and Maillard, 1955,
p. 37.

Present location unknown.

XV. 40
THE HAREM (Rose Nudes)
Gosol, summer, 1906.
Oil on canvas.
Size : 154.3 x 109.5 cm.
Signed top left : Picasso.

Exh. Carnegie Institute, Pittsburgh, 1928 : *27th International Exhibition,* No. 201, repr. Cleveland Museum of Art, 1929 : *French Art since 1800.*

Art Institute of Chicago, 1933 : *Century of Progress,* No. 400. Cleveland Museum of Art, 1936 : *20th Anniversary,* No. 331, repr. pl. LXXII. Jacques Seligmann, New York, 1936 : *Picasso, Blue and Rose Periods,* No. 28, repr. in cat.

Bibl. Z. I. 321. *Catalogue of the John Quinn Collection,* New York, 1926, p. 89. Merli, 1948, No. 142. Cleveland

Museum of Art, 1958, *In Memoriam Leonard C. Hanna, Jr.,* No. 29. Jan Runnqvist, 1959, p. 19. Palau i Fabre, No. 111 (repr. in color).

Coll. John Quinn, New York ; Leonard C. Hanna, Jr. ;

The Cleveland Museum of Art, Leonard C. Hanna, Jr., Collection.

In this important work, the nudes are grouped in attitudes which sum up poses in previous works (XV. 35, 36, 38, 39). At the same time, they anticipate later work which leads to the more stylized nudes arranging their hair (XVI. 5, 6, 7, 8, 9).

XV. 41
PORTRAIT OF FERNANDE
Summer, 1906.
Oil on canvas.
Size : 100 x 81 cm.
Signed on the back : Picasso.

Exh. New York and Chicago, 1939–1940 : *Picasso, Forty Years of his Art,* No. 58, repr. p. 53. Knoedler, New York, 1962 : *Picasso, an American Tribute,* No. 28, repr. University of California, Los Angeles, 1965 : *Years of Ferment.*

Bibl. Z. I. 254. Level, 1928, p. 27. Barr, *Forty Years,* p. 53. Barr, *Fifty Years,* p. 45. Elgar and Maillard, 1955 (catalogue). Sutton, 1955, No. 60.

Coll. A. Saint, Paris ;

Private collection, Cambridge, Massachusetts.

Dated Paris, 1905, by Zervos and Gosol, 1906, by Kahnweiler. The handling of this work will appear again in Picasso's second classical period, in 1918.

XV. 42
WOMAN WITH A WHITE MANTILLA
Paris, 1901 (see note).
Oil on canvas. Size : 52 x 60 cm.
Signed bottom left : Picasso.

Exh. Galerie Charpentier, Paris, 1945. Knoedler, New York, January 1951. Dallas Museum of Fine Arts, March 6–29, 1953. San Francisco, March–April, 1954.

Bibl. Z. VI. 733. *Art News Annual,* 1958, p. 44. *Catalogue of the Albert D. Lasker Collection,* p. 62 (color).

Coll. Paul Guillaume, Paris ; Mme Jean Walter, Paris ; Bought by Mrs. Lasker, in May 1950, for $22,025 ;

Collection Mrs. Albert D. Lasker, New York.

Usually dated 1905–06, this painting, according to the artist, is actually contemporary with the mother and child subjects of 1901 (VI. 28, 29, 30, 31). It is probably the mantilla which has confused it with works from Gosol. The colors and the handling are very different. Lacking conclusive evidence, we had followed the previous chronology. Picasso corrected the date himself when the illustration was already printed in this part of the catalogue.

XV. 43
FERNANDE
WITH A BLACK MANTILLA
Summer, 1906.
Oil.
Size : 100 x 81 cm.
Signed ?

Bibl. Z. I. 253 (dated Paris, 1906). Sutton, 1955, No. 62.

Present location unknown.

The margins of the illustration are cut (Zervos archives).

XV. 44
FERNANDE WITH A MANTILLA
Gosol, summer, 1906.
Oil on wood (see note).
Size : 81.5 x 62 cm. Unsigned.

Exh. Grand Palais, Paris, 1966–1967 :

Hommage à Pablo Picasso, No. 35, repr. in cat.
Bibl. Z. VI. 893.
Owned by the artist.

Painted on the headboard of a bed.

XV. 45
FERNANDE WITH A KERCHIEF
Gosol, summer, 1906.
Gouache and charcoal on paper.
Size : 66 x 49.5 cm.
Signed bottom right : Picasso.

Exh. New York and Chicago, 1939–1940 : *Picasso, Forty Years of his Art,* No. 62, repr. p. 54. Knoedler, New York, 1947 : *Picasso before 1907,* No. 24. Virginia, 1958. Des Moines, 1958. Knoedler, New York, 1962 : *Picasso, an American Tribute,* No. 27, repr. Toronto and Montreal, 1964 : *Picasso and Man,* No. 35, repr. p. 50. Tokyo, 1964 : *Picasso,* No. 8. Fort Worth Art Center Museum, February 8–March 26, 1967 : *Picasso,* No. 147 (incorrectly dated 1905).

Bibl. Z. I. 319. Barr, *Forty Years,* p. 54. *Catalogue, T. Catesby Jones Collection,* 1948, No. 82. Sutton, 1955, No. 26.

Coll. Valentine Dudensing, New York ; T. Catesby Jones, New York (1929–1947) ;

Virginia Museum of Fine Arts, T. Catesby Jones Collection

The Catalan notebook contains three studies related to this work (cf. D. XV. 25, 26, 27).

XV. 46
WOMAN WITH LOAVES
Gosol, summer, 1906 (see note).
Oil on canvas.
Size : 100 x 69.8 cm.
Signed and dated, bottom left : Picasso 1905.

Exh. Chicago, 1933 : *A Century of Progress.* Jacques Seligmann, New York, 1936 : *Picasso, Blue and Rose Periods,* No. 31, repr. Philips Memorial Gallery, Washington, D.C., 1938. New York and Chicago, 1939–1940 : *Picasso, Forty Years of his Art,* No. 56, repr. p. 51. Philadelphia, 1958 : *Picasso,* No. 26, repr. Grand Palais, Paris, November 1966–February 1967 : *Hommage à Pablo Picasso,* No. 36, repr.

Bibl. Z. VI. 735. Zervos, Milan, 1932, pl. 2. Barr, *Forty Years,* p. 51. Barr, *Fifty Years,* p. 47. Elgar and Maillard, 1955 (catalogue). Sutton, 1955, No. 35. John Canaday, 1959, p. 454. Palau i Fabre, No. 116 (repr. in color).

Coll. Ambroise Vollard, Paris (about 1907) ; Caussignac, Paris ; Paul Guillaume, Paris (1930) ; Marie Harriman Gallery, New York ; Charles E. Ingersoll ;

Philadelphia Museum of Art, Gift of Charles E. Ingersoll.

As Zervos and Barr have already indicated, Picasso dated this painting later. By mistake he wrote 1905 instead of 1906.

XV. 47
RECLINING NUDE (FERNANDE)
Gosol, summer, 1906.
Gouache on paper.
Size : 47.3 x 61.3 cm.
Signed bottom right : Picasso.

Exh. Milwaukee Art Institute, September 12–October 20, 1957 : *Inaugural Exhibition,* No. 88, repr. p. 65. Toronto and Montreal, 1964 : *Picasso and Man,* No. 36, repr. in cat. p. 51.

Bibl. Z. I. 317.

Coll. Paul Guillaume, Paris (1934) ; Mr. and Mrs. Michael Straight, Washington, D.C. ;

The Cleveland Museum of Art, Gift of Mr. and Mrs. Michael Straight, 1954.

XV. 48
GOSOL LANDSCAPE
Gosol, summer, 1906.
Oil on canvas.
Size : 69.8 x 99 cm.
Signed bottom right : Picasso.

Exh. New York and Chicago, 1957 :
Picasso, 75th Anniversary Exhibition,
repr. in cat. p. 28.

Bibl. Z. VI. 732. Palau i Fabre, No. 107.

Coll. Mr. and Mrs. Nate B. Spingold,
New York ;

Private collection, New York.

This is part of the village of Gosol,
seen from the road on which Picasso
left for Veillver on the back of a mule.

XV. 49
ROOSTERS *(Les Coqs)*
Gosol, summer, 1906.
Gouache on paper.
Size : 24.1 x 31.7 cm.
Signed bottom left : Picasso.

Exh. New York and Chicago, 1939–
1940 : *Picasso, Forty Years of his Art,*
No. 48, repr. p. 47.

Bibl. Z. VI. 725 (dated 1905). Barr,
Forty Years, p. 47.

Coll. Miss Harriet Lane Levy, San
Francisco ;

San Francisco Museum of Art, Bequest
of Harriet Lane Levy.

XV. 50
HOUSES OF GOSOL
Gosol, summer, 1906.
Oil on canvas.
Size : 54 x 38.5 cm.
Signed on back of canvas : Picasso.

Bibl. Z. I. 316. Leo Swane in *Kunst-*
mus, Aa. XVI–XVIII, 1929–1931, p. 78.
Erik Zahle, 1938, p. 18. Catalogue
Statens Museum, Copenhagen, 1929,
No. 92 ; 1948, No. 118. *Moderne*
Udenlansk Kunst, 1964, No. R. 92.

Coll. Christian Tetzen, Lund ; Sale of
the Chr. Tetzen collection, May 19,
1925, No. 104 ; Skaenket Museet
(1928) ;

Statens Museum for Kunst, Copen-
hagen.

Picasso saw these houses from his
room at the Gosol inn. They still exist
today (May, 1965).

XV. 51
THE ROOSTER *(Le Coq)*
Gosol, summer, 1906.
Watercolor and ink. Size : 24 x 31 cm.
Signed bottom left : Picasso.

Exh. Virginia Museum of Fine Arts,
October–November 1953 : *The Cone*
Collection. Smith College Museum of
Art, May–June 1964 : *Beauty in the*
Beast. Greensboro Library, N. Caro-
lina, April 1965 : *The Cone Collection.*
Phillips Gallery, Washington, D.C.,
February–March 1966 : *Birds in Con-*
temporary Art, No. 23, repr.

Bibl. Not in Z. *The Cone Collection,*
Catalogue, Baltimore, 1934, pl. 108.
Handbook of the Cone Collection,
Baltimore Museum of Art, 1955,
No. 92. *Great Drawings of all Time,*
vol. III, No. 857 (color). Ponge and
Chessex (on the back of cover).

Coll. Miss Etta and Dr. Claribel Cone,
Baltimore ;

Baltimore Museum of Art, The Cone
Collection.

XV. 52
HEAD OF A MAN
Gosol, summer, 1906.
Gouache and watercolor on Japan
paper. Size : 40.7 x 35 cm.
Signed top right : Picasso.

Exh. Philadelphia Museum of Art,
1940 : *Masterpieces of Philadelphia
Private Collections.* Idem, 1958 :
Picasso, No. 22, repr. in cat. p. 15.

Bibl. Z. I. 346.

Coll. Galerie Slater, Paris ; Purchased
at the Galerie Slater for $1,000 in 1930
by the present owners :

*Collection Mr. and Mrs. Rodolphe
Meyer de Schauensee, Philadelphia.*

XV. 53
HEAD OF A MAN
Gosol, summer, 1906.
Oil on canvas.
Size : 45.1 x 40.3 cm.
Signed top left : Picasso.

Exh. MMA, New York, Art Institute of
Chicago, St. Louis City Art Museum,
Museo de Arte Moderno, Mexico, San
Francisco, Denver, 1965–1966 : *The
School of Paris, Paintings from the*

*Florene May Schoenborn and Sam-
uel A. Marx Collection,* repr. p. 19.

Bibl. Z. VI. 769. Sabartés and Boeck,
p. 460, No. 36.

Coll. Mr. and Mrs. Samuel A. Marx,
Chicago ;

*Collection Florene M. Schoenborn and
Samuel A. Marx, New York.*

XV. 54
HEAD OF A MAN
Gosol, summer, 1906.
Conté crayon.
Size : 32.9 x 22.5 cm.
Unsigned.

Bibl. Z. VI. 770.

Coll. José Fontdevila, Gosol ;

Present location unknown.

In 1906 Picasso gave this drawing to
José Fontdevila, the innkeeper at
Gosol. Today a photograph of the
original drawing hangs in the dining
room of the inn (cf. the related works
XV. 52 and 53 ; also Z. VI. 765, 772,
773).

XV. 55
HEAD OF A WOMAN
Gosol, summer, 1906.
Gouache and crayon.
Dimensions not known.
Signed bottom right : Picasso.

Bibl. Z. VI. 763.

Present location unknown.

Related portraits of the same woman:
D. XV. 28, 37 and 38. See also Zervos
VI. 762, 764.

XV. 56
BOY WITH CATTLE
Gosol, summer, 1906.
Gouache.
Size : 62 x 47 cm.
Signed bottom right : Picasso.

Exh. Cincinnati Art Museum. AFA,
September 22, 1958–November 5,
1960 : *Adventures in Collecting* (traveling exhibition). Contemporary
Art Association, Houston.

Bibl. Z. I. 338. Barr, *Fifty Years,* p. 48.

Coll. Valentine Gallery, New York ;

*The Columbus Gallery of Fine Arts,
Ohio.*

XV. 57
STUDY FOR THE PEASANTS
Gosol, summer, 1906.
Ink on paper.
Size : 18 x 12 cm.
Signed on verso.
Verso : Head of a Woman (D. XV. 39).

Bibl. Unpublished.

Coll. G. and L. Bollag, Zurich ; Mme
B. Bollag, Zurich ;

*Collection M. and Mme F. Kirch-
heimer, Küsnacht.*

An unpublished drawing which is very
important in determining the origins
of the large, important oil, *The Peasants*
(XV. 62). This is certainly a scene
taken from life, at Gosol. It is developed
further in the following works : XV.
58–62.

XV. 58
FLOWER GIRL
(Study for *The Peasants*.)
Gosol or Paris, summer, 1906.
Pen drawing.
Size : 63.1 x 48.2 cm.
Signed bottom left : Picasso.

Exh. New York and Chicago, 1957 :
Picasso, 75th Anniversary (addenda).
MMA, New York, 1962. Toronto and
Montreal, 1964 : *Picasso and Man,*
No. 43, repr. in cat. p. 57.

Bibl. Not in Z.

Coll. Mrs. Stanley B. Resor, New
York ;

*Museum of Modern Art, New York,
Gift of Mrs. Stanley B. Resor, 1950.*

XV. 59
SKETCH : THE PEASANTS
Paris, August 17, 1906.
Pen drawing.
Size : 18 x 12 cm.

Bibl. Not in Z. Donald Gallup, *The
Flowers of Friendship (Letters to Gertrude Stein),* New York, 1953.

*Yale University, Gertrude Stein Collec-
tion (Collection of American Literature).*

This important sketch appears in
Picasso's letter to Leo Stein, written
in Paris August 17, 1906. It establishes
that *The Peasants* was done in Paris,
right after Picasso's return from Gosol
(cf. Appendix, p. 339), and note
XV. 62).

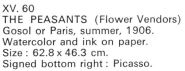

XV. 60
THE PEASANTS (Flower Vendors)
Gosol or Paris, summer, 1906.
Watercolor and ink on paper.
Size : 62.8 x 46.3 cm.
Signed bottom right : Picasso.

Exh. Museums Associated, Israel, 1955, No. 63. Toronto, Ottawa, Winnipeg, Minneapolis, Vancouver, San Francisco, Santa Barbara, Pasadena, Montreal, 1956–1957. New York and Chicago, 1957 : *Picasso, 75th Anniversary Exhibition,* repr. p. 28. Philadelphia, 1958 : *Picasso,* No. 34. Toronto and Montreal, 1964 : *Picasso and Man,* No. 42, repr. in cat. p. 56.

Bibl. Z. I. 311. Barr, *Fifty Years,* p. 48.

Coll. Ambroise Vollard, Paris ; Marie Harriman Gallery, New York ; Knoedler & Co., New York ; Perls Gallery, Beverly Hills ;

Collection Ayala and Sam Zacks, Toronto.

XV. 61
THE PEASANTS
Gosol or Paris, summer 1906.
Gouache on paper.
Size : 69 x 47 cm.
Signed bottom left : Picasso.

Exh. Musée de l'Orangerie des Tuileries, Paris, 1966 : *Collection Jean Walter-Paul Guillaume,* No. 94, repr. in cat. p. 198.

Bibl. Z. I. 312.

Coll. Paul Guillaume, Paris ; Mme Jean Walter, Paris ;

Musée de l'Orangerie, Par s, Collection Jean Walter-Paul Guillaume.

This gouache is the intermediary step between the watercolor (XV. 60) and the final composition (XV. 62). Here the young girl's body is elongated and closely matched to the forward movement of the man's (cf. XV. 58).

XV. 62
COMPOSITION : THE PEASANTS
Paris, August, 1906.
Oil on canvas.
Size : 218.5 x 129.5 cm.
Unsigned.

Bibl. Z. I. 384. Albert C. Barnes, *The Art in Painting,* New York, 1937, p. 59.

Coll. Ambroise Vollard, Paris ; Acquired in 1913 by Albert C. Barnes, Merion ;

Barnes Foundation, Merion, Pa.

This important large-scale composition is the result of the studies begun at Gosol (cf. XV. 56–61). According to Barr, it was inspired in part by El Greco, whose *Saint Joseph and the Infant Jesus* Picasso could have seen in reproduction. Picasso's letter to Leo Stein (cf. XV. 59 and Appendix, page 339) proves that this final version of *The Peasants* was done in Paris, in August, 1906, after his return from Gosol. Barr sees in the "free deformation of natural forms" in this major work the prefiguration of Cubism.

D. XV. 1
FEMALE NUDE FROM THE BACK, AND CHILD
Gosol, summer, 1906.
Charcoal on paper.
Size : 22 x 10 cm.
Signed bottom right : Picasso.

Bibl. Not in Z.

Coll. Kornfeld & Klipstein, Bern, May, 1964, Sale
No. 112, cat. No. 1081, repr. pl. 38 ;

Collection M. and Mme David Josefowitz, Geneva.

D. XV. 2
FEMALE NUDE AND CHILD
Gosol, summer, 1906.
Charcoal on paper.
Dimensions not available.
Signed bottom left : Picasso.

Bibl. Not in Z. *The Cone Collection,* Baltimore,
1934, pl. 104 b. Ponge and Chessex, pl. 40.

Coll. Miss Etta and Dr. Claribel Cone, Baltimore ;

Baltimore Museum of Art, The Cone Collection.

The model is probably Fernande (see also : D. XV. 1,
3 and 5).

D. XV. 3
FEMALE NUDE FROM THE BACK, AND CHILD
Gosol, summer, 1906.
Blue and sepia watercolor on paper.
Size : 24 x 16 cm.
Signed bottom right : Picasso.

Exh. Musée Réattu, Arles, 1957 : *Picasso,* No. 11.

Bibl. Z. VI. 719. Catalogue, Galerie Bollag, Zurich,
April, 1925, No. 159, pl. 30.

Coll. G. and L. Bollag, Zurich ; Max G. Bollag,
Zurich ;

Present location unknown.

D. XV. 4
NUDE FROM THE BACK
Summer, 1906.
Graphite pencil on paper.
Size : 16.5 x 10.5 cm.
Signed bottom right : Picasso.
Verso : Head of a Woman (D. XV. 21).

Bibl. Unpublished.

Coll. Cherbsky, Paris ;

Collection Georges Charensol, Paris.

D. XV. 5
NUDE FROM THE BACK, AND CLASPED HANDS
Gosol, summer, 1906.
Black crayon on paper.
Size : 31.5 x 25 cm.
Signed bottom right : Picasso.

Bibl. Not in Z.

Coll. Walter S. Brewster, Chicago ;

*Art Institute of Chicago, Bequest of Walter S.
Brewster.*

The clasped hands sketched on this sheet are the
ones of the woman and child in D. XV. 1, 2, 3.

D. XV. 6
NUDE CHILD
Gosol, summer, 1906.
Charcoal on paper.
Size : 24 x 15 cm.
Signed bottom right : Picasso.

Bibl. Not in Z. Ponge and Chessex, pl. 53.

Coll. G. and L. Bollag, Zurich ; Mme B. Bollag,
Zurich ;

Collection M. and Mme F. Kirchheimer, Küsnacht.

Study for the child in D. XV. 1, 2, and especially 3.

D. XV. 7
FEMALE NUDE FROM THE BACK
Summer, 1906.
Watercolor on paper.
Size : 37 x 24.5 cm.
Signed top left : Picasso.

Bibl. Z. I. 226. Merli, 1948.

Coll. Paul Guillaume, Paris ;

Present location unknown.

Zervos dates this 1905. But it is incontestably close to the series D. XV. 1–5, and to D. XV. 14.

D. XV. 8
WOMAN AND NUDE CHILD
Summer, 1906.
Watercolor on paper.
Dimensions not known.
Unsigned (?).

Bibl. Z. I. 315 (dated 1905).

Coll. E. Bonnet, Paris ;

Present location unknown.

We know this work only through the Zervos documentation.

D. XV. 9
NUDE CHILD
Summer, 1906.
Pen drawing.
Size : 38 x 27 cm.
Signed bottom left : Picasso.

Bibl. Not in Z. *The Cone Collection,* Baltimore, 1934, pl. 106 a. Helen Kay, 1965, p. 80.

Coll. Miss Etta and Dr. Claribel Cone, Baltimore ;

Baltimore Museum of Art, The Cone Collection.

D. XV. 10
NUDE YOUTH
Gosol, summer, 1906.
Pencil drawing.
Size : 17 x 10 cm.
Signed bottom left : Picasso.

Bibl. Not in Z.

Collection Berggruen, Paris.

Related to the series of preparatory drawings for *The Two Brothers* (XV. 9) and *The Two Youths* (XV. 10).

D. XV. 11
BOY WITH UNDERDRAWERS
Gosol, summer, 1906.
Pencil and wash.
Dimensions not available.
Unsigned.

Bibl. Z. I. 356. Ponge and Chessex, pl. 52.

Coll. Ambroise Vollard, Paris ;

Collection Berggruen, Paris.

Related to the young *Swineherd* (Z. VI. 876), and to the drawings Z. I. 358, Z. VI. 926 and 1462. See the following entry.

D. XV. 12
BOY WITH UNDERDRAWERS, FROM THE BACK
Gosol, summer, 1906.
Pencil drawing.
Size : 17 x 11 cm.
Signed bottom left : Picasso.

Bibl. Not in Z.

Coll. G. and L. Bollag, Zurich ; Galerie Bollag, Zurich, Sale, April 3, 1925, No. 166, repr. pl. 62 ;

Present location unknown.

D. XV. 13
NUDE ARRANGING HER HAIR, FROM THE BACK
1906.
Brush drawing and wash on paper.
Size : 41 x 27 cm.
Signed bottom right : Picasso.

Exh. Kunstmuseum, Basel, 1956 : *Collection R. Staechelin,* No. 53. Musée National d'Art Moderne, Paris, 1964 : *Fondation Rodolphe Staechelin,* No. 49, repr.

Bibl. Not in Z.

Rodolphe Staechelin Foundation, Basel.

D. XV. 14
NUDE ARRANGING HER HAIR, FROM THE BACK
1906.
Pen drawing on paper.
Size : 41 x 30 cm.
Signed on the back : Picasso.

Exh. Oslo, 1956 : *Picasso,* No. 9. Galerie Beyeler, Basel, 1966–1967 : *Picasso,* No. 10, repr.

Bibl. Not in Z.

Coll. Roede, Oslo ; Sotheby & Co., London, Sale, December 1, 1965 ;

Private collection, Lausanne.

A version, from the back, of *Nude Arranging her Hair* (Z. VI. 739 : a sheet from a sketchbook of 1906).

D. XV. 15
WOMAN AT HER TOILETTE
1906.
Pen drawing on paper.
Size : 35.5 x 25.5 cm.
Signed on the back : Picasso.

Exh. Musée de l'Athénée, Geneva, 1963 : *Picasso,* No. 11, repr.

Bibl. Not in Z.

Coll. Berggruen, Paris ;

Collection Mr. and Mrs. Leigh B. Block, Chicago.

D. XV. 16
STUDIES OF NUDES
1906.
Pen on paper.
Size : 31 x 41 cm.
Signed bottom left : Picasso.

Bibl. Not in Z.

Collection Berggruen, Paris.

D. XV. 17
STANDING NUDE, HANDS CLASPED
1906.
Pencil on paper.
Size : 17 x 11 cm.
Signed bottom left : Picasso.
Verso : Woman with Head Bent (D. XVI. 1).

Bibl. Not in Z.

Collection Siegfried Rosengart, Lucerne.

Related in pose to the nudes with clasped hands (XV. 25–28). Cf. in Z., a variant of the head of the same model (Z. VI. 852).

D. XV. 18
RECLINING NUDE
1906.
Pen drawing.
Size : 26 x 34 cm.
Signed bottom left : Picasso.

Bibl. Not in Z.

Collection Berggruen, Paris.

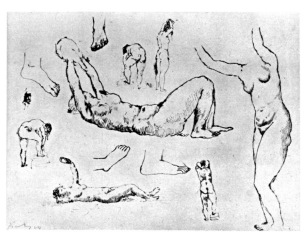

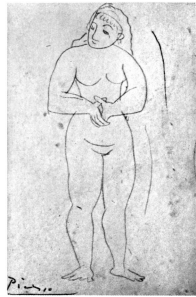

D. XV. 19
HEAD OF A DONKEY
Gosol, summer, 1906.
Ink on paper.
Size : 17 x 11 cm.
Unsigned. Signed on verso.
Verso : Woman on a Donkey (D. XV. 20).

Bibl. Unpublished.

Coll. G. and L. Bollag, Zurich ; Mme B. Bollag, Zurich ;

Collection M. and Mme F. Kirchheimer, Küsnacht.

D. XV. 20
WOMAN ON A DONKEY
(in front of the Pedraforca)
Gosol, summer, 1906.
Ink on paper.
Size : 17 x 11 cm.
Signed top left : Picasso.
Recto : Head of a Donkey (D. XV. 19).

Bibl. Unpublished.

Coll. Cf. D. XV. 19.

Collection M. and Mme F. Kirchheimer, Küsnacht.

Behind the woman is the Pedraforca, the mountain which overlooks Gosol in the Sierra del Cadi.

D. XV. 21
HEAD OF A WOMAN
1906.
Ink and wash on paper.
Size : 16.5 x 10.5 cm.
Signed top right : Picasso.
Recto : Nude from the Back (D. XV. 4).

Bibl. Unpublished.

Coll. Cherbsky, Paris ;

Collection Georges Charensol, Paris.

D. XV. 22
STANDING NUDE
Gosol, summer, 1906.
Graphite pencil on paper.
Size : 12 x 7.5 cm.
Unsigned.

Bibl. Not in Z. Douglas Cooper, *Picasso, Carnet Catalan*, p. 53.

Owned by the artist.

Page 53 of the Catalan notebook. According to Cooper this drawing is a study for an unpublished boxwood sculpture (h. about 1 m.).

D. XV. 23
WOMAN IN PROFILE
Gosol, summer, 1906.
India ink on paper.
Size : 12 x 7.5 cm.
Unsigned.

Bibl. Not in Z. Douglas Cooper, *Picasso, Carnet Catalan*, p. 3.

Owned by the artist.

Page 3 of the Catalan notebook. Study for a sculpture in wood (cf. note, D. XV. 22).

D. XV. 24
THREE FEMALE NUDES ON A STAND
Gosol, summer, 1906.
Graphite pencil on paper.
Size : 12 x 7.5 cm.
Unsigned.

Bibl. Not in Z. Douglas Cooper, *Picasso, Carnet Catalan*, p. 5. Blunt and Pool, No. 172. Palau i Fabre, No. 110.

Owned by the artist.

Page 5 of the Catalan notebook. According to Cooper, this is a study for an unexecuted sculpture *(The Three Graces).*

D. XV. 25
NUDE WITH KERCHIEF
Gosol, summer, 1906.
Graphite pencil on paper.
Size : 12 x 7.5 cm.
Unsigned.

Bibl. Not in Z. Douglas Cooper, *Picasso, Carnet Catalan,* p. 47.

Owned by the artist.

Page 47 of the Catalan notebook. Sketch for *Fernande with Kerchief* (XV. 45).

D. XV. 26
PROFILE OF FERNANDE WITH KERCHIEF
Gosol, summer, 1906.
Graphite pencil on paper.
Size : 12 x 7.5 cm.
Unsigned.

Bibl. Not in Z. Douglas Cooper, *Picasso, Carnet Catalan,* p. 10.

Owned by the artist.

Page 10 of the Catalan notebook. Sketch for *Fernande with Kerchief* (XV. 45). Cf. variants : Z. VI. 754, 755, 756, 760.

D. XV. 27
WOMAN IN CATALAN COSTUME
Gosol, summer, 1906.
India ink on paper.
Size : 12 x 7.5 cm.
Unsigned.

Bibl. Not in Z. Douglas Cooper, *Picasso, Carnet Catalan,* p. 70. Blunt and Pool, No. 171.

Owned by the artist.

Page 70 of the Catalan notebook.

D. XV. 28
THE COUPLE
Gosol, summer, 1906.
Pen drawing.
Size : 21 x 12.8 cm.
Signed bottom right : Picasso.

Bibl. Unpublished.

Coll. Bought from the artist in 1918 by G. and L. Bollag, Zurich ;

Private collection, Zurich.

Cf. variations of the same subject : Z. I. 339, Z. VI. 771, 780, 782 ; Ponge and Chessex, pl. 17.

D. XV. 29
TWO DANCING COUPLES
Gosol, summer, 1906.
India ink on paper.
Size : 7.5 x 12 cm.
Unsigned.

Bibl. Not in Z. Douglas Cooper, *Picasso, Carnet Catalan,* p. 67.

Owned by the artist.

Page 67 of the Catalan notebook. At the right : two clasped hands, with the note : *mano de mujer, derecha* (woman's right hand).

D. XV. 30
WOMAN IN CATALAN COSTUME
(and study of clasped hands)
Gosol, summer, 1906.
India ink on paper.
Size : 12 x 7.5 cm.
Unsigned.

Bibl. Not in Z. Douglas Cooper, *Picasso, Carnet Catalan,* p. 35.

Owned by the artist.

Page 35 of the Catalan notebook. The study at the right of the two clasped hands is related to the series of nudes with clasped hands (XV. 25–28).

D. XV. 31
NUDE : THE PITCHER-CARRIER'S POSE
Gosol, summer, 1906.
Graphite pencil on paper.
Size : 12 x 7.5 cm.
Unsigned.

Bibl. Not in Z. Douglas Cooper, *Picasso, Carnet Catalan,* p. 50.

Owned by the artist.

Page 50 of the Catalan notebook. Sketch of a nude in the same pose as the woman in the following entry.   Cf. also *The Adolescents* (XV. 11) and Z. VI. 516.

D. XV. 32
WOMAN CARRYING A PITCHER
Gosol, summer, 1906.
Black lead drawing.
Dimensions not available.
Signed top left : Picasso.

Bibl. Not in Z. *The Cone Collection,* Baltimore, 1934, pl. 107 b.

Coll. Miss Etta and Dr. Claribel Cone, Baltimore ;

Baltimore Museum of Art, The Cone Collection.

D. XV. 33
HEAD OF A WOMAN IN PROFILE
Gosol, summer, 1906.
India ink and wash.
Size : 40 x 30 cm.
Signed bottom right : Picasso.

Bibl. Not in Z.

Collection Berggruen, Paris.

The same profile and headdress of this woman appear again in the drawing D. XV. 36 (and in Z. VI. 633).

D. XV. 34
WOMAN RETURNING FROM MARKET
Gosol, summer, 1906.
Pen drawing.
Dimensions not available.
Signed bottom left : Picasso.

Bibl. Not in Z.   *The Cone Collection,* Baltimore, 1934, pl. 104 a. *Handbook of the Cone Collection,* Baltimore Museum of Art, 1955, p. 22. Elgar and Maillard, 1955, p. 49.

Coll. Miss Etta and Dr. Claribel Cone, Baltimore ;

Baltimore Museum of Art, The Cone Collection.

D. XV. 35
BUST OF FEMALE NUDE IN PROFILE
Gosol, summer, 1906.
Pen drawing.
Dimensions not available.
Unsigned (?).

Bibl. Not in Z. Waldemar George, 1926, pl. 2. *The Cone Collection,* Baltimore, 1934, pl. 107 a. Maurice Gieure, 1951, pl. 119. Ponge and Chessex, pl. 21.

Coll. Michael Stein, Vaucresson ;   Miss Etta and Dr. Claribel Cone, Baltimore ;

Baltimore Museum of Art, The Cone Collection.

D. XV. 36
YOUNG WOMAN STANDING IN PROFILE
Gosol, summer, 1906.
Black lead on paper.
Size : 59.6 x 45 cm.
Signed twice on the back : Picasso.

Exh. Toronto and Montreal, 1964 : *Picasso and Man,* No. 32, repr. p. 48.

Bibl. Not in Z. Wildenstein, *The Art of Drawing,* 1953, No. 126. Jean Sutherland Boggs in *The Connoisseur,* CLV, 1964, Fig. 2.

Coll. Huldschinsky, Berlin ;   Mme A. Furstenberg, Amsterdam ;   Wildenstein & Co., London ;   Since 1953 :

The National Gallery of Canada, Ottawa.

Cf. D. XV. 33 (and Z. VI. 633).

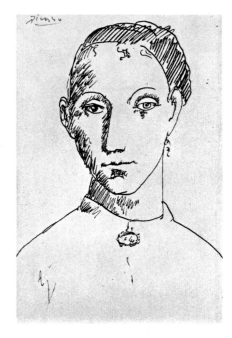

D. XV. 37
HEAD OF A WOMAN
Gosol, summer, 1906.
Pen drawing on paper.
Size : 21 x 13.5 cm.
Signed top left : Picasso.

Exh. Musée Réattu, Arles, 1957 : *Picasso,* No. 12, repr. in cat. pl. 6.

Bibl. Not in Z. Ponge and Chessex, pl. 16.

Collection Berggruen, Paris.

See note in following entry (D. XV. 38).

D. XV. 38
HEAD OF A WOMAN
Gosol, summer, 1906.
Pen on paper.
Size : 59 x 43 cm.
Signed bottom left : Picasso.

Bibl. Unpublished.

Coll. G. and L. Bollag, Zurich ; Galerie Bollag, Zurich, Sale, April 3, 1925, No. 157, pl. 58 ;

Present location unknown.

Related to the gouache XV. 55, and to the drawing D. XV. 28. Cf. the variants in Zervos : Z. VI. 762, 764, 780, 786.

D. XV. 39
HEAD OF A WOMAN
1906.
Pencil on paper.
Size : 18 x 12 cm.
Signed top left : Picasso.
Recto : Study for The Peasants (XV. 57).

Bibl. Not in Z. Ponge and Chessex, pl. 49.

Coll. G. and L. Bollag, Zurich ; Mme B. Bollag, Zurich ;

Collection M. and Mme F. Kirchheimer, Küsnacht.

D. XV. 40
TWO CHILDREN PLAYING BALL
1906.
India ink on paper.
Size : 21 x 18 cm.
Signed bottom right : Picasso.

Exh. Oslo, 1956 : *Picasso,* No. 30.

Bibl. Not in Z. Catalogue, Galerie Bollag, Zurich, April 1925, No. 168, pl. 62.

Coll. G. and L. Bollag, Zurich ; Galerie Bollag, Zurich, Sale, April 21, 1934, No. 97 ;

Collection Berggruen, Paris.

A variant of this theme is reproduced page 97. Cf. also Z. VI. 388 (incorrectly dated 1901–1902).

D. XV. 41
VASE OF FLOWERS
Summer, 1906.
Ink drawing.
Size : 26.3 x 18.4 cm.
Signed top left : Picasso.

Exh. The Solomon R. Guggenheim Museum, New York, 1965 : *Masterpieces of Modern Art from the Thannhauser Foundation,* No. 40, repr. p. 44.

Bibl. Not in Z. Champris, 1960, No. 251.

Coll. Justin K. Thannhauser, New York ;

The Solomon R. Guggenheim Museum, New York, Justin K. Thannhauser Foundation.

D. XV. 42
FLOWERS AND PITCHER
Gosol, summer, 1906.
Ink and watercolor.
Size : 40 x 30 cm.
Signed bottom right : Picasso.

Exh. Galerie Suzanne Bollag, Zurich, 1960 : *Contrastes II.*

Bibl. Z. VI. 723 (dated 1905). Catalogue, Galerie Bollag, Zurich, April 1925, No. 158, pl. 60. Idem, November 1930, No. 100, pl. XXIX.

Coll. G. and L. Bollag, Zurich ; Mme B. Bollag, Zurich ;

Collection Mlle Suzanne Bollag, Zurich.

NUDE ON RED BACKGROUND, PARIS, SUMMER-AUTUMN 1906, OIL.
COLLECTION JEAN WALTER – PAUL GUILLAUME, PARIS (XVI. 8).

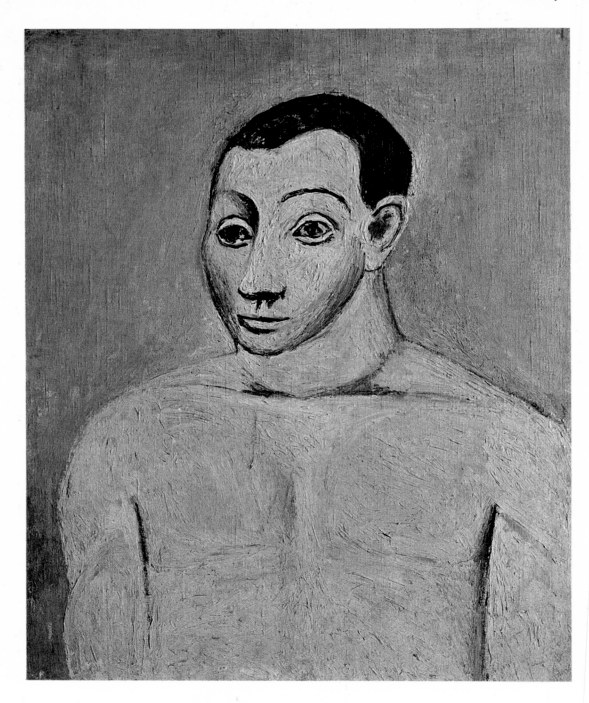

BUST OF A MAN, PARIS, AUTUMN 1906, OIL. COLLECTION OF THE ARTIST.
UNPUBLISHED IN COLOR (XVI. 26).

Toward Cubism, Paris, Autumn 1906

Unlike many of the previous canvases of 1906, the ones in this section have always been correctly attributed to the second half of 1906. It is clear enough that they are transitional, leading to the period that immediately preceded *Les Demoiselles d'Avignon*, and also they were seen by a considerable number of visitors at the Bateau-Lavoir. Picasso did not leave Paris in 1907. This fact has made it easier to classify works and, more important, to follow the technical stages by which the break with traditional painting occurred.

However, the difficulties are not all eliminated. Even if it is virtually impossible to recognize which canvases were actually completed at Gosol, considering the abrupt departure, it is not all that important for our purposes. Until the *Two Nudes* (XVI. 15), the dominant colors were still the reds of Gosol, with the one exception of the *Two Nudes* (XVI. 13), which is modeled in dull tones of brown and green, not unlike the palette

of the *Portrait of Gertrude Stein*. The self-portrait and the cylindrical female nudes are executed in very pale, washed colors. The last studies of women are in red on a white, usually unpainted ground. From now on, color assumes a different role. Forms are built up with hatching. Flat tones appear less often and seem composed of blended hatchings. And instead of curvilinear forms, Picasso regularly substitutes planes with rectilinear outlines.

The studies and preparatory drawings are exceptionally interesting because of these experiments in geometric simplification. We have included them among the paintings whenever they appeared essential to an understanding of Picasso's creative method.

The chronological limits of this period are largely arbitrary. We have concluded the catalogue with works done in the autumn of 1906 — in other words, at the turning-point when Picasso's works directly prefigure *Les Demoiselles d'Avignon*.

XVI. 1
TWO HEADS OF WOMEN
Summer–autumn, 1906.
Gouache. Size : 62 x 47 cm.
Signed bottom right : Picasso.

Exh. Contemporary Arts Museum, Houston, 1953. Houston Museum of Fine Arts, October 20–December 11, 1960 : *Gauguin to Gorky.*

Bibl. Z. I. 335.

Coll. Miss Ima Hogg, Houston ;

Museum of Fine Arts, Houston (on loan, Miss Ima Hogg Collection).

Related to D. XVI. 1.

XVI. 2
HEAD OF A WOMAN IN PROFILE
(Fernande)
Summer–autumn, 1906.
Gouache. Size : 32 x 40 cm.
Signed bottom right : Picasso.

Exh. Galerie Liljevalch, Stockholm, 1926, 1927 and 1938. National-museum, Stockholm, 1931. Kiruna,

Sweden, September 1965 : *Picasso i Kiruna,* No. 33.

Bibl. Not in Z.

Coll. Svensk-Franska Konstgalleriet, Stockholm, 1921, price : 1500 kronor ;

Prins Eugens Waldemarsudde Museum, Stockholm.

XVI. 3
WOMAN SEWING
Paris, summer–autumn, 1906.
Gouache on paper.
Size : 75 x 55 cm.
Signed top right : Picasso.

Exh. Musée Réattu, Arles, 1957 : *Picasso,* No. 14, repr. pl. 7.

Bibl. Z. I. 314 (dated 1905). Sutton, 1955, No. 63.

Coll. Ida Bienert, Germany ;

Private collection, France.

According to Douglas Cooper (Arles catalogue), Picasso did this gouache in Paris, after his return from Gosol. Cf. an unpublished study for this work reproduced in the Addenda, No. A. 21.

XVI. 4
WOMAN WITH HEAD BENT
FORWARD
Paris, summer–autumn, 1906.
Oil on canvas.
Size : 51 x 39.5 cm.
Signed on the back : Picasso.

Exh. Munich, Cologne, Hamburg, 1955–1956 : *Picasso 1900–1955,* No. 15, repr. in cat.

Bibl. Z. I. 351. Sutton, 1955, No. 55.

Coll. Paul von Mendelssohn-Bartholdy, Berlin ;

Staatsgalerie, Stuttgart.

One of the first examples of Picasso's experiments with the effects of perspective in the human face. The development of this style leads to the break with the classical rules of resemblance, as seen in the later works (end of 1906, and 1907).

XVI. 5
WOMAN WITH A COMB
Paris, summer–autumn, 1906.
Gouache. Size: 139 x 57 cm.
Signed bottom right: Picasso.

Exh. Musée de l'Orangerie des Tuileries, Paris, 1966: *Collection Jean Walter-Paul Guillaume,* No. 96, repr. in cat. p. 202.

Bibl. Z. I. 337. Waldemar George, *La grande peinture contemporaine à la collection Paul Guillaume,* p. 118.

Coll. Paul Guillaume, Paris; Mme Jean Walter, Paris;

Musée de l'Orangerie, Paris, Collection Jean Walter-Paul Guillaume.

This nude is related to the *Two Nudes* (XVI. 12–14). Picasso is interested here in the reality of his conception and in its tactile coherence. There is some evidence of concern with sculpture. But Picasso turns rarely to sculpture, as if it were only a means of controlling pictorial qualities (see XVI. 6). (Cf. the studies Z. VI. 627, 743.)

Color plate, page 93.

XVI. 6
KNEELING NUDE ARRANGING HER HAIR
Paris, summer–autumn, 1906.
Oil on wood panel.
Size: 35.7 x 21.6 cm.
Signed top left: Picasso.

Bibl. Not in Z. *City Art Museum Bulletin,* Vol. XIX, No. 4, St. Louis, October 1934.

Coll. Theodore Schempp;

City Art Museum of St. Louis.

This is a study in oil for the bronze sculpture *La Coiffure* (H. 42 cm., issued by Vollard, repr. Z. I. 329). Zervos catalogues two pencil sketches of the same subject (Z. I. 341, Z. VI. 751).

XVI. 7
LA COIFFURE
Paris, summer–autumn, 1906.
Oil on canvas. Size: 126 x 90.7 cm.
Signed bottom left: Picasso.

Exh. Chicago, 1933: *Century of Progress,* No. 406. Wadsworth Atheneum, 1934: *Picasso,* No. 19, repr. in cat. Jacques Seligmann, New York, 1936: *Picasso, Blue and Rose,* No. 33, repr. MMA, New York, 1955: *Paintings from Private Collections,* cat. p. 6. New York and Chicago, 1957: *Picasso, 75th Anniversary Exhibition,* repr. p. 30. Philadelphia, 1958: *Picasso,* No. 32, repr. New York, Chicago, St. Louis, Mexico, San Francisco, Denver,

1965–1966: *The School of Paris, Paintings from the Florene May Schoenborn and Samuel A. Marx Collection,* repr. in color in cat. p. 18.

Bibl. Z. I. 336 (dated 1905). Catalogue, *John Quinn Collection,* 1926, p. 87. C. J. Bulliet, 1936, pl. 107. Douglas Cooper, *Great Private Collections,* 1963, p. 287.

Coll. John Quinn, New York; Mrs. Edward A. Jordan, New York; Marie Harriman Gallery, New York; Mr. and Mrs. Samuel A. Marx, Chicago;

Collection Florene M. Schoenborn and Samuel A. Marx, New York.

XVI. 8
NUDE ON RED BACKGROUND
(Young Woman with Loose Hair)
Paris, summer–autumn, 1906.
Oil on canvas.
Size : 81 x 54 cm.
Signed top right : Picasso.

Exh. Galerie Georges Petit, Paris, 1932 : *Picasso,* No. 30. Kunsthaus, Zurich, 1932 : *Picasso,* No. 32. Musée de l'Orangerie, Paris, 1966 : *Collection Jean Walter-Paul Guillaume,* No. 95, repr. p. 200. Grand Palais, Paris, November 1966–February 1967 :

Hommage à Pablo Picasso, No. 37, repr. in cat.

Bibl. Z. I. 328 (dated 1905). Waldemar George, p. 119. Paul Eluard, 1944, p. 71. Daix, 1964, p. 54 (color).

Coll. Ambroise Vollard, Paris ; Paul Guillaume, Paris ; Mme Jean Walter, Paris ;

Musée de l'Orangerie, Paris, Collection Jean Walter-Paul Guillaume.

Color plate, page 317.

XVI. 9
NUDE COMBING HER HAIR
Paris, autumn, 1906.
Oil on canvas.
Size : 104.1 x 79.4 cm.
Signed top right : Picasso.

Exh. Galerie Georges Petit, Paris, 1932 : *Picasso* No. 39. Kunsthaus, Zurich, 1932 : *Picasso,* No. 34. Jacques Seligmann, New York, 1936 : *Picasso,* No. 34, repr. Tate Gallery, London, 1960 : *Picasso,* No. 31, repr. pl. 10 a.

Bibl. Z. I. 344.

Coll. Ambroise Vollard, Paris ; Jacques Ulmann, Paris ;

Private collection, Paris.

In this painting Picasso reappraises all the traditional plastic values of the female nude and the relations of its movements. The composition as a whole comes directly from the nudes combing their hair in the *Harem* (XV. 40).

XVI. 10
PORTRAIT OF GERTRUDE STEIN
Paris, autumn, 1906.
Oil on canvas (relined).
Size : 100 x 81.3 cm.
Unsigned.

Exh. Petit Palais, Paris, 1937 : *Les Maîtres de l'art indépendant,* No. 11. New York and Chicago, 1939–1940 : *Picasso, Forty Years of his Art,* No. 65, repr. Knoedler, New York, 1947 : *Picasso before 1907,* No. 33. San Francisco and Portland, 1948 : *Picasso, Gris, Miró,* No. 3. Yale University and Baltimore, 1951 : *Pictures for a Picture of Gertrude Stein,* No. 29. Paris, 1955 : *Picasso,* No. 12, repr. New York and Chicago, 1957 : *Picasso, 75th Anniversary,* repr. p. 29. Philadelphia, 1958 : *Picasso,* No. 36. Paris, 1966–1967 : *Hommage à Pablo Picasso,* No. 38, repr.

Bibl. Z. I. 352. Gertrude Stein, 1933, p. 56. R. Escholier, 1937, p. 81, G. Stein, 1938, pl. 22 (color). Barr, *Forty Years,* p. 56. Cassou, 1940, p. 41 (color). Wilenski, 1940, p. 200–219. Merli, 1942, p. 53. Wheeler, 1942, p. 52. Dorival, 1944, p. 230. Barr, *Fifty Years,* p. 50. Leo Stein,

1947, p. 174. P. O. Zennström, 1948, fig. 12. Florent Fels, 1950, p. 225. Lieberman, 1954, pl. 33 (color). Sabartés and Boeck, p. 460, No. 35. Elgar and Maillard, 1955 (cat.). J. Camón Aznar, 1956, fig. 272. Penrose, 1957, fig. 67. Vallentin, 1957, p. 136. Penrose, 1958, pl. IV, No. 1. A. B. Saarinen, 1958. L. G. Buchheim, 1959, p. 48. Golding, 1959, pl. 79 b. Daix, 1964, pl. 52 (color). Boudaille, 1964, pl. XVI (color).

Coll. Gertrude Stein, Paris ;

Metropolitan Museum of Art, New York, Bequest of Gertrude Stein, 1946.

This famous portrait was begun during the winter of 1905–06. In the spring Picasso rubbed out the head. He completed the painting in the autumn of 1906, after he returned from Gosol. Without seeing Gertrude Stein, he painted the mask-like face, a sign of his increasingly vigorous sculptural forms (see XVI. 15, 22–30, D. XVI. 22–24).

Color plate, page 95.

XVI. 11
TWO NUDES
Paris, autumn, 1906.
Watercolor and ink on paper.
Size : 21.2 x 13.5 cm.
Signed bottom left : Picasso Fecit.

Exh. Frankfurt and Hamburg, 1965, No. 30, repr. in color in cat.

Bibl. Not in Z. Ponge and Chessex, pl. 22.

Coll. Mme Gaston Bernheim de Villers, Monte Carlo ; Paul Rosenberg, Paris ; Galerie Berggruen, Paris ; Kornfeld & Klipstein, Bern, Sale No. 100, June 8, 1961, No. 81, repr. in color p. 161 ;

Collection Herbert Liesenfeld, Düsseldorf.

Study for XVI. 13. On the back : pencil sketch of a hand, and imprint of a French coin.

XVI. 12
TWO NUDES
Paris, autumn, 1906.
Gouache and charcoal.
Size : 64 x 48 cm.
Signed top left : Picasso.

Bibl. Not in Z. *The Cone Collection,* Catalogue, Baltimore, 1934, pl. 63. *Handbook of the Cone Collection,* Baltimore Museum of Art, 1955, No. 95.

Coll. Miss Etta and Dr. Claribel Cone, Baltimore ;

Baltimore Museum of Art, The Cone Collection.

Study for XVI. 13 and 14.

XVI. 13
TWO NUDES
Paris, autumn, 1906.
Oil on canvas.
Size : 151 x 100 cm.
Signed bottom right : Picasso.

Exh. Galerie Georges Petit, Paris, 1932 : *Picasso,* No. 40. Kunsthaus, Zurich, 1932 : *Picasso,* No. 35, repr. in cat. pl. V.

Bibl. Z. I. 360. Raynal and Lassaigne, 1950, p. 41 (color). Elgar and Mail-lard, 1955 (catalogue). Sutton, 1955, No. 58. Raynal, 1959, p. 37 (color).

Coll. Joseph Müller, Solothurn ;

Private collection, Switzerland.

The handling of the woman at the right is close to the almost mono-chrome and low-relief modeling of the Gosol period combined with the geometric simplifications of the face and the solidity which anticipate *Two Nudes* (XVI. 15).

XVI. 14
NUDE FROM THE FRONT
AND NUDE IN PROFILE
Paris, autumn, 1906.
Gouache on paper mounted on cloth.
Size : 58.5 x 43.2 cm.
Signed bottom right : Picasso.

Exh. New York, Milwaukee, Utica, Kansas City, 1941–1942 : *Picasso, Epochs of his Art.* Galerie Beyeler, Basel, November 1966–January 1967 : *Picasso 1900–1932,* No. 7, repr. in color in cat.

Bibl. Z. I. 361 and VI. 888.

Coll. Ambroise Vollard, Paris ; Marcel Fleischmann, Zurich ; J. K. Thann-hauser, New York ; Mr. and Mrs. Adolphe A. Juviler, New York ; Parke-Bernet, New York, Sale No. 2056, October 25, 1961 : *Collection of Mr. and Mrs. Adolphe A. Juviler,* No. 19, repr. in color in cat. p. 29 ;

Collection Walter D. Floersheimer, Orselina, Switzerland.

TWO NUDES, PARIS, AUTUMN 1906, OIL. THE MUSEUM OF MODERN ART, NEW YORK, GIFT OF
G. DAVID THOMPSON IN HONOR OF ALFRED H. BARR, JR. (XVI. 15).

XVI. 15
TWO NUDES
Paris, autumn, 1906.
Oil on canvas.
Size : 151.3 x 93 cm.
Signed bottom left : Picasso.

Exh. Galerie Georges Petit, Paris, summer, 1932 : *Picasso,* No. 41. Kunsthaus, Zurich, autumn, 1932 : *Picasso,* No. 36. Museum of Modern Art, New York, and The Art Institute of Chicago, 1939–1940 : *Picasso, Forty Years of his Art,* No. 67, repr. in cat. p. 58. Palazzo Reale, Milan, 1953 : *Picasso,* No. 6, repr. in cat. Museum of Modern Art, New York, May 31–September 7, 1955 : *Paintings from Private Collections,* cat. No. 111. MMA, New York, and The Art Institute of Chicago, 1957 : *Picasso, 75th Anniversary Exhibition,* repr. in cat. p. 31. Philadelphia Museum of Art, 1958 : *Picasso.* MMA, New York, October 8–November 9, 1958 : *Works of Art Given or Promised.* MMA, New York, 1962 : *Picasso, 80th Birthday Exhibition.*

Bibl. Z. I. 366. Barr, *Forty Years,* p. 58. Gómez de la Serna, 1944, pl. IX. Barr, *Fifty Years,* p. 52. Merli, 1948, p. 157. Cassou, 1949, pl. 20. Fernanda Wittgens, 1954, pl. 3 (repr. in color). Penrose, 1958, pl. IV, No. 5.

Coll. Paul Rosenberg, Paris ; Rosenberg & Helft, London ; Keith Warner, Vermont ; E. & A. Silberman Galleries, New York ; G. David Thompson, Pittsburgh ;

The Museum of Modern Art, New York, Gift of G. David Thompson in honor of Alfred H. Barr, Jr.

Color plate on preceding page.

XVI. 16
TWO FEMALE NUDES
Paris, autumn, 1906.
Charcoal drawing.
Size : 63 x 47 cm.

Exh. New York and Chicago, 1957 : *Picasso, 75th Anniversary,* repr. in cat. p. 30.

Bibl. Not in Z.

Collection Mr. and Mrs. Richard S. Davis, Wayzata.

The pose of the standing figure is also used in the pastel D. XVI. 13.

XVI. 17
WOMAN SEATED AND WOMAN STANDING
Paris, autumn, 1906.
Charcoal drawing.
Size : 61.5 x 47 cm.
Signed bottom right : Picasso.

Exh. New York and Chicago, 1957, p. 30. Philadelphia, 1958, No. 35. Toronto, 1964, No. 40. Fort Worth Art Center Museum, February 8—March 26, 1967 : *Picasso,* No. 152, repr. in cat. p. 16.

Bibl. Z. I. 368.

Philadelphia Museum of Art, Louise and Walter Arensberg Collection.

XVI. 18
TWO NUDES
Paris, autumn, 1906.
Pencil, stumped. Size : 63 x 47 cm.
Signed on the back : Picasso.

Exh. New York, 1944, p. 42. Chicago, 1946, No. 43. Toronto, 1949, No. 37. New York and Chicago, 1957, p. 31.

Bibl. Not in Z. Trier, 1956, p. 18. Ponge and Chessex, pl. 56.

Coll. Arthur B. Davies ; Frank Crowninshield ; John Graham ;

Art Institute of Chicago, Gift of Mrs. Potter Palmer.
Study for XVI. 15.

XVI. 19
STANDING NUDE
Paris, autumn, 1906.
Pencil on paper.
Size : 62.2 x 45 cm.
Signed bottom right : Picasso.

Exh. Galerie Knoedler, Paris, 1966, No. 29, repr. in cat. Fort Worth, 1967, No. 155.

Bibl. Not in Z.

Collection M. Knoedler & Co., New York.

Closely related to the figure at the left in the drawing XVI. 18. A study for *Two Nudes* (XVI. 15).

XVI. 20
STUDIES OF NUDES
Paris, autumn, 1906.
Pencil on paper.
Size : 13 x 20 cm.
Signed bottom left : Picasso.

Bibl. Not in Z.

Collection Berggruen, Paris.

A sketch which shows, at the left, the final pose of the *Two Nudes* (XVI. 15), and which foreshadows the first studies for *Les Demoiselles d'Avignon.* (Cf. *Three Nudes,* XVI. 32.)

XVI. 21
STUDIES FOR TWO NUDES (XVI. 15)
Paris, autumn, 1906.
Conté crayon on paper.
Size : 61 x 45.1 cm.
Signed bottom left : Picasso.

Bibl. Not in Z.

Coll. Leo Stein, Paris ; Pierre Matisse, New York ;

Museum of Fine Arts, Boston, Arthur Tracy Cabot Foundation.

XVI. 22
HEAD OF A WOMAN
Paris, autumn, 1906.
Oil on canvas.
Dimensions not known.
Unsigned (see note).

Bibl. Z. I. 372 and VI. 894. Sabartés and Boeck, p. 460, No. 37.

Formerly Roger Dutilleul Collection, Paris.

Our photograph is from the Kahnweiler archives. The painting was unsigned when it was taken.

XVI. 23
BUST OF A YOUNG WOMAN
Paris, autumn, 1906.
Oil.
Size : 54 x 42 cm.
Signed top left : Picasso.

Bibl. Z. I. 367. Waldemar George, *La*

grande peinture contemporaine à la collection Paul Guillaume, p. 121 (entitled *Jeune Fille*).

Formerly Paul Guillaume Collection, Paris.

XVI. 24
BUST OF A WOMAN
Paris, autumn, 1906.
Oil on canvas mounted on wood.
Size : 80.2 x 64.2 cm.
Signed top right : Picasso.

Exh. Valentine Gallery, New York, 1936 : *Picasso 1901–1934,* No. 31. Detroit, 1937 : *Walter P. Chrysler, Jr., Collection,* No. 18. San Francisco, 1939–1940 : *Seven Centuries of Painting.* No. 192. Chicago, 1940 : *Origins of Modern Art,* No. 68. Virginia and

Philadelphia, 1941 : *Collection of Walter P. Chrysler, Jr.,* No. 156, repr. Musée des Arts Décoratifs, Paris, 1955 : *Picasso,* No. 13, repr. New York, Chicago, St. Louis, Mexico, San Francisco, Denver, 1965-1966 : *School of Paris, The Florene May Schoenborn and Samuel A. Marx Collection,* repr. p. 16.

Bibl. Z. I. 374. Waldemar George, p. 114. Cassou, 1940, pl. 58.

Coll. Paul Guillaume, Paris ; Valentine Gallery, New York ; Walter P. Chrysler, Jr., New York ; Mr. and Mrs. Samuel A. Marx, Chicago ;

The Art Institute of Chicago, Gift of Mr. and Mrs. Samuel A. Marx.

This work, and the following one, show an increasing geometry of form. The main shapes are cylinders, spheres, and arcs.

XVI. 25
SEATED FEMALE NUDE
Paris, autumn, 1906.
Oil on canvas.
Size : 151 x 100 cm.
Signed top left : Picasso.

Exh. Tate Gallery, London, 1960 : *Picasso,* No. 32, repr. pl. 7 b. Paris, 1966 : *Paris-Prague,* No. 164.

Bibl. Z. I. 373.

National Gallery, Prague.

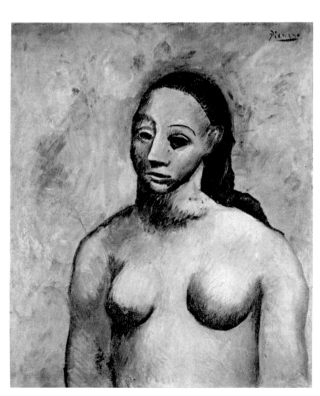

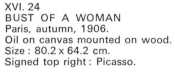

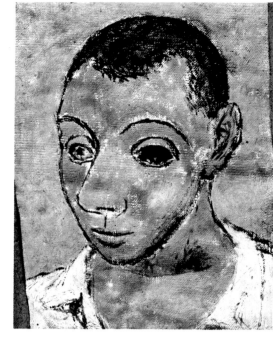

XVI. 26
BUST OF A MAN
Paris, autumn, 1906.
Oil on canvas.
Size : 65 x 54 cm.
Unsigned.

Bibl. Z. II. 1.

Owned by the artist.

This little known work that has never left the artist's private collection is closely related to the *Self-Portrait* (XVI. 28).

Color plate, page 318.

XVI. 27
HEAD OF A YOUNG MAN
Paris, autumn, 1906.
Oil on canvas.
Size : 27 x 19 cm.

Bibl. Z. I. 371. Elgar and Maillard, 1955, p. 47 (repr. in color). Sutton, 1955, No. 52.

Private collection, Paris.

XVI. 28
SELF-PORTRAIT WITH A PALETTE
Paris, autumn, 1906.
Oil on canvas.
Size : 92 x 73 cm.
Signed and dated, bottom left : Picasso 1906.

Exh. Wadsworth Atheneum, 1934, No. 20, repr. New York and Chicago, 1939–1940, No. 66, repr. New York, 1940 : *Gallatin Collection,* No. 102. Paris, 1955, No. 11, repr. Munich, Cologne, Hamburg, 1955–1956, No. 16, repr. New York and Chicago, 1957, repr. p. 29. Philadelphia, 1958, No. 41. London, 1960, No. 30, repr. pl. 10 b. Toronto and Montreal, 1964, No. 44, repr. p. 57. Paris, 1966–1967 : *Hom-*

mage à Pablo Picasso, No. 39, repr.

Bibl. Z. I. 375. Barr, *Forty Years,* p. 57. Barr, *Fifty Years,* p. 51. Sabartés, 1954, No. 92. Elgar and Maillard, 1955 (cat.). Penrose. 1958, pl. IV, No. 3. Canaday, 1959, p. 455. Gasser, 1963, p. 268 (color). Daix, 1964, p. 57 (color). Read, 1965, pl. 50.

Coll. A. E. Gallatin, New York ;

Philadelphia Museum of Art, A. E. Gallatin Collection.

See the studies : Addenda No. A. 22.

Color plate, frontispiece.

XVI. 29
HEAD OF A BOY
Paris, autumn, 1906.
Oil on canvas.
Size : 35.5 x 23 cm.
Signed on the back : Picasso.

Exh. Knoedler, New York, 1962 : *Picasso, an American Tribute,* No. 31, repr. in cat.
Bibl. Z. VI. 892. Helen Kay, 1965, p. 82.

Coll. Mme Helena Rubinstein (Princess Gourielli), New York ; Parke-

Bernet, New York, April 30, 1966 : *Sale of the Helena Rubinstein Collection* (Modern Paintings, First Part), No. 33, repr. in color in cat. p. 57, sold for $40.000 ;

Private collection, U.S.A.

The mask-like face in this small painting (very similar to No. XVI. 27), and especially the treatment of the eyes, are reminiscent of the Iberian sculptures in the Louvre.

XVI. 30
MAN, WOMAN, AND CHILD
Paris, autumn, 1906.
Oil on canvas.
Size : 115 x 88 cm.
Unsigned.

Exh. Paris, 1966–1967 : *Hommage à Pablo Picasso,* No. 40, repr.

Bibl. Z. II. 587. H. Kay, 1965, p. 84.

Owned by the artist.

This large canvas sums up previous experiments : the head of the man is close to XVI. 27 and 29, his torso to XVI. 26 ; the woman's face is similar to XVI. 23 and 15 (figure at the left), her pose to XVI. 20 (seated figure). It is a monochrome work, mainly in tones of grey.

XVI. 31
SEATED MALE NUDE
Paris, autumn, 1906.
Oil on canvas.
Size : 35 x 24 cm.
Unsigned (see note).

Bibl. Z. I. 363. Sutton, 1955, No. 57.

Present location unknown.

Documentation from the Kahnweiler archives. The photograph was taken when this painting had no signature.

XVI. 32
THREE NUDES (Study)
Paris, autumn, 1906.
Oil on canvas.
Size : 25 x 30 cm.
Unsigned.

Bibl. Z. I. 349. Barnes Foundation, Inventory, No. 211.

Barnes Foundation, Merion, Pennsylvania.

This small painting, related to the first studies for *Les Demoiselles d'Avignon,* has at the left a figure similar to the nude at the left in the *Two Nudes* (XVI. 15). See XVI. 18 and 19, and especially XVI. 20. There is also a study of the standing nude at the left in the Barnes Foundation which is a drawing, 18 x 10 cm, signed bottom right.

XVI. 33
NUDE IN PROFILE
Paris, autumn–winter, 1906.
Oil on canvas.
Approximate size : 26 x 21 cm.
Unsigned.

Bibl. Z. I. 350. Barnes Foundation, Inventory, No. 207.

Barnes Foundation, Merion, Pennsylvania.

This curious study is perhaps later than the first part of the winter, 1906 (the pose is the same as the woman in front of the curtain, at the left, in *Les Demoiselles d'Avignon*), but it is related to previous studies of nudes : cf. XVI. 15, 19, and 32.

D. XVI. 1
WOMAN WITH HEAD BENT FORWARD
Summer—autumn, 1906.
India ink and pencil on paper.
Size : 17 x 11 cm.
Signed top left : Picasso.
Verso : Standing Nude (D. XV. 17).

Bibl. Z. VI. 753. Millier, 1961.

Collection Siegfried Rosengart, Lucerne.

Study for *Two Heads of Women* (XVI. 1).

D. XVI. 2
HEAD OF A WOMAN, FROM THE BACK
Summer—autumn, 1906.
Pen and pencil drawing.
Size : 17 x 10.5 cm.
Unsigned.

Bibl. Not in Z.

Coll. Bought from the artist in 1918 by G. and L. Bollag, Zurich ;

Private collection, Zurich.

D. XVI. 3
HEAD OF A WOMAN IN PROFILE
Summer—autumn, 1906.
Watercolor on ruled paper.
Size : 20 x 12.5 cm.
Signed bottom right : Picasso.

Bibl. Z. VI. 752.

Present location unknown.

Related works : Z. VI. 677 and 800.

D. XVI. 4
HEAD OF A WOMAN
Summer—autumn, 1906.
Gouache and color wash on paper.
Size : 47 x 31 cm.
Signed bottom right : Picasso.

Exh. Lausanne, 1964, No. 230, repr. in cat.

Bibl. Z. VI. 787.

Coll. Bought from the artist in 1918 by G. and L. Bollag, Zurich ;

Private collection, Zurich.

D. XVI. 5
NUDE YOUNG GIRL
Paris, autumn, 1906.
Charcoal on cardboard.   Size : 100 x 73 cm.
Unsigned (signed on recto).
Recto : Mother and Child (X. 9).

Bibl. Unpublished.

Coll. Cf. X. 9.

Collection Stavros S. Niarchos, Paris.

Sketch on cardboard mounted on the back of the panel of No. X. 9. Inscribed top right : Picasso, 13 rue Ravignan, 18e. Label at the left : Galerie Vollard, 5072.

D. XVI. 6
NUDE COMBING HER HAIR
Summer—autumn, 1906.
Pencil drawing.
Size : 17 x 10 cm.
Signed top right : Picasso.

Exh. Manchester and Leeds, 1962.

Bibl. Unpublished.

Coll. Heinz Berggruen, Paris ;

Collection Dr. Henry M. Roland, England.

Study for *Nude Combing her Hair* (XVI. 9).

D. XVI. 7
WOMAN WITH LEFT HAND RAISED
Summer–autumn, 1906.
Crayon and gouache.
Size : 62 x 47 cm.
Unsigned (?).

Bibl. Z. I. 334 (dated 1905).

Formerly Ambroise Vollard collection, Paris.

Related to XVI. 8 and 12, and D. XVI. 11.

D. XVI. 8
NUDE WITH ARMS RAISED
Summer–autumn, 1906.
Pencil on paper.
Size : 16.9 x 10.7 cm.
Unsigned.
Recto : Man Carrying a Burden (D. XII. 22).

Bibl. Not in Z.

Coll. Klipstein, Bern, Sale, June 27, 1944, No. 366,
sold for 195 Swiss francs (recto and verso) ;

Department of Prints, Kunstmuseum, Basel.

D. XVI. 9
NUDE WITH ARMS RAISED
(and a study of a hand)
Summer–autumn, 1906.
Pencil on paper.
Size : 16.9 x 10.7 cm.
Unsigned.
Verso : Standing Nude (sketch).

Bibl. Not in Z.

*The Philadelphia Museum of Art, Louise and Walter
Arensberg Collection.*

Closely related to D. XVI. 8.

D. XVI. 10
STANDING NUDE
Summer–autumn, 1906.
Pencil drawing.
Size : 17 x 10.5 cm.
Unsigned.
Verso : Sketches of Figures.

Exh. Frankfurt and Hamburg, 1965, No. 18, repr.

Bibl. Not in Z.

Collection Max G. Bollag, Zurich.

D. XVI. 11
STANDING NUDE
Summer–autumn, 1906.
Pencil on paper.
Size : 17.2 x 10 cm.
Signed top right : Picasso.
Verso : Sketch of a man and the inscription : *Soto
Angel/Campio Nuevo/Chalet Victoria/Malaga.*

Bibl. Not in Z.

Coll. Galerie Rosengart, Lucerne ;

Private collection, Switzerland.

Authenticated by the artist, October 17, 1960.
Related to XVI. 8 and 12, and D. XVI. 7.

D. XVI. 12
STANDING NUDE
Paris, autumn, 1906.
Ink and charcoal on paper.
Size : 24 x 14 cm.
Signed top right : Picasso.

Exh. Musée Réattu, Arles, 1957, No. 16, repr. in
cat. pl. 8.

Bibl. Not in Z. Galerie Bollag, Zurich, catalogue,
April 1925, No. 165, pl. 62.

Coll. G. and L. Bollag, Zurich ; Galerie Berggruen,
Paris ;

Private collection, France.

D. XVI. 13
STANDING NUDE
Paris, autumn, 1906.
Pastel.
Size : 65 x 45 cm.
Signed bottom right : Picasso.

Bibl. Z. I. 357.

Present location unknown.

A pencil drawing, very similar to this pastel, is in the Rhode Island School of Design (Z. VI. 645). These drawings are related to the studies for *Two Nudes* (XVI. 15). Cf., especially, the standing nude in No. XVI. 16.

D. XVI. 14
RECLINING NUDE
Paris, autumn, 1906.
Pencil drawing.
Dimensions not available.
Signed top left : Picasso.

Bibl. Not in Z. Waldemar George, 1926, pl. 4. *The Cone Collection,* Baltimore, 1934, pl. 103 b. Maurice Gieure, 1951, pl. 120.

Coll. Miss Etta and Dr. Claribel Cone, Baltimore ;

Baltimore Museum of Art, The Cone Collection.

D. XVI. 15
NUDE AND FAUN
Paris, autumn, 1906.
Watercolor on paper.
Size : 20.3 x 13.3 cm.
Signed top left : Picasso.

Bibl. Not in Z.

Coll. Parke-Bernet, New York, Sale, April 20, 1950, No. 45, p. 10 ;

Collection Mrs. Alex L. Hillman, New York.

This belongs to a series of watercolors in the same format (Z. VI. 803, 805, 806, 808). The series is contemporary with *Nude from the Front and Nude in Profile* (XVI. 14).

D. XVI. 16
STUDY : SEATED MALE NUDE
Paris, autumn, 1906.
Pencil on paper.
Size : 30.5 x 20.3 cm.
Signed bottom left : Picasso.

Exh. Chicago, 1933, No. 1045.

Bibl. Not in Z.

The Art Institute of Chicago, Gift of Robert Allerton.

D. XVI. 17
RECLINING NUDE
Paris, autumn, 1906.
Watercolor on paper.
Dimensions not known.
Signed and dated, bottom left : Picasso 1906.

Bibl. Z. I. 348.

Present location unknown.

We know this work only through Zervos.

D. XVI. 18
SEATED MALE NUDE
Paris, autumn, 1906.
Conté crayon on paper.
Size : 33 x 20.3 cm.
Signed bottom right : Picasso.

Bibl. Not in Z.

Collection Mr. and Mrs. Lee A. Ault, New York.

These two studies (D. XVI. 16 and 18) are probably related to *Seated Male Nude* (XVI. 31).

D. XVI. 19
HEAD OF A MAN IN PROFILE
Paris, autumn, 1906.
Brush drawing.
Size : 62 x 46 cm.
Signed bottom right : Picasso.

Exh. Recklinghausen, 1959, No. 241. Bremen, 1961, No. L 22. Frankfurt and Hamburg, 1965, No. 26, repr.

Bibl. Not in Z.

Galerie des 20. Jahrhunderts, Berlin.

D. XVI. 20
SEATED NUDE IN AN ARMCHAIR
Paris, winter, 1906–1907.
Pastel and charcoal.
Size : 62 x 45 cm.
Signed bottom right : Picasso.

Bibl. Unpublished.

Coll. G. and L. Bollag, Zurich, Sale, April 3, 1925, No. 156, repr. pl. 60 ;

Present location unknown.

Sketch related to the first studies for *Les Demoiselles d'Avignon.* (Cf. the contemporary drawings : Z. VI. 826, 827, 829, 831.)

D. XVI. 21
TWO NUDES
Paris, autumn, 1906.
Ink and wash on paper.
Size : 48 x 32 cm.
Signed bottom right : Picasso.

Exh. Cassel, 1964, No. 6, repr. p. 188. Frankfurt and Hamburg, 1965, No. 31, repr. Galerie Knoedler, Paris, 1966, No. 28, repr.

Bibl. Z. I. 359.

Coll. Ambroise Vollard, Paris ; Galerie Berggruen, Paris ;

Contemporary Art Establishment, Zurich.

D. XVI. 22
HEAD OF A WOMAN
Paris, autumn, 1906.
Ink on paper.
Size : 31 x 23 cm.
Signed bottom right : Picasso.

Bibl. Not in Z.

The Philadelphia Museum of Art, Louise and Walter Arensberg Collection.

A study closely related to Z. I. 347.

D. XVI. 23
HEAD OF A WOMAN
Paris, autumn, 1906.
Ink and red gouache on paper.
Size : 62 x 47 cm.
Signed bottom right : Picasso.

Exh. Lyons, 1953, No. 102. Paris, 1959, No. 181. Frankfurt and Hamburg, 1965, No. 32, repr. in color in cat.

Bibl. Z. VI. 856.

Collection Gustav Zumsteg, Zurich.

D. XVI. 24
RED HEAD OF A WOMAN
Paris, autumn, 1906.
Red gouache on paper. Size : 63 x 47 cm.
Signed bottom right : Picasso.

Exh. Paris, 1953 : *Le Cubisme,* No. 6. Paris, 1964 : *Collection André Lefèvre,* No. 245.

Bibl. Not in Z.

Coll. André Lefèvre, Paris ; Palais Galliera, Paris, November 25, 1965 : *Second Sale of the André Lefèvre Collection,* No. 17, sold for 285,000 fr. ;

Formerly André Lefèvre Collection, Paris.

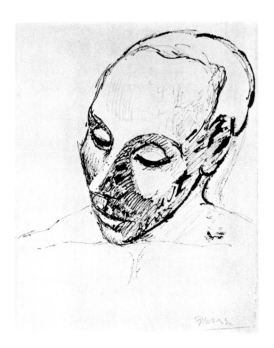

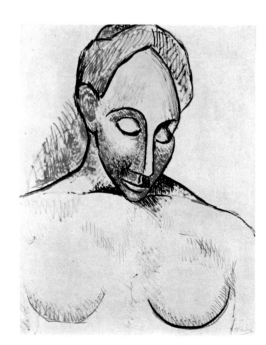

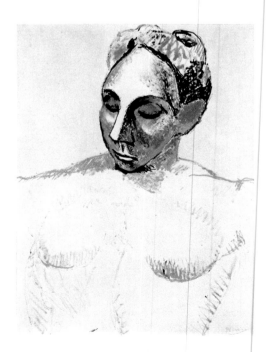

APPENDIX: DOCUMENTS

ARTICLE BY MIGUEL UTRILLO ("PINCELL")
in *Pèl y Ploma*, No. 77 (June, 1901), p. 15.

Exhibition of Pastels by Picasso at the Sala Parés, Barcelona, 1901.

PABLO R. PICASSO

Some talents of the future have already emerged from the center of modern art at Barcelona, among them some young strangers whom circumstances have brought to our city. Pablo R. Picasso, whose abilities as a painter no one would deny, would have developed an entirely different kind of art had he remained in sun-shattered Malaga. Transplanted to Barcelona, he found himself in an environment more congenial to his talents than the milieu of painters who use shrill colors and call themselves colorists because their palettes look like parrot feathers. At most, after winning some medals, he might have painted another "Flevit super illam," which up to now remains the masterpiece of that scorching land of the raisin.

At Barcelona Picasso may not have profited by the lessons which would have been given regularly at Llotja, but he has had the fortunate bad example of numerous painters who know how to paint without attending the official schools or participating in battles to win little traveling scholarships from which the artists' families reap most of the glory.

In comparison with his fellow painters, the young Andalusian (who speaks Castilian with the accent of Barcelona, according to the single number which appeared of the Madrid review, *Mercurio*) deserves greater credit than those who award medals to paintings as if they were art in chocolate-making. Some of the works exhibited at the *Quatre Gats* were quickly bought by the collectors who look for the most promising of the younger painters, while the Catalan review, *Joventut*, was the first to publish a drawing by Picasso. A year ago Picasso already made the pilgrimage to Paris; a bit dazzled by the vast possibilities open to the arts there, he piled innumerable croquis, as well as more complete works. He abandoned these on the first signs of success to make a trip to the south of Spain, of which his earlier memory no longer corresponded to his new ideas.

In Madrid, Picasso and the writer Soler founded the journal *Arte Joven*, which circulated widely from the first number, just because this taste for renewal, evident in the drawings of the young Andalusian painter. And there the same thing happened to him as happens to so many artists sooner or later: Paris, the Paris disparaged for its restless life, drew him again. He did not go to conquer it, as he dreamed in his first visit, but to acquire knowledge in this center where all the arts come to exuberant flower.

The art of Picasso is extremely youthful; child of a spirit of observation which does not pardon the weaknesses of the men of our time, he throws beauty into relief against horrors, noting it with the sobriety of those who draw because they see, and not because they remember. The pastels in the exhibition organized by our publication at the Sala Parés represent only one aspect of Picasso's talent, a talent which will be very much discussed, but no less appreciated, by those who abandon ready-made models to seek art in all its aspects.

In this number, we publish some album leaves which, like many others to be published later, demonstrate the quickness of the young painter's vision. (We also reproduce here his portrait by Casas.) We pay homage to the old masters, while assisting in as great a measure as possible the flight of those who may become the great men of tomorrow.

Picasso, who is not yet twenty, was given a nickname in Paris: with the large, wide-brimmed hat favored in Montmartre in bad weather, his lively but self-controlled Southern eyes, and his neck swathed in the legendary cravats of the ultra-Impressionists, his appearance inspired his French friends to call him "Little Goya." We trust that the outward appearance will not lie, and we know in our heart we are right.

Pincell.

EXPOSITION DE TABLEAUX

DE

F. ITURRINO

et de

P.-R. PICASSO

du 25 juin au 14 juillet 1901

GALERIES VOLLARD
6, rue Laffitte,
Paris

INVITATION

REVIEW BY FÉLICIEN FAGUS OF THE EXHIBITION AT THE GALERIE VOLLARD, in *La Revue Blanche*, Vol. XXVII (July 15, 1901), pp. 464-65, under the heading, "Gazette d'Art."

The Spanish Invasion: Picasso

The second ... a good invasion, or rather, the immigration of poor relations from their meagre home; these newcomers in no way resemble barbarians in a conquered country, to which unfortunately we are almost beginning to be accustomed. The men from across the Pyrenees, who have been flowing into Paris for several years, must no longer feel themselves foreigners: the qualities which bring success with them are collateral to ours; we are both Latins, and it becomes almost a defensive alliance. Indeed it is the second one. The first is famous, the period from Charles V to Philippe IV, an alliance full of chivalry and bravado, which gave the French a legacy other than the echo of the beautiful clinking of arms and of the richly sonorous words which heralded this irruption, all banners unfurled: a new vision—severe, strong, lofty, of man confronting himself, other men, and destiny. Our literature incorporated it freely, making it serve the goals of its genius: Corneille, Molière and others, including the poets from Ronsard to Malherbe, not to mention the burlesques; it drew from this vision a new, robust conception of the hero—Polyeucte, Alcestis or Don Juan—poised, antithetic, and complementary to the Anglo-Norman conception which Shakespeare and his satellites created at the same time. The world has subsisted on the image of these heroes, from Faust to Zarathustra. Three hundred years later the Anglo-Latin worlds have reached the critical hour of disintegration and stagnation.

The new hispanic expansion, purely artistic this time, which is significant, is manifested by a harsh imagination, somber, corrosive, sometimes magnificent, but then it is a consciously lugubrious magnificence. Above all, it is thoroughly indigenous.

All these artists have a profound family resemblance; beneath superficial influences, they follow their great ancestors, and this is good. Particularly Goya, the bitter, mournful genius. His influence is seen in Picasso, this brilliant newcomer. He is the painter, absolutely, beautifully the painter; his understanding of the material is sufficient evidence.

Like all pure painters he adores color for itself and each substance has its proper color. Hence he is enamoured of all subjects, and everything is his subject: flowers bursting wildly out of their vase toward the light, and the luminous air dancing around them; the multicolored swarming of crowds at the race track or by the sunlit sand of the bullring; the nudity of the female body—any female body—or the shrouding of these bodies, which are suggested, molded by the flexible folds of motley draperies. Some lucky finds here—three little girls dancing, the malachite green of one of their skirts against the white underclothing, the stiff white, boyish, very starched underclothing of little girls; the yellow and white of a woman's hat, etc.

Just as everything is his subject, he also translates everything, even argot, or Gongorism, that other argot, or even the vocabulary of a neighbor. Besides the great ancestors, one easily distinguishes many a probable influence—Delacroix, Manet (everything points to him, whose painting is a little Spanish), Monet, Van Gogh, Pissarro, Toulouse-Lautrec, Degas, Forain, Rops perhaps.... Each influence is transitory, set free as soon as caught: one sees that Picasso's haste has not yet given him time to forge a personal style; his personality is in this haste, this youthful, impetuous spontaneity (I understand he is not yet twenty, and covers as many as three canvases a day). The danger for him lies in just this impetuosity, which can well lead to facile virtuosity and easy success. Prolificness and fruitfulness are not synonymous, nor are violence and energy. And that would be profoundly regrettable in the face of such brilliant virility.

Félicien Fagus.

See the Introduction to Catalogue V, p. 154.

REVIEW BY FRANÇOIS CHARLES OF THE EXHIBITION AT THE GALERIE VOLLARD, in *L'Ermitage*, Paris, September 1901, p. 241.

... As for M. Picasso, who is, I am told, very young, he begins with such éclat that I am somewhat uneasy about his future. One can tell the source of each of his paintings, and there is too much variety. There is no doubt that he is gifted, but for his own good I would advise him not to paint one canvas a day.

F. C.

PREFACE BY ADRIEN FARGE TO THE CATALOGUE OF THE EXHIBITION AT THE GALERIE BERTHE WEILL, Paris, April 1-15, 1902.

M. Pedro Mañach, whether he proceeds by analogy or by antithesis, has a very happily developed sense of arrangement. He organized the preceding exhibitions so well that already amateurs are regularly making the pilgrimage to the little gallery on the Rue Victor-Massé. In these exhibitions he gathered together works which were related as much in their direction as in their execution. . . .

In the same way he now presents two painters of completely opposite temperaments, although one finds in both an equally sincere enthusiasm. Their different interpretations of a similar ideal have great charm. . . .

Picasso is all nerve, all verve, all impetuosity. With vehement brush strokes, thrown on the canvas with great rapidity to follow the flight of his conception, he builds brilliant, solid works which delight the eyes of those taken with dazzling painting in colors which are sometimes crudely brutal, sometimes rare and knowing. At times Picasso is carried away by his passion for color, and then he gives us the luxurious *Still Life* or the dazzling *Luxembourg*. There is also intense observation: the *Courtesan* on display, all her fingers encircled with rings and a jeweled collar stiffening her studied posture, calculated to show off the goods to advantage. There is *Trottin*, true flower of the pavement, tarnished by the impure atmosphere of the great city. There is the *Virgin with Golden Hair*, captivating us by the undefinable expression of her enigmatic glance, a suggestive and disturbing sphinx, with a sinuous body, a lustful mouth, curled hair, painted nails like petals on long supple hands, the female quivering voluptuously within the innocent virgin, longing with vague desire for the unknown. What an eloquent symbol is this strange figure! How much soulfulness also in the pensive head of the *Baby*, even now heavy with all that innocence foresees of the cruelty of life. Seated in a high chair, in a magnificent dress of royal blue, the child already is thoughtful beyond her years. Then there is a *Clown*, in glittering yellows, and a fanciful *Pierrot*, showing Picasso's facility in capturing attitudes, while a brilliant, clamorous *Fourteenth of July* combines the exaggerated movement and the intense life of the popular fête in the gaudiest of colors.

Adrien Farge.

See Catalogues V and VI.

REVIEW BY FÉLICIEN FAGUS OF THE EXHIBITION AT THE GALERIE BERTHE WEILL, in *La Revue Blanche*, September 1, 1902, under the heading "Gazette d'Art."

SPANISH PAINTERS (Excerpts)

. . . Picasso, only lately the positive reveler in color, concentrates himself on displays of energy. A small, serious child, almost stiff, with a stubborn chin, heavy forehead, suffering, suspicious, pitiless eyes, painted all in blue, posing like an historic personage. A girl in a tub, with skinny legs and thin body, who is standing sponging her hip, lifts high the shoulder of the arm which holds the sponge, and presents a slender beauty, distorted, serene in a strange way. *The Courtesan,* the strong outlines against dull blue, the unconscious dignity, the feline contortion of the shoulder and hands, the fixity of the stare under a hair style like that of an idol, with an enormous dark blue feathered hat, makes something hieratic out of her. This quasi-hieratic quality is more defined in the *Virgin with Golden Hair* (the same woman or her sister ?)—this very young girl, lying on her stomach, head raised, staring out at nothing, inhaling and sniffing suspiciously with her animal-like snub nose; here is the stupefied beast who would attain divinity; here is the sphinx. All this conveyed in vivid but mat flat tints enclosed by carefully elaborated, prominently marked outlines: this simplification stresses substantially the impression of stained-glass engendered by the spirit of these canvases. . . .

All of these Spanish artists (Zuloaga, Nonell, Iturrino, Losada, etc. . .) have temperament, race and individuality, each one in perfect control of a personal garden, very personal and at the same time closely related to the neighboring garden. They do not have their great man yet, the conqueror who subsumes and remolds all, makes everything start from him, who shapes an unlimited universe. They remember to advantage Goya, Zurbaran, Herrera; are stimulated by Manet, Monet, Degas, Carrière, our Impressionists. Which one—the time is ripe—will become their Greco?

Félicien Fagus.

See Catalogue VI.

HARLOR'S PREFACE TO THE CATALOGUE OF THE EXHIBITION AT THE GALERIE BERTHE WEILL, Paris, November 15–December 15, 1902.

Exhibition of paintings, pastels and drawings by Girieud, Launay, Picasso and Pichot.

Two Frenchmen, two Spaniards, all four are inspired by the same scorn for the conventional. Each vision is quite personal. They paint or draw wholeheartedly. They do not sacrifice to a desire to please. And if, at times, they show some uncertainty, it is not from catering to this or that opinion, but because they are themselves still searching. And one of their charms is that they find it natural to admit it.

A Provence which is burnt by the sun, whose waters, whose stones are, as it were, chemically transformed by the action of the implacable heat, this is the Provence of M. Girieud. . . .

With M. Launay, we are altogether in France. Which is to say, we are in Paris and the most French sort of Paris. . . .

The ardor of M. P. R. Picasso has already been noticed. He has a tireless passion to see everything, to express everything. He is not bound by a

manner, a genre. He has no set method. Here are three studies of women, cameo varieties of a painful reality, dedicated to misery, solitude, and exhaustion. A savage light surrounds these creatures. Shade and light play round about them violently. One especially wholly personifies distress, isolation among nature's unfeeling consolations: she is seated on a shore, bent double, with all the fatigue of mute despair, and she seems to resist the treacherous call of the ocean. . . .

How different is this little sketch of a nude woman in an elaborate pose suggested only by a contour line drawn sharply and purely. Here also a corner of Barcelona, a box at the theatre, and some notations of Paris, the Enclosure at Auteuil strewn with light-colored dresses, where a moving throng blooms; here also girls of the sort whose faces on the night streets, under hats too big for them, have an impudent touch of rouge . . . M. Picasso is impulsive, full of energy. His faculties of observation go instinctively to the most expressive beings and things.

We have a feverish description of Catalonia by M. Ramón Pichot. . . .

Harlor.

See the Introduction to Catalogues VII and VIII, page 206.

ARTICLE BY CHARLES MORICE in the *Mercure de France*, Paris, December 1902, page 804.

Exhibition of Picasso, Launay, Pichot and Girieud.

At Rue Victor-Massé, at Mlle Weill's, on the street-floor of a narrow store, these four artists, two French, two Spanish, have brought together their latest works. French; Spanish? Is this quite true? No. All four are citizens of Montmartre! Land of their desire, atmosphere of their labors and of their ambitions, of their art.

Young art (I do not say "art nouveau"!) with its extremisms and its successes, its weaknesses, its dangers: the time for inquiry into self and into nature. Picasso is twenty years old and his comrades are not much older than he. No doubt all are still far from mastery. They are not yet in command of themselves. But I know of nothing more fascinating or moving than this sort of pre-dawn of spirits—also nothing more significant: if you want to know the present direction of art, ask the artists who are in the process of searching for themselves, shaking off their training.

Those whose efforts I am considering would reply that they have already gone through Impressionism and that they will not go back to it. They recall it sometimes and could not without ingratitude deny what they owe to it; only their hearts are elsewhere. Where? I suspect that they would not find it easy to say exactly. Again, they are looking. They are looking and what they produce is quite as contemporary as the poetry of symbolists and the novel of the naturalists. There is much realism, "brutalism" even in the painting on view at Rue Victor-Massé. But, oddly enough, this servile devotion to immediate appearances of beings and things is combined with a fine decorative instinct. It is for this reason that this art in process of becoming, en route, is rich in precious indications of the general prevailing order.

For the time being, one encounters the negative, that fatal wall against which the generations without humanity come to grief. This is visible with all of them, less with Pichot and Girieud, more with Launay, still more with Picasso. It is extraordinary what sterile sadness weighs on the whole work of this very young man. His work is already uncountable. Picasso, who painted before he learned to read, seems to have been assigned the mission of expressing with his brush everything there is. One could talk of a young god who wishes to remake the world. But it is a somber god. The hundreds of faces he paints grimace—never smile. His world is not more habitable than his squalid settings. And his painting itself is sick—incurably ? I do not know. But certainly he has force, a gift, a talent. Such drawing—a crouching nude woman—gives you the feeling of a near-miracle. Such composition —at the theatre, two spectators, a man and a woman, in a box, turning away from the stage where the *danseuse* performs, far off, in bright light,—is as disturbing and provocative as a Flower of Evil. Beings of hardly either sex, "ordinary demons," with despairing eyes, head bowed, brow blackened with desperate or criminal thoughts.... After all, should one really hope that this painting will regain its health ? Is not this child with a terrible precocity destined to consecrate by the masterpiece the negative view of life, that sickness from which he suffers more than anyone else? ...

Charles Morice.

PREFACE BY CHARLES MORICE TO THE CATALOGUE OF THE EXHIBITION AT THE GALERIES SERRURIER, Paris, February 25–March 6, 1905.

Excerpts :

... He was not twenty years old and already he had this amazing certainty of line, of color harmonies, of composition which many artists still strive for after years of work. A miracle which nothing can explain. One could believe that in another life, with many years and works, this child with the insistent and sure eye had already learned everything ; thereafter, with no further need to study, he went on producing daily, tirelessly, and the drawings and the prints and the paintings covered the walls of his studio, and soon were lined up in any number of deep ranks....

... this premature twilight of spleen, which logically would have ended in the night of despair and death, is followed, by a merciful anomaly, by a sudden light : the dawn of pity rises, salvation is at hand.

C. M.

ARTICLE BY CHARLES MORICE in the *Mercure de France,* March 15, 1905, under the heading "Art Moderne."

Exhibition of works by Trachsel, Gérardin, Picasso (Galeries Serrurier, 37 Boulevard Haussmann).

... I have already had many times the occasion to speak about Picasso, to mention the extraordinary gifts of this very young artist and to deplore the negative direction of his effort towards sterile melancholy and towards the caricatured aspect of beings and things. These new works that he is showing at the Serrurier Galleries herald a radiant transformation of his talent. Not that nothing remains of his original somber vision. Picasso is Andalusian and perhaps this predilection for the gestures and accents of sorrow is an ineradicable racial trait in Spain. But today the poses are simpler, the units are grouped less shabbily, the canvas

lightens. There is no longer the taste for the sad and ugly for their own sake ; this premature twilight of spleen, which logically would have ended in the night of despair and death, is followed, by a merciful anomaly, by a ray of light : the dawn of pity rises—it is salvation. For what was especially sad in the first works of Picasso, otherwise already stamped with a powerful personality, was that he apparently relished the melancholy without sympathizing in it. His sensibility has deepened. Let us note also that his technique has improved and strengthened : his constructions are more solid than a short time ago and also simpler.

Charles Morice.

ARTICLE BY GUILLAUME APOLLINAIRE in *La Revue Immoraliste,* Paris, April 1905.

PICASSO, PAINTER AND DRAUGHTSMAN (Galeries Serrurier).

It is said that Picasso's work reveals a precocious disenchantment.

I think it is the opposite.

Everything enchants him and his undeniable talent seems to me at the disposal of a fantasy which blends exactly the delightful and horrible, the wretched and refined.

His naturalism enamoured of exactitude is enhanced by the mysticism that in Spain lurks in even the least religious spirits. Castelar was known to carry a rosary in his pocket, and if Picasso is indifferently religious (as I think), I would wager he has felt it advisable to keep up a subtle devotion to the saints, to St. Theresa or St. Isidore.

In Rome at Carnival there are maskers (Harlequin, Colombine, or *cuoca francese*) who in the morning after an orgy, finishing up sometimes with a murder, will go to St. Peter's to kiss the worn toe of the statue of the prince of apostles.

Such people would enchant Picasso.

Under the bright rags of his slender saltimbanques, you discern real youths of the masses, fickle, cunning, clever, poor and deceitful.

His mothers clench their thin hands just as young mothers of the common people have often done and his nude women are granted the escutcheon of fleece which traditional painters scorn, and which is the shield of Western modesty.

Guillaume Apollinaire.

ARTICLE BY GUILLAUME APOLLINAIRE in *La Plume,* May 15, 1905.

THE YOUNG : PICASSO, PAINTER

If we only knew, all the gods would awake. Born of the profound knowledge which man kept of himself, the pantheisms he worshipped in his own likeness have fallen asleep. But despite the eternal slumbers, there are eyes in which human nature reflects those divine and joyous phantoms.

These eyes are as attentive as flowers which want only to gaze on the sun. Ah, life-giving joy ! there are men who see with these eyes.

Picasso has observed the human images which float in the azure of our memories, and partake of divinity, in order to damn the metaphysicians. How pious are his skies, alive with flights, and his heavy sombre lights, like those of grottoes !

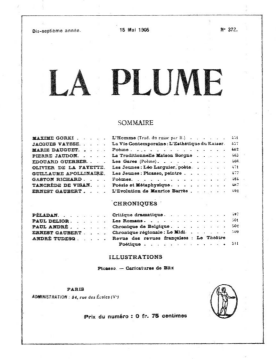

Diz-septième année. 15 Mai 1905 N° 372.

LA PLUME

SOMMAIRE

MAXIME GORKI . . . . . L'Homme (Trad. du russe par B.) 454
JACQUES VAYESE . . . . . La Vie Contemporaine : L'Esthétique du Kaiser. 457
MARIE DAUGUET. . . . . Poème 462
PIERRE JAUDON . . . . . La Traditionnelle Maison Borgne. 463
EDOUARD GUERBER . . . Les Gares (Poème) 468
OLIVIER DE LA FAYETTE. . Les Jeunes : Léo Larguier, poète. 471
GUILLAUME APOLLINAIRE. Les Jeunes : Picasso, peintre 477
GASTON RICHARD . . . . Poèmes. 484
TANCRÈDE DE VISAN. . . . Poésie et Métaphysique. 487
ERNEST GAUBERT . . . . L'Evolution de Maurice Barrès 492

CHRONIQUES

PÉLADAN. . . . . Critique dramatique. 497
PAUL DELIOR . . . . . . Les Romans 501
PAUL ANDRÉ. . . . . . . Chronique de Belgique. 506
ERNEST GAUBERT . . . . Chronique régionale : Le Midi. 509
ANDRÉ TUDESQ . . . . . Revue des revues françaises : Le Théâtre
                          Poétique 511

ILLUSTRATIONS

Picasso. — Caricatures de Bixx.

PARIS
ADMINISTRATION : 54, rue des Écoles (V°)

Prix du numéro : 0 fr. 75 centimes

There are children who have strayed off without having learned the catechism. They stop, and the rain stops falling. "Look, in front of those houses there are people whose clothes are shabby." These children, whom one does not caress, know so much. "Mama, love me to death !" They are tumblers and their successful feats are like mental evolutions.

These women no longer loved remember. By this time they have ruminated on their wearing ideas too often. They do not pray ; they worship memories. Like an old church, they crouch in the twilight. These women renounce everything, and their fingers are itching to plait crowns of straw. At daybreak they disappear ; they have consoled themselves in silence. They cross many a threshold ; mothers guard the cradles, so that the newborn may not inherit some taint ; when they bend over the cradles, the little babes smile, sensing their goodness.

They often give thanks, and the gestures of their forearms tremble like their eyelids.

Enveloped in frozen mist, old men wait unthinkingly, for it is only children who meditate. Stirred by remote countries, brute squabbles, locks of coarsened hair, these old men beg without humility.

Other beggars are worn out by life. These are the infirm, the cripples, the bums. They seem amazed to have reached the goal, which is still blue, but no longer the horizon. Old, they have become as foolish as kings who have too many troops of elephants bearing citadels. There are travelers who confound the flowers with the stars.

Grown old like oxen at twenty-five, the young have conducted nurselings to the moon.

In the clear light, women hold their peace ; their bodies are angelic, and their glances tremble.

As to danger, their smiles are inward. They wait for fear, to confess innocent sins.

For a year, Picasso lived this painting of tears, blue as the humid depths of the abyss, and full of pity.

Pity made Picasso more violent. The public squares were settings for a man who had hanged himself ; he was stretched against the houses above the oblique passerby. The condemned awaited a savior. Miraculously the rope swung free ; the windowpanes flamed with flowers.

In rooms penniless painters drew pubescent nudes by lamplight. Women's shoes left by the bed were expressive of tender haste.

Calm followed this frenzy.

The harlequins go in splendid rags while the painting is gathering, warming or whitening its colors to express the strength and duration of the passions, while the lines delimited by the tights curve, intersect, or flow impetuously.

In a square room, paternity transfigures the harlequin, whose wife bathes with cold water and admires her figure, as frail and slim as her husband, the puppet. A stove warms a nearby gipsy caravan. Fine lilts mingle, and elsewhere passing soldiers curse the day.

Love is good when it is set off, and the habit of spending one's time at home redoubles paternal feeling. The child brings the woman Picasso wanted glorious and immaculate closer to the father.

Primiparous mothers no longer expect the baby to arrive, perhaps because of certain ill-omened, chattering ravens. Miracle! They give birth to future acrobats in the midst of pet monkeys, white horses, and dogs like bears.

Adolescent sisters, treading in perfect balance the heavy balls of the saltimbanques, impose on these spheres the radiant motion of worlds. These still adolescent youngsters have the anxieties of innocence; animals instruct them in the religious mystery. Some harlequins match the splendor of the women, whom they resemble, being neither male nor female. The color has the flatness of frescoes; the lines are firm. But, placed at the frontiers of life, the animals are human, and the sexes are indistinct.

Hybrid beasts have the consciousness of Egyptian demigods; taciturn harlequins have their cheeks and foreheads paled by morbid sensibility.

You cannot confuse these saltimbanques with actors. The spectator must be pious for they are celebrating silent rites with a difficult agility. It is this that distinguishes this painter from the Greek vase painters although his drawing sometimes approaches theirs. There, on the painted earthenware, bearded, garrulous priests offered in sacrifice animals, resigned and powerless. Here, virility is beardless, but shows itself in the sinews of thin arms, in the flat planes of the face, and the animals are mysterious.

Picasso's taste for the line which eludes, changes and penetrates, and produces almost unique examples of linear drypoints in which the general appearance of the world is not altered by the light which modifies forms as it changes colors.

More than all the poets, sculptors and the other painters, this Spaniard scathes us like a sudden chill.

His meditations are laid bare in the silence. He comes from afar, from the opulence of composition and brutal decoration of the Spaniards of the 17th century.

Those who have been acquainted with him remember transient manifestations of ferocity which already were more than just experiments.

His insistence on the quest of beauty has governed his path. He has found himself more of a Latin in morals, more of an Arab in rhythms.

Guillaume Apollinaire.

See the Introduction to Catalogue XII.

EXCERPTS FROM: *SANDRICOURT*—In the Land of Firmans—History of a Government. With a preface by Eugène Marsan. Paris, Société d'éditions artistiques, 1906, pp. 11–13.

Exchange of dialogue between the author and his hero, Sandricourt, in the setting of the *Lapin Agile*, Rue des Saules:

"If you are tempted to think me paradoxical, I would ask you to observe the eloquent décor of this café which is frequented only, for I discount the curious, by the young men who pay with poverty for the leisure of their unlimited dreaming. You see on these walls, more expressive than a museum's walls, numberless illustrations of their thoughts: no doubt, some are burlesques without importance, as a joke, but also there are some beautiful bodies of nude women, a flayed Christ who is dying, and lastly this picture here...."

With his finger M. Sandricourt pointed out to me a compelling picture done in colors that were flat, as if burnt. He remarked of it: "This Harlequin and Colombine are hungry (notice the eyes), but they don't have twenty sous and, not being able to eat, they drink. They are not looking at each other at all; but I can tell that they care for each other. The young artist who painted that in two hours will become a genius, if Paris does not destroy him."

I objected, for I had at once recognized the hand that had fitted the yellow, red, green lozenges of their tights to the thin bodies of Harlequin and Colombine.

"The painter of this Harlequin," I said, "Monsieur, already has a reputation and tomorrow.... He is an Andalusian, and one who paints, as only a Spaniard could, the look and the tatters. You might call him, for mnemonics, the Callot of the saltimbanques, but rather make sure to remember his name: Picasso."

This excerpt from a work published in 1906 attests the comparative popularity of Picasso at this time. See At the Lapin Agile (XII. 23).

EXCERPT FROM *PICASSO AND HIS FRIENDS* by Fernande Olivier (Editions Stock, Paris, 1933).

The studio of the Bateau-Lavoir (pp. 25–26).

An icebox in winter, a sweatbox in summer, the tenants (of the Bateau-Lavoir) would meet there at the one and only fountain with pitcher in hand. Picasso had been settled there since 1903 *(sic)*, after his return from Spain. It was then that I saw him for the first time.... He was talking away to his fellow-countryman, the Catalan painter Ricardo Canals... The contrast between Picasso and Canals was striking to anyone who saw them together. Canals—tall, slim, pale, cold, with the blue eyes of a guileless child. Picasso—small, dark, stocky, disquieted and disquieting...

I was astonished confronting Picasso's work. Astonished and attracted. Their morbid air really embarrassed me a bit, but pleased me, too. This was the end of the "Blue period." Large, unfinished paintings stood around in the studio where everything reeked of work; but work in what disorder... dear God!

A mattress on four legs in a corner, a small cast-iron stove, all rusty, with a pottery washbasin on top of it, used for cleaning up; a towel, a sliver of soap, were lying on a wooden table to one side. In another corner a wretched little trunk painted black made a not very comfortable seat. A straw-bottomed chair, easels, canvases of every size, paint tubes scattered on the floor, brushes, containers for turpentine, a basin for etching, no curtains.... At that time, Picasso was working on a now well-known etching: a man and woman are sitting at a table in a wine shop, and the half-starved couple manifest poverty and alcoholism with frightening realism.... [1]

[1] *The Frugal Repast,* 1904.

The article by Miguel Utrillo (Pincell) about Picasso, printed in Pèl y Ploma, No. 77, June 14–17, 1901, Barcelona. Page 15 : above the title, a Picasso drawing : Café-Concert in Malaga

(D. III. 4). Page 17 : Picasso drawing, Head of a Woman. See page 333 for a translation of this article. Frick Art Reference Library, New York.

Portrait of Picasso by Ramón Casas, printed in Pèl y Ploma, June 14–17, 1901. The original drawing is in the Museum of Modern Art, New York.

La Revue blanche, July 15, 1901. Under the heading Gazette d'art, the article by Félicien Fagus : L'Invasion espagnole : Picasso (see page 333).

La Revue blanche, July 15, 1901, page 465 : end of the article by Félicien Fagus. The illustration is by Kees Van Dongen.

Portrait of Picasso by Sebastián Junyent, reproduced in the magazine Forma, Barcelona, 1904. Junyent has depicted his friend in front of La Vie (IX. 13). Frick Art Reference Library, New York.

185 Casajemas (Charles)   Février 1901   Tentative de meurtre et suicide

17   20 ans, né à Barcelone   Le 17 février vers 9 heures du soir, dans le débit
19   (Espagne) le   de vins situé 128 B⁴ de Clichy, le sieur Casajemas a
     fils de   tiré sur la delle Florentin Laure 20 ans, modèle 11 rue
                                       Chappe sans l'atteindre, un coup de revolver. Tour-
     artiste peintre d⁴ 130 ter B⁴   nant son arme contre lui même, il s'est ensuite tiré
     de Clichy.   un coup de revolver dans la tempe droite Transporté d'abord
Témoin Florentin (Laure) 20 ans   à la pharmacie Dajou 81 B⁴ de Clichy, ensuite à l'hôpi-
     modèle d⁴ 11 rue Chappe   tal Bichat dans la voiture de place R 62 appt au loueur
  - Lenoir (Louise)   modèle   Theis d⁴ 116 rue de Crimée conduite par le cocher Becker
     d⁴ 11 rue Chappe.   michel n° 57919, accompagné par le gardien Prat du 18ᵉ arᵗ
  - Pallarès (Manuel) 28 ans   il est décédé dans cet établissement le même jour à 11 h 30
sujets artiste peintre d⁴ B⁴ de Clichy 130 du soir. Il était amoureux de la d⁴ Florentin née Gar-
Espagnols   gallo Laure 20 ans qui n'était pas sa maîtresse.
  - Huguet (Manuel) 26 ans   Il avait dîné avec Pallarès Huguet et les deux femmes chez
     artiste peintre d⁴ B⁴ de Clichy 130 ter le m⁴ de vins établ. 128 B⁴ de Clichy. à la fin du dîner
                                       il avait donné un paquet de lettres à la d⁴ Florentin
     en la priant de les lire. Celle ci eut peur et s'éloigna. C'est alors que Casajemas
     tira sur elle sans l'atteindre. croyant l'avoir tuée il se logea une balle dans
     la tempe droite. (Certificat du Docteur Willette 27 rue Lepic.)
     La course du cocher Becker n'a pas été payée.

186 Rudolph (Jules) comptᵉ   Feu de Cheminée.

Casajemas (Charles) 20 years of age, born in Barcelona (Spain), the son of   , painter, residing at 130 ter Boulevard de Clichy.
Witnesses : Florentin (Laure) 20 years of age, artist's model, residing at 11 rue Chappe.
Lenoir (Louise), artist's model, residing at 11 rue Chappe.
Spanish Citizens { Pallarès (Manuel) 28 years of age, painter, residing at 130 ter Boulevard de Clichy.
Huguet (Manuel) 26 years of age, painter, residing at 130 ter Boulevard de Clichy.

185. ATTEMPTED MURDER AND SUICIDE

On February 17 at approximately 9 p.m., in the wine shop at 128 Boulevard de Clichy, Mr. Casajemas fired a revolver at Miss Florentin (Laure), 20 years old, a model, 11 rue Chappe, without wounding her. Turning his weapon against himself, he then fired a shot into his right temple. Carried first to Dajou's Pharmacy at 81 Boulevard de Clichy, then to the Bichat Hospital in cab No. 9262, belonging to cab-owner Theis, residing at 116 rue de Crimée, driven by the cabman Becker, Michel, No. 57919, accompanied by policeman Prat of the 18th *arrondissement*, he died at this establishment on the same day at 11.30 p.m. He was in love with Miss Florentin, *née* Gargallo, Laure, 20 years old, who was not his mistress. He had dined with Pallarès, Hugué, and the two ladies at the wine shop at 128 Boulevard de Clichy. At the end of dinner he had given a bundle of letters to Miss Florentin, asking her to read them. She was frightened and drew back. It was then that Casajemas fired at her but missed. Under the impression that he had killed her, he put a bullet into his right temple.
(Death certificate by Doctor Willette, 27 rue Lepic.)
The fare of cabman Becker has not been paid.

Excerpt from the register of the police station of the 9th *arrondissement*, Paris, February 1901. This previously unpublished information was obtained through the courtesy of M. Louis Amade, Counselor to the Chief Commissioner of Police, Paris.

The present appearance (1966) of the café where Casagemas killed himself in 1901. It is this café at 128 Boulevard de Clichy, and not the one in Montparnasse, which Picasso painted in 1901 in the painting now known as *The Café de La Rotonde* (V. 45).

Il me semble douteux
que vous puissiez parvenir
a comprendre la lettre
de Pablo mais je pense qu'
il est preferable de laisser
l'original tel qu'il est
dans ce francais plus ou
moins fantaisiste. Je suis
vraiment desolée, miss
Gertrude, de n' avoir point
recu, a gosol Little Jimmy
mais il vous faut savoir qu'
en Espagne on ne recoit
jamais, de ce qui semble
etre utile ou pouvoir amuser
les autorités postales car
dans ce cas ils confisquent
tout a leur profit
Quant à mon anglais!!!
inutile de vous en parler...
meilleures amitiés Fernande

17 Aut 06
Mon cher ami
Stein

Je ai recu votre
lettre et l'argent
merci.

J'ai travaillé à
Gosol et je travaille
ici - je vous montrerai
et vous causerai de
tout ça quand je

Letter from Picasso to Leo Stein, written in Paris, August 17, 1906. This letter, with the drawing sketched on one page, shows that the large composition, *The Peasants* (XV. 62), was painted in Paris, a few days after Picasso's return from Gosol. Top left, on a page of the same letter, a message to Gertrude Stein written by Fernande Olivier. The original letter belongs to the Yale University Library, Collection of American Literature.

vous verrai. Chaque jour
plus dificille et du
calme ou? - Je suis
en train defaire un
home avec une petite
fille ils portent del
fleur dan un panier
a cote de eux deux
voeufs et du bles
quelque chose comme ca

Mes meilleurs
souvenirs à votre soeur
et à vous de votre ami
Picasso

339

Picasso in 1901 in his studio, 130 Boulevard de Clichy. Photograph taken by his friend, Torrés Fuster. Standing at the left: Pedro Mañach. At the right: Fuentes and Madame Torrés Fuster. *Pierre Cailler, Geneva.*

June 1905 : Picasso in Schoorl, Holland, at the house of his friend, the writer Tom Schilperoort (seated). In the foreground, Nelly, Schilperoort's wife. *Pierre Cailler, Geneva.*

Barcelona, 1906 : photograph taken by Juan Vidal y Ventosa in his studio, *El Guayaba*, when Picasso stopped briefly in Barcelona on his way to Gosol. Picasso is seated between Fernande Olivier and his friend Ramón Reventos, the Catalan writer. *Pierre Cailler, Geneva.*

The inn *(Can Tempanada)* at Gosol where Picasso lived during the summer of 1906. Photograph taken by Georges Boudaille in 1965.

IV. H. C.
VILLAGE CORRIDA
Barcelona, 1901.
Oil on wood.
Size : 21.5 x 35.5 cm.
Signed bottom right : Picasso.

Exh. Lefevre Gallery, London, June 1931 : *Thirty Years of Pablo Picasso.*

Bibl. Not in Z.

Coll. Christie's, London, Sale, November 26, 1954, No. 119, sold for £2,835 ;

Private collection.

This little painting, sold in 1954 with a statement of authenticity signed by the artist, might be the *Courses de village,* No. 43 of the Vollard Exhibition in 1901 (See the introduction to Catalogue V, page 154). Related to *In Front of the Church* (V. 49). This work is *hors catalogue,* since the photograph was received after the book was in press.

ADDENDA

A. 1
CORRIDA
Barcelona, 1900.
Pastel, varnished.
Size : 12.5 x 19 cm.
Signed bottom right : P. Ruiz Picasso.

Exh. Galerie Knoedler, Paris, 1966, No. 7, repr. in cat.

Bibl. Not in Z.

Private collection, Paris.

This pastel, unpublished until the recent exhibition at the Galerie Knoedler, Paris, is contemporary with the bullfight scenes of 1900 (see II. 1–7).

A. 2
BULLFIGHT
Barcelona, 1900.
Pastel.
Size : 35 x 39.5 cm.
Signed bottom left : P. R. Picasso.

Bibl. Not in Z.   Unpublished.

Coll. Sir Chester Beatty, Dublin ; Sotheby & Co., London, Sale, June 28, 1967 : *10 Paintings from the Chester Beatty Collection,* No. 10, repr. in color in cat., sold for £42.150, acquired by :

Marlborough Fine Art Ltd., London.

A. 3
THE EMBRACE
Paris, 1900.
Pastel.
Size : 47.5 x 38.5 cm.
Signed bottom left : P. R. Picasso.

Exh. Galerie Beyeler, Basel, 1966–1967 : *Picasso 1900-1932,* No. 2 (entitled *Frenzy*), repr. in color in cat.

Bibl. Not in Z.

Coll. Silberman Galleries, New York ;

Collection Galerie Beyeler, Basel.

This is a variant in pastel of the famous oil in the Pushkin Museum, *The Embrace* (II. 14). It was published for the first time in the catalogue of the 1966–1967 exhibition at the Galerie Beyeler, Basel.

A. 4
CAFÉ IN MONTMARTRE
Paris, 1901.
Oil on cardboard.
Size : 43 x 53.5 cm.
Signed bottom left : Picasso.

Exh. Galerie Beyeler, Basel, 1966–1967 : *Picasso 1900-1932,* No. 1, repr. in color in cat.

Bibl. Not in Z.

Coll. Libaude, Paris (bought directly from the artist) ; Bellier, Paris ;

Collection Galerie Beyeler, Basel.

This previously unpublished work may have been No. 37 *(Brasserie)* at the Vollard exhibition in 1901 (see page 158).

A. 5
RUE LEPIC (or *Rue Ravignan,* see note)
Paris, 1901.
Oil on wood.
Size : 53 x 68 cm.
Signed bottom left : Picasso.

Bibl. Not in Z. Unpublished.

Coll. Libaude, Paris ; Galerie Bernheim-Jeune, Paris (acquired from Libaude, March 9, 1920) ; Kuroki, London (acquired from Galerie Bernheim-Jeune, April 26, 1921) ;

Collection Mrs. Richard J. Bernhard, New York.

When Picasso authenticated this unpublished work for us, May 1, 1967, he commented : "It was Rue Lepic or Rue Ravignan—in any case a street in Montmartre." This painting could have been exhibited at Berthe Weill's in October–November 1904 : No. 33, *Scène de rue* (cf. Le Sieutre's description, p. 238) ; or at the Galeries Serrurier in 1905 : No. 26, *La Rue Ravignan à Paris.*

A. 6
PORTRAIT OF CASAGEMAS DEAD
Paris, summer, 1901.
Oil on cardboard.
Size : 52 x 34 cm.
Unsigned.

Exh. Never exhibited.

Bibl. Not in Z. Unpublished.

Owned by the artist.

Picasso revealed this unknown work to Pierre Daix, in June 1967. It is related to the series inspired by the death of Casagemas (VI. 2, 4, 5, 6). As in VI. 5, Casagemas' right temple bears the wound of the bullet that killed him (cf. p. 338). Painted in 1901, this portrait in closely related to the head of the man with Casagemas' features in *La Vie* (IX. 13) of 1903. Photograph by Mme Jacqueline Picasso.

A. 7
WOMAN WITH A CROW
Paris, 1904.
Gouache and pastel.
Size : 60.5 x 45.5 cm.
Signed and dated, bottom right : Picasso 1904.

Exh. Grand Palais, Paris, 1966–1967 : *Hommage à Picasso*, No. 20, repr. in cat.

Bibl. Not in Z. Unpublished.

Coll. Olivier Sainsère, Paris ;

Private collection, France.

Picasso painted this replica of *Woman with a Crow* a few days after the first version (see XI. 10). It was revealed to the public for the first time at the Paris exhibition, 1966–1967.

DRAWINGS

A. 8
CARLOS CASAGEMAS, FULL-FACE AND IN PROFILE
Barcelona, 1900.
Charcoal on paper.
Size : 13 x 21 cm.
Unsigned.

Bibl. Not in Z. Palau i Fabre, No. 59.

Collection J. A. Samaranch, Barcelona.

Published for the first time, in 1966, by Josep Palau i Fabre. For other portrayals of Casagemas, see D. I. 7, 8, and D. II. 8. Casagemas committed suicide, February 17, 1901 (cf. p. 338). Picasso painted five works related to the death of his friend : VI. 2, 4, 5, 6, and Addenda No. A. 6.

A. 9
CAFÉ-CONCERT
Malaga or Madrid, 1901.
Pastel, varnished.
Size : 21.5 x 27 cm.
Signed bottom left : P. Ruiz Picasso.

Exh. Galerie Knoedler, Paris, 1966, No. 9, repr. in cat.

Bibl. Z. VI. 337.

Private collection, Paris.

A. 10
WOMEN IN THE STREET
Madrid or Barcelona, 1901.
Colored crayons.
Size : 14.5 x 22.5 cm.
Signed bottom right : Picasso.

Exh. Galerie Knoedler, Paris, 1966, No. 8, repr. in cat.

Bibl. Not in Z. Unpublished.

Collection Georges Saad, Paris.

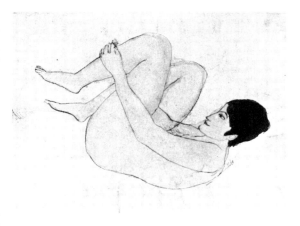

A. 11
RECLINING NUDE
Barcelona, 1901.
Ink and watercolor on paper.
Size : 16 x 22 cm.
Initialed bottom right : P.

Bibl. Not in Z. Jiri Padrta, *Picasso Sconosciuto*, Editori Riuniti, Rome 1962, p. 10, No. 3 (wrongly dated 1905-1906).

Coll. V. Kramar, Prague ;

National Gallery, Prague.

Related to *Reclining Nude with Picasso at her Feet* (D. IV. 5) and to *Parody of Manet's "Olympia"* (D. IV. 7). The head of the man behind the bed (Picasso in D. IV. 5, Sebastián Junyer holding a dish of fruit in D. IV. 7) has been cut out.

A. 12
NUDE WITH MIRROR
Barcelona, 1902.
Pencil and watercolor.
Size : 26.1 x 37.8 cm.
Signed bottom right : Picasso.

Exh. Petit Palais, Paris, 1966–1967 : *Hommage à Picasso*, No. 10, repr. in cat.

Bibl. Not in Z. Unpublished.

Owned by the artist.

Inscription, lower left : "Cuando tengas ganas de joder, jode."

A. 13
NUDE WOMAN
Barcelona, 1902.
Ink and watercolor.
Size : 24.6 x 31 cm.
Unsigned.

Exh. Petit Palais, Paris, 1966–1967 : *Hommage à Picasso*, No. 9, repr. in cat.

Bibl. Not in Z. Unpublished.

Owned by the artist.

Related to VII. 16 and D. VII. 3.

A. 14
THE TWO SISTERS (Study)
Barcelona, 1902.
Pencil drawing.
Size : 45.5 x 32.8 cm.
Unsigned.

Exh. Petit Palais, Paris, 1966–1967 : *Hommage à Picasso*, No. 11, repr. in cat.

Bibl. Not in Z. Unpublished.

Owned by the artist.

This previously unpublished drawing is a study for *The Two Sisters* (VII. 22). See also the studies D. VII. 4 and 6.

A. 15
WOMAN LEANING ON A TABLE
Barcelona, 1903.
Ink drawing.
Size : 31 x 22 cm.
Signed with the initial : P.

Exh. Galerie Knoedler, Paris, 1966, No. 20, repr. in cat.

Bibl. Not in Z. Unpublished.

Collection M. Knoedler & Co.

A. 16
MÉNAGE DE PAUVRES (Study)
Barcelona, April 1903.
Colored crayons on back of a Junyer commercial card.
Size : 13.5 x 9 cm.
Signed bottom right : Picasso.

Bibl. Not in Z. Palau i Fabre, No. 78 (repr. in color).

Private collection, Barcelona.

This drawing, published for the first time in 1966, is a sketch for *Ménage de Pauvres (Man and Woman in a Café)* [IX. 9]. The painting is dated April 1903.

A. 17
THE COUPLE (Study)
Paris, 1904.
Conté crayon and wash.
Size : 37 x 26.8 cm.
Unsigned.

Exh. Petit Palais, Paris, 1966–1967 : *Hommage à Picasso*, No. 12, repr. in cat.

Bibl. Not in Z. Unpublished.

Owned by the artist.

A previously unpublished study for *The Couple (Les Misérables)* [XI. 5].

A. 18
SHEET OF STUDIES WITH SELF-PORTRAIT
Paris, 1904.
Ink on paper.
Size : 37.3 x 26.8 cm.
Unsigned.

Exh. Petit Palais, Paris, 1966–1967 : *Hommage à Picasso*, No. 15, repr. in cat.

Bibl. Not in Z. Unpublished.

Owned by the artist.

The nude man is a sketch for *The Christ of Montmartre* (D. XI. 9). The head of Picasso with a cap is related to the self-portraits D. XI. 28 and 29.

A. 19
THE TWO BROTHERS (Study)
Gosol, summer, 1906.
Watercolor.
Size : 54.5 x 34 cm.
Signed bottom right : Picasso.

Exh. Galerie Knoedler, Paris, 1966, No. 22, repr. in cat.

Bibl. Z. VI. 714.

Private collection, Paris.

See XV. 3–9.

A. 20
LA TOILETTE
1905-1906.
Watercolor and ink.
Size : 31.2 x 41.8 cm.
Unsigned.

Exh. Petit Palais, Paris, 1966–1967 : *Hommage à Picasso*, No. 16, repr. in cat.

Bibl. Not in Z. Unpublished.

Owned by the artist.

Dated 1905 by Jean Leymarie (catalogue of the Paris exhibition), but this work seems related to the series D. XV. 1–3, D. XV. 7, 8.

A. 21
WOMAN SEWING (Study)
Paris, summer-autumn, 1906.
Conté crayon and charcoal.
Size : 60.7 x 47.8 cm.
Unsigned.

Exh. Petit Palais, Paris, 1966–1967 : *Hommage à Picasso*, No. 17, repr. in cat.

Bibl. Not in Z. Unpublished.

Owned by the artist.

A previously unpublished study for *Woman Sewing* (XVI. 3).

A. 22
STUDIES FOR SELF-PORTRAIT
WITH A PALETTE
Paris, autumn, 1906.
Pencil.
Size : 48.3 x 31.8 cm.
Unsigned.

Exh. Petit Palais, Paris, 1966–1967 : *Hommage à Picasso*, No. 18, repr. in cat.

Bibl. Not in Z. Unpublished.

Owned by the artist.

An unpublished sheet of studies for *Self-Portrait with a Palette* (XVI. 28).

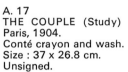

BIBLIOGRAPHY AND LIST OF EXHIBITIONS

BIBLIOGRAPHY

Index of abbreviations used in the catalogue raisonné.

This bibliography is limited to those works consulted by the authors and most particularly those referred to in the text and in the catalogue raisonné.

Editions in English are cited when possible.

ADHÉMAR, Jean: *Henri de Toulouse-Lautrec, Complete Lithographs and Drypoints.* New York: Abrams, 1965.

APOLLINAIRE 1905: Guillaume Apollinaire. *"Picasso, peintre et dessinateur,"* La Revue Immoraliste, April 1905 (Paris).

APOLLINAIRE 1905: Guillaume Apollinaire. "Les Jeunes: Picasso, peintre" (exhibition at the Galeries Serrurier), *La Plume,* No. 372, Paris, May 15, 1905 (with 5 reproductions of Picasso's works).

AZNAR, J. C. 1956: José Camón Aznar. *Picasso y el Cubismo.* Madrid, 1956.

BARNES, Albert C.: *The Art in Painting.* New York: Harcourt, Brace, 1937 (3rd edition).

BARR, *Forty Years:* Alfred H. Barr, Jr. *Picasso, Forty Years of his Art.* New York: Museum of Modern Art, 1939.

BARR, *Fifty Years:* Alfred H. Barr, Jr. *Picasso, Fifty Years of his Art.* New York: Museum of Modern Art, 1946.

BARR, *75th Anniversary:* Cf. List of exhibitions, New York, 1957.

BENET 1953: Rafael Benet. *Simbolismo.* Barcelona: Ediciones Omega, 1953.

BERGER 1965: John Berger. *Success and Failure of Picasso.* London and Baltimore: Penguin Books, 1965.

BLUNT and POOL: Sir Anthony Blunt and Phoebe Pool. *Picasso, The Formative Years.* London: Studio Books, 1962. New York: New York Graphic Society, 1963.

BOUDAILLE 1964: Georges Boudaille. *Le Musée de L'Ermitage.* Paris: N.E.F., 1964.

BOUDAILLE 1964: Georges Boudaille. *Picasso, périodes bleue et rose.* Paris: Le Musée Personnel, 1964.

BOURET 1950: Jean Bouret. *Picasso, Dessins.* Paris: Editions des Deux Mondes, 1950.

BRASSAÏ: *Conversations avec Picasso.* Paris: Gallimard, 1964.

BREESKIN 1952: Adelyn D. Breeskin, "Early Picasso Drawings in the Cone Collection," *Magazine of Art,* March 1952 (New York).

BUCHHEIM 1959: Lothar-Gunther Buchheim. *Picasso.* London, 1959.

BULLIET 1936: C. J. Bulliet. *The Significant Moderns.* New York, 1936.

CABANNE 1963: Pierre Cabanne. *The Great Collectors.* New York: Farrar, Straus, 1963; London: Cassell, 1963.

CAILLER, Pierre: *Guillaume Apollinaire, Documents iconographiques.* Geneva: Cailler, 1965.

CANADAY 1959: John Canaday. *Mainstreams of Modern Art.* New York, 1959.

CASSOU 1940: Jean Cassou. *Picasso.* Paris: Hypérion, 1940 (reprinted 1946).

CASSOU 1958: Jean Cassou. *Picasso.* Paris: Somogy, 1958.

CHAMPRIS 1960: Pierre de Champris. *Picasso, Ombre et Soleil.* Paris: Gallimard, 1960.

Cinquante chefs-d'œuvre, 1963: Paris, Editions Plaisir de France, 1963.

COCTEAU 1923: Jean Cocteau. *Picasso.* Paris: Stock, 1923.

COGNIAT 1959: Raymond Cogniat. *Picasso, Figures.* Lausanne: International Art Book, 1959.

CONE COLLECTION CATALOGUE 1934: *The Cone Collection of Baltimore, Maryland, Catalogue of Paintings, Drawings and Sculpture of the 19th and 20th Centuries.* Preface by George Boas. Baltimore, 1934.

COOPER, Douglas: *Picasso, le Carnet Catalan.* Facsimile reproduction of Picasso's sketchbook, with preface and notes by Douglas Cooper. Paris: Berggruen, 1958.

COOPER, Douglas: Cf. List of exhibitions, Marseilles, 1959; Dallas, 1967; Fort Worth, 1967.

C.-P.: Alejandro Cirici-Pellicer. *Picasso antes de Picasso.* Barcelona: Iberia Joaquin Gil, 1946. (French ed.: *Picasso avant Picasso.* Geneva; Pierre Cailler, 1950.)

COQUIOT 1914: Gustave Coquiot. *Cubistes, futuristes, passéistes.* Paris: Ollendorf, 1914.

DAIX 1964: Pierre Daix. *Picasso.* Paris: Somogy, 1964. London: Thames & Hudson, 1965.

DALE, M. 1929: Maud Dale. *Before Manet to Modigliani.* New York, 1929.

DALE, M. 1930: Maud Dale. *Picasso.* New York: Knopf, 1930.

DELEVOY 1965: Robert L. Delevoy. *Dimensions of the 20th Century, 1900–1945.* Geneva: Skira, 1965.

DIEHL 1960: Gaston Diehl. *Picasso.* Paris: Flammarion, 1960.

DORIVAL 1944: Bernard Dorival. *Les étapes de la peinture française contemporaine. Vol. II.* Paris, 1944.

DORIVAL 1961: Bernard Dorival. *The School of Paris in the National Museum of Modern Art, Paris.* Paris, 1961. New York: Abrams, 1962.

Drawings of the Masters, 20th Century, Vol. I. New York: Shorewood Press, 1964.

DUNCAN 1961: David Douglas Duncan. *Picasso's Picassos.* New York: Harper & Row, 1961.

EINSTEIN, Carl: *Die Kunst des 20. Jahrhunderts.* Berlin, 1926.

ELGAR AND MAILLARD 1955: Frank Elgar and Robert Maillard. *Picasso.* Paris: Hazan, 1955.

ELGAR 1956: Frank Elgar. *Picasso, Blue, Pink Periods.* (Paper.) New York, 1956.

ELUARD 1944: Paul Eluard. *A Pablo Picasso.* Geneva and Paris: Editions des Trois Collines, 1944.

ENCINA 1961: J. de la Encina. *La Pittura Espagnola.* Milan: Garzanti, 1961.

ERBEN 1947: Walter Erben. *Picasso und die Schwermut.* Heidelberg: Verlag Lambert Schneider, 1947.

ESCHOLIER 1937: Raymond Escholier. *La Peinture française, XXe siècle.* Paris: Floury, 1937.

FAGUS 1901: Félicien Fagus. "L'Invasion espagnole: Picasso" (review of the Vollard Exhibition), *La Revue blanche,* XXVII, No. 195, July 15, 1901 (Paris).

FAGUS 1902: Félicien Fagus. "Peintres espagnols" (review of the exhibition at the Galerie Berthe Weill), *La Revue blanche,* September 1, 1902 (Paris).

FELS 1950: Florent Fels. *L'Art vivant, de 1900 à nos jours.* Geneva: Cailler, 1950.

FRANCASTEL, Pierre: *Art et techniques aux XIXe et XXe siècles.* Paris: Editions de Minuit, 1962.

FRANCASTEL, Pierre: *Peinture et société.* Paris: Gallimard, 1965 (Lyons: Audin, 1951).

GALLUP, Donald C.: *The Flowers of Friendship, Letters to Gertrude Stein.* New York: Knopf, 1953.

GASSER 1963: Manuel Gasser. *Self-Portraits.* New York: (Appleton) Meredith, 1963.

GAYA NUÑO 1950: Juan Antonio Gaya Nuño. *Picasso.* Barcelona: Ediciones Omega, 1950.

GEISER: Bernhard Geiser. *Picasso, peintre-graveur,* catalogue illustré de l'œuvre gravé et lithographié, 1899–1931. Bern: (Author), 1933 (new edition 1955).

GEORGE, Waldemar: *La grande peinture contemporaine à la collection Paul Guillaume.* Paris: Editions des Arts, n. d. (*ca.* 1929).

GEORGE, W., 1926: Waldemar George. *Picasso, Dessins.* Paris: Editions des Quatre Chemins, 1926.

GIEURE 1951: Maurice Gieure. *Initiation à l'œuvre de Picasso.* Paris: Editions des Deux Mondes, 1951.

GOLDING 1959: John Golding. *Cubism.* London: Faber & Faber, 1959.

GÓMEZ DE LA SERNA: Ramón Gómez de la Serna. *Completa e veridica historia de Picasso y el Cubismo.* Turin: Chiantore, 1945.

Great Drawings of All Time. New York: Shorewood Press, 1962.

GUERRAND: Roger-H. Guerrand. *L'Art nouveau en Europe.* Preface by Aragon. Paris: Plon, 1965.

JACOB: Max Jacob. "Souvenirs sur Picasso," *Cahiers d'Art,* No. 6, 1927 (Paris).

JAFFÉ 1964: Hans Jaffé. *Picasso.* New York: Abrams, 1964.

JARDOT 1955: Cf. List of exhibitions, Paris, 1955.

JARDOT 1959: Maurice Jardot. *Pablo Picasso, Drawings,* New York: Abrams, 1959.

JARDOT, Stuttgart 1959: Maurice Jardot. *Picasso Zeichnungen.* Stuttgart: Verlag Gerd Hatje, 1959.

JAVORSKAÏA 1933: *Pablo Picasso.* ("Les Maîtres de la peinture moderne.") Moscow, 1933.

KAHNWEILER 1920: Daniel-Henry Kahnweiler. *Der Weg zum Kubismus.* Munich: Delphin Verlag, 1920. (Under the pseudonym Daniel Henry.)

KAHNWEILER 1958: Daniel-Henry Kahnweiler. *Der Weg zum Kubismus.* Stuttgart: Verlag Gerd Hatje, 1958.

KAHNWEILER and PARMELIN 1955: Daniel-Henry Kahnweiler and Hélène Parmelin. *Picasso, Œuvres des musées de Leningrad et de Moscou.* Paris: Cercle d'Art, 1955.

KAY, Helen, 1965: Helen Kay. *Picasso's World of Children.* New York: Doubleday, 1965.

LASSAIGNE 1949: Jacques Lassaigne. *Picasso.* Paris: Somogy, 1949.

LASSAIGNE 1952: Jacques Lassaigne. *Spanish Painting. Vol. II: From Velasquez to Picasso.* Geneva: Skira, 1952.

LASSAIGNE and RAYNAL. See Raynal and Lassaigne, 1950.

LEVEL 1928: André Level. *Picasso.* Paris: Crès, 1928.

LEYMARIE: Jean Leymarie. *Fauvism.* Geneva: Skira, 1959.

LEYMARIE, Jean: Cf. List of exhibitions, Paris, 1966–1967.

LIEBERMAN 1952: William S. Lieberman. *Picasso, Blue and Rose Periods.* New York: Abrams, 1952.

LIEBERMAN 1954: William S. Lieberman. *Picasso, Blue and Rose Periods.* New York: Abrams, 1954.

LIEBERMAN 1961: William S. Lieberman. *Picasso, Blue and Rose Periods.* New York: Abrams, 1961 (Paper).

Living Art 1923: *Living Art.* New York: The Dial Publishing Co., 1923.

MAHAUT 1930: Henri Mahaut. *Picasso.* Paris: Crès, 1930.

MERLI 1942: Joan Merli. *Picasso, el artista y la obra de nuestro tiempo.* Buenos Aires: Editorial Poseidon, 1942.

MERLI 1948: Reprinting of 1942 edition above.

MILLIER 1961: Arthur Millier. *The Drawings of Picasso.* Los Angeles: Borden, 1961.

MONGAN and SACHS: A. Mongan and Paul J. Sachs. *Drawings in the Fogg Art Museum.* Cambridge, Mass., 1940.

MORICE 1902: Charles Morice. "Exposition de MM. Girieud, Launay, Picasso et Pichot" (review of exhibition at Galerie Berthe Weill, November 15–December 15, 1902), *Mercure de France,* December 1902 (Paris).

MORICE 1905: Charles Morice. "Exposition d'œuvres de MM. Trachsel, Gérardin, Picasso"

(Galeries Serrurier, February 25–March 6, 1905), *Mercure de France*, March 15, 1905 (Paris).

O'HANA, Jacques: Cf. List of exhibitions, O'Hana 1960.

OLIVIER: Fernande Olivier. *Picasso and His Friends.* New York: (Appleton) Meredith, 1965. (Original edition, Paris: Stock, 1933.)

ORS 1930: Eugenio d'Ors. *Pablo Picasso.* Paris: Editions des Chroniques du Jour, 1930.

PALAU I FABRE: Josep Palau i Fabre. *Picasso en Cataluña.* Barcelona: Ediciones La Poligrafa S.A., 1966.

PARIS, Pierre: *Essai sur l'art et l'industrie de l'Espagne primitive.* Paris, 1903–1904.

PARIS, Pierre and ENGEL, Arthur: *Une forteresse ibérique à Osuna.* Paris, 1906.

PENROSE 1956: Roland Penrose. *Portrait of Picasso.* London: Lund Humphries, 1956.

PENROSE 1958: Roland Penrose. *Picasso, His Life and Work.* London: Gollancz, 1958.

PENROSE 1960: Cf. List of exhibitions, London, 1960.

Le Point: Special number devoted to Picasso. *Le Point,* No. XLII, October 1952 (Souillac). Articles by M. Raynal, D.-H. Kahnweiler, P. Reverdy, G. Besson, T. Tzara, P. Gay, E. Pignon, C. Roy.

PONGE and CHESSEX: Francis Ponge and Jacques Chessex. *Dessins de Pablo Picasso, époques bleue et rose.* Lausanne: Mermod, 1960.

PROKOFIEV 1962: *La Peinture française dans les musées de l'U.R.S.S.,* Moscow, 1962.

RAYNAL 1921: Maurice Raynal. *Picasso.* Munich: Delphin Verlag, 1921.

RAYNAL 1922: Maurice Raynal. *Picasso.* Paris: Crès, 1922. (French edition of the 1921 work.)

RAYNAL 1953: Maurice Raynal. *Picasso.* Geneva: Skira, 1953.

RAYNAL and LASSAIGNE 1950: Maurice Raynal and Jacques Lassaigne. *History of Modern Painting. Vol. III: From Picasso to Surrealism.* Geneva: Skira, 1950.

READ 1965: Herbert Read. *A Concise History of Modern Painting.* Paris, 1965. New York: Praeger, 1959.

RÉAU 1929: Louis Réau. *Catalogue de l'art français dans les musées russes.* Paris, 1929.

REWALD and WHEELER 1944: John Rewald and M. Wheeler. *Modern Drawings.* New York: Museum of Modern Art, 1944.

RICHARDSON 1962: Cf. List of exhibitions,

Knoedler, New York, 1962.

RICHARDSON 1964: John Richardson. *Picasso, aquarelles et gouaches.* Basel: Editions Phoebus, 1964.

RIPLEY 1959: E. Ripley. *Picasso.* Philadelphia: Lippincott, 1959.

ROSENBERG 1959: J. Rosenberg. *Great Draughtsmen from Pisanello to Picasso.* Cambridge: Harvard University Press, 1959.

RUNNQVIST 1959: Jan Runnqvist. *Minotauros— en Studie i forhallandet mellan Ikonografi och Form i Picassos Konst, 1900–1937.* Stockholm: Bonniers, 1959.

RUSSOLI, Franco: Cf. List of exhibitions, Milan, 1953.

SAARINEN 1958: Aline B. Saarinen. *The Proud Possessors.* New York: Random House, 1958.

SABARTÉS 1946: Jaime Sabartés. *Picasso, Portraits et Souvenirs.* Paris: Louis Carré and Maximilien Vox, 1946. (Spanish ed.: *Picasso, Retratos y Recuerdos,* Madrid, 1953.)

SABARTÉS 1954: Jaime Sabartés. *Picasso, Documents iconographiques.* Geneva: Cailler, 1954.

SABARTÉS 1963: Jaime Sabartés, preface. *Picasso, Les Bleus de Barcelone.* Paris: Editions Au Vent d'Arles, 1963.

SABARTÉS and BOECK: Jaime Sabartés and Wilhelm Boeck. *Pablo Picasso.* Paris: Flammarion, 1955.

SACHS 1954: Paul J. Sachs. *Modern Prints and Drawings.* New York: Knopf, 1954.

SCHOOLMAN and SLATKIN 1950: *Six Centuries of Master Drawings in America.* New York, 1950.

SCHÜRER 1927: Oskar Schürer. *Pablo Picasso.* Leipzig: Klinkhardt & Bierman, 1927.

STEIN, G., 1933: Gertrude Stein. *The Autobiography of Alice B. Toklas.* New York: Harcourt, Brace, 1933. (French ed., Paris: Gallimard, 1934.)

STEIN, G., 1938: Gertrude Stein. *Picasso.* Paris: Floury, 1938. (English ed., Boston: Beacon, 1959.)

STEIN, Leo 1947: Leo Stein. *Appreciation, Painting, Poetry, Prose.* New York, 1947.

STERLING 1957: Charles Sterling. *Great French Paintings in the Hermitage.* Paris 1957. New York: Abrams, 1958.

SUTTON 1955: Denys Sutton. *Picasso, peintures, époques bleue et rose.* Paris: Editions du Chêne, 1955 (original edition 1948).

SWEENEY, James Johnson: "Picasso and Iberian Sculpture," *Art Bulletin,* XXIII, No. 3, September 1941 (New York).

TERNOWIETZ 1935: *Le Musée d'Art Moderne Occidental* (album). Moscow, 1935.

TOUGUENHOLD 1914: "La collection française de S. I. Chtchoukine," *Apollon,* No. 1–2, 1914 (Petrograd).

TOUGUENHOLD 1923: *Le premier musée de la peinture occidentale moderne, ancienne collection S. I. Chtchoukine.* (Tschukin Collection.) Moscow–Petrograd 1923.

TRIER 1956: Eduard Trier. *Zeichner des XX. Jahrhunderts.* Berlin, 1956.

UHDE 1928: Wilhelm Uhde. *Picasso et la tradition française. Notes sur la peinture actuelle.* Paris: Editions des Quatre Chemins, 1928.

UTRILLO, Miguel: (Under the pseudonym "Pincell"), "Pablo R. Picasso," *Pèl y Ploma,* No. 77, June 14–17, 1901 (Barcelona). See translation, p. 333.

VALLENTIN 1957: Antonina Vallentin. *Pablo Picasso.* Paris: Albin Michel, 1957.

W.C.A.: *World Collectors Annuary.* Ed. by Fred A. van Braam. Delft: Verlag Brouwer.

WEILL, Berthe: *Pan! dans l'œil: Trente ans dans les coulisses de la peinture contemporaine, 1900–1930.* Paris: Lipschutz, 1933.

WHEELER 1942: M. Wheeler. *Twentieth Century Portraits.* New York, 1942.

WILENSKI 1940: R. H. Wilenski. *Modern French Painters.* London and New York, 1940.

WITTGENS 1954: Fernanda Wittgens. *Picasso.* Milan: Silvana, 1954.

ZAHLE 1938: Erik Zahle. *Fransk Maleri efter 1900.* Copenhagen, 1938.

ZENNSTRÖM 1948: P. O. Zennström. *Picasso,* 1948.

Z. I.: Christian Zervos. *Pablo Picasso.* Vol. I (1895–1906). 3rd edition. Paris: Editions Cahiers d'Art, 1957. (Original edition 1932.)

Z. VI.: Christian Zervos. *Pablo Picasso.* Vol. VI (supplement to vols. I–V). Paris: Editions Cahiers d'Art, 1962. (Original edition 1954.)

ZERVOS, Milan 1932: Christian Zervos. *Picasso.* Milan: Ulrich Hoepli, 1932 (new edition in 1946).

ZERVOS 1949: Christian Zervos. *Dessins de Picasso, 1892–1948.* Paris: Cahiers d'Art, 1949.

NOT IN Z.: Work which is not reproduced in volumes I or VI of the work of Christian Zervos (cf. Z. I. and Z. VI. above).

EXHIBITIONS

Index of abbreviations used in the catalogue raisonné.

This index is limited to those exhibitions which are referred to in the catalogue raisonné. To make them easier to find, they are listed alphabetically and not chronologically.

ARLES 1957: Musée Réattu, Arles, July 6–September 2, 1957: *Picasso, dessins-gouaches-aquarelles, 1898–1957* (110 works), catalogue by Douglas Cooper.

BERGGRUEN 1954: Galerie Berggruen, Paris, in collaboration with the Galerie Louise Leiris, May 25–July 24, 1954: *Picasso, dessins 1903–1907* (42 works), catalogue foreword by Daniel-Henry Kahnweiler.

BEYELER 1966–1967: Galerie Beyeler, Basel, November 26, 1966–January 31, 1967: *Picasso 1900–1932.*

BORDEAUX 1966: Musée des Beaux-Arts, Bordeaux, 1966: *La Peinture française dans les collections américaines,* catalogue by Gilberte Martin-Méry.

BOSTON 1938: Museum of Modern Art, Boston, October 19–November 11, 1938: *Picasso and Matisse.*

BOSTON 1940: Museum of Fine Arts, Boston, April 26–May 25, 1940: *Picasso, Forty Years of his Art* (236 of the 344 works shown in New York in 1939).

BREMEN 1961: Kunsthalle, Bremen, June 23–

August 6, 1961: *Picasso.*

BUENOS AIRES 1934: The first exhibition of Picasso's works in South America.

CASSEL 1964: Documenta III, Cassel, June 27–October 1964: *Picasso* (drawings).

CHICAGO 1930: Arts Club of Chicago, March–April 1930: *Paintings by Picasso.*

CHICAGO 1933: Art Institute of Chicago, 1933: *A Century of Progress Exhibition.*

CHICAGO 1934: Art Institute of Chicago, 1934: *A Century of Progress Exhibition.*

CHICAGO 1937: Arts Club of Chicago, January 8–31, 1937: *Collection of Walter P. Chrysler, Jr.*

CHICAGO 1937: Art Institute of Chicago, 1937: *Watercolors and Gouaches by Picasso.*

CHICAGO 1939: Arts Club of Chicago, January 3–27, 1939: *Drawings by Pablo Picasso loaned by Mr. Walter P. Chrysler, Jr.*

CHICAGO 1939: Art Institute of Chicago, March 23–May 14, 1939: *International Watercolor Exhibition.*

CHICAGO 1940: Art Institute of Chicago, February 1–March 3, 1940: *Picasso, Forty Years of his Art* (236 of the 344 works shown in New York).

CHICAGO 1946: Art Institute of Chicago, 1946: *Drawings Old and New.*

CHICAGO 1957: Art Institute of Chicago, October 29–December 8, 1957: *Picasso, 75th Anniversary Exhibition.*

CINCINNATI 1940: Cincinnati Museum of Art, September 28–October 27, 1940: *Picasso,*

Forty Years of his Art (170 of the 344 works shown in New York).

CLEVELAND 1940: Cleveland Museum of Art, November 7–December 8, 1940: *Picasso, Forty Years of his Art* (170 works).

COLOGNE 1912: Sonderbund Internationale Kunstausstellung, Cologne, May 25–September 30, 1912 (16 oils and gouaches by Picasso).

COLOGNE 1913: Der Rheinischer Kunstsalon, Cologne, March–April 1913: *Pablo Picasso* (53 paintings, 13 drawings).

DALLAS 1967: Dallas Museum of Fine Arts, February 8–March 26, 1967: *Picasso* (86 paintings), catalogue by Douglas Cooper.

DETROIT 1937: Detroit Institute of Arts, October 1937: *Selected Exhibition of the Walter P. Chrysler, Jr. Collection.*

DETROIT 1941: Detroit Institute of Arts, 1941: *Masterpieces of 19th and 20th Century Drawings.*

FORT WORTH 1967: Fort Worth Art Center Museum, February 8–March 26, 1967: *Picasso* (72 drawings, watercolors and pastels), catalogue by Douglas Cooper.

FRANKFURT and HAMBURG 1965: Frankfurter Kunstverein, May 29–July 4, 1965: *Picasso, 150 Handzeichnungen aus sieben Jahrzehnten,* catalogue by Ewald Rathke and Sylvia Rathke-Köhl; Kunstverein, Hamburg, summer 1965.

GENEVA 1963: Musée de l'Athénée, Geneva, July 11–September 21, 1963: *Picasso,* catalogue foreword by André Verdet.

HOUSTON 1955 : Houston Contemporary Art Association, January 14–February 20, 1955 : *Picasso.*

KNOEDLER, NEW YORK 1947 : M. Knoedler & Co., Inc., New York, October 15–November 8, 1947 : *Picasso before 1907.*

KNOEDLER, NEW YORK 1962 : M. Knoedler & Co., Inc., New York, April 25–May 12, 1962 : *Picasso, an American Tribute, 1895–1909* (44 works), catalogue by John Richardson.

KNOEDLER, PARIS 1966 : Galerie Knoedler, Paris, November–December 1966 : *Picasso, dessins et aquarelles 1899–1965,* catalogue by Lionel Prejger.

KNOKKE-LE-ZOUTE 1950 : Casino Communal, Knokke-le-Zoute, 1950 : *Exposition d'œuvres de Picasso.*

LAUSANNE 1964 : Palais de Beaulieu, Lausanne, 1964 : *Chefs-d'œuvre des collections suisses, de Manet à Picasso,* catalogue by François Daulte.

LEFEVRE GALLERY 1931 : Alex Reid & Lefevre Gallery, London, June 1931 : *Thirty Years of Pablo Picasso.*

LEFEVRE GALLERY 1943 : Alex Reid & Lefevre Gallery, London, March 1943 : *Picasso and his Contemporaries.*

LEFEVRE GALLERY 1953 : Alex Reid & Lefevre Gallery, London, May-June 1953 : *Picasso 1898–1936.*

LONDON 1951 : The Institute of Contemporary Arts, London, October 11–November 24, 1951 : *Picasso, Drawings and Water Colours since 1893.*

LONDON 1960 : Arts Council of Great Britain, Tate Gallery, London, July 6–September 18, 1960 : *Picasso* (270 works), catalogue by Roland Penrose.

LOS ANGELES 1961 : University of California Art Gallery, Los Angeles, October 25–November 12, 1961 : *Bonne Fête Monsieur Picasso.*

LYONS 1953 : Musée de Lyon, June 1953 : *Picasso* (179 works), notes by Jean Cassou, D.-H. Kahnweiler, Christian Zervos, René Jullian, Marcel Michaud ; catalogue compiled by Madeleine Rocher-Jauneau.

MARSEILLES 1959 : Musée Cantini, Marseilles, May 11–July 31, 1959 : *Picasso* (58 works), catalogue by Douglas Cooper.

MEXICO 1944 : Sociedad de Arte Moderno, Mexico, June 1944 : *Picasso.*

MILAN 1953 : Palazzo Reale, Milan, September–November 1953 : *Picasso,* catalogue by Franco Russoli.

MINNEAPOLIS 1941 : Minneapolis Institute of Arts, February 1–March 2, 1941 : *Picasso, Epochs in his Art.*

MUNICH, COLOGNE, HAMBURG 1955–1956 : Haus der Kunst, Munich, October 25–December 18, 1955 : Rheinisches Museum, Cologne-Deutz, December 30, 1955–February 29, 1956 ; Kunsthalle, Hamburg, March 10–April 29, 1956 : *Picasso 1900–1955.*

MMA, NEW YORK 1941–1942 : Museum of Modern Art, New York (and Utica, Durham, Kansas City, Milwaukee, Grand Rapids, Hanover, Poughkeepsie) : *Picasso, Epochs in his Art.*

MMA, NEW YORK : Museum of Modern Art, New York, May 15–September 18, 1962 : *Picasso in the Museum of Modern Art ; 80th Birthday Exhibition* (no catalogue).

NEW GALLERY, NEW YORK 1962 : The New Gallery, New York, April 25–May 12, 1962 : *Picasso, an American Tribute* (drawings), catalogue by John Richardson.

NEW YORK and CHICAGO 1939–1940 : The Museum of Modern Art, New York, November 15, 1939–January 7, 1940 : *Picasso, Forty Years of his Art* (344 works), catalogue by Alfred H. Barr, Jr. The Art Institute of Chicago, February 1–March 3, 1940 : *same exhibition* (236 of the 344 works shown in New York).

NEW YORK 1944 : The Museum of Modern Art, New York, 1944 : *Modern Drawings.*

NEW YORK and CHICAGO 1957 : The Museum of Modern Art, New York, May 22–September 8,

1957 : *Picasso, 75th Anniversary Exhibition,* catalogue by Alfred H. Barr, Jr. The Art Institute of Chicago, October 29–December 8, 1957 : *same exhibition.*

NEW YORK, etc. 1965–1966 : The Museum of Modern Art, New York ; The Art Institute of Chicago ; St. Louis City Art Museum ; Museo de Arte Moderno, Mexico ; San Francisco Museum of Art ; Denver Art Museum, 1965–1966 : *The School of Paris, Paintings from the Florene May Schoenborn and Samuel A. Marx Collection,* catalogue foreword by Alfred H. Barr, Jr., introduction by James Thrall Soby.

O'HANA 1960 : Sidney Janis Gallery, New York, April 25–May 21 ; O'Hana Gallery, London, June 23–July 28 ; Stoneleigh Abbey, Warwickshire, July 30–August 14 ; Galerie Motte, Geneva, August 23–September 10, 1960 : *Picasso, His Blue Period,* pastels, watercolors and drawings from the Junyer Vidal collection, Barcelona ; catalogue by Jacques O'Hana.

OSLO 1956 : Kunstnernes Hus, Oslo, November 1–December 31, 1956 : *Picasso.*

PARIS 1953 : Musée National d'Art Moderne, Paris, January 30–April 9, 1953 : *Le Cubisme, 1907–1914.*

PARIS 1954 : Maison de la Pensée Française, Paris, June 1954 : *Picasso, œuvres des musées de Leningrad et de Moscou, 1900–1914,* catalogue by Maurice Raynal.

PARIS 1955 : Musée des Arts Décoratifs, Paris, June–October 1955 : *Picasso, peintures 1900–1955* (141 works), catalogue by Maurice Jardot.

PARIS 1959 : Petit-Palais, 1959 : *Chefs-d'œuvre de la peinture française de Géricault à Matisse.*

PARIS 1960 : Musée National d'Art Moderne, Paris, 1960 : *Les Sources du XXᵉ siècle, Les arts en Europe de 1844 à 1914,* catalogue by Jean Cassou, Emile Langui, Nikolaus Pevsner.

PARIS 1964 : Musée National d'Art Moderne, Paris, March–April 1964 : *La Collection André Lefèvre.*

PARIS 1966 : Musée National d'Art Moderne, Paris, March 1966 : *Paris–Prague* (the Cubist works in The National Gallery of Prague), catalogue foreword by Adolf Hoffmeister.

PARIS 1966–1967 : Grand Palais, Paris (284 paintings), and Petit Palais (205 drawings), November 1966–February 1967 : *Hommage à Pablo Picasso,* catalogue by Jean Leymarie.

PERLS GALLERIES, New York 1939 : March 27–April 29, 1939 : *Picasso before 1910.*

PERLS, Kate, Paris 1937 : Galerie Kate Perls, Paris 1937 : *Picasso 1900–1910.*

PETIT, Galerie Georges, 1932 : Galerie Georges Petit, Paris, June 16–July 30, 1932 : *Picasso,* catalogue by Charles Vranken.

PHILADELPHIA 1958 : The Philadelphia Museum of Art, January 8–February 23, 1958 : *Picasso, a Loan Exhibition.*

RECKLINGHAUSEN 1959 : Kunsthalle, Recklinghausen, May 23–July 5, 1959 : *Die Handschrift des Künstlers.*

ST. LOUIS 1940 : The City Art Museum of St. Louis, March 16–April 14, 1940 : *Picasso, Forty Years of his Art* (236 works).

SAN ANTONIO 1954 : The Marion Koogler McNay Art Institute, San Antonio, Texas, November 4–December 5, 1954 : *Picasso* (Opening exhibition).

SAN FRANCISCO 1939–1940 : M. H. de Young Memorial Museum, San Francisco, December 29, 1939–January 28, 1940 : *Seven Centuries of Painting.*

SAN FRANCISCO 1940 : San Francisco Museum of Art, April 26–May 25, 1940 : *Picasso, Forty Years of his Art* (236 works).

SAN FRANCISCO and PORTLAND 1948 : San Francisco Museum of Art and Portland Art Museum (Oregon), 1948 : *Picasso, Gris, Miró.*

SELIGMANN, New York 1936 : Jacques Seligmann & Co., Inc., New York, November 2–26, 1936 : *Picasso, Blue and Rose Periods* (34 paintings).

SELIGMANN, New York 1937 : Jacques Seligmann & Co., Inc., New York, November 1–20, 1937 :

Twenty Years in the Evolution of Picasso, 1903–1923.

SERRURIER, Paris 1905 : Galeries Serrurier, Paris, February 25–March 6, 1905 : *Exposition d'œuvres de MM. Trachsel, Gérardin, Picasso,* catalogue foreword by Charles Morice.

TATE GALLERY 1960 : Cf. LONDON 1960.

TATE GALLERY 1961 : Tate Gallery, London, December 16, 1960–January 29, 1961 : *The John Hay Whitney Collection,* catalogue by John Rewald.

TEL AVIV 1966 : Tel Aviv Museum, Helena Rubinstein Pavilion, 1966 : *Picasso* (69 paintings, 79 graphics), catalogue foreword by Dr. Haïm Gamzu and Daniel-Henry Kahnweiler, introduction by Maurice Jardot.

THANNHAUSER, Munich, 1913 : Moderne Galerie, Heinrich Thannhauser, Munich, February 1913: *Pablo Picasso* (76 paintings, 38 drawings).

TOKYO 1964 : National Museum of Art, Tokyo, May 23–July 5, 1964 : *Picasso,* catalogue by Sinichi Segui. Same exhibition : Kyoto, July 10–August 3, 1964 : Nagoya, August 7–18, 1964.

TORONTO 1949 : The Art Gallery of Toronto, April 1949 : *Picasso.*

TORONTO and MONTREAL 1964 : The Art Gallery of Toronto, January 11–February 16, 1964 and The Montreal Museum of Fine Arts, February 28–March 31, 1964 : *Picasso and Man* (273 works), catalogue by Jean Sutherland Boggs.

VALENTINE GALLERY, New York 1936 : October 26–November 21, 1936 : *Picasso 1901–1934, Retrospective Exhibition.*

VEVEY 1962 : Musée Jenisch, Vevey, July 7–September 23, 1962 : *De Cézanne à Picasso, Maîtres de l'aquarelle au XXᵉ siècle.*

VIRGINIA and PHILADELPHIA 1941 : The Virginia Museum of Fine Arts, January 16–March 4, 1941, and The Philadelphia Museum of Art, March 29–May 11, 1941 : *The Collection of Walter P. Chrysler, Jr.* (The first exhibition of the entire collection, 341 works, of which 88 were by Picasso, catalogue by Douglas Fox.

VOLLARD 1901 : Galeries Ambroise Vollard, Paris, June 25–July 14, 1901 : *Exposition de tableaux de F. Iturrino et de P. R. Picasso* (64 paintings and some drawings by Picasso), catalogue foreword by Gustave Coquiot.

WADSWORTH ATHENEUM 1934 : Wadsworth Atheneum, Hartford, Connecticut, February 6–March 1, 1934 : *Pablo Picasso.*

WEILL, Berthe, 1902 : Galerie Berthe Weill, Paris, April 1–15, 1902 : *Tableaux et pastels de Louis Bernard-Lemaire et de Picasso* (15 works by Picasso), exhibition arranged by Pedro Mañach, catalogue foreword by Adrien Farge.

WEILL, Berthe, 1902 : Galerie Berthe Weill, Paris, June 2–15, 1902 : A group exhibition : Matisse, Villon, Marquet, Maillol, Picasso, etc. (1 work by Picasso : No. 24, *Grand Prix d'Auteuil*), exhibition arranged by Pedro Mañach, catalogue foreword by Emile Seyden.

WEILL, Berthe, 1902 : Galerie Berthe Weill, Paris, November 15–December 15, 1902 : *Peintures, pastels et dessins de MM. Girieud, Launay, Picasso et Pichot* (9 works and some drawings by Picasso), catalogue foreword by Harlor.

WEILL, Berthe, 1904 : Galerie Berthe Weill, Paris, October 24–November 20, 1904 : *Exposition de MM. Charbonnier, Clary-Baroux, Raoul Dufy, Girieud, Picabia, Picasso, Thiesson* (11 paintings and some drawings by Picasso), catalogue foreword by Maurice Le Sieutre.

YALE UNIVERSITY and BALTIMORE 1951 : Yale University Art Gallery, February–March 1951, and The Baltimore Museum of Art, March–April 1951 : *Pictures for a Picture of Gertrude Stein.*

ZURICH 1932 : Kunsthaus, Zurich, September 11–October 30, 1932 (extended until November 13): *Picasso* (325 works), catalogue by Charles Vranken, introduction by W. Wartmann (exhibition based on that held at the Galerie Georges Petit, Paris, summer, 1932).

TABLE OF COLOR PLATES

In chronological order.
The number in parentheses refers to the catalogue.

PHOTOGRAPHS

Harry N. Abrams Inc., New York ; Albright-Knox Art Gallery, Buffalo ; Victor Amato, Washington, D. C. ; Ashmolean Museum, Oxford ; Bachmann, Zurich ; Baltimore Museum of Art ; Galerie Beyeler, Basel ; Paul Bijtebier, Brussels ; Paul Boissonnas, Geneva ; Museum of Fine Arts, Boston ; Georges Boudaille, Paris ; Museum Boymans-van Beuningen, Rotterdam ; Brenwasser, New York ; Alice Brill, Sao Paulo ; Brompton Studio, London ; Editions Cahiers d'Art, Paris ; Editions Pierre Cailler, Geneva ; Cauvin, Paris ; Galerie Charpentier, Paris ; Art Institute of Chicago ; Hermann Claasen, Cologne ; Cleveland Museum of Art ; Columbus Gallery of Fine Arts ; A. C. Cooper & Sons, London ; Paul Cordes, New York ; Detroit Institute of Arts ; Walter Dräyer, Zurich ; Dumont & Babinot, Rheims ; Edita S. A., Lausanne ; Fogg Art Museum, Cambridge, Mass. ; Frick Art Reference Library, New York ; Galerie A. Gattlen, Lausanne ; Glasgow Art Gallery and Museum ; Göteborgs Konstmuseum ; Musée Goya, Castres ; Galerie Wilhelm Grosshennig, Düsseldorf ; Solomon R. Guggenheim Museum, New York ;

Hannema-de Stuers Foundation, Heino ; Hans Hinz, Basel ; Houston Museum of Fine Arts ; Alain Jacot-Descombes, Neuchâtel ; Michael Katz, New York ; M. Knoedler & Co. Inc., New York ; Galerie Knoedler, Paris ; Kunsthaus, Zurich ; Kupferstichkabinett, Basel ; Louis Laniepce, Paris ; Galerie Louise Leiris, Paris ; Los Angeles County Museum of Art ; Marion Koogler McNay Art Institute, San Antonio ; Metropolitan Museum of Art, New York ; Morin, Cannes ; Muller, Paris ; National Gallery of Art, Washington, D. C. ; National Gallery of Canada, Ottawa ; Nasjonalgalleriet, Oslo ; Nationalmuseum, Stockholm ; Norton Gallery and School of Art, Florida ; Ny Carlsberg Glyptotek, Copenhagen ; O'Hana Gallery, London ; Philadelphia Museum of Art ; Phillips Collection, Washington, D.C. ; Phoenix Art Museum, Arizona ; Piccardy, Grenoble ; Mme Jacqueline Picasso, Mougins ; Picasso Museum, Barcelona ; Ediciones La Poligrafa, Barcelona ; Eric Pollitzer, Long Island ; Pushkin Museum, Moscow ; National Gallery of Prague ; Prins Eugens Waldemarsudde, Stockholm ; Queensland Art Gallery,

Brisbane ; Domínguez Ramos, Madrid ; Réunion des musées nationaux, Versailles ; Museum of Art, Rhode Island School of Design ; Rijksmuseum Kröller-Müller, Otterlo ; Rochester Memorial Art Gallery, University of Rochester ; Galerie Rosengart, Lucerne ; San Francisco Museum of Art ; Staatsgalerie, Stuttgart ; Statens Museum for Kunst, Copenhagen ; St. Louis City Art Museum ; Soichi Sunami, Museum of Modern Art, New York ; Szépmüvészeti Muzeum, Budapest ; Tate Gallery, London ; Toledo Museum of Art, Ohio ; Arthur Tooth & Sons Ltd., London ; Heinrich Urwyler, Zurich ; Marc Vaux, Paris ; Jacques Verroust, Neuilly-sur Seine ; Virginia Museum of Fine Arts, Richmond ; Von der Heydt-Museum der Stadt Wuppertal ; Whitworth Art Gallery, University of Manchester ; Wildenstein & Co. Inc., New York ; Worcester Art Museum ; Yale University Art Gallery, New Haven ; Yale University Library, Collection of American Literature.

3660 4

PRINTED IN SWITZERLAND